HANDBOOK OF NEUROPSYCHOLOGY, 2nd Edition

VOLUME 4

DISORDERS OF VISUAL BEHAVIOR

HANDBOOK OF NEUROPSYCHOLOGY, 2nd Edition

Series Editors

FRANÇOIS BOLLER
INSERM, Unité 324, Centre Paul Broca, 75014 Paris, France

and

JORDAN GRAFMAN
National Institute of Neurological Disorders and Stroke, National Institutes of Health, Bethesda, MA 20892, USA

Volume 4

DISORDERS OF VISUAL BEHAVIOR

Editor

MARLENE BEHRMANN
Department of Psychology, Carnegie Mellon University, Pittsburgh, PA 15213-3890, USA

ELSEVIER
Amsterdam – London – New York – Oxford – Paris – Shannon – Tokyo
2001

ELSEVIER SCIENCE B.V.
Sara Burgerhartstraat 25
P.O. Box 211, 1000 AE Amsterdam, The Netherlands

First edition 2001

Library of Congress Cataloging in Publication Data
A catalog record from the Library of Congress has been applied for.

ISBN series 0 444 50376 5 (HB)
ISBN series 0 444 50377 3 (PB)
ISBN this edition (hardbound) 0 444 50360 9
ISBN this edition (paperback) 0 444 50369 2

♾ The paper used in this publication meets the requirements of ANSI/NISO Z39.48-1992 (Permanence of Paper).
Printed in The Netherlands

Preface

We are pleased to present the fourth volume of the second edition of the Handbook of Neuropsychology. As already demonstrated by the first three volumes, neuropsychology is a field of science that has undergone extraordinary growth and changes in recent years. Planning for the first edition of the Handbook started over fifteen years ago. Even though the more recent volumes of the first edition were designed to reflect some of the changes that have taken place, we have decided, with the encouragement of the Publisher, that it would be worthwhile to prepare a new edition. As the series co-editors, we intend to ensure that the new edition of the Handbook of Neuropsychology remains the principal reference source in the field, continuing to provide comprehensive and current coverage of both experimental and clinical aspects of neuropsychology. To this end, we have asked the authoritative chapter authors to produce new in-depth reviews that go beyond a summary of their results and point of view. Each chapter is up-to-date, covering the latest developments in methodology and theory. Discussion of 'bedside' evaluations, laboratory techniques, as well as extensive discussions of theoretical models are all to be found in the Handbook. The Handbook also presents the latest findings and methodologies of functional neuroimaging techniques such as PET, fMRI, and transcranial magnetic stimulation (TMS).

We are confident that the Handbook will continue to be an essential reference source for clinicians such as neuropsychologists, neurologists, psychiatrists, and psychologists, as well as for all scientists engaged in research in the cognitive neurosciences. This second all-new edition is designed to update chapters covering research domains where considerable developments have occurred. In addition, there has been an in-depth reorganization of content areas that have spawned new approaches since the first edition. All the chapters included in this new edition will provide the most recent data and references for further studies and research.

The first volume included an introduction section that focused on practical and theoretical issues of general interest. Two chapters covered, in a novel and comprehensive fashion, clinical evaluation and neuropsychological assessment, with an emphasis not so much on the description of tests, but on their rationale. One of the features of neuropsychology in recent years has been the spectacular comeback of single case studies and that is why the chapter on statistical approaches compared statistical procedures appropriate for groups to that of single cases. Hemispheric specialization remains an important topic, which was examined in the introduction under two different points of view. One chapter summarized the contribution to neuropsychology provided by the commissurotomy ('split brain') model, while another chapter reviewed experimental assessments of hemispheric specialization in normal individuals. An introduction to current neuroimaging used language disorders as an illustration. Neurophysiological techniques were reviewed with emphasis on evoked potentials (ERP). Several chapters dealt with the application of theoretical models to neuropsychology, including a discussion of the lesion method and of computer modeling.

In addition to the Introduction, the first volume included a section on attention edited by Giacomo Rizzolatti. It included four chapters. Two of them concerned selective attention.

The first was essentially devoted to visuo/spatial attentional phenomena, while the focus of the second was on the temporal aspects of attention. The phenomenon of failure to orient, neglect and neglect-related phenomena was dealt with in the third chapter. This chapter included a large section devoted to the anatomical localization of lesions producing neglect in humans. Finally, the last chapter reviewed the anatomy and the neurophysiological properties of the circuits whose lesion produces neglect deficits in primates. In that chapter, the various theories of neglect were reviewed and their validity discussed from a neurophysiological perspective.

The second volume of the Handbook was a special 'in memoriam' volume. It was dedicated to the memory of Laird Cermak who, despite his grave illness, vigorously and resolutely took on the task of preparing a new section on memory and its disorders. The volume included chapters on animal models and neuropsychological assessment. Memory was discussed from the anatomical and clinical viewpoints, and memory disorders resulting from specific diseases such as Herpes simplex and Alzheimer's disease were considered in detail. The section further provided a cognitive neuropsychological analysis of various forms of memory, including explicit memory, remote memory and semantic memory. Chapters on confabulation and on functional amnesia were also included. We were all deeply saddened by the news of Laird's untimely death. We are very much indebted to Mieke Verfaellie for supervising the final stages of preparing this volume for the revised handbook.

The third volume, edited by Rita Sloan Berndt, covered traditional approaches to, as well as new techniques for, investigating language disorders by leading researchers in the field of language and aphasia research. The volume is divided into four parts. The first part, entitled 'The Study of Aphasia', included a chapter on historical developments, a discussion of the relationship between neuroanatomy and language, one on sign language, one on cross-lingual studies and a review of aphasia in bilinguals and polyglots. The second part ('Understanding the Symptoms of Aphasia') discussed and analyzed the symptoms of aphasia and related disorders including reading and writing. The next section goes further into related disorders with chapters that discuss the relations between language and memory and attention as well as disorders of skilled movements, of body representation and of number processing. The volume concluded with a review of emerging methods for the study of language and aphasia including neuroimaging, ERP, TMS and studies of 'split brain' subjects.

Marlene Behrmann is the editor of the fourth volume, which we present here. The volume begins with a chapter reviewing the neurophysiology of spatial vision with special emphasis on single unit recordings in nonhuman primates. The next three chapters review the recent work on recognition deficits for faces (prosopagnosia), objects (visual object agnosia) and words (peripheral dyslexias). Disorders of spatial representation, of color processing and of mental imagery are presented next including a detailed discussion of the neuropsychological behavior as well as the underlying neural substrate of these disorders. Additional chapters deal with Balint's syndrome, with blindsight and with visuospatial or constructional disorders. Finally, the relationship between eye movements and brain damage is described in detail.

The fifth volume is edited by Guido Gainotti. It covers emotional behavior and its disorders. It begins with chapters dealing with the basic theoretical and anatomical issues in the neuropsychological study of emotions. A central part of this volume will address the problem of hemispheric asymmetries in emotional representation and a final group of chapters examines the neural mechanisms of the stress response and reviews the main emotional disorders. In the introductory chapters, an effort is made to present both neurobiologically oriented and cognitively oriented theories of emotion. Both the detailed anatomo-clinical and theoretical aspects of the anatomical substrates of emotions are covered in depth. In the central part of the volume, the claims for right hemisphere dominance for emotions and emotional communication are contrasted with those assuming a different hemispheric specialization for positive vs. negative emotions and with models assuming asymmetric cortico-limbic control of human emotion. Finally, in the last chapters of the volume, individual differences in the hemispheric control of the stress response are discussed and the neural mechanisms of affective/emotional disturbances are approached with neuropsychological methods and with functional neuroimaging techniques.

The sixth volume, edited by François Boller and Stefano Cappa, is devoted to topics related to aging and dementia. The volume will be introduced by two chapters dealing with age-related cognitive and neurobiological alterations in animals, including a detailed review of data obtained with transgenic and knockout technology. The next chapter will review the cognitive changes associated with normal aging. The gamut of symptoms that occur in Alzheimer's disease (AD) will then be described and analyzed. They will include effects on attention, memory, language, non-verbal functions, non-cognitive symptoms, olfaction and the motor system. The discussion of dementia will be presented in two sections. The first will concern AD, which will be discussed from the points of view of epidemiology, pathology, neurochemistry and treatment. The other section will deal with non-AD dementias including fronto-temporal dementias and specific conditions such as Parkinson's and Huntington's disease, as well as HIV infection. The volume will include a review of brain imaging and cerebral metabolism findings in aging and dementia. Three final chapters will review non-cognitive symptoms, the relations between culture and dementia and the special syndrome of severe dementia.

The revised edition of the Handbook will continue with two child neuropsychology volumes edited by Sid Segalowitz and Isabelle Rapin. In childhood, the impact of acquired and degenerative disorders is strongly colored by the immaturity of the brain, so that what is said in other volumes of the Handbook rarely applies directly to children. This section starts with a consideration of aberrant brain development and the limits of plasticity of the immature brain when it is damaged. The epidemiology of the developmental disorders follows a discussion of left handedness and the emergence of cerebral dominance. The next seven chapters consider the strengths and limitations of the techniques of neuroimaging and electrophysiology as they apply to normal and handicapped children and of clinical neuropsychological testing in infancy, preschool and school-age children. The following six chapters are devoted to developmental disorders of motor and somatosensory perception, and to the functional impact of impaired vision and hearing. Inadequate language acquisition and language disorders are among the most frequent developmental disorders bringing children to neuropsychologists. Chapters on language development, developmental language disorders and acquired aphasias are followed by discussions of the ubiquitous academic problems, reading disability and dyscalculia. Learning disabilities and academic difficulties also arise from other cognitive losses, discussed in chapters devoted to deficits of memory in children, some of whom present with severe mental deficiency and autistic behaviors, and of attention, including criteria for its diagnosis and pharmacological management. Executive disorders have come to center stage in both adult and pediatric neuropsychology in the last decade, and their role in a variety of developmental disorders is explored. In addition to the pervasive focus on cognitive disorders, child neuropsychology needs to consider aberrant drive and affect and some of their potential correlates with major societal impact such as substance abuse and eating disorders. These disorders have their roots in childhood even though they may not appear until later in life. Epilepsy and autistic spectrum disorders have separate chapters because of their particularly high prevalence in children. Finally, while neuropsychological syndromes in children often directly inform us about normal brain–behavior relations, the neuropsychology of normal development is also based on data obtained from nonclinical paradigms. Such developments are described in separate chapters on normal cognitive and affective development.

This new edition of the Handbook will also include a completely revamped section on the frontal lobes edited by Jordan Grafman. Chapters on the history of science's attempt to understand the function of the frontal lobes and the neural architecture/anatomy of the prefrontal cortex lead off this volume. Animal research has contributed greatly to our understanding of the special capability of the frontal lobes to respond to a variety of input from 'lower order' sensory and posterior association cortex and this and other observations are reported in this volume. Functions dependent on the frontal lobes emerge late in ontogeny and appear to decline early in normal aging. These findings are reviewed and their implications for neuropsychology discussed. Over the last 15 years, the functioning of the frontal lobes has become associated with the term working memory. In this volume the concept of working memory is discussed in relation to both functional neuroimaging and patient studies. Gross distinctions in the functioning of the prefrontal cortex have divided it topographically into dorsolateral and ventromedial sectors. This volume offers chapters highlighting the role of each sector from both neuroimaging and lesion perspectives. Many of the views of the prefrontal cortex characterize it as involved in 'processing.' A chapter in this volume takes a slightly different perspective and attempts to characterize the nature of knowledge representation within the frontal lobes. Many theories of the frontal lobes suggest that they are concerned with maintaining information across time. A chapter reviews the role of the frontal lobes in temporal processing. Since the frontal lobes are affected by many neuropsychiatric disorders, a chapter in this volume places their dysfunction in the context of the parallel fronto-subcortical networks and suggests that each network, when damaged, contributes specific symptoms to the patient's clinical presentation. Finally, computational modeling has taken center-stage in cognitive neuroscience and its usefulness in testing different theoretical stances about the role of the frontal lobes in information processing is presented in a concluding chapter.

The final volume on rehabilitation, edited by Jordan Grafman and Ian Robertson, contains topics not specifically covered in the previous edition of the Handbook. In particular, we were so impressed by the advances and current direction of studies on neuroplasticity and rehabilitation that we thought the time was right to include these topics in the new edition of the Handbook of Neuropsychology. Neuroplasticity is among the most exciting areas of research in cognitive neuroscience. In this volume, there are chapters on animal models of neuroplasticity, cortical map changes with practice and following brain damage, cross-modal reassignment of function, auditory system reassignment following learning and cerebral-damage, the effects of amputation on phantom limb and pain perceptions, the effects of age on plasticity, the ability of the non-damaged hemisphere to take over functions of the damaged hemisphere, and the effects of cognitive skill learning on neural organization and function. A section describing how basic science findings can be translated into practical rehabilitation of patients follows. Rehabilitation programs for neglect, language, executive functions, motor skills are described. The use of functional neuroimaging to provide a neural window on cognitive plasticity is discussed. The last section of the Handbook has traditionally been reserved for a discussion of the state-of-the-art of new technologies. Here we provide updates on MRI, fMRI, PET, transcranial magnetic stimulation, and other technologies that have burst upon the cognitive neuroscience scene in the last ten years.

Besides the printed second edition of the Handbook of Neuropsychology that you have in your hands, there are already plans for a web-based version. This will make it easier to adapt the Handbook to changes that will undoubtedly occur in the near future. For example, neuroimaging techniques are rapidly developing, opening new in-roads into the mapping of brain and behavior relationships. The rising interest in the aging population is also very likely to increase even further, as new advances will occur concerning the early detection of cognitive impairment and the maintenance of cognitive functions into old age. The same advances will undoubtedly also occur for the developing brain.

Many people have contributed to the successful preparation of the Handbook. We again wish to emphasize our appreciation for the commitment of the volume editors who have spent long hours in the planning stage and in the actual compiling of the various sections. Throughout the development and production of the Series, the editorial staff of Neurology and Neuroscience of Elsevier Science B.V. in Amsterdam has provided invaluable assistance.

F. Boller

J. Grafman

List of contributors

Bartolomeo, P. INSERM Unit 324, Centre Paul Broca, 2 ter rue d'Alesia, Paris, F-65014, France and Neuropsychology Unit, Henri-Mondor Hospital, Cretéil, France
E-mail: paolo@broca.inserm.fr

Barton, J.J.S. Department of Neurology, KS 452, Human Vision and Eye Movement Laboratory, Beth Israel Deaconess Medical Center, Harvard Medical School, 330 Brookline Avenue, Boston, MA 02215, USA *and* Department of Bioengineering, Boston University, Boston, MA 02215, USA
E-mail: jbarton@caregroup.harvard.edu

Behrmann, M. Department of Psychology, Carnegie Mellon University, Baker Hall 331H, Pittsburgh, PA 15213-3890, USA
E-mail: behrmann@cnbc.cmu.edu

Chokron, S. Laboratoire de Psychologie Expérimentale, CNRS ep 617, Grenoble, France
E-mail: sylvie@petlab.mssm.edu

Colby, C.L. Department of Neuroscience and Center for the Neural Basis of Cognition, University of Pittsburgh, 446 Crawford Hall, Pittsburgh, PA 15232, USA
E-mail: ccolby@cnbc.cmu.edu

Coslett, H.B. University of Pennsylvania School of Medicine, 3400 Spruce St., Philadelphia, PA 19140, USA
E-mail: hbc@mail.med.upenn.edu

Farah, M.J. Department of Psychology, University of Pennsylvania, 3815 Walnut Street, Philadelphia, PA 19104-6198, USA
E-mail: farah@cattell.psych.upenn.edu

Feinberg, T.E. Neurobehavior and Alzheimer's Disease Center, Beth Israel Medical Center, 317 East 17th Street, Fierman Hall, 9th Floor, New York, NY 10003, USA
E-mail: tfeinberg@bethisraelny.org

Goldberg, M.E. Laboratory of Sensorimotor Research, National Eye Institute, Bldg 49 Room 2A50, NIH, Bethesda, MD 20892, USA *and* Department of Neurology, Georgetown University School of Medicine, Washington, DC 20007, USA
E-mail: meg@Isr.nei.nih.gov

Grossi, D. Second Neurologic Department, School of Medicine, Federico II University, Nuovo Policlinico – Ed 17, Via S Pansini 5, 80131 Napoli, Italy
E-mail: dagrossi@unina.it

Humphreys, G.W. Behavioural Brain Sciences Research Centre, School of Psychology, University of Birmingham, Birmingham B15 2TT, UK
E-mail: humphreg@psycho1.bham.ac.uk

Moscovitch, M. Rotman Research Institute, Baycrest Centre for Geriatric Care, 3560 Bathurst Street, North York, ON M6A 2E1, Canada
E-mail: momos@credit.erin.utoronto.ca

Rafal, R. School of Psychology, University of Wales, Bangor, The Brigantia Building, Penrallt Road, Bangor LL57 2AS, Wales, UK
E-mail: r.rafal@bangor.ac.uk

Riddoch, M.J. Behavioural Brain Sciences Research Centre, School of Psychology, University of Birmingham, Birmingham B15 2TT, UK
E-mail: riddochj@psg-fs2.bham.ac.uk

Roane, D.M. Department of Psychiatry, Beth Israel Medical Center, 317 East 17th Street, Fierman Hall, 9th Floor, New York, NY 10003, USA
E-mail: droane@bethisraelny.org

Saffran, E.M. Department of Communication Sciences, Temple University Hospital, 3401 N. Broad Street, Philadelphia, PA 19140, USA
E-mail: saffran@vm.temple.edu

Tranel, D. Department of Neurology, Division of Behavioral Neurology and Cognitive Neuroscience, University of Iowa College of Medicine, 200 Hawkins Drive, Iowa City, IA 52242, USA
E-mail: daniel-tranel@uiowa.edu

Trojano, L. Salvatore Maugeri Foundation, Rehabilitation Center of Telese (BN), I.R.C.C.S., Via Bagni Vecchi, 82037 Telese Terme (BN), Italy
E-mail: lutroj@tin.it

Weiskrantz, L. Department of Experimental Psychology, University of Oxford, South Parks Road, Oxford OX1 3UD, UK
E-mail: larry.weiskrantz@psy.ox.ac.uk

Contents

Handbook of Neuropsychology, 2nd Edition, Vol. 4
M. Behrmann (Ed)

CHAPTER 1

Central color processing and its disorders

Daniel Tranel

Department of Neurology, Division of Behavioral Neurology and Cognitive Neuroscience, University of Iowa College of Medicine, 200 Hawkins Drive, Iowa City, IA 52242, USA

Introduction

The 'central' processing of color information refers to the stages of color processing that occur at the level of primary visual cortex and beyond, i.e. at higher brain levels. The brain regions known to be important for color perception include primary visual cortex and early visual association cortices in the lingual and fusiform gyri (Fig. 1). These correspond to parts of Brodmann areas 17 and 18/19, which are also known as areas V1, V2/V3, and V4 (cf. Felleman and Van Essen, 1991). Acquired damage to these regions, and to higher order visually related cortices in the occipitotemporal junction, can produce various disturbances of color processing, including impaired color perception, color imagery, color recognition, and color naming (Tranel, 1997). This chapter reviews these conditions, and their neu-

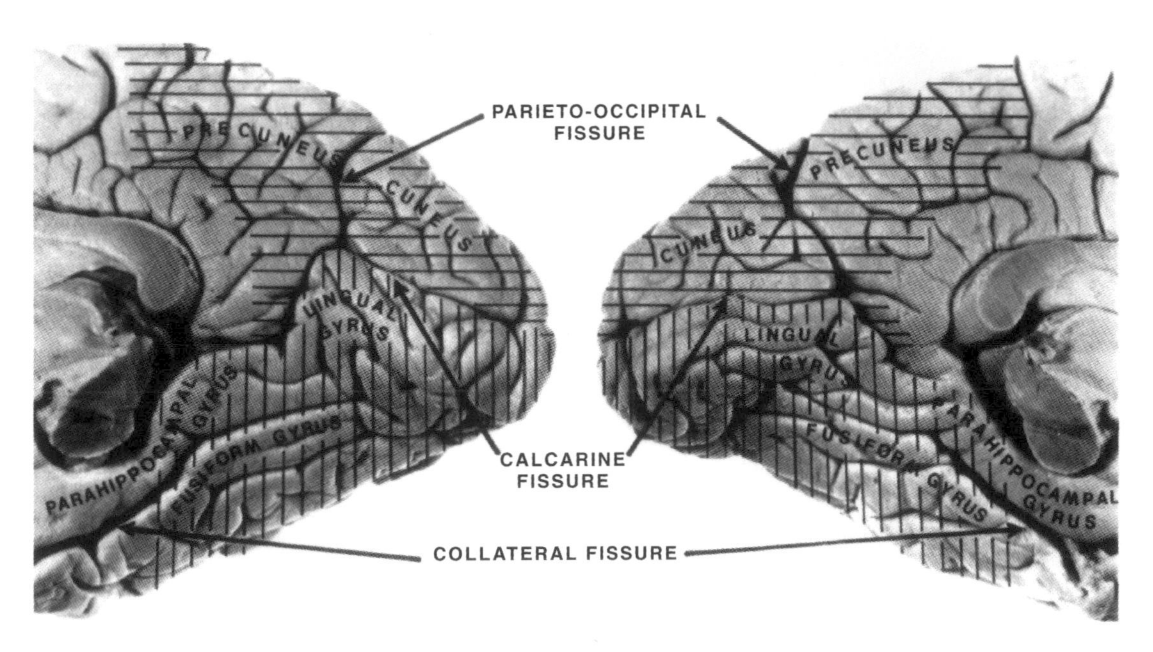

Fig. 1. Mesial view of the human brain, showing major sulci and gyri. The regions that are important for various aspects of color processing include the lingual gyrus and the posterior portion of the fusiform gyrus, located below the calcarine fissure in the medial and ventral aspects of the hemispheres. From Damasio, Tranel and Rizzo (2000), used with permission from the authors and publishers.

ral correlates, with an emphasis on what has been learned about brain–behavior relationships in regard to color processing from the scientific study of these conditions. I should emphasize again that my focus here is on disorders of central processing of color that occur as a consequence of acquired brain injury, and not on impairments of color vision that are peripheral, developmental, or congenital in nature [1]. This is an important distinction, since a relatively large number of individuals, particularly males, have some degree of inherited color 'blindness'. For instance, it has been estimated that about 1% of males are red-blind and about 2% are green-blind (Gouras, 1991). A working assumption throughout this chapter, then, is that an individual's premorbid color vision was normal.

Terminology

As alluded to above, four more-or-less separate aspects of central color processing can be distinguished: color perception, color imagery, color recognition, and color naming. Color perception simply refers to the capacity of seeing color, i.e. with primary and early secondary visual cortices. Color imagery refers to the capacity of imagining colors, or of imagining entities in color, e.g. bringing into one's mind's eye the image of a colorful scene, such as exemplified in Fig. 2. Color recognition is somewhat difficult to define, but it essentially refers to the assignment of psychological meaning to color information. It includes capacities such as knowing the difference between various colors, knowing the colors in which various entities normally appear, and knowing that colors can vary as functions of properties such as brightness, saturation, and hue. In fact, such color knowledge is, from a psychological perspective, quite robust: for example, there is wide consensus about typical colors for entities (Joseph and Proffitt, 1996; Saunders and van Brakel, 1997), and persons make very reliable judgments about which colors are characteristic of particular entities (Siple and Springer, 1983). Color naming refers to the capacity of applying a lexical term to a color, e.g. naming the color of grass as 'green'.

[1] A fascinating study of the peripheral processing of color (i.e. in the retina) can be found in Roorda and Williams (1999).

Measurement

Before discussing disorders of color processing, it is worthwhile to spend a few moments on issues of measurement. I will cover measurement of color perception, color recognition, and color naming. Measurement of color imagery really depends on the self-report of the patient, and I am not aware of a quantitative, objective means by which this can be accomplished. Rizzo, Smith, Pokorny and Damasio (1993) have outlined a variety of state-of-the-art testing procedures for quantifying various color-related processing capacities.

Color perception

Color-plate tests (e.g. the Ishihara Color Plate Test) and color arrangement tests (e.g. the Farnsworth-Munsell 100-Hue Test) are used to measure color perception. The color arrangement tests in particular are useful with patients who may have naming impairments (including aphasic patients), since the tests do not depend on the production of verbal responses. It is important to measure color perception separately in all four quadrants of vision, since the most common disorders of color perception affect either a quadrant or hemifield, and to explore both peripheral and central vision. For example, by using a well-saturated colored object (e.g. the color chips from the Token Test of the Multilingual Aphasia Examination), the examiner can pass the object back and forth slowly between the patient's quadrants of vision, and inquire as to whether the color of the object appears to change when either the horizontal or vertical midlines are crossed. Patients with color perception defects will give characteristic responses in this paradigm: for example, when the object moves from peripheral to central vision, or crosses one of the midlines, the patients will indicate that the color of the object has "dimmed", or "changed", or even "disappeared".

Color recognition

Both verbal and nonverbal procedures should be used to assess color recognition. Verbal tasks consist of asking the patient questions about color knowledge, and two types of questions should be posed, one in which a color name constitutes the response (e.g. "What color is a banana?"), and one in which a color

Fig. 2. A scene from west-central Wyoming, showing spectacular colors in the Rocky Mountains.

name is in the question (e.g. "What are some things that are blue?"). A nonverbal task involves presenting the patient with black-and-white line drawings of characteristically colored entities (e.g. a carrot or snowman), and asking the patient to select from colored foils the correct color for the entity (Fig. 3). In these tasks, it is important to include at least some items whose color names are uncommon verbal associates (e.g. eggplant), to provide a more rigorous test of true color knowledge, because for many common entities, the verbal association between the color name and object name is quite prepotent, and may be sufficient for the patient to answer the question accurately even if color knowledge is impaired (e.g. "blue" sky, "green" grass). We have shown for other verbal sets of this type that knowledge about the lexical items that complete the set does not imply knowledge about the entities referred to by the lexical items (Damasio and Tranel, 1990).

Color naming

Two types of tasks can be used to assess color naming, one in which the patient is asked to produce color names to colored stimuli (e.g. "What color is this [a yellow pencil]?"), and one in which the patient is asked to point to colored stimuli, given a color name (e.g. "Point to all the objects in this tray that are orange".). It is often worthwhile to ask for both oral and written responses in the first task, particularly with aphasic patients, because one may observe important dissociations between the ability to produce color names orally versus in writing. Testing should cover the basic set of 6–10 colors that are widely known by normal individuals (cf. Berlin and Kay, 1969; Bornstein, 1985). More extensive investigation is not recommended, since the effects of special expertise become the predominant influence on performance (e.g. testing a visual artist) and idiosyncratic, nongeneralizable findings may result.

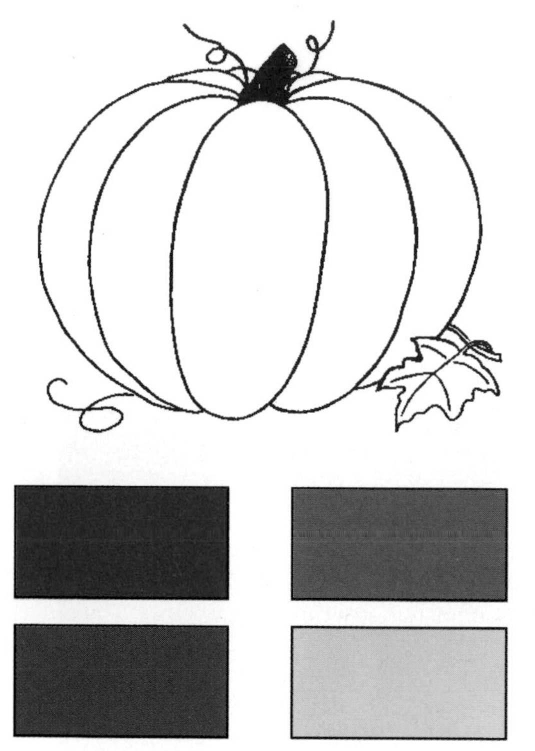

Fig. 3. An example of an item from a color matching test. The patient is required to select from the four color foils the one that best 'fits' the picture (orange — pumpkin).

Disorders of color perception (central achromatopsia)

Central achromatopsia is defined as an impairment of color perception caused by an acquired cerebral lesion. Mechanisms that have been proposed for this disorder include reduced hue discrimination (e.g. Heywood et al., 1987; Victor, Maiese, Shapley et al., 1989) and defective color constancy (Zeki, 1990), but so far, this issue remains poorly understood (Hurlbert, Bramwell, Heywood and Cowey, 1998; Ruttiger, Braun, Gegenfurtner et al., 1999). In any event, the core feature of central achromatopsia is an acquired inability to perceive color normally, in the setting of intact or relatively intact processing of many other components of visual perception, especially form, motion, and depth (e.g. Heywood, Kentridge and Cowey, 1998). A neurobiological model of central color processing has been recently proposed (Wray and Edelman, 1996).

Clinical presentation

Central achromatopsia is relatively rare, especially in full field; more commonly, a quadrant or hemifield of vision is affected (Damasio et al., 1980; Kolmel, 1988; Meadows, 1974; Paulson, Galetta, Grossman and Alavi, 1994; Rizzo et al., 1993). Within the affected portion of vision, it is common for the periphery to be more affected than central vision; in fact, the portion of the visual field near the fovea is often entirely spared. Affected patients usually do not complain that they have entirely lost the capacity to see color. Instead, they tend to present with complaints that colors look "washed out", "dim", or "dirty", although, in severe cases, the patient may note that the visual panorama has turned entirely to black and white and shades of gray. Another common complaint is that the ambient lighting is poor, and this complaint may persist even in naturally or artificially well-lit environments. Achromatopsic patients do tend to be exquisitely sensitive to poor lighting conditions, which invariably exacerbate the perceived severity of their color perception problems. Such patients are frequently aided, at least psychologically, by simple measures, such as increasing the level of ambient lighting (e.g. using 100-W bulbs throughout the house).

Neuro-ophthalmological features

When patients present with complaints of altered color perception, it is important to obtain careful neuro-ophthalmological assessment, so that it can be accurately determined just what is and is not wrong with the patient's vision in various parts of the field. As alluded to above, the vast majority of patients with central achromatopsia will manifest blindness (anopsia) in at least part of the visual field, usually a hemifield or quadrant. One common pattern is for there to be blindness in one quadrant of a hemifield, and achromatopsia in the other quadrant of the same hemifield. In the non-blind, but achromatopsic portion of the field, however, the patients usually do not have impairments of other aspects of vision, including spatial contrast sensitivity, flicker and motion perception, and depth perception (Cavanagh, Henaff, Michel et al., 1998; Rizzo et al., 1993).

Neuropsychological features

Achromatopsia (and the typically associated quadrant- or hemianopia) can occur as an isolated manifestation of acquired cerebral disease, especially if the responsible lesion is highly circumscribed; however, it is more common for there to be co-existent neuropsychological deficits, particularly in object recognition and reading. The object recognition impairment is known as visual agnosia, and this usually affects recognition of certain categories of entities, but not others. The most commonly affected class is faces, i.e. the patient loses, along with color perception, the ability to recognize familiar faces (prosopagnosia). Recognition of stimuli from other categories can also be affected, e.g. the patient may lose the ability to recognize animals, or fruits and vegetables, or tools. Visual object recognition impairments, in fact, almost always affect some categories of entities more than others, and striking category-related dissociations of object recognition have been the focus of a good deal of recent scientific inquiry (Damasio, Damasio, Tranel and Brandt, 1990; Farah, Meyer and McMullen, 1996; Hillis and Caramazza, 1991; Sartori, Job, Miozzo et al., 1993; Tranel, Damasio and Damasio, 1997a,b; Tranel, Logan, Frank and Damasio 1997c; Warrington and McCarthy, 1994; Warrington and Shallice, 1984). It is important to emphasize that the co-existence of achromatopsia and visual agnosia does not imply any cause-and-effect relationship, because many patients with severe color perception deficits can recognize entities normally, and conversely, most entities are recognized nearly as easily when presented in black-and-white as when presented in color, although color does have an influence on recognition, especially latency (Joseph and Proffitt, 1996; Siple and Springer, 1983). Instead, the reason why these neuropsychological manifestations tend to occur together has to do with neuroanatomical factors: the neural systems important for color perception are very close to those required for visual recognition of various entities, and thus, a single lesion has a good chance of damaging both sets of neural structures. An example of a patient with achromatopsia and prosopagnosia is shown in Fig. 4.

An acquired impairment of reading, known as acquired alexia, is another neuropsychological manifestation frequently associated with central achromatopsia. So-called 'pure alexia' (also known as 'alexia without agraphia'), in which the patient loses the ability to read, but can write normally, occurs with left-sided inferior occipital/occipitotemporal lesions that also produce right-field hemiachromatopsia; this is the most common pattern associated with the conjunction of these symptoms. As in the case of visual agnosia described above, the co-occurrence of the neuropsychological manifestations of alexia and achromatopsia is due to the close proximity of neural structures important for these two functions, so that a single lesion can easily damage both systems (Damasio and Damasio, 1983), and not because reading depends in any way on color perception. Incidentally, the reading deficits that develop following acquired brain injury may be relatively subtle, especially in the chronic phase of recovery (i.e. months or years after the onset of brain injury). Thus, it is important to use sensitive tests to measure reading, one example of which is the Iowa-Chapman Reading Test recently developed and standardized in our laboratory (Manzel and Tranel, 1999).

One other neuropsychological manifestation that sometimes occurs together with achromatopsia is topographical disorientation. In this condition, patients lose the ability to navigate familiar routes, or to learn new ones (see Barrash, 1998, for review). Again, the co-occurrence of these disorders is attributable to the proximity of neural structures required for each function, and not because route learning is dependent on normal color vision. For example, a recent large-scale lesion study has demonstrated that topographical learning is highly dependent on structures in right and left mesial occipitotemporal regions (Barrash, Damasio, Adolphs and Tranel, 2000). Also, functional imaging studies have consistently demonstrated activation, usually bilaterally, of the mesial occipital/occipitotemporal cortices during learning and recall of topographical information (e.g. Aguirre and D'Esposito, 1997; Aguirre, Detre, Alsop and D'Esposito, 1996; Maguire, Burgess, Donnett et al., 1998). As noted, the ability to perceive color does not appear to be critical for normal topographical orientation; however, the extent to which topographical learning and recall may depend to some extent on color knowledge remains an unanswered question.

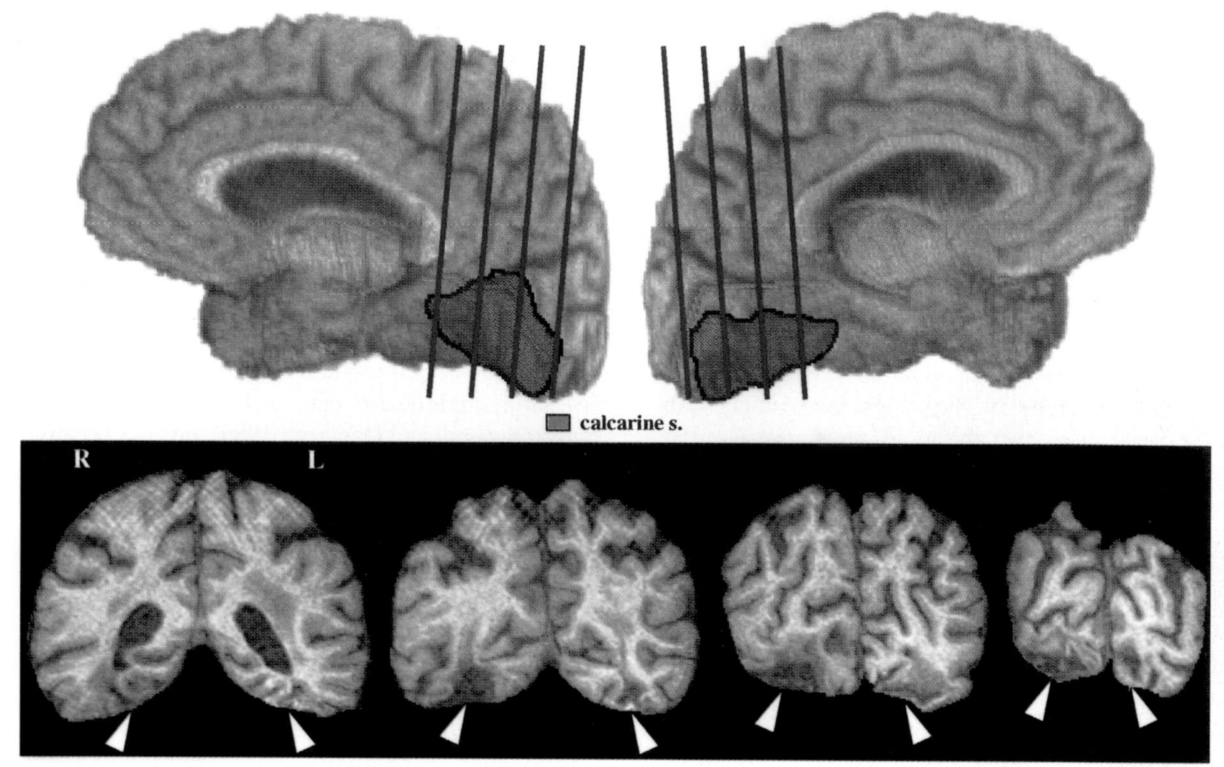

Fig. 4. Top: mesial views of a three-dimensional MRI reconstruction of a patient who sustained bilateral infarcts in the infracalcarine visual association cortices. Bottom: the lesions are shown in coronal MRI sections (arrows). The patient had bilateral superior quadrantanopia. In the lower fields, form vision was normal, but color perception was impaired. From Tranel, Grabowski and Damasio (1998b), used with permission from the authors and publishers.

Neural correlates

Lesion studies

Bilateral lesions in the inferior occipital region and in the occipitotemporal junction, in and near the lingual and fusiform gyri, have been associated with full-field central achromatopsia (Damasio et al., 1980). Unilateral lesions in the same region are associated with hemiachromatopsia in the field contralateral to the lesion. As noted earlier, the most common presentation of central achromatopsia involves a combination of quadrantanopia and quadrantachromatopsia: in the hemifield opposite the lesion, the patient will be blind in the upper quadrant, and have a loss of color perception in the lower quadrant. Right-sided occipital/occipitotemporal lesions may produce a relatively pure pattern of this type; comparable left-sided lesions typically produce alexia along with achromatopsia. In both cases, some degree of visual agnosia and topographical disorientation may be manifest. An example of a patient with a left occipitotemporal lesion causing right-field hemiachromatopsia, 'pure' alexia, and category-specific visual object agnosia is presented in Fig. 5.

Studies using the lesion method have pointed to damage in the middle third of the lingual gyrus as the most consistent neuroanatomical correlate of central achromatopsia (Rizzo et al., 1993). Another common correlate is damage to the white matter immediately behind the posterior tip of the lateral ventricle. A recent case study reported an intriguing pattern of deficits in which a patient with a circumscribed lesion in the right fusiform gyrus developed color and form perception impairments in the left superior quadrant, but maintained normal motion perception in this quadrant (Merigan, Freeman and Meyers, 1997). The relationship between color perception and motion perception has been

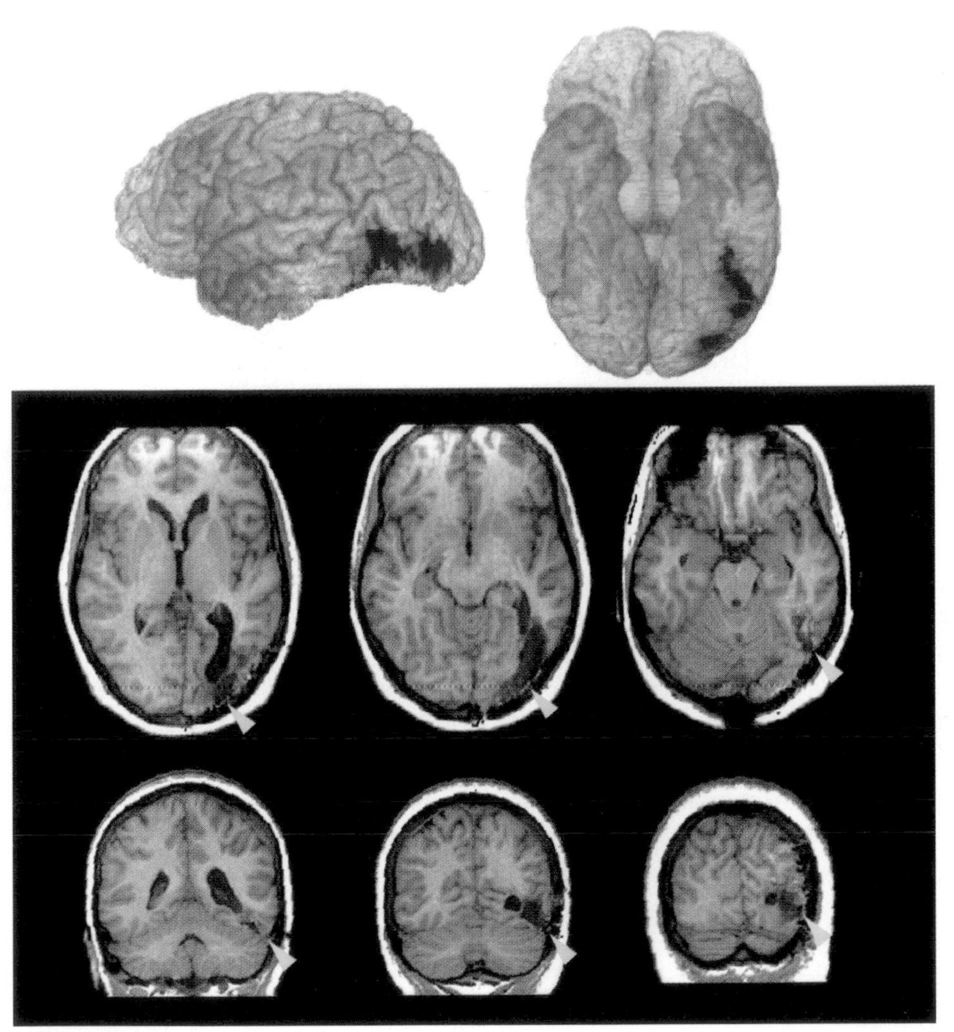

Fig. 5. Three-dimensional reconstruction of a T1-weighted MRI in a patient with hemiachromatopsia, pure alexia, and category-specific visual object agnosia (animals impaired; tools normal). The lesion is centered in the left occipitotemporal region and involves parts of the lingual and fusiform gyri. From Tranel, Grabowski and Damasio, (1998b), used with permission from the authors and publishers.

investigated carefully in other recent lesion studies (Cavanagh et al., 1998; Heywood et al., 1998), and the findings have indicated clear anatomical separation for these capacities, consistent with a large body of experimental neurophysiological work in nonhuman primates (e.g. Hubel and Livingstone, 1987; Livingstone and Hubel, 1984, 1987).

Functional imaging studies

Functional imaging approaches to the investigation of the neural basis of color processing, including PET and fMRI, have corroborated and extended findings from the lesion work summarized above. For example, when subjects are asked to view colored stimuli, there is selective activation of areas in the region of the lingual and fusiform gyri, or the putative human area V4 (Chao and Martin, 1999; Clark, Parasuraman, Keil et al., 1997; Corbetta, Miezin, Dobmeyer et al., 1990, 1991; Lueck, Zeki, Friston et al., 1989; Sakai, Watanabe, Onodera et al., 1995; Zeki, Watson, Lueck et al., 1991). An interesting finding emphasized in the study by Clark et al. (1997) was that face processing and color processing tasks both tended to activate ventral occipitotemporal cortices, suggesting that the neural structures used for processing faces and colors have considerable overlap. This finding is consistent with the lesion studies adduced above, which have shown a strong association between achromatopsia and prosopagnosia.

Similar findings have been obtained in paradigms using electrophysiological measures (Allison, Begleiter, McCarthy et al., 1993; Plendl, Paulus, Roberts et al., 1993; Rosler, Heil and Henninghausen, 1995). One interesting and unresolved issue is that while the weight of the lesion work has been towards the importance of the lingual gyrus for color perception, the functional imaging work has emphasized the importance of the fusiform gyrus. This may have to do with the nature of the task demands in the functional imaging studies (or, relatedly, the types of 'control' tasks employed), or to a certain degree of imprecision in the lesion work (e.g. relatively large lesions that make it difficult to separate the relative contributions of the lingual and fusiform gyri), but in any event, the differences are worth exploring in more detail.

Disorders of color imagery

As noted earlier, the assessment of color imagery depends on the self-report of the patient. Patients may complain that they cannot imagine colors, or imagine entities with characteristic colors, or they may complain that they cannot remember the colors that objects should have. To explore such complaints, the examiner can inquire about what the world looks like in the patient's 'mind's eye'; responses absent of color information may suggest a color imagery deficit. Asking the patient to describe (from imagery) entities that do not have characteristic colors is also a useful approach (e.g. "What color is your car? Your favorite shirt? Your dog?"), as is asking about items whose color is determined by social convention (e.g. "What color is a yield sign? A mile-marker sign? The spades suit in a card deck?"). Because the coloration of such entities is idiosyncratic or arbitrary, the patient probably has to imagine the entities, in color, in order to answer such questions accurately (De Vreese, 1991; Farah, 1984). The examiner should also inquire about dreaming, i.e. does the patient dream in color? In particular, the patient should be asked whether there has been any change in the presence of color in dreams since the onset of a brain injury, since there is wide inter-individual variation in the extent to which persons dream in color.

Color imagery is intimately associated with color perception. In fact, one of the most contentious issues in this field is the question of whether the same brain regions used for color perception are used for color imagery (this is true of other aspects of visual perception and visual imagery, as well). Earlier work, based on lesion studies, suggested that achromatopsia is invariably accompanied by defective color imagery (Beauvois and Saillant, 1985; De Renzi and Spinnler, 1967), suggesting that the perception of color is dependent upon the same neural regions that support color imagery (Farah, 1988). Functional imaging studies have lent some support to this position, as well, showing that when subjects imagined and named the colors associated with various entities, similar neural regions were activated, specifically, the fusiform gyrus, bilaterally. However, some recent lesion studies are at variance with this position, suggesting that perception and imagery of color can be dissociated. The patient reported by De Vreese (1991) was noted to have preserved color perception, but impaired color imagery, and patients with the opposite dissociation — impaired color perception, but intact color imagery — have been reported by Shuren, Brott, Schefft and Houston (1996) and Bartolomeo, Bachoud-Levi and Denes (1997). And Chao and Martin (1999), using a PET paradigm, found that the retrieval of color knowledge (presumably related to some extent to color imagery) activated different neural regions from those activated by color perception, results which are also consistent with the notion that color imagery and color perception do not depend on exactly the same neural structures.

At this point, it is probably safe to conclude that the processes of perceiving color and of imagining color must rely on neural structures that are very close, if not identical. At the least, these structures would appear to include part of the fusiform gyrus, and perhaps part of the lingual gyrus. This issue is unresolved, though, and deserving of further study. Functional imaging paradigms, with the potential to provide a fairly high degree of spatial resolution, may help settle this question. As alluded to above, a comparable debate has been waged in regard to other aspects of visual perception, e.g. the extent to which the perception of objects and the imagery of objects depend on the same neural structures (e.g. D'Esposito, Detre, Aguirre et al., 1997; see Kosslyn, 1994, for a fuller discussion of this issue).

Disorders of color recognition (color agnosia)

For the purpose of this discussion, a strict definition of agnosia will be adopted, viz., a normal percept stripped of its meaning (cf. Teuber, 1968; Tranel and Damasio, 1996). Accordingly, color agnosia is defined as the loss of the ability to retrieve color knowledge pertinent to a given stimulus, that cannot be attributed to faulty perception or to impaired naming. Thus, patients with color agnosia will be impaired on tasks in which the retrieval of color knowledge is crucial: e.g. remembering the characteristic colors of various entities, recalling entities that appear in certain colors, choosing the correct color for an entity, and retrieving basic knowledge about color (e.g. knowing that mixing red and yellow will make orange).

Color agnosia is rare, and its study has been hampered by the confusing and sometimes contradictory ways in which the condition has been defined. Some authors, for example, have designated patients who cannot name colors correctly as having color agnosia (a similar confusion has punctuated the literature on visual object recognition; see Tranel and Damasio (1999) for discussion). In other cases, patients designated as color agnosic clearly had significant color perception defects, making the application of the term 'agnosia' somewhat dubious. Nonetheless, several well-studied cases of color agnosia have been reported (Farah, Levine and Calvanio, 1988; Kinsbourne and Warrington, 1964; Luzzatti and Davidoff, 1994; Schnider, Landis, Regard and Benson, 1992), although the neuropsychological specification of these cases is considerably better than the neuroanatomical description.

The neuroanatomical correlates of color agnosia include the occipitotemporal region, either unilaterally on the left or bilaterally; however, it remains unclear how this pattern differs from that which has been described in connection with central achromatopsia (e.g. Benton and Tranel, 1993). Presumably, the two conditions — color agnosia and achromatopsia — cannot share identical neuroanatomical substrates, but the studies available to date do not permit an unequivocal separation. In the two patients reported by Luzzatti and Davidoff (1994), one had a "left temporal" lesion, and the other had a "left temporo-parieto-occipital" lesion; the authors did not provide further anatomical detail. In the patient reported by Schnider et al. (1992), the lesion held responsible for the patient's color agnosia was described as "left inferotemporo-occipital". It would appear from the available evidence that color agnosia is probably associated with lesions that are somewhat anterior to those responsible for central achromatopsia; however, until further published cases provide better clarification of this issue, it has to be concluded that the neuroanatomical correlates of color agnosia remain elusive.

Functional imaging studies have recently provided some pertinent information on this issue. For example, PET studies from Martin's laboratory (Chao and Martin, 1999; Martin, Haxby, Lalonde et al., 1995) have shown activations in the left inferior temporal region, bilateral fusiform gyrus, and right lingual gyrus during a condition in which subjects were asked to retrieve previously acquired color knowledge. Martin and colleagues have emphasized that these regions do not overlap, at least completely, with those that have been identified as being activated by color perception per se, and are probably somewhat anterior and lateral to color perception substrates. Thus, the functional imaging work to date supports the same conclusion hinted at by previous lesion studies, namely, that the neural substrates for color perception and color knowledge are at least partially separable.

We had the opportunity to study a patient who premorbidly, was an expert in painting with oils. After sustaining bilateral occipitotemporal lesions, the patient found that he could no longer mix paints to obtain desired colors. Careful evaluation revealed that he suffered neither achromatopsia nor color anomia; he performed normally on all standard tests of color perception, and could name colors accurately. Interestingly, he even remained capable of articulating verbally the precise process he should apply to achieve certain colors (e.g. "I need to mix this dark red with this light blue and a hint of black to get the color I want for the shaded portion of this mountain scene ... "), but he could not perform the process 'intuitively', i.e. by mixing just the right amounts together to achieve the desired color. Arguably, this patient can be considered to have genuine loss of color knowledge, viz., color agnosia, albeit against a background of special expertise in this domain. As noted, the lesions in this patient were in the occipitotemporal region, bilaterally, and slightly anterior to those that have been associated most frequently with achromatopsia, providing some additional support for the notion that this lesion locus is a reliable correlate of color agnosia.

The most common neuropsychological correlates of color agnosia are visual object agnosia and, in rare cases, visual confrontation anomia, i.e. difficulty recognizing and naming objects, respectively. When visual object agnosia is present, it typically affects some conceptual categories more than others, with the most common pattern being a pronounced impairment in the recognition of living entities (especially animals) with relative or complete sparing of recognition of artifactual entities (e.g. tools and utensils). These findings converge well with recent studies of the neuroanatomical correlates of object recognition, which have suggested a crucial role for mesial occipital and occipitotemporal structures in the retrieval of conceptual knowledge for animals, whereas retrieval of knowledge for tools is associated with structures in the left occipito-temporo-parietal junction (Tranel et al., 1997a).

Disorders of color naming (color anomia)

Color anomia is defined as an impairment in the ability to name colors or to point to colors given their names, that is not due to aphasia and that cannot be attributed to defective color perception. The condition should not be diagnosed in patients who have severe general cognitive disturbance (e.g. dementia), or whose visual attention and perception are severely impaired. In the most typical presentation of color anomia, the patient will manifest a right homonymous hemianopia, but intact color and form perception in the left hemifield. Pure alexia (a reading defect without a writing impairment) is a highly frequent neuropsychological correlate of color anomia (Damasio and Damasio, 1983); in fact, color anomia almost never occurs without some degree of acquired reading defect (Davidoff and De Bleser, 1994; Mohr, Leicester, Stoddard and Sidman, 1971). Naming colors can be impaired selectively, i.e. without any defects in the perception, imagery, and recognition of colors (Damasio, McKee and Damasio, 1979; Geschwind and Fusillo, 1966; Rizzo and Damasio, 1989; Rizzo et al., 1993).

Color anomia is associated with lesions in the left mesial occipitotemporal region, in a subsplenial position (Davidoff and De Bleser, 1994; Damasio, Tranel and Rizzo, 2000). Such a lesion typically affects visual cortex or optic radiations in such a way so as to produce a right hemianopia; hence, the processing of visual information is confined to the right visual cortex. Also, the lesion is situated in a manner that prevents primary language areas in the left hemisphere from receiving information related to color, yielding the color naming impairment.

Interestingly, the naming of colors is actually one ability that is frequently spared in patients who otherwise have pronounced defects in naming for many other categories of stimuli. For example, Goodglass, Wingfield, Hyde and Theurkauf (1986) found, in a large study of many aphasic patients, that color naming frequently stood out as being unimpaired, even when severe naming defects for other stimuli were present, and this finding is consistent with an older case study (Yamadori and Albert, 1973). We have made similar observations in several recent large-scale studies of naming disorders, specifically, that the vast majority of patients with pronounced naming defects do not have impaired naming of colors (Damasio et al., 1990; Damasio and Damasio, 1992; Tranel et al., 1997b; Tranel, Damasio and Damasio, 1998a).

It is somewhat puzzling that the condition of color anomia has received such scant attention in the scientific literature in recent years. In fact, very little has been published on this topic since the definitive paper by Damasio et al. (1979), which is now more than two decades old. One can conjecture, though, on at least a couple of reasons why this might be the case. For one, the disorder is very rare; in fact, as noted above, color naming often stands out as a preserved naming capacity in patients who otherwise have severe naming deficits for many other categories of stimuli. There are a number of potential explanations for this phenomenon, but one factor that undoubtedly contributes is the fact that color names, and the stimuli to which they apply, comprise a very small, and essentially closed, set of items. Specifically, most individuals can name reliably less than a dozen or so colors, and beyond this, in-between, hybrid terms are usually applied (e.g. "blueish-green", "light red"). And new terms (and new stimuli) are not typically added to the prevailing cultural repertoire (cf. Saunders and van Brakel, 1997), that is, the class is 'closed'. Compare this to a category, such as prepositions, which is also 'closed' and generally considered to be relatively small, but actually contains upwards of a 100 different items (Landau and Jackendoff, 1993), or to the better-studied categories of nouns or even verbs, which have thousands of members. Hence, insofar as color naming is concerned, the task may be highly resistant to impairment by virtue of its simplicity and circumscribed nature.

Another factor may be the challenge of trying to separate experimentally the processes of word retrieval and conceptual knowledge retrieval, especially in normal individuals who are the typical subjects in functional imaging studies. In these studies, the characteristic method of assessing knowledge retrieval is to ask the subjects to name various stimuli, but of course, this directly confounds the processes of naming and recognition. Even in the best studies available to date, this problem cannot be dismissed (cf. Chao and Martin, 1999; Martin et al., 1995). In the Chao and Martin study, for example, which is probably the best study of this type available to date, the investigators found that naming the color of colored objects, relative to naming the colored objects, activated the left lingual gyrus and the inferior temporal cortex bilaterally. The authors noted that these areas of activation were essentially identical to those that were activated by tasks calling for color perception (lingual gyrus) or retrieving color knowledge (inferior temporal cortex). The experimental design, however, does not permit an unequivocal separation of color naming from other aspects of color processing, because the subjects in the study could not be prevented from engaging different aspects of color processing while performing the different experimental tasks. In short, such paradigms have yet to yield unequivocal information regarding the neural underpinnings of color naming, teased apart from the processes of color perception and retrieving other knowledge about color.

Summary

Although rare, disorders of color processing have provided a number of important insights into neuropsychological and neuroanatomical correlates of visual processing. Human lesion studies have furnished many testable hypotheses regarding color processing, and recent functional imaging approaches, including PET and fMRI, have begun to corroborate many of the clues derived from the lesion work. While many details have yet to be worked out, the available evidence points consistently to a role for mesial and ventral occipital and occipitotemporal regions for color processing. And for several color processing capacities, a predominant role for left-hemisphere occipital and occipitotemporal structures has been supported consistently. One of the most important findings from the literature, for which there is considerable convergent evidence from a wide range of different experimental approaches, is that color processing depends on neural structures which are separable, at least partially, from those that support other aspects of vision, including processing of form, depth, and motion.

Acknowledgements

This research was supported by Program Project Grant NINDS NS19632.

References

Aguirre GK, D'Esposito M: Environmental knowledge is subserved by separable dorsal/ventral neural areas. Journal of Neuroscience: 17; 2512–2518, 1997.

Aguirre GK, Detre JA, Alsop DC, D'Esposito M: The parahippocampus subserves topographical learning in man. Cerebral Cortex: 6; 823–829, 1996.

Allison T, Begleiter A, McCarthy G, Roessler E, Nobre AC, Spencer DD: Electrophysiological studies of color processing in human visual cortex. Electroencephalography and Clinical Neurophysiology: 88; 343–355, 1993.

Barrash J: A historical review of topographical disorientation and its neuroanatomical correlates. Journal of Clinical and Experimental Neuropsychology: 20; 807–827, 1998.

Barrash J, Damasio H, Adolphs R, Tranel D: The neuroanatomical correlates of route learning impairment. Neuropsychologia: 38; 820–836, 2000.

Bartolomeo P, Bachoud-Levi A-C, Denes G: Preserved imagery for colours in a patient with cerebral achromatopsia. Cortex: 33; 369–378, 1997.

Beauvois MF, Saillant B: Optic aphasia for colours and colour agnosia: a distinction between visual and visuo-verbal impairments in the processing of colours. Cognitive Neuropsychology: 2; 1–48, 1985.

Benton AL, Tranel D: Visuoperceptual, visuospatial, and visuoconstructive disorders. In Heilman KM, Valenstein E (Eds), Clinical Neuropsychology, 3rd ed. New York: Oxford University Press, pp. 165–213, 1993.

Berlin B, Kay P: Basic Color Terms. Berkeley, CA: University of California Press, 1969.

Bornstein MH: On the development of color naming in young children: data and theory. Brain and Language: 26; 72–93, 1985.

Cavanagh P, Henaff M-A, Michel F, Landis T, Troscianko T, Intriligator J: Complete sparing of high-contrast color input to motion perception in cortical color blindness. Nature Neuroscience: 1; 242–247, 1998.

Chao LL, Martin A: Cortical regions associated with perceiving, naming, and knowing about colors. Journal of Cognitive Neuroscience: 11; 25–35, 1999.

Clark VP, Parasuraman R, Keil K, Kulansky R, Fannon S, Maisog JM, Ungerleider LG, Haxby JV: Selective attention to face identity and color studied with fMRI. Human Brain Mapping: 5; 293–297, 1997.

Corbetta M, Miezin FM, Dobmeyer S, Shulman GL, Petersen SE: Attentional modulation of neural processing of shape, color, and velocity in humans. Science: 248; 1556–1559, 1990.

Corbetta M, Miezin FM, Dobmeyer S, Shulman GL, Petersen SE: Selective and divided attention during visual discriminations of shape, color, speed: functional anatomy by positron emission tomography. Journal of Neuroscience: 11; 2383–2402, 1991.

Damasio AR, Damasio H: The anatomic basis of pure alexia. Neurology: 33; 1573–1583, 1983.

Damasio AR, Damasio H: Brain and language. Scientific American: 267; 88–95, 1992.

Damasio AR, Damasio H, Tranel D, Brandt JP: The neural regionalization of knowledge access: preliminary evidence. Quantitative Biology: 55; 1039–1047, 1990.

Damasio AR, McKee J, Damasio H: Determinants of performance in color anomia. Brain and Language: 7; 74–85, 1979.

Damasio AR, Tranel D: Knowing that 'Colorado' goes with 'Denver' does not imply knowledge that 'Denver' is in 'Colorado'. Behavioural Brain Research: 40; 193–200, 1990.

Damasio AR, Tranel D, Rizzo M: Disorders of complex visual processing. In Mesulam MM (Ed), Principles of Behavioral and Cognitive Neurology. Philadelphia: Davis, pp. 332–372, 2000.

Damasio AR, Yamada T, Damasio H., Corbett J, McKee J: Central achromatopsia: behavioral, anatomic and physiologic aspects. Neurology: 30; 1064–1071, 1980.

Davidoff J, De Bleser R: Impaired picture recognition with preserved object naming and reading. Brain and Cognition: 24; 1–23, 1994.

D'Esposito M, Detre JA, Aguirre GK, Stallcup M, Alsop DC, Tippet LJ, Farah MJ: A functional MRI study of mental image generation. Neuropsychologia: 35; 725–730, 1997.

De Renzi E, Spinnler H: Impaired performance on color tasks in patients with hemispheric lesions. Cortex: 3; 194–217, 1967.

De Vreese LP: Two systems for colour-naming deficits: verbal disconnection vs colour imagery disorder. Neuropsychologia: 29; 1–18, 1991.

Farah MJ: The neurological basis of mental imagery: a componentional analysis. Cognition: 18; 245–272, 1984.

Farah MJ: Is visual imagery really visual? Overlooked evidence from neuropsychology. Psychological Review: 95; 307–317, 1988.

Farah MJ, Levine DN, Calvanio R: A case study of mental imagery deficit. Brain and Cognition: 8; 147–164, 1988.

Farah MJ, Meyer MM, McMullen PA: The living/nonliving dissociation is not an artifact: giving an a priori implausible hypothesis a strong test. Cognitive Neuropsychology: 13; 137–154, 1996.

Felleman DJ, Van Essen, DC: Distributed hierarchical processing in the primate cerebral cortex. Cerebral Cortex: 1; 1–47, 1991.

Geschwind N, Fusillo M: Color naming defects in association with alexia. Archives of Neurology: 15; 137–146, 1966.

Goodglass H, Wingfield A, Hyde MR, Theurkauf JC: Category specific dissociations in naming and recognition by aphasic patients. Cortex: 22; 87–102, 1986.

Gouras P: The perception of color. In Vision and Visual Dysfunction, Vol. VI. London: Macmillan, 1991.

Heywood CA, Kentridge RW, Cowey A: Form and motion from colour in cerebral achromatopsia. Experimental Brain Research: 123; 145–153, 1998.

Heywood CA, Wilson B, Cowey A: A case study of cortical colour "blindness" with relatively intact achromatic discrimination. Journal of Neurology, Neurosurgery, and Psychiatry: 50;20–29, 1987.

Hillis AE, Caramazza A: Category-specific naming and comprehension impairment: a double dissociation. Brain: 114; 2081–2094, 1991.

Hubel DH, Livingstone, MS: Segregation of form, color, and stereopsis in primate area 18. Journal of Neuroscience: 7; 3378–3415, 1987.

Hurlbert AC, Bramwell DI, Heywood C, Cowey A: Discrimination of cone contrast changes as evidence for colour constancy in cerebral achromatopsia. Experimental Brain Research: 123; 136–144, 1998.

Joseph JE, Proffitt DR: Semantic versus perceptual influences of color in object recognition. Journal of Experimental Psychology: Learning, Memory, and Cognition: 22; 407–429, 1996.

Kinsbourne M, Warrington EK: Observations on colour agnosia. Journal of Neurology, Neurosurgery and Psychiatry: 27; 296–299, 1964.

Kolmel HW: Pure homonymous hemiachromatopsia: Findings with neuro-ophthalmologic examination and imaging procedures. European Archives of Psychiatry and Neurological Sciences: 237; 237–243, 1988.

Kosslyn SM: Image and Brain: The Resolution of the Imagery Debate. Cambridge, MA: MIT Press, 1994.

Landau B, Jackendoff R: 'What' and 'where' in spatial language and spatial cognition. Behavioral and Brain Sciences: 16; 217–265, 1993.

Livingstone MS, Hubel DH: Anatomy and physiology of a color system in the primate visual cortex. Journal of Neuroscience: 4; 309–356, 1984.

Livingstone MS, Hubel DH: Psychophysical evidence for separate channels for the perception of form, color, movement, and depth. Journal of Neuroscience: 7; 3416–3468, 1987.

Lueck CJ, Zeki S, Friston, KJ et al.: The color centre in the cerebral cortex of man. Nature: 340; 386–389, 1989.

Luzzatti C, Davidoff J: Impaired retrieval of object-colour knowledge with preserved colour naming. Neuropsychologia: 32; 933–950, 1994.

Maguire EA, Burgess N, Donnett JG, Frackowiak RSJ, Frith CD, O'Keefe J: Knowing where and getting there: a human navigation network. Science: 280; 921–924, 1998.

Manzel K, Tranel D: Development and standardization of a reading test for brain-damaged patients. Developmental Neuropsychology: 15; 407–420, 1999.

Martin A, Haxby JV, Lalonde FM, Wiggs CL, Ungerleider LG: Discrete cortical regions associated with knowledge of color and knowledge of action. Science: 270; 102–105, 1995.

Meadows JC: Disturbed perception of colors associated with localized cerebral lesions. Brain: 97; 615–632, 1974.

Merigan W, Freeman, A, Meyers SP: Parallel processing streams in human visual cortex. NeuroReport: 8; 3985–3991, 1997.

Mohr JP, Leicester J, Stoddard LT, Sidman M: Right hemianopia with memory and color deficits in circumscribed left posterior cerebral artery territory infarction. Neurology: 21; 1104–1113, 1971.

Paulson HL, Galetta SL, Grossman M, Alavi A: Hemiachromatopsia of unilateral occipitotemporal infarcts. American Journal of Ophthalmology: 118; 518–523, 1994.

Plendl H, Paulus W, Roberts IG, Botzel K, Towell A, Pitman JR, Scherg M, Halliday AM: The time course and location of cerebral evoked activity associated with the processing of colour stimuli in man. Neuroscience Letters: 150; 9–12, 1993.

Rizzo M, Damasio AR: Acquired central achromatopsia. In Kulikowski JJ, Dickinson CM, Murray IJ (Eds), Seeing Contour and Color. Oxford: Pergamon Press, pp. 758–763, 1989.

Rizzo M, Smith V, Pokorny J, Damasio AR: Color perception profiles in central achromatopsia. Neurology: 43; 995–1001, 1993.

Roorda A, Williams DR: The arrangement of the three cone classes in the living human eye. Nature: 397; 520–522, 1999.

Rosler F, Heil M, Henninghausen E: Distinct cortical activation patterns during long-term memory retrieval of verbal, spatial, and color information. Journal of Cognitive Neuroscience: 7; 51–65, 1995.

Ruttiger L, Braun DI, Gegenfurtner KR, Petersen D, Schonle P, Sharpe LT: Selective color constancy deficits after circumscribed unilateral brain lesions. Journal of Neuroscience: 19; 3094–3106, 1999.

Sakai K, Watanabe E, Onodera Y, Uchida I, Kato H, Yamamoto E, Koizumi H, Miyashita, Y: Functional mapping of the human colour centre with echo-planar magnetic resonance imaging. Proceedings of the Royal Society of London B: 261; 89–98, 1995.

Sartori G, Job R, Miozzo M, Zago S, Marchiori G: Category-specific form-knowledge deficit in a patient with herpes simplex virus encephalitis. Journal of Clinical and Experimental Neuropsychology: 15; 280–299, 1993.

Saunders BAC, van Brakel, J: Are there nontrivial constraints on colour categorization? Behavioral and Brain Sciences: 20; 167–228, 1997.

Schnider A, Landis T, Regard M, Benson DF: Dissociation of color from object in amnesia. Archives of Neurology: 49; 982–985, 1992.

Shuren JE, Brott TG, Schefft BK, Houston W: Preserved color imagery in an achromatopsic. Neuropsychologia: 34; 485–489, 1996.

Siple P, Springer, RM: Memory and preference for the colors of objects. Perception and Psychophysics: 34; 363–370, 1983.

Teuber HL: Alteration of perception and memory in man. In Weiskrantz L (Ed), Analysis of Behavioral Change. New York: Harper and Row, pp. 268–375, 1968.

Tranel D: Disorders of color processing (perception, imagery, recognition, and naming). In Feinberg TE, Farah, MJ (Eds), Behavioral Neurology and Neuropsychology. New York: McGraw Hill, pp. 257–265, 1997.

Tranel D, Damasio AR: The agnosias and apraxias. In Bradley WG, Daroff RB, Fenichel GM, Marsden CD (Eds), Neurology in Clinical Practice, 2nd ed. Stoneham, MA: Butterworth, pp. 119–129, 1996.

Tranel D, Damasio AR: The neurobiology of knowledge retrieval. Behavioral and Brain Sciences: 22; 303, 1999.

Tranel D, Damasio H, Damasio AR: A neural basis for the retrieval of conceptual knowledge. Neuropsychologia: 35; 1319–1327, 1997a.

Tranel D, Damasio H, Damasio AR: On the neurology of naming. In Goodglass H, Wingfield A (Eds), Anomia: Neuroanatomical and Cognitive Correlates. New York: Academic Press, pp. 65–90, 1997b.

Tranel D, Damasio H, Damasio AR: The neural basis of lexical retrieval. In Parks RW, Levine DS, Long DL (Eds), Fundamentals of Neural Network Modeling: Neuropsychology and Cognitive Neuroscience. Cambridge, MA: MIT Press, pp. 271–296, 1998a.

Tranel D, Grabowski TJ, Damasio H: Behavorial neurology. In Rosenberg RN (Ed.), Atlas of Clinical Neurology. Philadelphia: Butterworth-Heinemann/Current Medicine, Inc., Chapter 7, 1998b.

Tranel D, Logan, CG, Frank RJ, Damasio AR: Explaining category-related effects in the retrieval of conceptual and lexical knowledge for concrete entities: operationalization and analysis of factors. Neuropsychologia: 35; 1329–1339, 1997c.

Victor JD, Maiese K, Shapley R, Sidtis J, Gazzaniga MS: Acquired central dyschromatopsia: analysis of a case with preservation of color discrimination. Clinical Vision Sciences: 4; 183–196, 1989.

Warrington EK, McCarthy RA: Multiple meaning systems in the brain: a case for visual semantics. Neuropsychologia: 32; 1465–1473, 1994.

Warrington EK, Shallice T: Category specific semantic impairments. Brain: 107; 829–853, 1984.

Wray J, Edelman GM: A model of color vision based on cortical reentry. Cerebral Cortex: 6; 701–716, 1996.
Yamadori A, Albert ML: Word category aphasia. Cortex: 9; 83–89, 1973.
Zeki S: A century of cerebral achromatopsia. Brain, 113, 1727–1777, 1990.
Zeki SM, Watson JDG, Lueck CJ, Friston KJ, Kennard C, Frackowiak RSJ: A direct demonstration of functional specialization in human visual cortex. Journal of Neuroscience: 11; 641–649, 1991.

Handbook of Neuropsychology, 2nd Edition, Vol. 4
M. Behrmann (Ed)

CHAPTER 2

Brain damage and eye movements

Jason J.S. Barton *

Department of Neurology, KS 452, Human Vision and Eye Movement Laboratory, Beth Israel Deaconess Medical Center, Harvard Medical School, 330 Brookline Avenue, Boston, MA 02215, USA
Department of Bioengineering, Boston University, Boston, MA, USA

Introduction

Given the highly developed nature of the human visual system, eye movements play an important role in how we perceive and interact with the environment. More is known about the cerebral control of the ocular motor system than about that of any other motor response. On the one hand, the limited degrees of freedom in the natural range of eye movements simplifies their study, when compared to movements of limbs containing multiple joints. On the other, the existence of parallel subsystems of ocular motor responses reveals a sophisticated repertoire of responses dependent upon the type of sensory input and volitional state of the subject. The investigation of eye movements can provide insight not only about the control of motor behavior but also indirectly about perceptual and attentional processing.

This review is narrowed to the changes in eye movements due to focal lesions of the cerebral hemispheres, such as strokes, hemorrhages and tumors. These effects are more subtle than those due to focal lesions of the cerebellum and brainstem, which are reviewed elsewhere in detail (Leigh and Zee, 1999). The effects of diffuse or degenerative conditions of the cerebrum, such as Alzheimer's disease (Fletcher and Sharpe, 1986; Fletcher and Sharpe, 1988), AIDS (Johnston, Miller and Nath, 1996), and parkinsonism (Kennard and Lueck, 1989), are also not discussed, because these are less informative about the localization of function. Knowledge about the effects of focal lesions should aid the interpretation of ocular motor deficits from more diffuse cerebral lesions.

Disorders of ocular motor generation and control

The ocular motor system is traditionally divided into a number of subsystems, including saccades, smooth pursuit, vergence, fixation, and the gaze stabilization systems of optokinetic and vestibulo-ocular responses. In this section, we review the effects of cerebral lesions upon each of these systems separately. In addition, the complementary information gained from the newer technologies of functional imaging and transcranial magnetic stimulation will be discussed.

Saccades

Saccades are voluntary eye movements that shift fixation of the fovea rapidly from one object to another. They are among the most extensively studied volitional movements. Also, because they are closely allied to attention, they have been studied as indirect markers of the attentive and perceptual experience of the observer. In general, most unilateral cerebral lesions do not cause symptoms related to saccadic dysfunction, and the signs are difficult to detect without eye movement recordings. Bilateral lesions are more evident clinically.

* Tel.: +1 (617) 667-1243; Fax: +1 (617) 975-5322;
E-mail: jbarton@caregroup.harvard.edu

The standard laboratory saccadic paradigm has a subject fixate a light in the midst of a bland background, which then disappears at the same time a peripheral target for the saccade appears. Unlike brainstem and cerebellar lesions, most cerebral lesions do not alter basic characteristics, such as velocity and accuracy of these *visually guided saccades*, and latencies are minimally affected if at all. Rather, more complex experimental designs are required to reveal cortical deficits in saccadic control.

Gap and *overlap* tasks (Saslow, 1967) desynchronize the disappearance of the central fixation point and the appearance of the saccadic target. This dissociates two processes: the disengagement of fixation from a currently viewed location and the generation of a saccade to a new location. In the gap task, the fixation light disappears before the target appears, creating a period of about 200 ms without a visible light. The disengagement of fixation prior to target appearance reduces saccadic latency and generates a subpopulation named *express saccades*, with latencies around 110 ms (Fischer, 1986). In the overlap task, having the fixation light remain on for more than 100 ms after the target appears increases mean latency to 250 ms.

With *memory-guided saccades*, subjects look at the fixation light, which remains on while the target is flashed briefly, only making the saccade to the location of the vanished target when the fixation light disappears a few seconds later. Thus they must suppress the tendency to make an immediate *anticipatory* saccade and retain the target location in spatial working memory.

Target sequences are also used. In the *double saccadic target* paradigm (Becker and Jürgens, 1979; Wheeless, Boynton and Cohen, 1966), two targets are flashed sequentially before a saccade is initiated. If the second target appears just before the subject responds, then two saccades are generated, one to the location of the first target followed by another to that of the second. The size of the second saccade must take into account the change in retinal coordinates of the second target's location after the gaze shift caused by the first saccade (Fig. 1). This requires updating of saccadic programming with eye position data.

Complex sequences of several target steps can be shown, with instructions to look at each location in the correct order. This tests the ability to generate and store a temporo-spatial pattern of saccadic activity (Fig. 2).

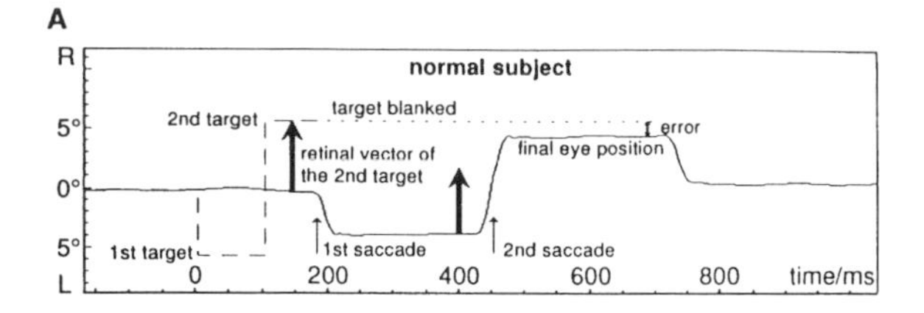

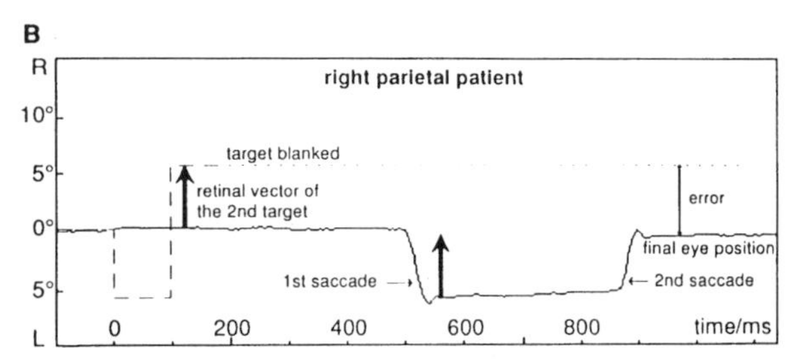

Fig. 1. Double saccadic target paradigm. Horizontal target (dotted line) and eye position (solid line) are plotted as a function of time. The target moves left, then right, and disappears, all before either subject makes the first saccade leftward. After the first saccade, the normal subject (top graph) takes into account both the retinal vector of the last target position as well as the amplitude of their first saccade, to compute a second saccade that is accurate to the last location of the target. The patient with a parietal lesion (bottom graph) does not take into account his initial saccade, and his second saccade approximates the retinal vector of the second target position. (From Heide et al., 1995, with permission.)

Last, there is the *antisaccade* (Hallett, 1978; Hallett and Adams, 1980). Instead of directing a saccade at a suddenly appearing target, subjects must make a saccade in the opposite direction (Fig. 3). Thus they must both suppress an automatic response (the visually guided saccade) and execute a novel one (the antisaccade).

Brain regions active during saccades: functional imaging

Human areas with saccade-related activity have been identified with a variety of functional techniques. A xenon study of regional cerebral blood flow (Melamed and Larsen, 1979) mapped the frontal eye field (FEF) to a region extending from the middle of the precentral gyrus, between the mouth and hand regions, to the posterior part of the middle

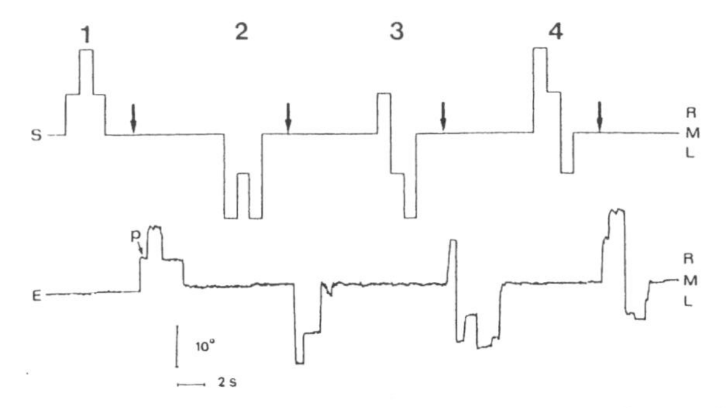

Fig. 2. Saccadic sequences. Horizontal target (top line) and eye (bottom line) are plotted as a function of time. The target jumps in a sequence of three positions before returning to the mid-position. The subject continues to fixate the mid-position until a signal is given at the arrows, when they are supposed to duplicate the sequence performed by the target. This subject with an SEF lesion performs trial 1 well, but not the others. (From Gaymard et al., 1993, with permission.)

frontal gyrus. This FEF localization has been confirmed with more recent PET (Fox, Fox, Raichle and Burde, 1985) and fMRI studies (Bodis-Wollner, Bucher, Seelos et al., 1997; Darby, Nobre, Thangaraj et al., 1996), which all indicate that human FEF is located in Brodmann areas 4 and 6, rather than in area 8, as it is in monkeys (Paus, 1996). Human FEF

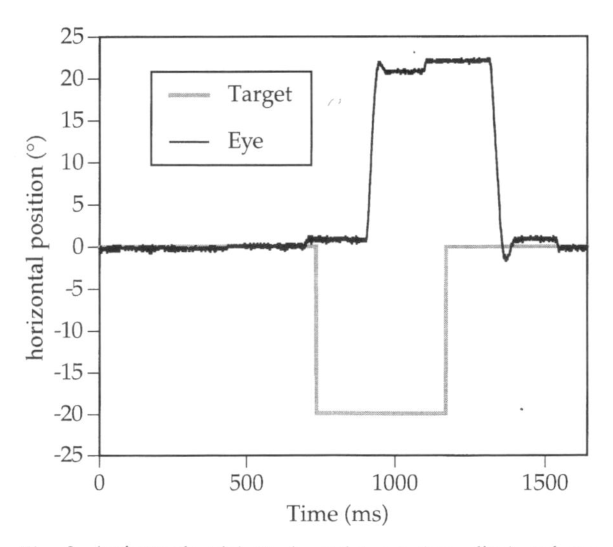

Fig. 3. Antisaccade trial. Horizontal target (gray line) and eye position (black line) are plotted as a function of time. The target moves leftward at about 700 ms, and this normal subject makes a correct antisaccade in the opposite direction, after a latency of 175 ms.

is activated both by horizontal and vertical saccades to visual targets (Melamed and Larsen, 1979) and by saccades to auditory or internally generated targets in darkness or with eyes closed (Bodis-Wollner et al., 1997; Darby et al., 1996; Fox et al., 1985). It is even activated by imagined saccades (Bodis-Wollner et al., 1997).

A second area activated during saccades, in the posterior part of the superior frontal gyrus, has been identified as the human supplemental eye field (SEF). In addition to activity during visually guided saccades (Petit, Orssaud, Tzourio et al., 1996), the SEF signal is enhanced during memory-guided saccades (Anderson, Jenkins, Brooks et al., 1994; Sweeney, Mintun, Kwee et al., 1996) and the execution of learned sequences of saccades (Petit et al., 1996). Other anterior cortical areas with increased activity during visually guided and memory-guided saccades include the cingulate, insula and dorsolateral prefrontal cortex (PFC) (Anderson et al., 1994; O'Sullivan, Jenkins, Henderson et al., 1995; Sweeney et al., 1996).

Posteriorly, a 'parietal eye field' with saccadic responses has been located in the monkey's lateral intraparietal area (LIP) (Andersen, Brotchie and Mazzoni, 1992; Colby, Duhamel and Goldberg, 1993), which has strong connections with the FEF. In human functional imaging, visually guided saccades elicit activity in the inferior parietal lobe (Anderson et al., 1994; Petit et al., 1996; Sweeney et al., 1996), more narrowly located to the intraparietal sulcus by some (Luna, Thulborn, Strojwas et al., 1998; Müri, Iba-Zizen, Derosier et al., 1996). Striate and lateral temporo-occipital cortex are also active during saccades, but only with visible targets (Bodis-Wollner et al., 1997; Darby et al., 1996; Fox et al., 1985; Melamed and Larsen, 1979).

Subcortical regions active during saccades have been less studied. Superior cerebellar vermal activity has been noted with visually guided, memory-guided saccades, and learned saccadic sequences (Anderson et al., 1994; O'Sullivan et al., 1995; Petit et al., 1996; Sweeney et al., 1996). Signal in the basal ganglia or thalamus were found in some studies of simple saccades (Petit et al., 1996; Sweeney et al., 1996), but not in others (Anderson et al., 1994). Memory-guided saccades also increase activity in the putamen, substantia nigra and thalamus (Anderson et al., 1994; O'Sullivan et al., 1995).

Studies comparing antisaccades with visually guided saccades have produced variable results. Most show greater activation in the PFC (Doricchi, Perani, Incoccia et al., 1997; Müri, Heid, Nirkko et al., 1998; Sweeney et al., 1996), though not all (O'Driscoll, Alpert, Matthysse et al., 1995). Increased activation in the FEF, SEF, parietal cortex, putamen and thalamus are seen in some (Doricchi et al., 1997; Sweeney et al., 1996), with greater involvement of the first three regions in the right hemisphere (Sweeney et al., 1996). Decreased activity during antisaccades have been found in ventromedial prefrontal cortex and anterior cingulate cortex (Sweeney et al., 1996), though another study found increased cingulate activity (Doricchi et al., 1997).

Saccades and lesions of the frontal eye field

FEF lesions cause little change (Guitton, Buchtel and Douglas, 1985; Moser and Kömpf, 1990) or only a slight increase in latency (Pierrot-Deseilligny, Rivaud, Penet and Rigolet, 1987) with visually guided saccades. When white matter is affected more extensively, particularly in the anterior limb of the internal capsule or near the frontal horns, contralateral saccades are more delayed: such lesions are likely to interrupt converging outputs from several cortical regions (Pierrot-Deseilligny et al., 1987). Latency effects of FEF lesions are better revealed in tasks with greater processing demands. In the overlap paradigm, there is increased latency of saccades in both horizontal directions, reminiscent of spasm of fixation (see below). Memory-guided saccades and antisaccades are also delayed (Rivaud, Müri, Gaymard et al., 1994). The frequency of express saccades is decreased in some patients (Rivaud et al., 1994).

In accuracy, there is a mainly contralateral hypometria in a variety of tasks (Fletcher and Sharpe, 1986; Rivaud et al., 1994), though memory-guided saccades may be hypometric in both right and left directions (Pierrot-Deseilligny, Rivaud, Gaymard, et al., 1991b). Unlike the case with parietal or fronto-parietal lesions (Duhamel, Goldberg, Fitzgibbon et al., 1992; Heide, Blankenburg, Zimmerman and Kömpf, 1995), one patient made accurate second saccades in a double-step task, suggesting that information about the first saccade was used in planning the second (Rivaud et al., 1994).

Scanning patterns can be altered by FEF damage. Such patients spend less time searching the contralateral side of complex visual scenes (Heide and Kömpf, 1998; Moser and Kömpf, 1990). This may represent an exploratory or intentional type of hemineglect, and indeed it can be associated with mild neglect signs on tests, such as line bisection and shape cancellation (Heide and Kömpf, 1998). There are older speculations that disorganized scanning after frontal lesions may cause a type of simultanagnosia (Luria, Karpov and Yarbuss, 1966).

Rivaud et al. (1994) also investigated the effect of eye position on saccadic performance: there do not appear to be craniotopic saccadic defects analogous to those described for smooth pursuit after frontal damage (Morrow and Sharpe, 1995). Therefore the changes in saccadic performance are related more to the direction of eye movement than to the starting or ending position of the eye, consistent with the coding of eye movements as vectors in the FEF in monkeys.

Saccades with lesions of other frontal regions

PFC lesions delay visually guided saccades ipsilaterally, contralaterally or bilaterally in some, but not all patients (Pierrot-Deseilligny, Rivaud, Gaymard and Agid, 1991a). Bilateral delays and inaccuracies are found with saccades requiring spatial memory, such as memory-guided saccades (Pierrot-Deseilligny et al., 1991b) and saccades guided by recalled spatial information from the vestibular system (Israël, Rivaud, Gaymard et al., 1995). Likewise, with the double-saccade paradigm, patients may fail to initiate the second saccade if it is directed contralaterally (Heide and Kömpf, 1998). Patients with right or left PFC lesions also have trouble inhibiting visually guided saccades to targets in either hemifield on the antisaccade task, though the latencies of their correct antisaccades are normal (Guitton et al., 1985; Pierrot-Deseilligny et al., 1991a). A non-ocular motor parallel is provided by data showing that patients with PFC lesions have more errors in novel stimulus–response keypress matches, but no increase in the latency difference between novel and practiced tasks (Godefroy and Rousseaux, 1997). Hence the major antisaccade deficit from PFC lesions is in suppressing automatic responses, not in generating the novel action. A similar finding is difficulty in suppressing anticipatory saccades with PFC lesions (Israël et al., 1995).

A single patient with a lesion of the ventrolateral frontal cortex also had difficulty suppressing visual saccades in an antisaccade task (Walker, Husain, Hodgson et al., 1998). This was thought related to deficits in working memory, as shown with non-ocular motor tests, than to problems with reflexive saccadic suppression, since he was able to suppress anticipatory saccades in tests of memory-guided saccades or during fixation sustained in the presence of peripheral targets. Ventrolateral frontal damage is evident in the diagrams of some patients in prior antisaccade studies, but the degree to which this damage as opposed to PFC damage was responsible for antisaccade errors is unclear.

Patients with lesions of the left SEF cannot perform a sequence of saccades correctly after a short delay (Gaymard, Rivaud and Pierrot-Deseilligny, 1993; Heide and Kömpf, 1998), implying a role in motor sequencing for this area (Fig. 2). With the double-step paradigm, the latencies of second saccades directed contralaterally are prolonged (Heide and Kömpf, 1998). SEF lesions also impair the accuracy of saccades which use vestibular information about a recent head turn to generate the desired saccadic amplitude in darkness (Israël et al., 1995).

Unilateral occipito-parietal lesions and saccades

It has been suggested that the posterior parietal cortex (PPC) is responsible for triggering reflexive visually guided saccades (Pierrot-Deseilligny, Rivaud, Gaymard et al., 1995). Unilateral PPC lesions increase the latency of such saccades, mainly contralaterally (Heide et al., 1995; Heide and Kömpf, 1998; Sundqvist, 1979), but sometimes in both horizontal directions (Pierrot-Deseilligny et al., 1987). Similar increases in latency of visually guided saccades can occur with lesions of the posterior internal capsule (Pierrot-Deseilligny et al., 1987). There may be a hemispheric effect, with both right- and left-sided lesions causing increases for contralateral saccades, but only right-sided lesions causing a smaller increase for ipsilateral saccades (Heide et al., 1995; Pierrot-Deseilligny et al., 1991a). A similar result has been found with memory-guided saccades (Pierrot-Deseilligny et al., 1991b). There are fewer express and anticipatory saccades, and more variable latencies in both directions, more so contralaterally (Braun, Weber, Mergner and Schulte-Mönting, 1992). In addition to latency effects, a mild contralateral hypometria has been found (Heide et al., 1995).

More complex saccadic behavior is affected. In monkeys, cells in the LIP can use extraretinal information about eye movements to update retinotopic maps of target location for saccadic planning (Colby et al., 1993). Heide et al. (1995) used double-step targets to study the effects of lesions on spatial coding of target position. There were errors in the execution and size of the second saccade to an ipsilateral second target, after a first saccade to a contralateral target, which suggested that the patient lacked extraretinal information about contralateral eye movements when they planned the second saccade (Fig. 1). A similar finding was reported in a patient with a right frontoparietal lesion (Duhamel et al., 1992). In contrast, saccades based on vestibular information are not affected by PPC lesions (Israël et al., 1995).

The effect of prediction on saccadic latencies has also been studied in patients with parietal lesions, with mixed results. Some patients could not use prediction to reduce latency in either direction, but others could (Ron, Schmid and Orpaz, 1989).

Bilateral parietal lesions and saccades

Abnormal saccades with biparietal injury have been described with 'visual disorientation' or Bálint's syndrome (Cogan, 1965; Hécaen and de Ajuriaguerra, 1954; Holmes, 1918; Husain and Stein, 1988). There are usually other eye movement problems, including impaired optokinetic responses, pursuit and convergence. The nature of the saccadic problem is not clear: the literature is marred by differences in definition and description and the lack of precise data in many. In fact, the saccadic disturbance may have several dissociable elements.

One abnormality is a severe *saccadic inaccuracy* (Holmes, 1918; Luria, Pravdina-Vinarskaya and Yarbuss, 1962), which can occur with bilateral lesions of the inferior parietal lobules (Pierrot-Deseilligny, Gray and Brunet, 1986). Patients cannot make accurate saccades to visual or tactile targets, though some can make saccades to command. Their eyes wander in search of a target until they stumble upon it. Once fixated, they may have trouble maintaining fixation (Holmes, 1918). However, others maintain fixation excessively, suggesting a second impairment, of *difficulty initiating saccades* to visual objects (Cogan, 1965; Hécaen and de Ajuriaguerra, 1954). Some patients could not make reflexive saccades to unexpected noises also (Hécaen and de Ajuriaguerra, 1954). The cause of impaired saccadic initiation is unclear. It may be *fixation spasm* (Holmes, 1930) but the data required to determine whether these cases meet modern criteria for fixation spasm (Johnston, Sharpe and Morrow, 1992) do not exist (see below). Alternatively, Cogan (1965) noted that his patients had a full range of randomly performed saccades but could not execute saccades to command or shift gaze between objects, which he labeled '*ocular motor apraxia*', to indicate a disorder of volitional saccadic generation.

Another controversy is the relation of the saccadic dysfunction to the other components of Bálint's syndrome, namely simultanagnosia and the spatial disorientation that leads to optic ataxia. Luria et al. (1962) held that the inaccurate saccadic search was due to simultanagnosia, since an organized visual search would be disrupted if elements of the scene kept slipping from awareness. However, Holmes (1918) concluded that saccadic inaccuracy did not simply reflect visuospatial disturbance, since some patients could not make saccades to parts of their own body. Dissociations between the components of Bálint's syndrome in patients suggest that these elements are indeed independent entities (Rizzo, 1993). For example, patients with simultanagnosia can have normal saccadic accuracy, latencies, and ocular search strategies (Rizzo and Hurtig, 1987).

Combined bilateral frontal and parietal lesions

In monkeys, the combination of bilateral parietal and frontal lesions causes much more profound impairments of saccades than bilateral ablations of either area alone (Lynch, 1992). In humans, a similar combination of lesions has been reported as Bálint's syndrome (Hausser, Robert and Giard, 1980; Hécaen and de Ajuriaguerra, 1954) or acquired ocular motor apraxia without optic ataxia or simultanagnosia (Dehaene and Lammans, 1991; Pierrot-Deseilligny, Gautier and Loron, 1988). The eye movement abnormalities in these cases are severe. The eyes are often immobile. There are no saccades to command or to visual targets, though sometimes there are preserved saccades to unexpected noises (Hausser et al., 1980). Gaze shifts are accompanied by head turns, which generate slow vestibular movements in the opposite direction, which may then be followed by a saccade (Pierrot-Deseilligny et al., 1988). There is no optokinetic response, pursuit, or convergence either.

Subcortical lesions and saccades

Despite the evidence of subcortical activation during saccades in functional imaging, little is known about the effects of focal lesions of these structures. Vermesch, Müri, Rivaud et al. (1996) studied nine patients with anoxia or carbon monoxide poisoning associated with bilateral damage to the lentiform nuclei on imaging. Visual saccades and antisaccades were performed normally, but tasks requiring an internal target representation to be briefly maintained in working memory, such as memory-guided saccades, predictive saccades, and saccadic sequences, were impaired in accuracy and/or frequency. Another patient with bilateral infarcts of the bodies of the caudate nuclei similarly had impaired accuracy and prolonged latency of memory-guided saccades but normal performance of visual saccades and antisaccades (Vermesch, Gaymard, Rivaud-Pechoux et al., 1999).

Transcranial magnetic stimulation (TMS) studies of saccades

TMS can produce a transient focal alteration of cortical function. Both excitatory and inhibitory effects can be achieved. TMS provides information complementary to that of functional imaging, since task-related activation in the latter does not tell us whether a specific region is critical to task performance or merely active in association with it. The acute inhibitory 'lesions' of TMS are more focal than most natural lesions, and because their effects are studied immediately, the results are less contaminated by adaptation and recovery.

In general, saccades cannot be elicited by single pulses or rapid trains of TMS to the frontal or parietal regions while the eyes are in another ocular motor state, such as fixation in light, fixation in dark, and smooth pursuit (Li, Olson, Anand and Hotson, 1997; Wessel and Kömpf, 1991; Zangemeister,

Canavan and Hoemberg, 1995). However, Li et al. (1997) showed in a double-saccade paradigm that a rapid train of TMS impulses triggered by the first of two saccades could generate a burst of small saccades whose frequency was related to TMS frequency. The direction of these evoked saccades varied among subjects and between test blocks within subjects, being sometimes contralateral to the TMS site, sometimes in the direction of the first intentional saccade, and sometimes in that of the second. Compared with fixation, the double-saccade condition may have facilitated TMS by lowering thresholds in the frontal eye field. Two to four TMS impulses may also be needed, as others have not been able to evoke saccades with single TMS pulses during or just after single visually guided saccades (Zangemeister et al., 1995).

More data are available on the negative effects of TMS on saccades. Visually guided saccades or saccades triggered by an auditory cue are delayed 30–60 ms by TMS applied to the parietal or frontal cortex in the interval between the stimulus/trigger and the saccade (Elkington, Kerr and Stein, 1992; Priori, Bertolasi, Rothwell et al., 1993; Thickbroom, Stell and Mastaglia, 1996; Zangemeister et al., 1995). This is true for saccades following both unpredictable and predictable target shifts (Zangemeister et al., 1995). The effect varies with TMS intensity and may be most effective in the interval 50–80 ms prior to mean saccadic latency (Priori et al., 1993; Zangemeister et al., 1995). Latency histograms suggest that 'fast regular' saccades may be particularly vulnerable to TMS, and that the reduction in their numbers accounts for much of the prolonged latency (Elkington et al., 1992; Priori et al., 1993). In contrast, express saccades are not affected by TMS in a gap paradigm (Priori et al., 1993).

The effect of TMS on other parameters of visually guided saccades is unclear. One study found no change in amplitude or duration of 11° saccades (Priori et al., 1993), but another found reductions in amplitude and changes in the duration/amplitude and peak-velocity/amplitude relationships, particularly for smaller saccades of around 6° (Zangemeister et al., 1995). These were interpreted as evidence of reductions in both the height and width of the pulse of increased neuronal activity generated by the saccadic control signal.

TMS studies of more complex saccadic paradigms provide data on the time course of ocular motor processing. TMS of the parietal cortex degraded the amplitude and directional accuracy of contralateral memory-guided saccades, but only when given within the first few hundred milliseconds after target appearance (Brandt, Ploner, Meyer et al., 1998; Müri, Vermesch, Rivaud et al., 1996). In contrast, saccadic accuracy was only impaired either bilaterally or contralaterally by TMS of the PFC when applied in the 'memory phase', between 500 and 1500 ms after the target had appeared and disappeared. This is consistent with hypotheses that the parietal cortex is involved in the early sensorimotor transformations of saccadic processing, and that the PFC is involved in spatial memory of target location.

An antisaccade study showed increases in latency of correct responses bilaterally when TMS was applied to the PPC at 80 ms and to frontal cortex at 100 ms after target onset (Terao, Fukuda, Ugawa et al., 1998). TMS also increased contralaterally directed errors when applied at 80 ms in a wide variety of locations. The results for frontal cortex are more similar to lesion effects in the FEF (Rivaud et al., 1994) than in the PFC, where bilaterally directed errors without increases in latency are observed (Guitton et al., 1985; Pierrot-Deseilligny et al., 1991a).

In the future, TMS can be expected to yield more data on the timing of information flow within the components of the saccadic system. A major limitation at present is the imprecision in cortical target location, which is not negligible given the variability in regional anatomy between subjects. Preliminary use of structural and functional MRI for TMS targeting has begun (Terao et al., 1998) and should advance the findings from TMS.

Summary of saccadic data

The data at present support a saccadic system which consists of a network of cortical areas, including the FEF, PPC, SEF, and PFC at a minimum, and the basal ganglia subcortically (Table 1, Fig. 4). It has been suggested that the PPC triggers 'reflexive' visually guided saccades and the FEF triggers saccades requiring greater volitional control (Pierrot-Deseilligny et al., 1995). This is partly supported by data showing that contralateral visually guided saccades are delayed by PPC lesions and antisaccades and

TABLE 1

Effects of unilateral cerebral lesions on saccades

Type of saccade	Visual guided	Overlap	Express	Memory-guided		Antisaccade	Anticipatory	Double target	Sequences
				Visual	Vestibular				
Frontal regions									
FEF	delay (C) hypo (C)	delay (B)	decrease	delay hypo (B)		delay		normal	
PFC	delay (B, I, C)			error (B) delay (B)	error (B) delay (B)	error	increase	2nd saccade failure	
Ventral FC						error	normal		
SEF				normal	error (B)			2nd saccade delay	error
Basal ganglia				error					error
Parietal regions									
PPC	delay (C, B) hypo (C)		decrease (C)	delay	normal		decrease (C)	2nd saccade error	
PIVC					error (C)				

FC, frontal cortex; FEF, frontal eye field; PFC, prefrontal cortex; SEF, supplemental eye field; PIVC, parieto-insular vestibular cortex; PPC, posterior parietal cortex; B, bilateral; C, contralateral; I, ipsilateral; hypo, hypometric.

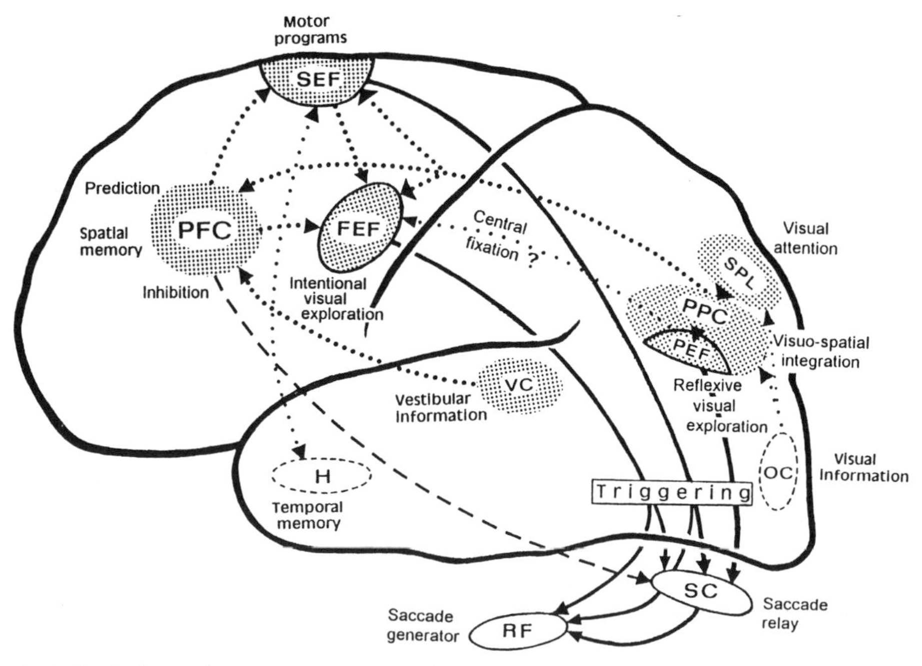

Fig. 4. Cortical saccadic control. See text for details. H, hippocampus; OC, occipital cortex; PPC, posterior parietal cortex; RF, reticular formation; SC, superior colliculus; SPL, superior parietal lobule; VC, vestibular cortex (PIVC) (From Pierrot-Deseilligny et al., 1995, with permission.)

visual memory-guided saccades are delayed by FEF lesions. However, the fact that memory-guided saccades are delayed by some PPC lesions and visually guided saccades by some FEF lesions shows that this distinction is not absolute. The PPC also performs sensorimotor transformations for saccadic targeting, leading to hypometria and failure to use contralateral saccadic data in updating subsequent saccades in the double-step paradigm when it is lesioned. The PFC is important in spatial memory and suppression of reflexive responses, with lesions leading to delays and errors in visual memory-guided, vestibular memory-guided, and double-step saccades, and the escape of anticipatory saccades and antisaccade errors. The SEF and basal ganglia also play a role in the temporal organization of saccades, and their lesions cause errors on the memory-guided tasks and saccadic sequences, and delays in the double-step paradigm. The role of the cingulate cortex has yet to be defined by lesion studies.

Smooth pursuit

Pursuit is another function originating in foveate animals. The goal of ocular tracking of a moving target is to keep the image of the target at or near the fovea, where visual resolution is best. This is usually accomplished by a mix of saccades and smooth pursuit eye movements. The smooth pursuit system responds to motion of the image of a small target across the retina by generating eye velocities that try to match the velocity of the target. If the match is successful the velocity of the target's retinal image will be reduced to zero. Thus smooth pursuit is an example of a negative feedback system: indeed, velocity traces of pursuit reveal the small oscillations around mean eye velocity that are characteristic of such systems (Goldreich, Krauzlis and Lisberger, 1992). When the match is inadequate, as with higher target frequencies and velocities or subject inattention, the eye falls behind the target until at some point saccades are triggered to move the fovea back to the target.

Studies of smooth pursuit use one of two basic stimuli. One is a target in constant motion, usually along a sinusoidal path (Fig. 5), sometimes on a 'triangular' path, in which the target moves at constant speed, switching directions periodically. The ratio of peak eye velocity to target velocity is pursuit gain,

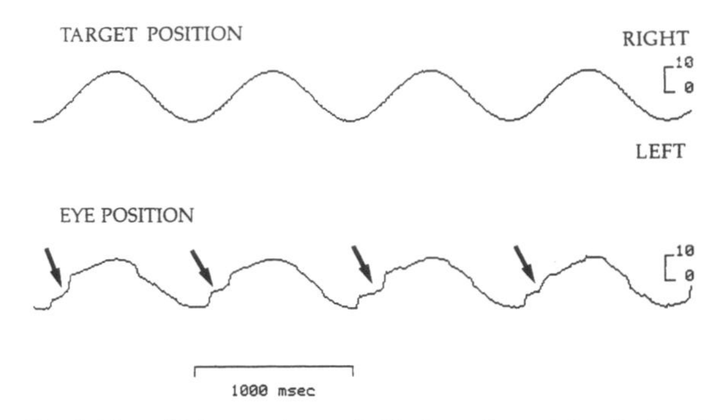

Fig. 5. Sinusoidal smooth pursuit. Horizontal target (top line) and eye position (bottom line) are plotted as a function of time. When the target moves rightward (ipsidirectionally), pursuit gain is too low (arrows) in this patient with a right occipitotemporal lesion, prompting substitution of 'catch-up' saccades. (From Barton et al., 1996a, with permission.)

and the comparison of the time of eye reversal to target direction reversal gives the phase lag or lead. The gain and phase characterize the steady-state or maintained pursuit response. The frequency and amplitude (and peak velocity for sinusoidal targets) can be varied to obtain a profile of pursuit performance. Normal subjects tend to show both a frequency and acceleration saturation for pursuit gain (Zackon and Sharpe, 1987).

The second type of stimulus is the step-ramp paradigm (Fig. 6). The subject watches a stationary spot which jumps suddenly to a peripheral location (the step) and immediately begins to move at a constant velocity and direction (the ramp). After a period of about 130 ms, a pursuit response begins and is usually interrupted at about 200 ms by a saccade correcting for the shift in position of the target (Morrow and Sharpe, 1993b). Given the pursuit latency of 130 ms, the continuing pursuit movement in the first 130 ms after the saccade is still a response to the motion of the target when it was in the retinal periphery, before it was foveated by the saccade. Both pre- and post-saccadic pursuit velocity can be analyzed to give a measure of pursuit initiation, rather than pursuit maintenance, before negative feedback has time to influence the system's response. With appropriate choice of steps, the response of the pursuit system to target motion in various retinal locations can also be assessed. Responses are usually expressed as a velocity gain. Latency of the pre-saccadic pursuit response is sometimes reported, though identification

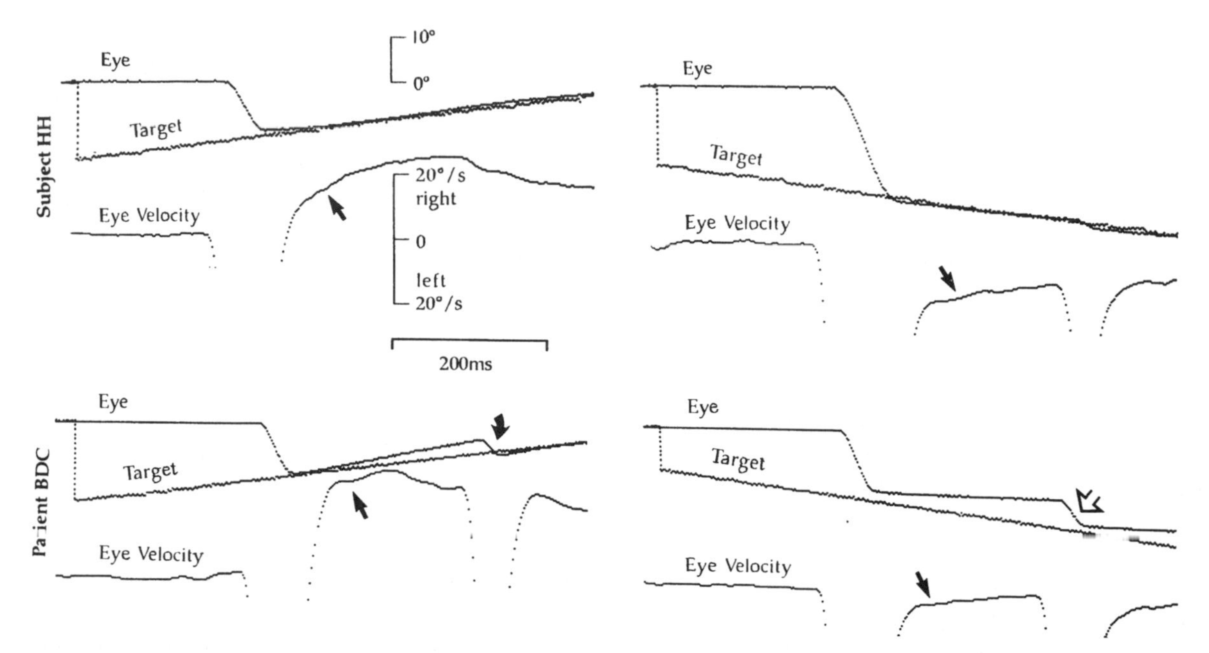

Fig. 6. Step-ramp pursuit. Horizontal eye and target position as well as eye velocity are plotted as a function of time for a normal subject (HH) and one with a left occipitotemporal lesion (BDC). Post-saccadic velocities are indicated by arrows. In the normal subject, this is well-matched to target speed. In BDC, pursuit with a rightward moving target (left graph) is too fast, and a 'back-up' saccade is made to move the eye back to the target (curved arrow). With a leftward moving target pursuit is too slow, and a 'catch-up' saccade is made to stay with the target (arrowhead). (Modified from Barton et al., 1998, with permission.)

of pursuit onset is problematic because of the low velocities. Acceleration can be measured also, but is usually imprecise.

Variations on these methods can be used to examine other issues in smooth pursuit. Predictive aspects of pursuit behavior can be reduced — but never eliminated (Kowler, 1990) — in the pursuit maintenance method by using trajectories that are the sum of several superimposed sinusoidal motions. Similarly, step-ramps can use targets with unpredictable step locations, step latencies, ramp directions, and ramp velocities. On the other hand, step-ramps predictable in speed, direction and latency, sometimes with occasional omissions of actual target motion, can be used to assess prediction and anticipation in pursuit initiation (Kao and Morrow, 1994).

Brain regions active during smooth pursuit: functional imaging

There is much less functional imaging data on pursuit than for saccades. Technically, identifying pursuit-related activity is complicated by two issues. First, since subjects track moving objects with a combination of smooth pursuit and small saccades, signal changes during tracking contain a mix of saccadic and pursuit-related activity. Second, as the eye pursues a moving object, the retinal image of the stationary part of the environment moves in the opposite direction. Also, some slip of the moving object's retinal image is inevitable, as eye speed rarely matches target speed perfectly. Therefore some of the activity during pursuit will reflect perception of target and background motion. To isolate pursuit, the saccadic component can be minimized with targets moving predictably at low frequency and acceleration (Barton, Simpson, Kiriakopoulos et al., 1996b; Lisberger, Evinger, Johanson and Fuchs, 1981), and visual motion can be minimized — but not eradicated — with small targets moving predictably in the dark (Barton et al., 1996b). Ideally, control tasks with saccades and motion perception with the eyes stationary are required.

In monkeys, area V5 (middle temporal, MT) is an extra-striate region with responses selective for visual motion. Adjacent to MT is area V5a (medial superior temporal, MST). Neurons in both MT and

MST show activity during pursuit, but the activity in MT appears related only to the visual image motion generated during pursuit. In humans, a visual motion area analogous to the V5 complex of monkeys has been shown in lateral occipito-temporal cortex, in the junction between Brodmann areas 19 and 37 (Tootell, Reppas, Kwong et al., 1995). Pursuit-related activity has been demonstrated in this region, greater than that associated with visual motion alone (Barton et al., 1996b; Freitag, Greenlee, Lacina et al., 1998) or saccades (O'Driscoll, Strakowski, Alpert et al., 1998).

It is also known that there are pursuit-related responses in the frontal eye fields in monkeys. O'Driscoll et al. (1998) claimed to show such activity in humans also with PET; however, they did not find greater activity during sinusoidal smooth pursuit than saccades, and since they did not monitor eye movements, it cannot be certain that the activity they demonstrated was not attributable to a saccadic component of ocular tracking. However, Petit, Clark, Ingeholm and Haxby (1997) showed that the activation with a triangular pursuit task was more lateral and inferior in the FEF than the region activated during saccades alone. This regional dissociation provides stronger evidence of pursuit activity in the FEF.

Compared with saccades, pursuit is associated with greater activity in the lingual gyrus and dorsomedial cuneus, probably related to visual motion (Dupont, Orban, de Bruyn et al., 1994). Activity in a dorsal occipito-parietal region has also been noted with pursuit (Freitag et al., 1998).

Directional pursuit defects after cerebral lesions

Directional defects impair pursuit of targets moving in a specific direction, regardless of location in the visual field. They can often be observed clinically. Like all cerebral pursuit defects, they are asymptomatic.

Most directional defects in pursuit are *ipsidirectional*, in that they impair pursuit towards the side of the lesion (Fig. 5). Ipsidirectional smooth pursuit defects were first noted with hemispherectomies (Sharpe, Lo and Rabinovitch, 1979; Troost, Daroff, Weber and Dell'Osso, 1972), then in small reports of cases with parietal and occipito-temporal lesions (Baloh, Yee and Honrubia, 1980; Bogousslavsky and Regli, 1986; Leigh and Tusa, 1985). Larger patient series confirm ipsidirectional defects of predictable targets with unilateral occipito-parietal lesions (Lekwuwa and Barnes, 1996; Morrow and Sharpe, 1990; Thurston, Leigh, Crawford et al., 1988). Studies with unpredictable step-ramp targets in the same patients (Morrow and Sharpe, 1993a) show ipsidirectional defects in pursuit initiation with more ventral temporo-parieto-occipital lesions (junction of areas 19/37/39).

Frontal lesions can cause pursuit defects also. Ipsidirectional pursuit defects, sometimes with milder reductions of contradirectional pursuit, are reported with lesions of the FEF, SEF, or PFC (Morrow and Sharpe, 1990, 1995; Rivaud et al., 1994). Others report that ipsidirectional pursuit defects correlate with damage to SEF, whereas lesions of the FEF cause symmetric bidirectional defects (Lekwuwa and Barnes, 1996): this requires confirmation.

Ipsidirectional pursuit defects may also arise from lesions of the posterior limb of the internal capsule (Barton, Sharpe and Raymond, 1996a; Brigell, Babikian and Goodwin, 1984; Lekwuwa and Barnes, 1996; Morrow and Sharpe, 1990), affecting descending cortical output to brainstem nuclei (Kjallman and Frisén, 1986; Tusa and Ungerleider, 1988). Indeed, one study found that chronic ipsidirectional defects in pursuit correlated better with lesions of this descending tract than any one cortical region, and noted that the lesions in most previous pursuit studies involve white matter extensively (Barton et al., 1996a). Hence it may be that damage to output or connecting tracts may be of more significance than damage to single cortical regions in creating persistent pursuit defects, given the network of cortical areas that likely participate in its generation.

The basis of the pursuit asymmetry is of interest. While some patients have a low amplitude nystagmus whose fast phase is towards the side of the lesion, it is unlikely that the asymmetry in pursuit simply results from the superimposition of this nystagmus upon the pursuit response. The velocity of the slow phase is too low to account for the magnitude of the difference in ipsi and contradirectional pursuit velocity, and not all patients with asymmetries in horizontal smooth pursuit have nystagmus (Barton et al., 1996a; Sharpe et al., 1979). Impairments in motion perception are not found in most patients with decreased ipsidirectional smooth pursuit, and chronic lesions of the lateral occipitotemporal cortex alone impair motion perception, but not pursuit (Barton et al., 1996a). One step-ramp study has shown that the most consistent abnormality is an increase in contradirectional pursuit initiation (Fig. 6), likely arising from an acute velocity bias affecting the entire pursuit system, followed by a direction-specific adaptation (see 'recovery' below) (Barton and Sharpe, 1998).

The influence of background visibility has also been studied. Older reports of bi-parietal injury mention impaired pursuit with a visible background, but normal pursuit in darkness (Hécaen and de Ajuriaguerra, 1954; Luria et al., 1962). Lawden, Bagelmann, Crawford et al. (1995) found that a visible background abnormally decreased pursuit in patients with lesions of Brodmann area 40 or frontal white matter.

A few patients have *contradirectional* pursuit defects (Lawden et al., 1995; Lekwuwa and Barnes, 1996; Reeves, Perret, Jenkyn and Saint-Hilaire, 1984). This has been attributed to hemineglect or hemianopia (Lawden et al., 1995), though other studies have not found a similar effect of visual or attentional defects (Barton et al., 1996a; Thurston et al., 1988). The localization of this anomaly is unclear: it has been reported with both occipito-parietal and frontal lesions. *Bidirectional* defects were also found with frontal, parietal and thalamic lesions and attributed to impaired attention (Lekwuwa and Barnes, 1996). However, one patient with a right parietal lesion that caused bidirectional reduction in pursuit initiation to step ramp targets had good saccadic accuracy and latencies to the same targets and to stationary targets (Barton and Sharpe, 1998). This argues against a generalized inattention underlying the impaired pursuit performance. Also, the patient performed well on tests for hemineglect. It was suggested that his bidirectional deficit may have been due to damage to the parietal eye field (as evidenced by increased contralateral saccadic latencies) and neighboring areas.

Are there hemispheric differences? Some found that right-sided lesions caused a higher incidence of pursuit defects (Morrow and Sharpe, 1995; Thurston et al., 1988), but others did not (Lawden et al., 1995), while yet others reported that right-sided lesions caused more severe ipsidirectional defects (Lekwuwa and Barnes, 1996). Bogousslavsky and Regli (1986) stated that left-sided lesions caused ipsidirectional defects while right-sided ones caused bidirectional ones. The issue is not yet settled.

The potential and course of recovery of pursuit defects has been inadequately studied. In some patients with hemorrhages (Brigell et al., 1984; Leigh, 1989), subsequent improvement may have been due to improvement in the lesion rather than cerebral adaptation. In one patient with a lesion including the posterior internal capsule (Fig. 7), the acute deficit was associated with a velocity bias that not only decreased ipsidirectional pursuit initiation, but also increased contradirectional pursuit, and imparted a slow contradirectional drift to fixation immediately after saccades to stationary targets (Barton and Sharpe, 1998). Over a few months, the ipsidirectional pursuit recovered, but the contradirectional pursuit remained abnormal, coming to resemble the findings in other patients with chronic capsular lesions. This suggests that the lesion generated a velocity drift affecting all pursuit initiation, followed by a direction-specific adaptation during recovery over the next few months.

Retinotopic and craniotopic pursuit defects after cerebral lesions

Retinotopic defects impair pursuit of targets within specific regions of the contralateral hemifield, regardless of the direction of motion. These are detected only with laboratory step-ramp stimuli. They are unusual because of the rarity of natural posterior lesions sparing both striate cortex and optic radiations: poor pursuit in hemianopic regions simply reflects blindness and is not a pursuit defect. Nevertheless, a few patients with intact visual fields have been studied. Thurston et al. (1988) found two patients with lesions of Brodmann areas 39/40 who had both ipsidirectional and retinotopic pursuit defects, and one patient with a lesion in area 19/37 with a retinotopic defect alone. Morrow and Sharpe (1993a) had one patient with a lesion in areas 21/22 who had a retinotopic defect. Frontal lobe lesions do not cause retinotopic defects (Morrow and Sharpe, 1995).

Morrow (1996) described craniotopic pursuit deficits with FEF. Pursuit is impaired when the eyes are located to the contralateral side of midline. All patients also had ipsidirectional pursuit defects, and some, but not all, had ipsilateral gaze deviation and impaired contralateral saccades.

Fixation

The ability to keep gaze steady upon an object is itself an ocular motor behavior. In part, this 'zero eye movement' is defined by the ability to suppress unwanted eye movements. Separating this negative suppressive function from the positive act of fixating is often difficult. Little is known about either from monkeys. Some cells in area 7 of the posterior parietal cortex discharge continuously during visual fixation and pursuit of motivationally relevant visual targets (Mountcastle, Lynch, Georgopoulos et al., 1975). In the FEF, there is activity related to the countermanding or suppression of saccades just prior to their execution (Schall and Thompson, 1999). In humans, functional imaging studies show fixation-related activation in the FEF (Melamed and Larsen, 1979) and PFC (Anderson et al., 1994). Compared to optokinetic responses, steady fixation also yields greater activation in the SEF and anterior cingulate cortex (Dieterich, Bucher, Seelos and Brandt, 1998).

Spasm of fixation is an impairment in shifting fixation from one target to another (Alfano, 1955; Holmes, 1930). Holmes attributed this to a heightened fixation reflex. Modern criteria for spasm of fixation requires ocular motor recordings showing that saccadic latencies to suddenly appearing targets are prolonged when the central fixation light remains continuously visible (overlap paradigm), but normal when the central light disappears simultaneous with the appearance of the peripheral target (Johnston et al., 1992). Spasm of fixation is thought to result from cerebral damage that disinhibits the pars reticulata of the substantia nigra, which in turn inhibits the superior colliculus. The lesions responsible for spasm of fixation are still not certain, but could include the FEF.

The converse defect is *impersistence of fixation*. Patients with medial frontal lobe lesions affecting the supplementary motor area have difficulty suppressing saccades when an object suddenly appears in the visual field contralateral to the lesion, whereas ventrolateral frontal lesions impair this suppressive function with targets appearing in either hemifield (Paus, Kalina, Patockova et al., 1991). The latter is reminiscent of the high antisaccade error rate reported with a ventrolateral frontal lesion and attributed to deficits in working memory rather than suppressive capability (Walker et al., 1998). High antisaccade error rates (Guitton et al., 1985; Pierrot-Deseilligny et al., 1991a) and anticipatory saccades in memory-guided paradigms (Israël et al., 1995) indicate a similar problem in patients with PFC lesions.

A subset of patients with asymmetries in pursuit or vestibulo-ocular responses after cerebral lesions have a small amplitude *nystagmus* with the slow phase drifting away from the side of the lesion, during fixation (Sharpe et al., 1979). This is generally asymptomatic: the slow phase is only a few degrees per second, a velocity insufficient to degrade visual resolution. It is presumed to represent an imbalance of tonic inputs to the ocular motor system from the hemispheric structures involved in pursuit generation.

Sometimes confused with nystagmus are *square wave jerks*, a type of saccadic intrusion. When these occur, the eyes are taken away from the desired fixation by a small saccade of a few degrees, and then returned to fixation by a similar movement after 200 ms or so. In contrast with nystagmus, there is no slow drift of the eye and their occurrence is not rhythmic. Normal subjects make less than eight square wave jerks a minute, but a variety of lesions increase their frequency, including cerebral lesions, of which they correlate more with size than location (Sharpe, Herishanu and White, 1982). While generally asymptomatic, extremely frequent and large square wave jerks have been thought to contribute to the impaired reading of patients with progressive supranuclear palsy (Friedman, Jankovic and McCrary, 1992).

Vergence

With the development of a fovea and the shift of orbital locations from lateral to frontal placement in the skull, it becomes desirable to train the two foveas upon the same visual target. The slightly different views of an object by the two eyes creates stereoscopic depth perception. With objects at different distances from the observer, the eyes must change

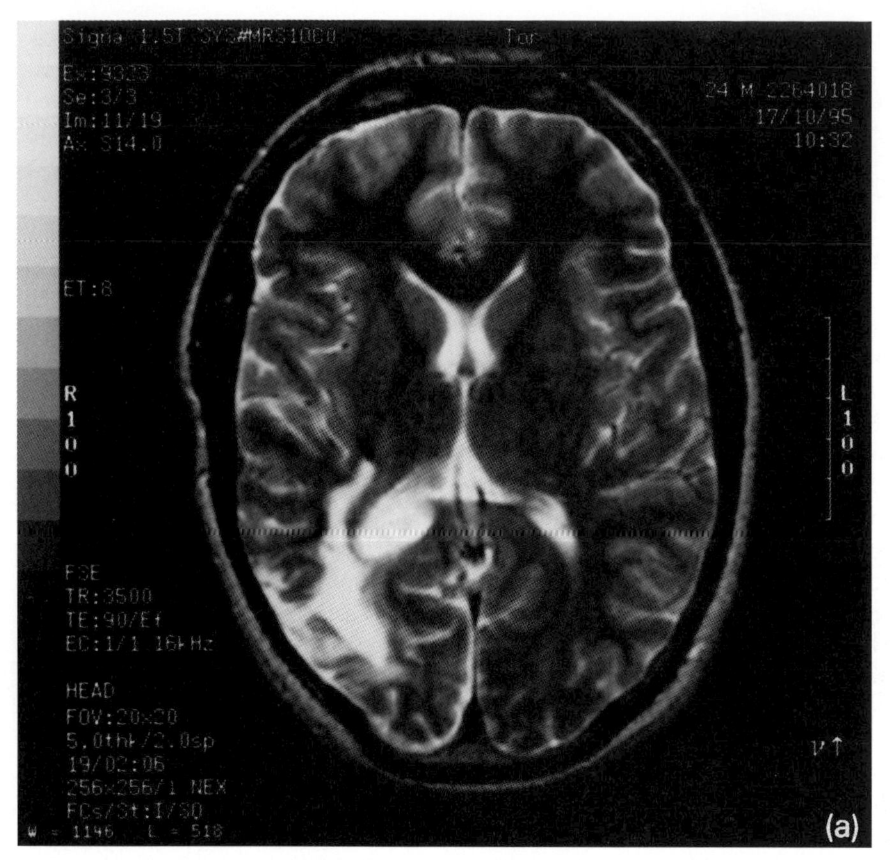

Fig. 7. Recovery of step-ramp pursuit. (a) This patient had a lesion of not only the human motion area in lateral occipitotemporal cortex, but also of the posterior limb of the internal capsule. (b) Pursuit velocity after the first saccade to the target was measured, as in Fig. 6, to targets stepping into the right hemifield and then ramping right or left at different speeds indicated on the x-axis. Negative values indicate leftward motion. At 1 month after his right-sided stroke, the patient had low ipsidirectional and high contradirectional pursuit velocities. Also, for stationary targets (target velocity of zero), his eyes had a leftward (contradirectional) drift, instead of the normal rightward post-saccadic drift. Five months later, this drift with stationary targets and ipsidirectional pursuit was normal, but contradirectional pursuit remained abnormally high. (Modified from Barton et al., 1998, with permission.)

their gaze direction relative to each other to maintain single fixation, diverging for far objects and converging for near objects. The consequence of vergence failure is horizontal diplopia.

Little is known about the cerebral control of vergence eye movements. In monkeys, cells tuned to stereodisparity exist in area MST (Roy, Komatsu and Wurtz, 1992), which also contains neurons that have activity related to pursuit within a single depth plane. Whether lesions of this area impair vergence movements generated by stereodisparity is not known; however, lesions of the partly homologous area LS in the cat result in abnormal vergence (Takagi, Toga and Bando, 1993). Area LIP (Gnadt and Mays, 1995) and a region just anterior to the FEF (Gamlin, Yoon and Zhang, 1996) contain neurons with vergence-related responses also. In humans, there are no functional imaging studies of vergence yet. However, one PET study of stereodisparity perception found responses in peri-striate cortex, the parietal lobe and prefrontal cortex (Gulyás and Roland, 1994).

Some patients with parietal damage have a divergent misalignment of the eyes, attributed to loss of convergent tone (Fowler, Wade, Richardson and Stein, 1996; Ohtsuka, Maekawa, Takeda et al., 1988). Often, this takes the pattern of *convergence insufficiency*, not unlike that encountered after non-specific head trauma (Kerkhoff and Stögerer, 1994). More definitive studies are required to establish that this deficit is specific for parietal damage.

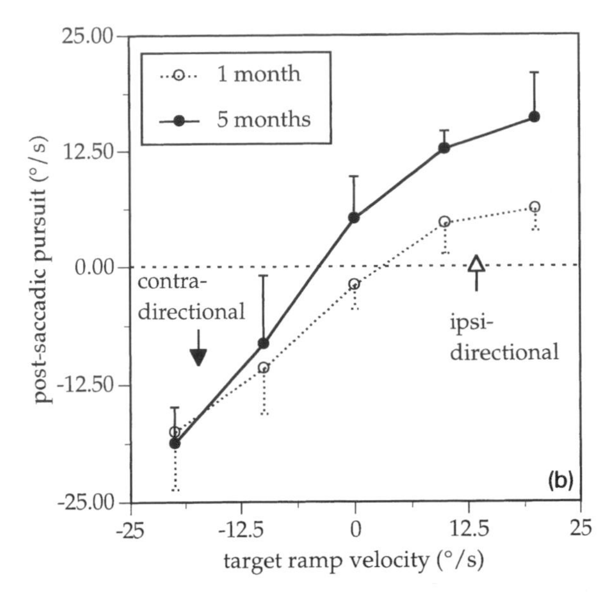

Fig. 7 (continued).

Optokinetic and vestibular-ocular responses

These stabilize gaze in space while the observer's head is moving, preventing degradation of the retinal image by motion. Two types of head motion occur: angular acceleration, in which the head rotates or turns, and linear acceleration, in which the head translates or shifts horizontally or vertically. These are detected by the semicircular canals and otoliths, respectively, which together constitute the vestibular apparatus. The vestibulo-ocular responses (VOR) use these vestibular signals to generate eye movements in the direction opposite to head motion, to keep direction of gaze stable. These are mediated primarily by brainstem structures.

Also, if the eyes were carried by the head as it moved, the retinal image of the stationary environment would move in the opposite direction. Motion of large portions of the visual field, which normally occurs only with eye motion, stimulates the optokinetic system, which generates slow eye movements to match the visual motion, keeping gaze steady and reducing retinal image motion to zero. In afoveate animals the optokinetic response is a slow rise in eye velocity mediated by brainstem nuclei, the nucleus of the optic tract and the accessory optic system (Simpson, 1984). In primates, this slow optokinetic response is supplemented by a quickly rising tracking response, mediated by cortical structures related to the smooth pursuit system. The optokinetic response and VOR are complementary rather than redundant systems. The optokinetic response is most effective at low rather than high frequencies and speeds, whereas the opposite is true of the VOR.

Functional imaging during vestibular or optokinetic stimulation

Cerebellar and brainstem structures are primarily responsible for the VOR. Nevertheless, single-cell recordings in non-human primates have shown vestibular activity in several cortical regions (Guldin and Grusser, 1998). Chief among these is the parieto-insular vestibular cortex (PIVC) (Akbarian, Berndl, Grusser et al., 1988; Guldin, Akbarian and Grusser, 1992). Additional regions include area 7a in the parietal lobe, the cervical region in area 3a of the sensorimotor strip, area 2v, and the 'visual posterior sylvian area', among others (Guldin and Grusser, 1998; Kawano, Sasaki and Yamashita, 1980). All of these areas show responses to optokinetic and somatosensory stimuli also (Grusser, Pause and Schreiter, 1990). In addition, area MST contains neurons that respond to specific optic flow stimuli (Graziano, Andersen and Snowden, 1994).

In humans, stimulation of semicircular canals with caloric irrigation leads to increases in regional blood flow in the superior temporal region (Friberg, Olsen, Roland et al., 1985). Galvanic stimulation, which may stimulate the otolithic apparatus preferentially, also activates on fMRI the parieto-temporal region, likely the human homologue of PIVC, as well as the central sulcus (area 3a) and anterior intraparietal sulcus (area 2v) (Lobel, Kleine, Leroy-Willig et al., 1999).

Optokinetic stimuli with nystagmus activates a large number of cortical and subcortical regions which in other studies are active during either motion perception or saccadic and pursuit responses, as well as the PIVC region (Dieterich et al., 1998). On the other hand, optic flow stimuli alone appear to activate a medial parieto-occipital area, but de-activate the human PIVC region, suggesting a reciprocal inhibition rather than complementary activation between visual and vestibular cues to self motion (Brandt, Bartenstein, Janek and Dieterich, 1998).

Effects of cerebral lesions on vestibulo-ocular responses

The most commonly measured VOR clinically is the eye movement elicited by activity in the horizontal semicircular canals. Irrigation of the external ear with warm or cool water also stimulates these canals, generating vestibular slow phases and a 'caloric' nystagmus. Older studies reported directional asymmetries in the slow phases of caloric nystagmus with cerebral lesions. One found this with tumors in a wide variety of locations, with no relation of the direction of asymmetry to the side of the lesion (Kluzer and Hahn, 1954). A larger study noted that caloric responses were affected specifically by posterior temporal lesions, with the slow nystagmus phases consistently reduced towards the lesion, and that this was independent of asymmetries in optokinetic responses (Carmichael, Dix and Hallpike, 1954). A better quantitative study in hemidecorticate subjects showed that similar reductions in the response to ipsidirectional sinusoidal head rotations could be accounted for by a superimposed nystagmus during fixation, which was attributed to imbalance in the pursuit system (Sharpe and Lo, 1981). Whether such nystagmus was present in the patients with focal lesions reported by Carmichael et al. (1954) is not stated. At present, therefore, it is not clear whether the VOR to horizontal angular acceleration is specifically modified by posterior temporal lesions or merely reflects superimposed asymmetries from the pursuit system. Nevertheless, there is some data from cat studies indicating that focal lesions of area 7 can generate both spontaneous nystagmus and decrease in ipsidirectional slow phases of the VOR without a concomitant abnormality in at least one ocular tracking response, VOR cancellation (see below) (Ventre, 1985).

It has also been reported that patients with lesions of the non-dominant parieto-temporal region do not experience vertigo with caloric stimulation (Takeda, Tanaka-Tsuji, Sawada et al., 1995): this likewise needs to be confirmed.

Deficits of static vestibular function in the roll plane (perpendicular to the sagittal axis) have been investigated (Brandt and Dieterich, 1994; Brandt and Dieterich, 1999). Unlike the situation with brainstem or peripheral vestibular lesions, which cause a torsional tilt and skew deviation (vertical misalignment) of the eyes, no ocular motor effects are found with cortical lesions, though subjective estimates of the environmental vertical are tilted in the absence of visual cues. The subjective tilt is contraversive (top tilted away from the side of the lesion) with lesions of the parieto-insular cortex but either ipsi or contraversive with posterolateral thalamic lesions.

When saccades are made to targets while the head is freely moving, vestibular information may be required to maintain targeting accuracy. With a memory-guided paradigm in which the retained targeting data was vestibular rather than visual, errors emerged with targets contralateral to lesions of the PIVC, but not of the PPC (Israël et al., 1995).

Effect of cerebral lesions on optokinetic responses

Decreased gain of ipsidirectional slow phases of optokinetic nystagmus have long been described after parietal lesions (Carmichael et al., 1954; Fox and Holmes, 1926). However, in modern studies, these are correlated closely with pursuit defects and have been ascribed to damage to the pursuit system from parietal (Baloh et al., 1980; Sharpe and Lo, 1981) or FEF lesions (Rivaud et al., 1994). An older case study claimed a dissociation between preserved pursuit and impaired optokinetic slow phases after bilateral middle cerebral artery infarctions (Blackwood, Dix and Rudge, 1975), but this was poorly quantified and has yet to be reproduced.

Lesions of the parieto-insular cortex are associated with decreased illusions of self-motion with optokinetic displays restricted to the contralateral hemifield (Straube and Brandt, 1987), but whether this is associated with impaired ocular responses is not known.

Related to the optokinetic responses are a number of visual–vestibular interactions. The VOR in darkness is augmented when the patient is tested in the light, with a visible stationary background. On the other hand, with a small target moving in concert with the head, subjects can suppress or cancel their VOR in order to keep gaze directed at the moving target. Asymmetries in visual enhancement of the VOR and VOR cancellation again correlate with asymmetries in pursuit (Baloh et al., 1980; Sharpe and Lo, 1981).

Eye movements reflecting perceptual and attentional disorders

The previous section discussed ocular motor alterations caused by damage to regions considered to be directly involved in the generation and control of eye movements. However, as with all actions, eye movements are a response to the environment, and hence reflect many other factors in that interaction, including the perception of stimuli, attention, and intentional set, among others. Disorders in these processes can also alter ocular motor patterns, and the study of eye movements can provide data about the nature of the underlying dysfunction or the adaptation of the system to the problem.

Hemianopia

Fixation and saccades in hemianopia

In hemianopic patients, the point of central fixation is shifted slightly into contralateral space (Barton, Behrmann and Black, 1998; Gassel and Williams, 1963). This coincides with perceptual shifts of center, as revealed in line bisection tasks (Barton et al., 1998; Barton and Black, 1998; Liepmann and Kalmus, 1900), which in turn may represent a normal central bias to horizontal spatial judgments with stimuli restricted to a single hemifield (Nielsen, Intriligator and Barton, 1999).

Patients with hemianopia cannot see targets in their blind hemifield. If cued to the appearance of randomly located targets on the hemianopic side, as by the offset of a central fixation light, they make a series of small searching saccades until the target is found (Girotti, Casazza, Musicco and Avanzini, 1983; Meienberg, Zangemeister, Rosenberg et al., 1981). This inability to localize unpredictably positioned targets can be used as a bedside test to exclude functional hemianopia (Meienberg, 1983). Of interest, a similar series of small saccades is used by these patients towards auditory stimuli, implying that hemianopia influences a common motor program used for multi-modal targets, possibly at the level of the superior colliculus (Traccis, Puliga, Ruiu et al., 1991). With predictable auditory or visual stimuli, however, patients eventually make accurate single saccades as they learn the target location (Meienberg et al., 1981; Rizzo and Hurtig, 1992; Schoepf and Zangemeister, 1996; Traccis et al., 1991). Over time, some patients develop a more efficient strategy for unknown targets, making one very large contralateral saccade that in most cases places the target in the seeing hemifield, so that it can then be reached with an accurate ipsilateral saccade (Meienberg et al., 1981). Children do not develop this adaptive strategy naturally (Mezey, Harris, Shawkat et al., 1998). Some rehabilitative approaches try to foster this 'search hypermetria', with reported subjective improvement (Kerkhoff, Elke and Meier, 1994).

Hemianopia also alters the responses to targets in the ipsilateral seeing hemifield. Latencies of both manual responses (Rizzo and Robin, 1996) and saccades to moving or stationary targets (Barton and Sharpe, 1998; Meienberg et al., 1981; Sharpe et al., 1979; Traccis et al., 1991) are increased. It has been speculated that this may be due to altered interhemispheric cortical connections (Rizzo and Robin, 1996), or to loss of a facilitation of saccadic triggering in the superior colliculus (Traccis et al., 1991).

Ocular motor search patterns in hemianopia

The data about saccadic scanning in hemianopia are mixed. Some studies found little impact of hemianopia on the scanning of complex drawings (Chédru, Leblanc and Lhermitte, 1973; Rizzo and Hurtig, 1992), but these used fairly coarse parameters, such as number of fixations and exploration time per hemispace. Using a more fine-grained division of visual space, one study found that left hemianopic patients searching letter arrays had a horizontal gradient of fixations increasing towards contralateral space (Behrmann, Watt, Black and Barton, 1997). This contrasted with an even distribution of saccades in normal subjects, and the opposite gradient in patients with left hemineglect (Fig. 8). Thus, while neglect patients display a pathologic gradient, hemianopic patients develop an adaptive gradient that increases fixations in their blind hemispace.

How does hemianopia alter saccadic search with stimuli and tasks that do not generate an even distribution of salient elements in normal subjects? Line bisection is one such task: though the physical characteristics (luminance and contrast) of the line stimulus are evenly distributed across space, the instruction to bisect generates fixation patterns concentrated around line center in normal subjects (Barton

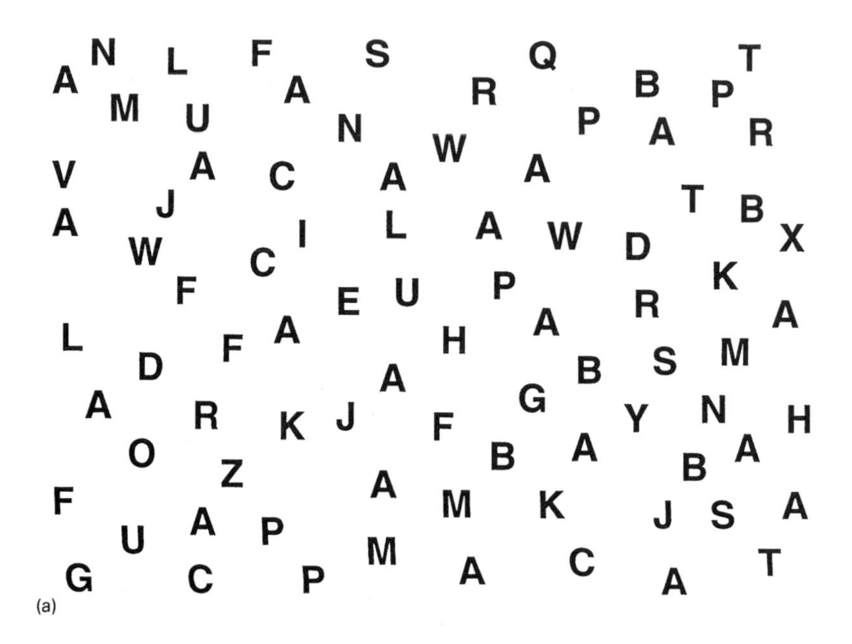

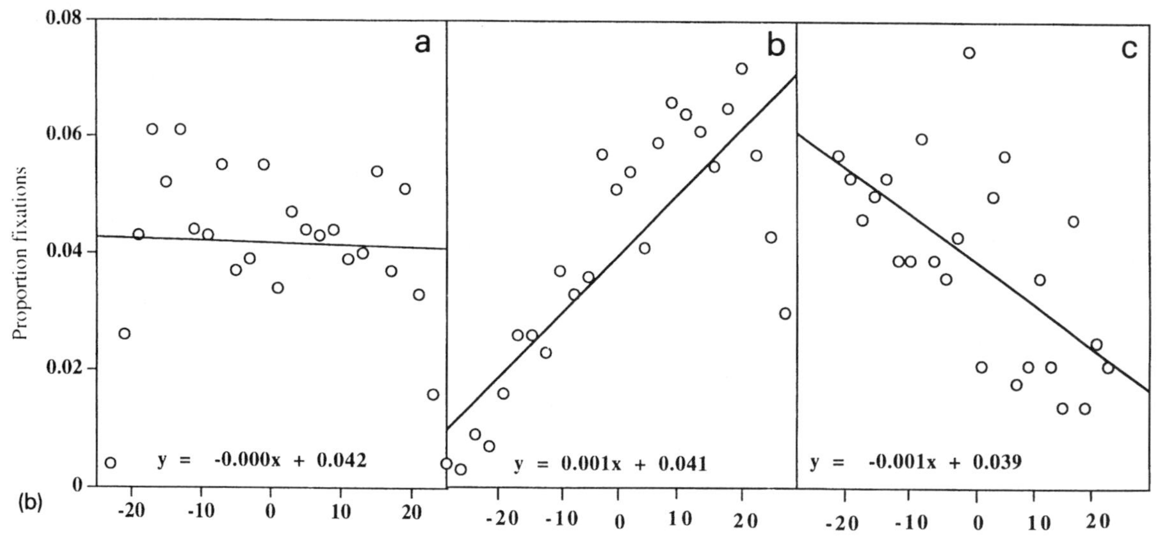

Fig. 8. Scanning of a letter array. (a) The array used: the subject counts the number of As. (b) Proportions of fixations made to different 2° regions of horizontal space by three different subject groups. Lines represent linear regressions, whose constants are given in the equations shown. Normal subjects (left graph) distribute fixations evenly across the horizontal extent of the array. Patients with left hemineglect (center graph) show a pathologic gradient, with fewer fixations towards the left of the array, whereas patients with left hemianopia show an adaptive gradient with more fixations towards the left side. (From Behrmann et al., 1997, with permission.)

et al., 1998; Ishiai, Furukawa and Tsukagoshi, 1987; Ishiai, Furukawa and Tsukagoshi, 1989), indicating greater salience of this mid-region. Hemianopic patients demonstrate twin peaks of fixations (Fig. 9), one concentrated on the contralateral edges of lines (Barton et al., 1998; Ishiai et al., 1987; Ishiai et al., 1989) and a central peak slightly offset into contralateral space (Barton et al., 1998). The slight contralateral offset of the central peak may be a product of the adaptive attentive and ocular motor gradient favoring contralateral hemispace (Behrmann et al., 1997). Alternatively, it may reflect the greater

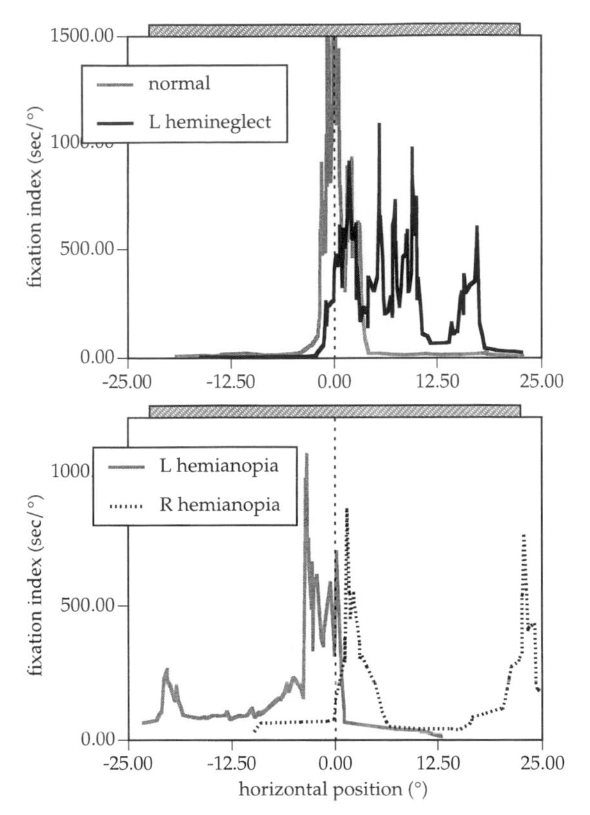

Fig. 9. Scanning during line bisection. The line's extent is shown as the bars above each graph. The fixation index is a measure of the time spent in the vicinity of each fixation, taking into account both number and duration of fixations, made by each group of subjects. Normal subjects (gray line, top graph) fixate the central portion of the line exclusively, whereas patients with left hemineglect (black line, top graph) generate a broad scatter of fixations on the right portion of the line. Hemianopic patients (bottom graph) have a central peak skewed slightly into their blind hemispace, and a second peak at the end of the line in blind hemispace.

emphasis of the central visual field in cortical representation, as discussed above (Nielsen et al., 1999). The peak at the contralateral line end presumably represents a point of great salience to a hemianopic patient instructed to find line center, since they cannot see the full contralateral extent of the line unless they fixate its end.

Hemifield defects that encroach upon the parafoveal region impair reading, causing *hemianopic dyslexia*. With languages written from left to right, patients with left hemianopia have trouble when they finish one line and must find the beginning of the next, since the left margin is now in their scotoma. Instead of one or two large return saccades, they resort to a staircase of searching leftward saccades (Trauzettel-Klosinski and Brendler, 1998; Zihl, 1995). Right hemianopia limits the amount of text visible to the right of fixation and impedes the planning of the rightward saccades that scan the text (Leff, Scott, Crewes et al., 2000). This increases the frequency and reduces the amplitude of saccades during the process of reading the line from left to right, and the left-to-right flow is interrupted by more regressive saccades (De Luca, Spinelli and Zoccolotti, 1996; Trauzettel-Klosinski and Brendler, 1998; Zihl, 1995). Zihl (1995) found that individual fixations during the left-to-right reading phase were prolonged, but De Luca et al. (1996) found increased fixation times only for subjects with reduced contrast sensitivity in their remaining vision. Overall reading speed is more prolonged for patients with right hemianopia than for those with left hemianopia (De Luca et al., 1996; Trauzettel Klosinski and Brendler, 1998). All these parameters for both types of hemianopia are correlated with the degree of central field involvement, not surprisingly: patients with at least 5° of macular sparing are only mildly affected (Trauzettel-Klosinski and Brendler, 1998). Over time, reading performance can improve in patients as they learn adaptive strategies (Trauzettel-Klosinski and Brendler, 1998). Subjects who can use prediction to increase the accuracy of their saccades to regularly occurring targets have better adapted reading behavior (Schoepf and Zangemeister, 1996).

Hemineglect

Unilateral hemineglect is considered to result from an abnormal bias in spatial attention or exploration. Abnormalities in ocular motor behavior have long been recognized in this disorder, and it has even been considered in the past that the eye movement changes may have caused hemineglect (Scott, Jeannerod and Zahin, 1966). However, abnormal ocular search probably does not cause hemineglect but reflects underlying defects in orienting and attention (Riddoch and Humphreys, 1987). The precise relation between attention and eye movements continues to be debated (Posner, 1980; Sheperd, Findlay and Hockey, 1986). It is clear that attention can be dissociated from saccades, in that it can be deployed towards a spatial location without an associated eye movement (Posner, 1980). Despite this, data from monkey suggest that such attentional shifts are associated with generation or modification of activity in ocular motor structures like the superior colliculus (Kustov and Robinson, 1996): hence the apparent behavioral dissociation may not be borne out on a physiologic level. Furthermore, the opposite dissociation appears less likely: there is evidence that a shift in attention to the region of the saccadic goal is needed to execute a voluntary saccade (Hoffman and Subramanian, 1995; Kowler, Anderson, Dosher and Blaser, 1995). Overall, the distribution of saccades and eye fixations during scanning is considered an index of 'overt' attention (Umiltà, 1988). The relation of overt attention to the distribution of overall attention must be subject to some general, but not rigid, constraints, much as the tip of an iceberg is presumed to be above its submarine body, but not necessarily related to its mass or spatial dimension in any precise manner.

Saccades in hemineglect

How does hemineglect influence the generation of saccades? With the standard saccadic tests, hemineglect patients frequently fail to make saccades towards left-sided targets, even when their occurrence is predictable (Butter, Rapscak, Watson and Heilman, 1988; Girotti et al., 1983; Rizzo and Hurtig, 1992). This may reflect failure to perceive the target ('sensory inattention'), failure to react to the perceived target (lack of 'motor intention'), or both (Butter et al., 1988). Tests to dissociate the sensory and motor components have been done. Làdavas, Zeloni, Zaccara and Gangemi (1997) had 10 patients try to maintain fixation at center and react to the appearance of the targets by a manual key press, and Butter et al. (1988) used an antisaccade paradigm, in which their single patient looked in the direction opposite to the target. Both studies found evidence of failure to perceive the target, as deduced from trials lacking any manual or ocular responses, most often in the contralateral, but also in the ipsilateral hemifield. This inattention followed a gradient from left-most to right-most horizontal space, at least in patients with parietal lesions (Làdavas et al., 1997).

In addition, these studies showed that patients had difficulty suppressing unwanted saccades. In the antisaccade task, the patient was unable to suppress reflexive saccades to targets, initially more so when they were in the ipsilateral hemifield, then, as the sensory inattention to contralateral stimuli resolved, more for targets in the contralateral hemifield (Butter et al., 1988). This is not unlike the antisaccade deficit described in other patients with similar prefrontal lesions (Guitton et al., 1985), and hence may not be part of his neglect phenomenology. On the other hand, Làdavas et al. (1997) found, in a task requiring steady fixation, that patients failed to suppress saccades also, more so when targets appeared in the ipsilateral hemifield. This was true of both patients with parietal lesions only and those with fronto-parietal lesions, though more dramatic in the former. Some of the patients with frontal lesions made reflexive saccades without manual responses when left-sided targets appeared, and even denied seeing these targets. This was interpreted as evidence for dissociation between attention and saccadic control.

There are little data on directional eye movement effects in hemineglect. The rapid eye movements of sleep show more rightward than leftward movements with hemineglect (Doricchi, Guargiglia, Paolucci and Pizzamiglio, 1993). Similar, but less pronounced, ipsidirectional (rightward) biases were also seen in patients with hemianopia alone, however. Saccades made during line bisection did not show a similar tendency in either saccadic amplitude or number for a group of hemineglect patients, though short segments of fixations in some patients showed a directional drift due to asymmetries in sequential rightward and leftward saccadic amplitudes (Barton et al., 1998).

Ocular motor search patterns in hemineglect

A subject viewing a stimulus makes a series of alternating saccades and fixations. These searching eye movements are one means of exploring attentional distribution. Furthermore, functional imaging studies have suggested that attention and saccades generate activity in closely parallel cortical networks and may be anatomically as well as functionally linked (Corbetta, Akbudak, Conturo et al., 1998). The distribution of fixations in any visual task is the result of a number of interacting factors. Eye movements tend to be made to prominent or 'salient' visual features. Salience is determined both by the physical properties of the stimulus, such as contrast, color, motion and form, and by the instructional set of the subject (in the experimental context, the task they have been asked to do). The scan of salient features interacts further with any internal attentional biases of the subject, which are held to be minimal in normal individuals, but significant in patients with hemineglect.

With letter or symbol arrays, left hemispatial exploration time is decreased in severe hemineglect (Chédru et al., 1973), and correlates inversely with neglect severity (Johnston and Diller, 1986). With letter arrays that generate an even distribution of fixations (and presumably salience) across horizontal space in normal subjects, patients with left hemineglect show a horizontal gradient of fixations (Fig. 8), even within the right hemispace (Behrmann et al., 1997). This indicates an internal attentional bias manifest as a left-to-right gradient, consistent with neglect theories of biased attentional vectors (Bisiach and Vallar, 1988; Kinsbourne, 1987).

Decreased left hemispatial searching also occurs with displays of line drawings and photographs (Chain, Leblanc, Chédru and Lhermitte, 1979; Karnath, 1994; Rizzo and Hurtig, 1992) or even while searching for a non-existent target in the dark (Harnak, 1992; Karnath and Fetter, 1995). The latter technique has been used in conjunction with 30° body tilts to show that the ocular search bias follows body coordinates rather than gravitational coordinates (Karnath, Fetter and Niemeier, 1998). The implication is that previously demonstrated shifts in neglect coordinates with tilt might be related more to visual environmental coordinates than to gravitational ones.

Line bisection is a simple stimulus which generates centrally skewed search patterns in normal subjects. Although earlier reports found no difference between the number of fixations to the right or left of line center in patients with left hemineglect (Ishiai et al., 1987), more detailed analyses have revealed a consistent rightward shift of all horizontal scanning parameters, including the median, right-most and left-most fixation positions, and the longest fixation (Barton et al., 1998). Examination of the data of individuals shows that, even with this relatively simple line stimulus, there is considerable variation in scan patterns. Some patients fixate most often on a position to the right of midline and only make eye movements to points right of this frequently visited position. Though their coexistent hemianopia means that they never saw the portions of the line to the left of this frequently fixated point, they nevertheless mark this point as line center, which Ishiai and colleagues (Ishiai et al., 1989; Ishiai, Sugishita, Mitani and Ishizawa, 1992) called a line completion effect. The implication is that these patients have an imagined representation of a part of the line they have not actually seen. In contrast, other patients make leftward fixations that do not appear to influence the markedly rightward bisection placement they eventually make (Barton et al., 1998; Ishiai, Seki, Koyama and Gono, 1996). It is as if the data obtained during the left-most fixations had disappeared. The distribution of fixations may also vary. Some demonstrate twin peaks, while others distribute fixations over a range shifted to the right, and make a bisection judgment located somewhere in the middle of this range, much as if a simple frame-shift of their spatial coordinates had occurred (Barton et al., 1998). Whether these variations between patients represent differences in the temporal stage of neglect or differences in lesion anatomy is unclear. It is also possible that some variations reflect premorbid differences in scanning behavior, which is notoriously idiosyncratic (Groner, Walder and Groner, 1984; Walker-Smith, Gale and Findlay, 1977).

Reading is one of the most complex perceptual tasks. Left hemineglect can cause *neglect dyslexia*, manifest by reading errors restricted to the left side of the page and/or the left side of individual words (Behrmann, Moscovitch, Black and Mozer, 1990). Recordings in one patient during reading showed the ocular counterpart to the failure to read the left side of pages: return leftward sweeps made after reaching the ends of lines failed to extend past the midline (Karnath and Huber, 1992). The authors concluded that this resulted from an attentional bias referenced to an environmental rather than a retinotopic frame. However, we have noted reading patterns in which the left-most point fixated in a line moves progressively rightwards as the patient moves down the page

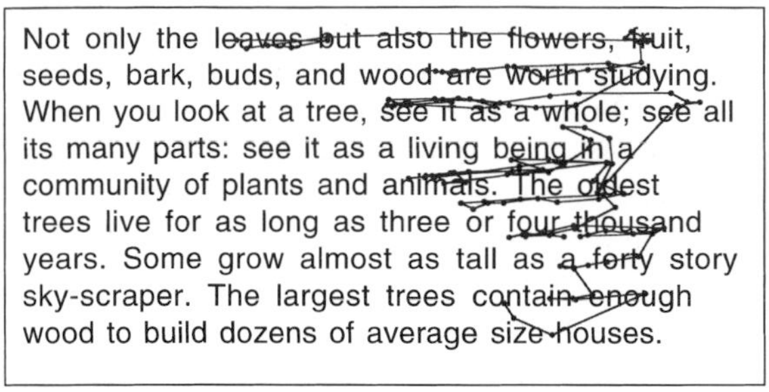

Not only the leaves but also the flowers, fruit,
seeds, bark, buds, and wood are worth studying.
When you look at a tree, see it as a whole; see all
its many parts: see it as a living being in a
community of plants and animals. The oldest
trees live for as long as three or four thousand
years. Some grow almost as tall as a forty story
sky-scraper. The largest trees contain enough
wood to build dozens of average size houses.

Fig. 10. Fixations during paragraph reading. A patient with left hemineglect begins just to the left of the middle of the page, then, with successive lines, begins each line further and further to the right. This pattern is not predicted by hemineglect with only a spatiotopic reference frame.

(Fig. 10), which might result from a combination of retinotopic and environmental neglect biases.

Blindsight

Blindsight is the presence of remnant visual function despite the subject's denial of perception. There are several hypotheses about the anatomic basis of blindsight. One is that blindsight represents functioning of the superior colliculus in patients without striate cortex or input (Pöppel, Held and Frost, 1973). However, blindsight for pattern and motion are not easily explained by known tectal response properties, leading to suggestions that tectal projections to the pulvinar may provide indirect visual input to extra-striate cortex (Weiskrantz, Warrington, Sanders and Marshall, 1974). This retino-tecto-pulvino-cortical relay in turn cannot explain blindsight color perception as tectal neurons lack color opponency, leading to a proposal that direct projections from lateral geniculate neurons to extra-striate cortex are responsible (Cowey and Stoerig, 1991).

Blindsight eye movements in animals

Much of the early impetus for human studies on blindsight derived from residual visual abilities found in behavioral experiments on de-striated monkeys (Weiskrantz, 1972). Monkeys with striate lesions retain or can learn to make saccades to targets in blind regions (Keating, 1980; Mohler and Wurtz, 1977; Zee, Tusa, Herdman et al., 1987). To parallel human blindsight, though, it must be shown that the monkeys are not aware of these targets. Moore, Rodman, Repp and Gross (1995) found that monkeys made accurate saccades to targets in blind hemifields if they were cued to its appearance by the offset of the central fixation light, but did not look for it if the cue was not provided. This failure to respond was interpreted as lack of awareness of blind field targets.

Whether monkeys have smooth pursuit to targets moving in blind fields is unclear. Zee et al. (1987) found that pursuit returned to nearly normal gain, but with increased latency 1–6 months after bilateral striate resections, but other studies found no pursuit of targets in the contralateral hemianopic field after unilateral striate resection (Goldberg, Bruce, Ungerleider and Mishkin, 1982; Segraves, Goldberg, Deng et al., 1987).

The little data about the anatomic basis of residual eye movements to blind field stimuli in monkeys without striate cortex are confusing. Saccadic localization is lost when the striate lesion is followed by resection of the superior colliculus (Mohler and Wurtz, 1977), but there is only temporary impairment after adding resection of preoccipital cortex, with subsequent pulvinar degeneration (Keating, 1980). This suggests that residual function in de-striated monkeys requires a functioning colliculus, but not pulvinar and extra-striate cortex. However, Page, King, Merigan and Maunsell (1994) showed that complete lesions of the lateral geniculate nucleus abolished smooth pursuit initiation and saccadic localization in the contralateral hemifield, without recovery over at least 18 months.

Blindsight human saccades

Early hypotheses about blindsight centered on the role of the superior colliculus in the absence of functioning striate cortex. Since saccadic localization is a well-known tectal function, this has been an extensively studied blindsight function. Pöppel et al. (1973) first described a weak correlation between saccadic size and target position in four patients with incomplete hemianopia, mainly a small increase in saccadic amplitude for targets up to 30° eccentric. Poor correlation was noted at larger eccentricities, which was explained as due to the rarity of large centrifugal head-fixed saccades in daily behavior. Similarly, patient D.B. had a weak correlation of saccades with targets only for targets between 5 and 25°: for the entire range the correlation was insignificant (Sanders, Warrington, Marshall and Weiskrantz, 1974; Weiskrantz et al., 1974). Most of the positive correlation derived from reduced saccadic size for the nearest target at 5°, a portion of the visual field which recovered on later perimetry (Weiskrantz, 1987). Perenin and Jeannerod (1975) found some saccadic localization in two patients with cortical hemianopia; again, mainly for targets less than 30° eccentric.

In contrast, Blythe and colleagues (Blythe, Bromley, Kennard and Ruddock, 1986; Blythe, Kennard and Ruddock, 1987) found that only patients with conscious residual vision localized targets with saccades. Two of their five patients with residual vision had surprisingly good saccadic localization up to 30°. Meienberg et al. (1981) did not find any saccadic localization in three patients with cerebral hemianopia. In a larger study of 10 patients with chronic lesions, only two patients had a weak correlation of saccadic amplitude with the position of either moving or stationary targets (Barton and Sharpe, 1997). Paradoxically, these patients were not those with focal medial occipital lesions, in whom greater potential for blindsight had been hypothesized.

It has been suggested that saccadic localization might improve with training, as in monkeys (Mohler and Wurtz, 1977). In humans, the accuracy of a saccadic search strategy (as opposed to the accuracy of initial saccades) was weak or non-existent in six subjects before a training program, but afterwards improved to equal that of the normal hemifield (Zihl, 1980; Zihl and Werth, 1984). However, this may have represented learning of an adaptive strategy rather than development of blindsight, which should have been evident as more accurate initial saccades.

Hemidecorticate patients provide interesting data, since they indicate what is possible without striate and extra-striate cortex. Braddick, Atkinson, Hood et al. (1992) studied two infants for directional gaze shifts. These infants were more likely to look to their blind hemifield when a target was presented there than when there was no target at all, indicating some rudimentary target detection by the sub-cortical saccadic system.

Blindsight human pursuit and optokinetic responses
Ter Braak, Schenk and van Vliet (1971) reported one man with cortical blindness in whom some optokinetic responses recovered 5 months after his stroke. Four children with cortical blindness were shown to have optokinetic nystagmus (Van Hof-van Duin and Mohn, 1983). However, confirming complete loss of vision in children is difficult. One of the blind children avoided walls when walking and another had residual visual evoked potentials, though the implications of such electrophysiologic results in cortical blindness are still uncertain (Celesia, Archer, Kuroiwa and Goldfader, 1980). In the two children with congenital cortical blindness, the optokinetic responses elicited by monocular stimulation had faster slow-phase velocities for stimuli moving towards rather than away from the nose. This temporo-nasal asymmetry is thought characteristic of the subcortical optokinetic system (Simpson, 1984). In contrast to these studies, optokinetic responses were not found in another cortically blind patient (Perenin, Ruel and Hécaen, 1980) nor from within the blind hemifield of a series of older hemianopic patients (Perenin, 1991). Likewise, pursuit initiation to focal moving targets was not present in adult patients with chronic lesions confined to the medial occipital lobe (Barton and Sharpe, 1997).

Overall, the data for residual ocular motor function in blindsight are tenuous. The correlations for saccadic localization are weak or non-existent. There is no convincing evidence that practice can create blindsight saccadic localization, and none that any such ability is functionally useful to the patient. For optokinetic and pursuit responses, the data are even less encouraging.

Visual agnosia

Little is known about the impact of higher level visual disturbances on eye movements. In part, this reflects our modest understanding of the interaction of higher level visual perception and eye movements in normal subjects. Existing data show that normal subjects differ widely in the way they scan complex visual stimuli. However, this variability does not imply that fixations are randomly distributed. Indeed, preliminary experiments suggested that a given subject tended to scan a given stimulus with a fairly stereotyped series of saccades and fixations, which were termed *scanpaths* (Noton and

Stark, 1971a). It was even considered that complex perception might be accomplished through a series of linked sequences of perceptions whose spatial structure was tagged by the sequence of eye movements that generated them — so-called feature rings (Noton and Stark, 1971b,c). In the absence of overt saccades, such spatial tagging might be accomplished by shifts of covert attention. However, not all subjects show scanpaths, and those who do differ greatly in the pattern of their scanpaths for any given picture and show different scanpaths for different pictures within similar categories (Groner et al., 1984; Noton and Stark, 1971b). Also, these experiments used large, poorly visible line drawings, with the assumption that this would make overt as eye movements a serial form of pattern processing. The generalization of the findings to more natural stimuli and the validity of the assumption of serial pattern processing can be questioned.

Since the eye movements of normal subjects viewing complex visual stimuli differ so widely, detecting abnormal patterns in patients with visual agnosia is a challenge. Data on eye movements during normal face perception confirm great variability between subjects. For a given subject, though, there are regularities in their preference to fixate certain features and to follow certain sequences of fixations (Groner et al., 1984; Walker-Smith et al., 1977). In two *prosopagnosic* patients, an analysis of the predictability of scanpath sequences showed, first, that their scanning of faces in general was similar to that of normal subjects, and second, that this predictability was much lower for familiar than for unfamiliar faces (Rizzo, Hurtig and Damasio, 1987). This was interpreted as evidence of a still existing internal schema for the familiar faces that influenced fixations covertly.

In contrast to face perception, there is a large body of data on the eye movements during reading (Rayner, 1998). This reflects the fact that reading is a serial process, and hence the temporal sequences of eye movements are naturally of interest. Data on eye movements during reading by hemianopic and hemineglect patients have already been presented above. Surprisingly, though, there are little data on the eye movements in patients with *pure alexia*. These patients have impaired reading though they can still write. In less severe forms, they are still able to read, but with effort, proceeding letter-by-letter. Unlike normal subjects, their reading displays a characteristic word-length effect, in which reading speed correlates with the number of letters in a word. One study of two alexic patients showed a word-length effect for the number of fixations within a word also (Behrmann, Shomstein, Black and Barton, 2001). The same study also examined for linguistic effects upon fixations, and found that fixation number and duration correlated with the linguistic frequency and imageability of the word. This is also found in normal subjects reading text under sub-optimal conditions or in novice readers, suggesting that the alexic patients are still using a degraded left hemisphere reading process rather than a radically different visual processing system in the right hemisphere.

Conclusion

Eye movements are subtly altered by a large variety of cortical lesions. The pattern of dysfunction has revealed much detail about the organization of saccadic and pursuit generation by networks of specialized cortical modules, predominantly in the frontal and parietal cortices: on the other hand, information about the cortical contribution to fixation, vergence and vestibular eye movements is still rudimentary. Eye movements during specific tasks are also perturbed by perceptual and attentional disorders. While these secondary effects upon eye movements can sometimes contribute to our understanding of perceptual dysfunction, the relation of eye movements to perception is complex and interpretations of the data must be considered with caution. Nevertheless, eye movements can provide a valuable index of the behavioral consequences of phenomena, such as hemianopia, hemineglect, blindsight, and possibly even more complex perceptual dysfunction.

Acknowledgements

This work was supported by a grant from the National Institute for Neurologic Diseases and Stroke (NINDS).

References

Akbarian S, Berndl K, Grusser O, Guldin W, Pause M, Schreiter U: Responses of single neurons in the parietoinsular vestibular cortex of primates. Annals of the New York Academy of Sciences: 545; 187–202, 1988.

Alfano J: Spasm of fixation. American Journal of Ophthalmology: 40; 724–730, 1955.

Andersen R, Brotchie P, Mazzoni P: Evidence for the lateral intraparietal area as the parietal eye field. Current Biology: 2; 840–846, 1992.

Anderson T, Jenkins I, Brooks D, Hawken M, Frackowiak R, Kennard C: Cortical control of saccades and fixation in man. A PET study. Brain: 117; 1073–1084, 1994.

Baloh R, Yee R, Honrubia V: Optokinetic nystagmus and parietal lobe lesions. Annals of Neurology: 7; 269–276, 1980.

Barton J, Behrmann M, Black S: Ocular search during line bisection. The effects of hemi-neglect and hemianopia. Brain: 121; 1117–1131, 1998.

Barton J, Black S: Line bisection in hemianopia. Journal of Neurology, Neurosurgery and Psychiatry: 64; 660–662, 1998.

Barton J, Sharpe J: Saccades and smooth pursuit of moving targets in blind hemifields. A comparison of medial occipital, lateral occipital, and optic radiation lesions. Brain: 120; 681–699, 1997.

Barton J, Sharpe J: Ocular tracking of step-ramp targets by patients with unilateral cerebral lesions. Brain: 121; 1165–1183, 1998.

Barton J, Sharpe J, Raymond J: Directional defects in pursuit and motion perception in humans with unilateral cerebral lesions. Brain: 119; 1535–1550, 1996a.

Barton J, Simpson T, Kiriakopoulos E, Stewart C, Guthrie B, Wood M, Mikulis D: Functional magnetic resonance imaging of lateral occipitotemporal cortex during pursuit and motion perception. Annals of Neurology: 40; 387–398, 1996b.

Becker W, Jürgens R: An analysis of the saccadic system by means of double step stimuli. Vision Research: 19; 967–983, 1979.

Behrmann M, Moscovitch M, Black S, Mozer M: Perceptual and conceptual factors in neglect dyslexia: two contrasting case studies. Brain: 113; 1163–1183, 1990.

Behrmann M, Shomstein S, Black S, Barton JS: Eye movements during paragraph reading by letter-by-letter readers: effects of word length and lexical variables. Neuropsychologia, in press.

Behrmann M, Watt S, Black S, Barton JS: Impaired visual search in patients with unilateral neglect: an oculographic analysis. Neuropsychologia: 35; 1445–1458, 1997.

Bisiach E, Vallar G: Hemineglect in humans. In Boller F, Grafman J (Eds.), Handbook of Neuropsychology. Amsterdam: Elsevier, pp. 195–222, 1988.

Blackwood W, Dix M, Rudge P: The cerebral pathways of optokinetic nystagmus: a neuro-anatomical study. Brain: 98; 297–308, 1975.

Blythe I, Bromley J, Kennard C, Ruddock K: Visual discrimination of target displacement remains after damage to the striate cortex in humans. Nature: 320; 619–621, 1986.

Blythe I, Kennard C, Ruddock K: Residual vision in patients with retrogeniculate lesions of the visual pathways. Brain: 110; 887–905, 1987.

Bodis-Wollner I, Bucher S, Seelos K, Paulus W, Reiser M, Oertel W: Functional MRI mapping of occipital and frontal cortical activity during voluntary and imagined saccades. Neurology: 49; 416–420, 1997.

Bogousslavsky J, Regli F: Pursuit gaze defects in acute and chronic unilateral parieto-occipital lesions. European Neurology: 25; 10–18, 1986.

Braddick O, Atkinson J, Hood B, Harkness W, Jackson G, Vargha-Khadem F: Possible blindsight in infants lacking one cerebral hemisphere. Nature: 360; 461–463, 1992.

Brandt T, Bartenstein P, Janek A, Dieterich M: Reciprocal inhibitory visual-vestibular interaction. Visual motion stimulation deactivates the parieto-insular vestibular cortex. Brain: 121; 1749–1758, 1998.

Brandt T, Dieterich M: Vestibular syndromes in the roll plane: topographic diagnosis from brainstem to cortex. Annals of Neurology: 36; 337–347, 1994.

Brandt T, Dieterich M: The vestibular cortex. Its locations, functions and disorders. Annals of the New York Academy of Sciences: 871; 293–312, 1999.

Brandt S, Ploner C, Meyer B-U, Leistner S, Villringer A: Effects of repetitive transcranial magnetic stimulation over dorsolateral prefrontal and posterior parietal cortex on memory-guided saccades. Experimental Brain Research: 118; 197–204, 1998.

Braun D, Weber H, Mergner T, Schulte-Mönting J: Saccadic reaction times in patients with frontal and parietal lesions. Brain: 115; 1359–1386, 1992.

Brigell M, Babikian V, Goodwin J: Hypometric saccades and low-gain pursuit resulting from a thalamic hemorrhage. Annals of Neurology: 15; 374–378, 1984.

Butter C, Rapscak S, Watson R, Heilman K: Changes in sensory inattention, directional motor neglect and 'release' of the fixation reflex following a unilateral frontal lesion: a case report. Neuropsychologia: 26; 533–545, 1988.

Carmichael E, Dix M, Hallpike C: Lesions of the cerebral hemispheres and their effects upon optokinetic nystagmus. Brain: 77; 345–372, 1954.

Celesia G, Archer C, Kuroiwa Y, Goldfader P: Visual function of the extra-geniculo-calcarine system in man: relationship to cortical blindness. Archives of Neurology: 37; 704–706, 1980.

Chain F, Leblanc M, Chédru F, Lhermitte F: Négligence visuelle dans les lésions postérieures de l'hémisphere gauche. Revue Neurologique (Paris): 135; 105–126, 1979.

Chédru F, Leblanc M, Lhermitte F: Visual searching in normal and brain-damaged subjects (contribution to the study of unilateral inattention). Cortex: 9; 94–111, 1973.

Cogan D: Ophthalmic manifestations of bilateral non-occipital cerebral lesions. British Journal of Ophthalmology: 49; 281–297, 1965.

Colby C, Duhamel J-R, Goldberg M: The analysis of visual space by the lateral intraparietal area of the monkey: the role of extraretinal signals. Progress in Brain Research: 95; 307–316, 1993.

Corbetta M, Akbudak E, Conturo T, Snyder A, Ollinger J, Drury H, Linenweber M, Petersen S, Raichle M, van Essen

D, Shulman G: A common network of functional areas for attention and eye movements. Neuron: 21; 761–773, 1998.
Cowey A, Stoerig P: The neurobiology of blindsight. Trends in Neuroscience: 14; 140–145, 1991.
Darby D, Nobre A, Thangaraj V, Edelman R, Mesulam M-M, Warach S: Cortical activation in the human brain during lateral saccades using EPISTAR functional magnetic resonance imaging. Neuroimage: 3; 53–62, 1996.
de Luca M, Spinelli D, Zoccolotti P: Eye movement patterns in reading as a function of visual field defects and contrast sensitivity loss. Cortex: 32; 491–502, 1996.
Dehaene I, Lammans M: Paralysis of saccades and pursuit. Neurology: 41; 414–415, 1991.
Dieterich M, Bucher F, Seelos K, Brandt T: Horizontal or vertical optokinetic stimulation activates visual motion-sensitive, ocular motor and vestibular cortex areas with right hemispheric dominance. An fMRI study. Brain: 121; 1479–1495, 1998.
Doricchi F, Guargiglia C, Paolucci S, Pizzamiglio L: Disturbances of the rapid eye movements (REMs) of REM sleep in patients with unilateral inattentional neglect: clue for the understanding of the functional meanings of REMs. Electroencephalography and Clinical Neurophysiology: 87; 105–116, 1993.
Doricchi F, Perani D, Incoccia C, Grassi F, Cappa S, Bettinardi V, Galati G, Pizzamiglio L, Fazio F: Neural control of fast-regular saccades and antisaccades: an investigation using positron emission tomography. Experimental Brain Research: 116; 50–62, 1997.
Duhamel J-R, Goldberg M, Fitzgibbon E, Sirigu A, Grafman J: Saccadic dysmetria in a patient with a right frontoparietal lesion. Brain: 115; 1387–1402, 1992.
Dupont P, Orban G, de Bruyn B, Verbruggen A, Mortelmans L: Many areas in the human brain respond to visual motion. Journal of Neurophysiology: 72; 1420–1424, 1994.
Elkington P, Kerr G, Stein J: The effect of electromagnetic stimulation of the posterior parietal cortex on eye movements. Eye: 6; 510–514, 1992.
Fischer B: Express saccades in man and monkey. Progress in Brain Research: 64; 155–160, 1986.
Fletcher W, Sharpe J: Saccadic eye movement dysfunction in Alzheimer's disease. Annals of Neurology: 20; 464–471, 1986.
Fletcher W, Sharpe J: Smooth pursuit dysfunction in Alzheimer's disease. Neurology: 38; 272–277, 1988.
Fowler M, Wade D, Richardson A, Stein J: Squints and diplopia seen after brain damage. Journal of Neurology: 243; 86–90, 1996.
Fox P, Fox J, Raichle M, Burde R: The role of cerebral cortex in the generation of voluntary saccades: a positron emission tomographic study. Journal of Neurophysiology: 54; 348–367, 1985.
Fox J, Holmes G: Optic nystagmus and its value in the localization of cerebral lesions. Brain: 49; 333–371, 1926.
Freitag P, Greenlee M, Lacina T, Scheffler K, Radü E: Effect of eye movements on the magnitude of functional magnetic resonance imaging responses in extrastriate cortex during visual motion perception. Experimental Brain Research: 119; 409–414, 1998.
Friberg L, Olsen T, Roland P, Paulson O, Lassen N: Focal increase in blood flow in the cerebral cortex of man during vestibular stimulation. Brain: 108; 609–623, 1985.
Friedman D, Jankovic J, McCrary J: Neuro-ophthalmic findings in progressive supranuclear palsy. Journal of Clinical Neuro-ophthalmology: 12:; 104–109, 1992.
Gamlin P, Yoon K, Zhang H: The role of the cerebro-ponto-cerebellar pathways in the control of vergence eye movements. Eye: 10; 167–171, 1996.
Gassel M, Williams D: Visual function in patients with homonymous hemianopia II. Oculomotor mechanisms. Brain: 86; 1–36, 1963.
Gaymard B, Rivaud S, Pierrot-Deseilligny C: Role of the left and right supplementary motor areas in memory-guided sequences. Annals of Neurology: 34; 404–406, 1993.
Girotti F, Casazza M, Musicco M, Avanzini G: Oculomotor disorders in cortical lesions in man: the role of unilateral neglect. Neuropsychologia: 21; 543–553, 1983.
Gnadt J, Mays L: Neurons in monkey parietal area LIP are tuned for eye movement parameters in three-dimensional space. Journal of Neurophysiology: 73; 280–297, 1995.
Godefroy O, Rousseaux M: Novel decision making in patients with prefrontal or posterior brain damage. Neurology: 49; 695–701, 1997.
Goldberg M, Bruce C, Ungerleider L, Mishkin M: Role of the striate cortex in the generation of smooth pursuit eye movements (Abstract). Annals of Neurology: 12; 113, 1982.
Goldreich D, Krauzlis R, Lisberger S: Effect of changing feedback delay on spontaneous oscillations in smooth pursuit eye movements of monkeys. Journal of Neurophysiology: 67; 625–638, 1992.
Graziano M, Andersen R, Snowden R: Tuning of MST neurons to spiral motions. Journal of Neuroscience: 14; 54–67, 1994.
Groner R, Walder F, Groner M: Looking at faces: local and global aspects of scanpaths. In Gale A, Johnson F (Eds), Theoretical and Applied Aspects of Eye Movement Research. Amsterdam: Elsevier, pp. 523–533, 1984.
Grusser O, Pause M, Schreiter U: Vestibular neurones in the parieto-insular cortex of monkeys (Macaca fascicularis): visual and neck receptor responses. Journal of Physiology: 430; 559–583, 1990.
Guitton D, Buchtel H, Douglas R: Frontal lobe lesions in man cause difficulties in suppressing reflexive glances and in generating goal-directed saccades. Experimental Brain Research: 58; 455–472, 1985.
Guldin W, Akbarian S, Grusser O: Cortico-cortical connections and cytoarchitectonics of the primate vestibular cortex: a study in squirrel monkeys (Saimiri sciureus). Journal of Comparative Neurology: 326; 375–401, 1992.
Guldin W, Grusser O: Is there a vestibular cortex? Trends in Neuroscience: 21; 254–259, 1998.
Gulyás B, Roland P: Binocularity disparity discrimination in human cerebral cortex: functional anatomy by positron emission tomography. Proceedings of the National Academy of

Sciences of the United States of America: 91; 1239–1243, 1994.

Hallett P: Primary and secondary saccades to goals defined by instructions. Vision Research: 18; 1279–1296, 1978.

Hallett P, Adams B: The predictability of saccadic latency in a novel voluntary oculomotor task. Vision Research: 20; 329–339, 1980.

Harnak J: Ocular exploration in the dark by patients with visual neglect. Neuropsychologia: 30; 547–552, 1992.

Hausser C, Robert F, Giard N: Bálint's syndrome. Canadian Journal of the Neurological Sciences: 7; 157–161, 1980.

Hécaen H, de Ajuriaguerra J: Bálint's syndrome (psychic paralysis of visual fixation) and its minor forms. Brain: 77; 373–400, 1954.

Heide W, Blankenburg M, Zimmerman E, Kömpf D: Cortical control of double-step saccades: implications for spatial orientation. Annals of Neurology: 38; 739–748, 1995.

Heide W, Kömpf D: Combined deficits of saccades and visuo–spatial orientation after cortical lesions. Experimental Brain Research: 123; 164–171, 1998.

Hoffman J, Subramanian B: The role of visual attention in saccadic eye movements. Perception and Psychophysics: 57; 787–795, 1995.

Holmes G: Disturbances of visual orientation. British Journal of Ophthalmology: 2; 449–468, 506–516, 1918.

Holmes G: Spasm of fixation. Transactions of the Ophthalmological Societies of the United Kingdom: 50; 253–262, 1930.

Husain M, Stein J: Rezsö Bálint and his most celebrated case. Archives of Neurology: 45; 89–93, 1988.

Ishiai S, Furukawa T, Tsukagoshi H: Eye fixation patterns in homonymous hemianopia and unilateral spatial neglect. Neuropsychologia: 25; 675–679, 1987.

Ishiai S, Furukawa T, Tsukagoshi H: Visuo-spatial processes of line bisection and the mechanisms underlying spatial neglect. Brain: 112; 1485–1502, 1989.

Ishiai S, Seki K, Koyama Y, Gono S: Ineffective leftward search in line bisection and mechanisms of left unilateral spatial neglect. Journal of Neurology: 243; 381–387, 1996.

Ishiai S, Sugishita M, Mitani K, Ishizawa M: Leftward search in left unilateral spatial neglect. Journal of Neurology, Neurosurgery and Psychiatry: 55; 40–44, 1992.

Israël I, Rivaud S, Gaymard B, Berthoz A, Pierrot-Deseilligny C: Cortical control of vestibular-guided saccades in man. Brain: 118; 1169–1183, 1995.

Johnston C, Diller L: Exploratory eye movements and visual hemi-neglect. Journal of Clinical and Experimental Neuropsychology: 8; 93–101, 1986.

Johnston J, Miller J, Nath A: Ocular motor dysfunction in HIV-1-infected subjects. Neurology: 46; 451–457, 1996.

Johnston J, Sharpe J, Morrow M: Spasm of fixation: a quantitative study. Journal of the Neurological Sciences: 107; 166–171, 1992.

Kao G, Morrow M: The relationship of anticipatory smooth eye movement to smooth pursuit initiation. Vision Research: 34; 3027–3036, 1994.

Karnath H-O: Spatial limitation of eye movements during ocular exploration of simple line drawings in neglect syndrome. Cortex: 30; 319–330, 1994.

Karnath H-O, Fetter M: Ocular space exploration in the dark and its relation to subjective and objective body orientation in neglect patients with parietal lesions. Neuropsychologia: 33; 371–377, 1995.

Karnath H-O, Fetter M, Niemeier M: Disentangling gravitational, environmental and egocentric reference frames in spatial neglect. Journal of Cognitive Neuroscience: 10; 680–690, 1998.

Karnath H-O, Huber W: Abnormal eye movement behaviour during text reading in neglect syndrome: a case study. Neuropsychologia: 30; 593–598, 1992.

Kawano K, Sasaki M, Yamashita M: Vestibular input to visual tracking neurons in the posterior parietal association cortex of the monkey. Neuroscience Letters: 17; 55–60, 1980.

Keating E: Residual spatial vision in the monkey after removal of striate and preoccipital cortex. Brain Research: 187; 271–290, 1980.

Kennard C, Lueck C: Oculomotor abnormalities in diseases of the basal ganglia. Revue Neurologique: 145; 587–595, 1989.

Kerkhoff G, Elke K, Meier M: Neurovisual rehabilitation in cerebral blindness. Archives of Neurology: 51; 474–481, 1994.

Kerkhoff G, Stögerer E: Recovery of fusional convergence after systematic practice. Brain Injury: 8; 15–22, 1994.

Kinsbourne M: Mechanisms of unilateral neglect. In Jeannerod M (Ed.), Neurophysicological and neuropsychological aspects of spatial neglect. Amsterdam: Elsevier, pp. 69–86, 1987.

Kjallman L, Frisén L: The cerebral ocular pursuit pathways. Journal of Clinical Neuro-ophthalmology: 6; 209–214, 1986.

Kluzer G, Hahn R: Considérations sur la prédominance unilatérale du nystagmus vestibulaire provoqué chez des sujets atteints de tumeur d'un hémisphere cérébral. Revue d'Oto-Neuro-Ophtalmologie: 26; 257–266, 1954.

Kowler E: The role of visual and cognitive processes in the control of eye movement. In Kowler E (Ed), Eye Movements and their Role in Visual and Cognitive Processes. Amsterdam: Elsevier, pp. 1–70 1990.

Kowler E, Anderson E, Dosher B, Blaser E: The role of attention in the programming of saccades. Vision Research: 35; 1897–1916, 1995.

Kustov A, Robinson D: Shared neural control of attentional shifts and eye movements. Nature: 384; 74–77, 1996.

Làdavas E, Zeloni G, Zaccara G, Gangemi P: Eye movements and orienting of attention in patients with visual neglect. Journal of Cognitive Neuroscience: 9; 67–74, 1997.

Lawden M, Bagelmann H, Crawford T, Matthews T, Kennard C: An effect of structured backgrounds on smooth pursuit eye movements in patients with cerebral lesions. Brain: 118; 37–48, 1995.

Leff A, Scott S, Crewes H, Hodgson T, Cowey A, Howard D, Wise R: Impaired reading in patients with right hemianopia. Annals of Neurology: 47; 171–178, 2000.

Leigh R: The cortical control of ocular pursuit movements. Revue Neurologique (Paris): 145; 605–612, 1989.

Leigh R, Tusa R: Disturbance of smooth pursuit caused by infarction of occipitoparietal cortex. Annals of Neurology: 17; 185–187, 1985.

Leigh R, Zee D: The Neurology of Eye Movements. Oxford: Oxford University Press, 1999.

Lekwuwa G, Barnes G: Cerebral control of eye movements. I. The relationship between cerebral sites and smooth pursuit deficits. Brain: 119; 473–490, 1996.

Li J, Olson J, Anand S, Hotson J: Rapid-rate transcranial magnetic stimulation of human frontal cortex can evoke saccades under facilitating conditions. Electroencephalography and Clinical Neurophysiology: 105; 246–254, 1997.

Liepmann H, Kalmus E: Über einer Augenmaßstörung beu Hemianopikern. Berlin Klinische Wochenschritte: 38; 838–842, 1900.

Lisberger S, Evinger C, Johanson G, Fuchs A: Relationship between eye acceleration and retinal image velocity during foveal smooth pursuit in man and monkey. Journal of Neurophysiology: 46; 229–249, 1981.

Lobel E, Kleine J, Leroy-Willig A, van de Moortele P, Le Bihan D: Cortical areas activated by bilateral galvanic vestibular stimulation. Annals of the New York Academy of Sciences: 871; 313–323, 1999.

Luna B, Thulborn K, Strojwas M, McCurtain B, Berman R, Genovese C, Sweeney J: Dorsal cortical regions subserving visually guided saccades in humans: an fMRI study. Cerebral Cortex: 8; 40–47, 1998.

Luria A, Karpov B, Yarbuss A: Disturbances of active visual perception with lesions of the frontal lobes. Cortex: 2; 202–212, 1966.

Luria A, Pravdina-Vinarskaya E, Yarbuss A: Disorders of ocular movement in a case of simultanagnosia. Brain: 86; 219–228, 1962.

Lynch J: Saccade initiation and latency deficits after combined lesions of the frontal and posterior eye fields in monkeys. Journal of Neurophysiology: 68; 1913–1916, 1992.

Meienberg O: Clinical examination of saccadic eye movements in hemianopia. Neurology: 33; 1311–1315, 1983.

Meienberg O, Zangemeister W, Rosenberg M, Hoyt W, Stark L: Saccadic eye movements in patients with homonymous hemianopia. Annals of Neurology: 9; 537–544, 1981.

Melamed E, Larsen B: Cortical activation pattern during saccadic eye movements in humans: localization by focal cerebral blood flow increases. Annals of Neurology: 5; 79–88, 1979.

Mezey L, Harris C, Shawkat F, Timms C, Kriss A, West P, Taylor D: Saccadic strategies in children with hemianopia. Developmental Medicine and Child Neurology: 40; 626–630, 1998.

Mohler C, Wurtz R: Role of striate cortex and superior colliculus in visual guidance of saccadic eye movements in monkey. Journal of Neurophysiology: 40; 74–94, 1977.

Moore T, Rodman H, Repp A, Gross C: Localization of visual stimuli after striate cortex damage in monkeys: parallels with human blindsight. Proceedings of the National Academy of Sciences of the United States of America: 92; 8215–8217, 1995.

Morrow M: Craniotopic defects of smooth pursuit and saccadic eye movement. Neurology: 46; 514–521, 1996.

Morrow M, Sharpe J: Cerebral hemispheric localization of smooth pursuit asymmetry. Neurology: 40; 284–292, 1990.

Morrow M, Sharpe J: Retinotopic and directional deficits of smooth pursuit initiation after posterior cerebral hemispheric lesions. Neurology: 43; 595–603, 1993a.

Morrow M, Sharpe J: Smooth pursuit initiation in young and elderly subjects. Vision Research: 33; 203–210, 1993b.

Morrow M, Sharpe J: Deficits of smooth-pursuit eye movement after unilateral frontal lobe lesions. Annals of Neurology: 37; 443–451, 1995.

Moser A, Kömpf D: Unilateral visual exploration deficit in a frontal lobe lesion. Neuro-ophthalmology: 10; 39–44, 1990.

Mountcastle V, Lynch J, Georgopoulos A, Sakata H, Acuna C: Posterior parietal association cortex on the monkey: command functions for operations within extrapersonal space. Journal of Neurophysiology: 38; 871–908, 1975.

Müri R, Heid O, Nirkko A, Ozdoba C, Felbinger J, Schroth G, Hess C: Functional organisation of saccades and antisaccades in the frontal lobe in humans: a study with echo planar functional magnetic resonance imaging. Journal of Neurology, Neurosurgery and Psychiatry: 65; 374–377, 1998.

Müri R, Iba-Zizen M, Derosier C, Cabanis E, Pierrot-Deseilligny C: Location of the human posterior eye field with functional magnetic resonance imaging. Journal of Neurology, Neurosurgery and Psychiatry: 60; 445–448, 1996.

Müri R, Vermesch A-I, Rivaud S, Gaymard B, Pierrot-Deseilligny C: Effects of single-pulse transcranial magnetic stimulation over the prefrontal and posterior parietal cortices during memory-guided saccades in humans. Journal of Neurophysiology: 76; 2102–2106, 1996.

Nielsen K, Intriligator J, Barton J: Spatial representation in the normal visual field. A study of hemifield line bisection. Neuropsychologia: 37; 267–277, 1999.

Noton D, Stark L: Scanpaths in eye movements during pattern perception. Science: 171; 308–311, 1971a.

Noton D, Stark L: Eye movements and visual perception. Scientific American: 224; 34–43, 1971b.

Noton D, Stark L: Scanpaths in saccadic eye movements while viewing and recognizing patterns. Vision Research: 11; 929–942, 1971c.

O'Driscoll G, Alpert N, Matthysse S, Levy D, Rauch S, Holzman P: Functional neuroanatomy of antisaccadic eye movements investigated with positron emission tomography. Proceedings of the National Academy of Sciences of the United States of America: 92; 925–929, 1995.

O'Driscoll G, Strakowski S, Alpert N, Matthyse S, Rauch S, Levy D, Holzman P: Differences in cerebral activation during smooth pursuit and saccadic eye movements using positron-emission tomography. Biological Psychiatry: 44; 685–689, 1998.

O'Sullivan E, Jenkins I, Henderson L, Kennard C, Brooks D: The functional anatomy of remembered saccades: a PET study. NeuroReport: 6; 2141–2144, 1995.

Ohtsuka K, Maekawa H, Takeda M, Uede N, Chiba S: Convergence insufficiency after left middle cerebral artery occlusion. American Journal of Ophthalmology: 106; 60–64, 1988.

Page W, King W, Merigan W, Maunsell J: Magnocellular or parvocellular lesions in the lateral geniculate nucleus of monkeys cause minor deficits of smooth pursuit eye movements. Vision Research: 34; 223–239, 1994.

Paus T: Location and function of the human frontal eye field: a selective review. Neuropsychologia: 34; 475–483, 1996.

Paus T, Kalina M, Patockova L, Angerova Y, Cerny R, Mecir P, Bauer J, Krabec P: Medial vs lateral frontal lobe lesions and differential impairment of central-gaze fixation maintenance in man. Brain: 114; 2051–2067, 1991.

Perenin M-T: Discrimination of motion direction in perimetrically blind fields. NeuroReport: 2; 397–400, 1991.

Perenin M-T, Jeannerod M: Residual function in cortically blind hemifields. Neuropsychologia: 13; 1–7, 1975.

Perenin M-T, Ruel J, Hécaen H: Residual visual capacities in a case of cortical blindness. Cortex: 6; 605–612, 1980.

Petit L, Clark V, Ingeholm J, Haxby J: Dissociation of saccade-related and pursuit-related activation in human frontal eye fields as revealed by fMRI. Journal of Neurophysiology: 77; 3386–3390, 1997.

Petit L, Orssaud C, Tzourio N, Crivello F, Berthoz A, Mazoyer B: Functional anatomy of a prelearned sequence of horizontal saccades in humans. Journal of Neuroscience: 16; 3714–3726, 1996.

Pierrot-Deseilligny C, Gautier J-C, Loron P: Acquired ocular motor apraxia due to bilateral frontoparietal infarcts. Annals of Neurology: 23; 199–202, 1988.

Pierrot-Deseilligny C, Gray F, Brunet P: Infarcts of both inferior parietal lobules with impairment of visually guided eye movements, peripheral inattention and optic ataxia. Brain: 109; 81–97, 1986.

Pierrot-Deseilligny C, Rivaud S, Gaymard B, Agid Y: Cortical control of reflexive visually-guided saccades. Brain: 114; 1473–1485, 1991a.

Pierrot-Deseilligny C, Rivaud S, Gaymard B, Agid Y: Cortical control of memory-guided saccades. Experimental Brain Research: 83; 607–617, 1991b.

Pierrot-Deseilligny C, Rivaud S, Gaymard B, Müri R, Vermersch A-I: Cortical control of saccades. Annals of Neurology: 37; 557–567, 1995.

Pierrot-Deseilligny C, Rivaud S, Penet C, Rigolet M-H: Latencies of visually-guided saccades in unilateral hemispheric cerebral lesions. Annals of Neurology: 21; 138–148, 1987.

Pöppel E, Held R, Frost D: Residual visual function after brain wounds involving the central visual pathways in man. Nature: 243; 295–296, 1973.

Posner M: Orienting of attention. Quarterly Journal of Experimental Psychology: 32; 3–25, 1980.

Priori A, Bertolasi L, Rothwell J, Day B, Marsden C: Some saccadic eye movements can be delayed by transcranial magnetic stimulation of the cerebral cortex in man. Brain: 116; 355–367, 1993.

Rayner K: Eye movements in reading and information processing: 20 years of research. Psychological Bulletin: 124; 372–422, 1998.

Reeves A, Perret J, Jenkyn L, Saint-Hilaire J-M: Pursuit gaze and the occipitoparietal region. Archives of Neurology: 41; 83–84, 1984.

Riddoch M, Humphreys G: Perceptual and action systems in unilateral visual neglect. In Jeannerod M (Ed), Neurophysiological and Neuropsychological Aspects of Spatial Neglect. Amsterdam: Elsevier, pp. 151–180, 1987.

Rivaud S, Müri R, Gaymard B, Vermesch A, Pierrot-Deseilligny C: Eye movement disorders after frontal eye field lesions in humans. Experimental Brain Research: 102; 110–120, 1994.

Rizzo M: Bálint's syndrome and associated visuospatial disorders. Baillière's Clincal Neurology: 2; 415–437, 1993.

Rizzo M, Hurtig R: Looking but not seeing: attention, perception, and eye movements in simultanagnosia. Neurology: 37; 1642–1648, 1987.

Rizzo M, Hurtig R: Visual search in hemi-neglect: what stirs idle eyes? Clinical Vision Sciences: 7; 39–52, 1992.i

Rizzo M, Hurtig R, Damasio A: The role of scanpaths in facial recognition and learning. Annals of Neurology: 22; 41–45, 1987.

Rizzo M, Robin D: Bilateral effects of unilateral visual cortex lesions in human. Brain: 119; 951–963, 1996.

Ron S, Schmid R, Orpaz D: Applying a model of saccadic prediction to patients' saccadic eye movements. Brain Behaviour and Evolution: 33; 179–182, 1989.

Roy J-P, Komatsu H, Wurtz R: Disparity sensitivity of neurons in monkey extrastriate area MST. Journal of Neuroscience: 12; 2478–2492, 1992.

Sanders M, Warrington E, Marshall J, Weiskrantz L: 'Blind sight': vision in a field defect. Lancet: 20; 707–708, 1974.

Saslow M: Effects of components of displacement-step stimuli upon latency for saccadic eye movement. Journal of the Optometry Society of America: 57; 1024–1029, 1967.

Schall J, Thompson K: Neural selection and control of visually guided eye movements. Annual Review of Neuroscience: 22; 241–259, 1999.

Schoepf D, Zangemeister W: Target predictability influences the distribution of coordinated eye-head gaze saccades in patients with homonymous hemianopia. Neurological Research: 18; 425–439, 1996.

Scott B, Jeannerod M, Zahin M: L'agnosie spatiale unilatérale: perturbation en secteur des méchanismes d'exploration et de fixation du regard. Journal Medicine Lyon: 47; 169–195, 1966.

Segraves M, Goldberg M, Deng S-Y, Bruce C, Ungerleider L, Mishkin M: The role of striate cortex in the guidance of eye movements in the monkey. Journal of Neuroscience: 7; 3040–3058, 1987.

Sharpe J, Herishanu Y, White O: Cerebral square wave jerks. Neurology: 37; 1389–1392, 1982.

Sharpe J, Lo A: Voluntary and visual control of the vestibuloocular reflex after cerebral hemidecortication. Annals of Neurology: 10; 164–172, 1981.

Sharpe J, Lo A, Rabinovitch H: Control of the saccadic and smooth pursuit systems after cerebral hemidecortication. Brain: 102; 387–403, 1979.

Sheperd M, Findlay J, Hockey R: The relationship between eye movements and spatial attention. Quarterly Journal of Experimental Psychology: 38A; 475–491, 1986.

Simpson J: The accessory optic system. Annual Review of Neuroscience: 7; 13–41, 1984.

Straube A, Brandt T: Importance of the visual and vestibular cortex for self-motion perception in man (circularvection). Human Neurobiology: 6; 211–218, 1987.

Sundqvist A: Saccadic reaction-time in parietal-lobe dysfunction. Lancet: i; 870, 1979.

Sweeney J, Mintun M, Kwee S, Wiseman M, Brown D, Rosenberg D, Carl J: Positron emission tomography study of voluntary saccadic eye movements and spatial working memory. Journal of Neurophysiology: 75; 454–468, 1996.

Takagi M, Toga H, Bando T: Extrastriate cortical neurons correlated with ocular convergence in the cat. Neuroscience Research: 17; 141–158, 1993.

Takeda N, Tanaka-Tsuji M, Sawada T, Koizuka I, Kubo T: Clinical investigation of the vestibular cortex. Acta Otolaryngologica Supplement: 520; 110–112, 1995.

Ter Braak J, Schenk V, van Vliet A: Visual reactions in a case of long-lasting cortical blindness. Journal of Neurology, Neurosurgery and Psychiatry: 34; 140–147, 1971.

Terao Y, Fukuda H, Ugawa Y, Hikosaka O, Hanajima R, Furubayashi T, Sakai K, Miyauchi S, Sasaki Y, Kanazawa I: Visualization of the informational flow through human oculomotor cortical regions by transcranial magnetic stimulation. Journal of Neurophysiology: 80; 936–946, 1998.

Thickbroom G, Stell R, Mastaglia F: Transcranial magnetic stimulation of the human frontal eye field. Journal of the Neurological Sciences: 144; 114–118, 1996.

Thurston S, Leigh R, Crawford T, Thompson A, Kennard C: Two distinct deficits of visual tracking caused by unilateral lesions of cerebral cortex in humans. Annals of Neurology: 23; 266–273, 1988.

Tootell R, Reppas J, Kwong K, Malach R, Born R, Brady T, Rosen B, Belliveau J: Functional analysis of human MT and related visual cortical areas using magnetic resonance imaging. Journal of Neuroscience: 15; 3215–3230, 1995.

Traccis S, Puliga M, Ruiu M, Marras M, Rosati G: Unilateral occipital lesion causing hemianopia affects acoustic saccadic programming. Neurology: 41; 1633–1638, 1991.

Trauzettel-Klosinski S, Brendler K: Eye movements in reading with hemianopic field defects: the significance of clinical parameters. Graefe's Archive for Clinical and Experimental Ophthalmology: 236; 91–102, 1998.

Troost B, Daroff R, Weber R, Dell'Osso L: Hemispheric control of eye movements II. Quantitative analysis of smooth pursuit in a hemispherectomy patient. Archives of Neurology: 27; 449–452, 1972.

Tusa R, Ungerleider L: Fiber pathways of cortical areas mediating smooth pursuit eye movements in monkeys. Annals of Neurology: 23; 174–183, 1988.

Umiltà C: Orienting of attention. In Boller F, Grafman J (Eds), Handbook of Neuropsychology. Amsterdam: Elsevier, pp. 175–193, 1988.

Van Hof-van Duin J, Mohn G: Optokinetic and spontaneous nysintagmus children with neurological disorders. Behavioural Brain Research: 10; 163–175, 1983.

Ventre J: Cortical control of oculomotor functions. II. Vestibulo-ocular reflex and visual vestibular interactions. Behavioural Brain Research: 17; 221–234, 1985.

Vermesch A-I, Gaymard B, Rivaud-Pechoux S, Ploner C, Agid Y, Pierrot-Deseilligny C: Memory guided saccade deficit after caudate nucleus lesion. Journal of Neurology, Neurosurgery and Psychiatry: 66; 524–527, 1999.

Vermesch A-I, Müri R, Rivaud S, Vidailhet M, Gaymard B, Agid Y, Pierrot-Deseilligny C: Saccade disturbances after bilateral lentiform nucleus lesions in humans. Journal of Neurology, Neurosurgery and Psychiatry: 60; 179–184, 1996.

Walker R, Husain M, Hodgson T, Harrison J, Kennard C: Saccadic eye movement and working memory deficits following damage to human prefrontal cortex. Neuropsychologia: 36; 1141–1159, 1998.

Walker-Smith G, Gale A, Findlay J: Eye movement strategies involved in face perception. Perception: 6; 313–326, 1977.

Weiskrantz L: Behavioural analysis of the monkey's visual nervous system. Proceedings of the Royal Society of London B: 182; 427–455, 1972.

Weiskrantz L: Residual vision in a scotoma: a follow-up study of 'form' discrimination. Brain: 110; 77–92, 1987.

Weiskrantz L, Warrington E, Sanders M, Marshall J: Visual capacity in the hemianopic field following a restricted occipital ablation. Brain: 97; 709–728, 1974.

Wessel K, Kömpf D: Transcranial magnetic stimulation: lack of oculomotor response. Experimental Brain Research: 86; 216–218, 1991.

Wheeless L, Boynton R, Cohen G: Eye-movement responses to step and pulse-step stimuli. Journal of the Optometric Society of America: 56; 956–960, 1966.

Zackon D, Sharpe J: Smooth pursuit in senescence. Effects of target acceleration and velocity. Acta Otolaryngologica: 104; 290–297, 1987.

Zangemeister W, Canavan A, Hoemberg V: Frontal and parietal transcranial magnetic stimulation (TMS) disturbs programming of saccadic eye movements. Journal of the Neurological Sciences: 133; 42–52, 1995.

Zee D, Tusa R, Herdman S, Butler P, Gücer G: Effects of occipital lobectomy upon eye movements in primate. Journal of Neurophysiology: 58; 883–907, 1987.

Zihl J: 'Blindsight': improvement of visually guided eye movements by systematic practice in patients with cerebral blindness. Neuropsychologia: 18; 71–77, 1980.

Zihl J: Eye movement patterns in hemianopic dyslexia. Brain: 118; 891–912, 1995.

Zihl J, Werth R: Contributions to the study of 'blindsight' — II. the role of specific practice for saccadic localization in patients with postgeniculate visual field defects. Neuropsychologia: 22; 13–22, 1984.

Published by Elsevier Science B.V.
Handbook of Neuropsychology, 2nd Edition, Vol. 4
M. Behrmann (Ed)

CHAPTER 3

Spatial representations

Carol L. Colby [a,b,*] and Michael E. Goldberg [c,d]

[a] *Department of Neuroscience, of Pittsburgh, Pittsburgh, 446 Crawford Hall, PA 15232, USA*
[b] *Center for the Neural Basis of Cognition, University of Pittsburgh, Pittsburgh, PA 15232, USA*
[c] *Laboratory of Sensorimotor Research, National Eye Institute, Bldg. 49 Room 2A50, NIH, Bethesda, MD 20892, USA*
[d] *Department of Neurology, Georgetown University School of Medicine, Washington, DC 20007, USA*

Introduction

As we move through the world and interact with it, a major challenge to the nervous system is to construct a representation of the space around us and the locations of salient objects within it. The brain uses inputs from all modalities to extract spatial information and build internal representations designed to support interactions with the environment. These representations must be capable of guiding the many kinds of motor output that depend on spatial information. In this review, we describe the neural basis of spatial representation. The first section gives an overview of the functional organization of cortical brain regions involved in spatial processing. The following sections examine the specific kinds of spatial representations constructed in different cortical regions.

Functional organization of spatial processing

Dorsal stream extrastriate areas process visuospatial information

Among primates, visual inputs are the primary and most accurate source of information about extrapersonal space. Within the visual system, information is processed serially by a succession of cortical areas that are progressively more distant from primary visual cortex in the occipital lobe. Within this hierarchical system, there are two parallel streams of information flow (Ungerleider and Mishkin, 1982). The ventral stream, leading into the temporal lobe, consists of a series of anatomically linked extrastriate areas. Single neurons in these areas encode information about stimulus size, shape, orientation and color, among other qualities. Neurons in inferior temporal cortex, the endpoint of the ventral stream, are selective for complex forms and objects. Lesions of this cortex produce deficits in object discrimination and recognition. Overall, the ventral stream provides the substrate for understanding what things are, hence it is often referred to as the 'what' stream. In contrast, the dorsal stream is referred to as the 'where' stream and contains neurons selective for stimulus characteristics useful for determining the location of a stimulus. Lesions of parietal cortex, an endpoint of the dorsal stream, produce deficits in localization of objects, but do not impair object recognition. This double dissociation between the effects of parietal and temporal lobe lesions in monkeys led to the fundamental insight that the dorsal and ventral streams subserve distinct perceptual goals. Subsequent anatomical, physiological and functional imaging studies have underscored the importance of this basic division.

The dorsal stream is specialized for spatial perception in several ways. First, the visual field representation in individual dorsal stream areas is uni-

* Corresponding author. Tel.: +1 (412) 268-7295; Fax: +1 (412) 268-5060; E-mail: ccolby@cnbc.cmu.edu

formly broader than that found in ventral stream areas. The latter represent only the central 35–40° of visual angle, while dorsal stream areas such as MT (middle temporal) and MST (medial superior temporal) represent the entire visual field, out to 90°, and dorsal stream area PO (parieto-occipital) actually overrepresents the visual field periphery, relative to other areas (Colby, Gattass, Olson and Gross, 1988). Second, single neurons in several dorsal stream areas are specialized for the detection and analysis of moving visual stimuli, including speed and direction. Third, neurons in several dorsal stream areas are sensitive to the depth at which a stimulus appears relative to the animal. Some neurons are also selective for special properties, such as motion and rotation in depth. The full range of response properties in the dorsal stream is still being explored, but it is clear that considerable information about stimulus shape is also present (Sakata, Taira, Kusunoki et al., 1998; Sereno and Maunsell, 1998). This information is particularly important for providing the sensory basis for functions, such as shaping of the hand prior to grasping an object. The primary difference between the dorsal and ventral streams is not in the types of visual information processed per se, but rather in the uses to which that information is put, i.e. object recognition as compared to spatial coding. Finally, the dorsal stream intersects in the parietal lobe with a comparable somatosensory hierarchy. As will be described below, some dorsal stream areas in parietal cortex contain bimodal neurons that combine visual and somatosensory information. In addition, some parietal neurons respond to visual and auditory, or visual and vestibular information. Although we usually think of visual input as being the most important for spatial operations, awareness of space is more than just a visual function. We can appreciate the shape of an object, and we can tell where it is, regardless of whether we see it or sense it through hearing or touch. Supramodal as well as unimodal representations of space are constructed in the parietal cortex.

A network of association areas contributes to spatial cognition

The parietal cortex is thought to be pre-eminent among cortical areas responsible for spatial perception because lesions of parietal cortex lead to the most devastating and specific impairments of spatial function. However, many other cortical areas mediate cognitive functions that depend in some way on the use of spatial information. Association cortex occupies a continuous swath of the cerebral hemispheres, encompassing large parts of frontal, cingulate, temporal, parahippocampal and insular cortices. These regions are anatomically connected to each other and to parietal cortex by reciprocal pathways (Goldman-Rakic, 1988; Pandya and Yeterian, 1985). The spatial functions of some of these other association areas have been investigated in humans and non-human primates. For example, lesions of the parahippocampal cortex in humans can lead to topographic amnesia, a specific deficit in the ability to learn new environments or to navigate through previously familiar ones (Habib and Sirigu, 1987). In monkeys, single unit studies indicate that frontal cortex generates voluntary actions in extrapersonal space and mediates working memory for spatially directed responses (Funahashi, Bruce and Goldman-Rakic, 1993). As will be seen below, specific regions of parietal cortex are connected to particular zones within frontal cortex and neurons in linked regions operate in the same coordinate framework. Overall, spatial processing depends on both the parietal cortex and the distributed network of areas with which it is connected.

Multiple representations of space

Types of representations

Our subjective experience strongly suggests that we have direct access to a single coherent and overarching representation of space. Whether we localize a stimulus by sight, smell, hearing or touch, we can respond to it with equal ease and with any motor system at our command. This introspection is misleading. There is no evidence for the existence of a single, explicit, topographic representation of space suitable for incorporating every kind of sensory input and generating every kind of motor output. On the contrary, the evidence points to multiple representations of space, in a variety of coordinate frames, and linked to separate output systems designed to guide specific motor effectors.

The particular reference frame in use at any time depends on the task being performed. For example, if you were to draw out a route for a hiking trip on a map, the route would be in the coordinates of the map, the piece of paper. If you were then going to walk along that route, it would be necessary first to locate your current position within the coordinate frame of the map and then construct a representation of the route with respect to your starting point. The first, map-based reference frame is an example of an allocentric frame, in which locations are represented in reference frames independent of the observer. Allocentric reference frames include those centered on an object of interest (object-centered) and those in environmental (room-centered or world-centered) coordinates. The second reference frame, centered on your current location, is an example of an egocentric, or viewer-based, frame, in which locations are represented relative to the observer. Egocentric reference frames have been further subdivided to distinguish among those that are eye-centered, head-centered, hand-centered or body-centered (see Behrmann, 2000).

Evidence for multiple representations from studies of neglect

Damage to parietal cortex produces dramatic impairments of spatial perception and action. The most striking of these deficits is neglect, the tendency to ignore objects in the half of space opposite to the side of the lesion Bisiach and Valler (2000) (see Bartolomeo and Chokron, 2001, this volume). A patient with a right parietal lobe lesion may fail to notice or respond to objects on the left, including food on the left side of a plate or words on the left side of a page. Neglect occurs in all sensory modalities and can be expressed relative to any of several spatial reference frames. A patient with right parietal damage is typically unaware of objects on the left but 'left' may be defined with respect to a variety of axes. Patients may neglect objects on the left with respect to the body, or with respect to the line of sight, or with respect to the object to which they are attending (Driver and Halligan, 1991; Farah, Brunn, Wong et al., 1990; Gazzaniga and Ladavas, 1987; Karnath, Schenkel and Fischer, 1991; Moscovitch and Behrmann, 1994). For example, a neglect patient may shave only one half of his face (head-centered frame), or dress only one side of her body (body-centered frame). Neuropsychological observations thus suggest that the brain constructs multiple egocentric representations.

Studies in patients also indicate that neglect can be expressed relative to spatial reference frames that are extrinsic to the observer (see Behrmann, 2000 for review). A particularly striking example of a deficit expressed in an allocentric spatial reference frame has been described by Moscovitch and Behrmann (1994). They showed that patients neglected a somatosensory stimulus on the left side of the wrist (towards the thumb) when the right hand was palm down. When the hand was turned over so that the palm faced up, the neglected region shifted to the other side (towards the little finger). This demonstrates that the impairment is not of a somatosensory map of the skin surface but rather of an abstract representation of somatosensory space. The dynamic nature of the impairment, changing from moment to moment as a function of body posture, indicates that this representation is constantly being updated. Impairments in different kinds of representations can co-exist and individual patients exhibit different impairments under different behavioral demands (Behrmann and Moscovitch, 1994). Multiple frames of reference may even be used simultaneously (Behrmann and Tipper, 1994; Tipper and Behrmann, 1996). In sum, neuropsychological and behavioral studies support the view that multiple spatial representations are called into play according to the specific demands of the task (Carlson-Radvansky and Irwin, 1994; Sirigu, Duhamel, Cohen et al., 1996; Tipper, Lortie and Baylis, 1992).

Deficits in spatially directed actions are also common after parietal lobe damage. Milner and Goodale (1995) have emphasized the role of parietal cortex in generating spatial representations for the guidance of action, especially for reaching. Patients with misreaching, or optic ataxia, exhibit a variety of dissociable deficits. In a task that requires a subject to reach in a particular direction and orient the hand to match the orientation of a visual stimulus, subjects may misreach or misorient the hand or both (Perenin and Vighetto, 1988). Optic ataxia may also be lateralized, occurring only when the patient is required to point to objects in one visual hemifield or only when one hand is used for pointing. Optic ataxia is not simply a problem with visuospatial perception, as indicated by the fact that performance with one hand may be perfectly normal. It is also not a purely motor problem, as indicated by the observation that patients unable to reach accurately for visual targets can commonly touch points on their own bodies accurately under proprioceptive guidance. Optic ataxia is best characterized as a failure in the use of visuospatial information to guide arm movements.

Another example of the close linkage between parietal function and motor actions is the specificity of neglect for stimuli presented at particular distances. Some patients tend to ignore stimuli presented near the body, in peripersonal space, while responding normally to distant stimuli, or vice versa (Bisiach, Perani, Vallar and Berti, 1986; Cowey, Small and Ellis, 1994; Duhamel and Brouchon, 1990; Halligan and Marshall, 1991). Interestingly, this form of neglect is apparent only when the subject must produce a motor response to the stimulus, and not when spatial perception alone is tested (Pizzamiglio, Cappa, Vallar et al., 1989). This dependence on action indicates that spatial representations in parietal cortex incorporate both sensory information about distance and information about intended actions.

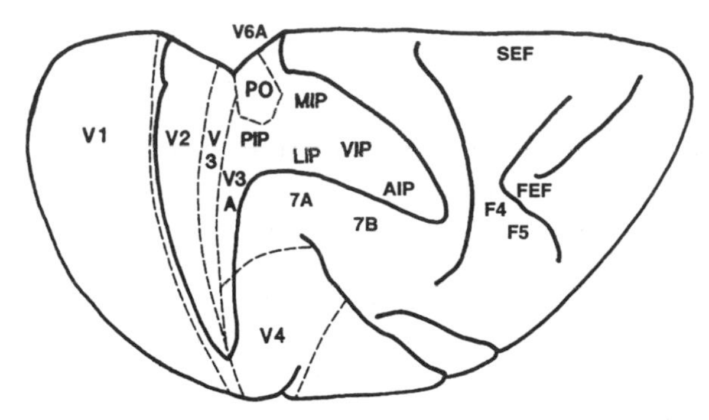

Fig. 1. Dorsal view of macaque right hemisphere with lunate and intraparietal sulci opened to show the locations of functionally defined extrastriate and parietal areas, along with frontal areas involved in spatial representation and behavior. Adapted from Colby et al. (1988).

Spatial representations in cortex

Types of representations in the brain

The brain mechanisms underlying spatial representation in cortex have been studied primarily in monkeys. To understand more precisely how parietal cortex contributes to spatial perception and action, several groups of investigators have carried out recordings from single neurons in alert monkeys trained to perform spatial tasks. Physiologists have specified the sensory and motor conditions under which parietal neurons are activated, using tasks that typically require a hand or an eye movement toward a visual target (Hyvarinen and Poranen, 1974; Mountcastle, Lynch, Georgopoulos et al., 1975; Robinson, Goldberg and Stanton, 1978). This work in monkeys has provided direct evidence that parietal cortex contains several distinct functional areas (Fig. 1) and multiple representations of space (Andersen, Snyder, Bradley and Xing, 1997; Caminiti, Ferraina and Johnson, 1996; Colby and Duhamel, 1991, 1996; Colby et al., 1988; Jeannerod, Arbib, Rizzolatti and Sakata, 1995; Lacquaniti, Guigon, Bianchi et al., 1995; Rizzolatti, Fogassi and Gallese, 1997; Stein, 1992). Parietal cortical areas are strongly linked with areas of frontal cortex (premotor cortex and the frontal and supplementary eye fields), which themselves encode object locations relative to a variety of reference frames (Gentilucci, Scandolara, Pigarev and Rizzolatti, 1983; Goldberg and Bruce, 1990; Graziano, Hu and Gross, 1997; Graziano, Yap and Gross, 1994; Gross and Graziano, 1995; Rizzolatti, Riggio and Sheliga, 1994; Rizzolatti, Scandolara, Matelli and Gentilucci, 1981b; Olson and Gettner, 1995). The spatial reference frames used in parietal and frontal cortex have been described either in terms of the body parts to which they are anchored (eye, head, limb) or in terms of the actions to which they contribute (looking, reaching, grasping). Some brain regions also contain neurons selective for the distance of the stimulus from the observer: within the grasp of the hand; within reach of the mouth; or distant from the viewer. These response selectivities underscore the degree to which spatial representations can be constructed in the service of action guidance. Finally, beyond these egocentric representations, recent work has demonstrated the existence at the single unit level of more abstract, allocentric representations that encode stimulus locations and actions in coordinates that are independent of the observer (Olson and Gettner, 1995, 1996).

The following sections describe evidence for five distinct spatial reference frames used in parietal and frontal cortex: reaching-related, grasp-related, head-centered, eye-centered, and object-centered. In the first four egocentric representations, neural activity is related to the distinct workspaces in which movements could occur, but does not specify whether such movements will occur. In the fifth, allocentric, representation, neural activity automatically encodes an abstract depiction of stimulus location, but likewise does not specify motor action.

Reaching-related spatial representations

Several kinds of representations in parietal and premotor cortex provide spatial information for reaching, including eye-centered (Batista, Buneo, Snyder and Andersen, 1999; Henriques, Klier, Smith et al., 1998), head-centered (Boussaoud, 1995) and arm-centered (Caminiti, Johnson, Galli et al., 1991). An arm-centered spatial representation is one in which the visual receptive field is anchored to the skin surface of the limb: when the arm is moved, the visual receptive field moves with it. The most direct evidence for such a representation comes from experiments in which visual receptive fields are mapped with the arm in different positions. Neurons in premotor cortex have visual receptive fields that move with the arm (Graziano et al., 1994) and some neurons encode targets in arm-centered coordinates (Caminiti et al., 1991). Neurons in the arm region of ventral premotor cortex (area F5) encode more than just the locations of targets. They also carry information about the shapes of object, information necessary for orienting and shaping the hand correctly to grasp an object (Murata, Fadiga, Fogassi et al., 1997).

Inputs to the arm region of premotor cortex arise from specific portions of parietal cortex where reaching-related activity is common, including the medial intraparietal (MIP) area and the parieto-occipital cortex (Johnson, Ferraina and Caminiti, 1993; Johnson, Ferraina, Bianchi and Caminiti, 1996). Neurons in the medial intraparietal area (area MIP) are specialized for responding to stimuli within reaching distance and for acting on them by reaching (Colby and Duhamel, 1991). Many types of neurons are found in area MIP, from purely somatosensory, to bimodal, to purely visual. Purely somatosensory neurons typically have receptive fields on the contralateral limbs, most often on the hand. Bimodal neurons have visual responses to the onset of a stationary visual stimulus as well as somatosensory responses to passive touch. These bimodal neurons are strongly activated when the monkey reaches for a visual target and are specific for both the location of the target and for the arm that is used to reach toward it. Area MIP also contains visual neurons, and some of these respond more strongly when the visual stimulus is moved to within reaching distance. These ‘near’ cells presumably signal the presence of a target that can be acquired by reaching with the arm, i.e. objects that are within the workspace of the reaching system. In a directional reaching task, more dorsal (predominantly somatosensory) neurons exhibit selectivity for movement direction at the time of the movement, whereas more ventral (predominantly visual) neurons show direction selectivity around the time of stimulus presentation (Johnson et al., 1996). Parietal neurons with reaching-related activity also encode stimulus features, such as location and direction of stimulus motion (Andersen et al., 1997; Eskandar and Assad, 1999; Snyder, Batista and Andersen, 1998). The mixture of sensory and movement-related signals present in area MIP is also characteristic of neurons in the parieto-occipital area called V6A (Battaglia-Mayer, Ferraina, Mitsuda et al., 2000; Galletti, Fattori, Kutz and Battaglini, 1997). These parietal regions collectively may be the source of the spatial information used by frontal cortex to guide reaching movements (Caminiti et al., 1996).

Reaching-related representations must be plastic enough to accommodate expansions of the workspace available for reaching. For many kinds of tool use, we experience the tool as an extension of our limb. Some intriguing recent experiments suggest that bimodal neurons in monkey intraparietal cortex likewise extend their visual receptive fields when the monkey uses a tool (Iriki, Tanaka and Iwamura, 1996). In these experiments, monkeys were trained to use a rake to retrieve distant objects and mapped visual receptive fields before and immediately after tool use. While the somatosensory receptive fields were unchanged, the visual receptive fields expanded when the monkey used the rake as an extension of its hand. The authors interpret this as a change in the body image, or schema: the enlargement of the visual receptive field reflects the neural correlate of a representation of the hand that now incorporates the tool. The visual receptive fields return to their original size within a few minutes after tool use is discontinued, and they do not expand at all if the monkey simply holds the rake without intending to use it. These rapid changes in visual receptive field size indicate that the connections that support the expansion must be in place all along. These MIP neurons, like those in the lateral intraparietal (LIP) area, have access to visual information well beyond the immediately apparent receptive field.

The plasticity apparent in parietal receptive fields can be interpreted as a modification of the workspace available for action. An intriguing recent case study suggests that similar modifications occur in humans (Berti and Frassunatti, 2000). A patient with a right parietal lobe lesion could accurately bisect a line placed far away when she used a laser pointer, but performed poorly both when she bisected a line in an ordinary pencil and paper task and when she attempted to bisect the distant line using a long stick. In both of the latter conditions, she was operating in the workspace accessible by reaching. As was the case for the monkeys in Iriki's task, the workspace available for reaching expanded when she used a tool (the long stick) that allowed her to act on stimuli at a distance in the same way that she acted on similar stimuli nearby. The neglect she exhibited for the left side of objects 'within reach' was not apparent when she bisected the far line by pointing at it with the laser pointer. This action must depend on spatial information encoded with respect to a different workspace.

Grasp-related spatial representation

Reaching and grasping are dissociable behaviors and each can be selectively impaired following brain damage (Jeannerod et al., 1995). Grasping an object requires aligning the hand with the object and shaping the hand to match the size of the object. Neurons in two parietal regions process the kinds of information necessary for grasping and manipulating objects. Neurons in the anterior intraparietal (AIP) area respond selectively to visual stimuli that the monkey can manipulate. Visual neurons in both the caudal intraparietal sulcus (cIPS) and in the AIP are sensitive to the shape and orientation of objects (Sakata Taira, Murata and Mine, 1995; Shikata, Tanaka, Nakamura et al., 1996). Moreover, some neurons in the AIP are activated in conjunction with specific hand movements. And in a memory-guided reaching task, these neurons are most strongly activated when the monkey is remembering an object with the neuron's preferred object shape (Murata, Gallese, Kaseda and Sakata, 1996). Reversible inactivation of area AIP interferes with the monkey's ability to shape its hand appropriately for grasping an object, but does not produce a deficit in reaching per se (Gallese, Murata, Kaseda et al., 1994). The spatial representation in the AIP is different from those in other cortical areas in that the spatial dimension represented is the desired shape of the hand rather than its position in egocentric space. Area AIP sends projections to area F5, the region of premotor cortex that controls hand shape and grip (Gallese, Fadiga, Fogassi et al., 1997). In sum, AIP neurons are involved in constructing an action-relevant representation that translates visual information into a form usable to specify motor action. This contrasts with the processing of shape information in ventral stream visual areas, such as V4 and inferior temporal cortex, which process similar information, but for a different purpose, namely object recognition.

Head-centered spatial representation

Movements of the head toward or away from a target rely on spatial information coded with respect to the head. In a head-centered representation, visual receptive fields are anchored to the head. As long as the head is stationary, the visual receptive field covers the same part of space, regardless of the position of the eyes or the rest of the body. In the ventral intraparietal (VIP) area, neurons encoding a head-centered representation co-exist with those encoding a simple retinocentric spatial representation (Duhamel, Bremmer, BenHamed and Graf, 1997). Area VIP is located in the depths of the intraparietal sulcus, where inputs from high-order visual and somatosensory cortex converge. Single neurons in area VIP respond vigorously to moving visual stimuli, yet they can also be driven well by somatosensory stimuli (Colby and Duhamel, 1991; Duhamel, Colby and

Goldberg, 1991, 1998). In the visual domain, VIP neurons are characterized by direction and speed selectivity, and thus resemble neurons in other dorsal stream visual areas that process stimulus motion. In the somatosensory domain, these same neurons respond to light touch on the head and face. The somatosensory and visual receptive fields of individual neurons exhibit strong spatial correspondence: they match in location, in size, and even in their preferred direction of motion.

The existence of spatially matched receptive fields raises an interesting question: what happens when the eyes move away from primary position? If the visual receptive fields were simply retinotopic, they would have to move in space when the eyes do and so would no longer match the location of the somatosensory receptive field. Instead, for some VIP neurons, the visual receptive field moves to a new location on the retina when the eyes move away from the straight ahead position. For example, the neuron illustrated in Fig. 2 has a somatosensory receptive field near the mouth and responds best to a visual stimulus moving toward the mouth from any direction (left column, A and C). It does not respond to the same visual stimulus on a trajectory toward the brow (right column, B and D). This pattern of response indicates that the stimulus is not being encoded in a simple retinotopic coordinate frame: stimuli moving through the same portion of visual space evoke quite different responses depending on the projected point of contact. Rather, this neuron is encoding visual information in a head-centered coordinate frame. This was confirmed by having the monkey shift its gaze to different locations (Fig. 2E–G). Regardless of where the monkey looked, the cell continued to respond best to visual stimuli on any trajectory heading toward the mouth and failed to respond to stimuli moving along similar trajectories, but directed toward other points on the face. This neuron has a head-centered receptive field: it responds to stimulation of a certain portion of the skin surface and to the visual stimulus aligned with it, no matter what part of the retina is activated. Similar trajectory selective neurons have been described by Rizzolatti and coworkers (Fogassi, Gallese, di Pellegrino et al., 1992; Fogassi, Gallese, Fadiga et al., 1996) in regions of premotor cortex that receive input from area VIP. Recent work shows that head-centered visual receptive fields are not limited to trajectory selective neurons: a quantitative study of VIP neuron responses to fronto-parallel motion indicates that many neurons have head-centered receptive fields (Bremmer, Duhamel, Ben Hamed and Graf, 1997; Duhamel et al., 1997).

The presumed function of the head-centered representation in area VIP is to delineate a workspace for potential movements of the head, especially reaching with the mouth. This was suggested by the observation of an unusual class of neurons which are selectively responsive to visual stimuli presented at very close range, within 5 cm of the face (Colby, Duhamel and Goldberg, 1993b). These 'ultranear' neurons are equally well activated by monocular or binocular stimulus presentation, which indicates that their distance tuning depends on cues other than disparity. Ultranear neurons could signal the presence of a stimulus that can be acquired by reaching with the mouth. This idea about the function of the head-centered representation in area VIP fits with the results of anatomical studies showing that area VIP projects to the specific region of premotor cortex involved in the control of head and mouth movements (Lewis and Van Essen, 1996; Matelli, Luppino, Murata and Sakata, 1994). Neurons in this premotor region, known as area F4, also have bimodal receptive fields, many of which respond best to visual stimuli presented within a few centimeters of the skin surface (Gentilucci, Fogassi, Luppino et al., 1988; Rizzolatti et al., 1981a; Rizzolatti, Scandolara, Matelli and Gentilucci, 1981b). Like the trajectory-selective neurons in area VIP, these premotor neurons also maintain visual responsiveness to stimuli approaching the tactile receptive field, regardless of the direction in which the monkey was looking (Fogassi et al., 1992, 1996). In both areas VIP and F4, locations are represented in terms appropriate for a specific kind of action, namely moving the head.

More than one type of spatial representation is present in area VIP. The response properties of many neurons are consistent with a spatial representation in head-centered coordinates: both the ultranear and the trajectory selective neurons encode stimulus location relative to the head, as do many bimodal neurons. Results from electrical stimulation support the idea that some neurons contribute to a head-centered representation. Microstimulation in this region

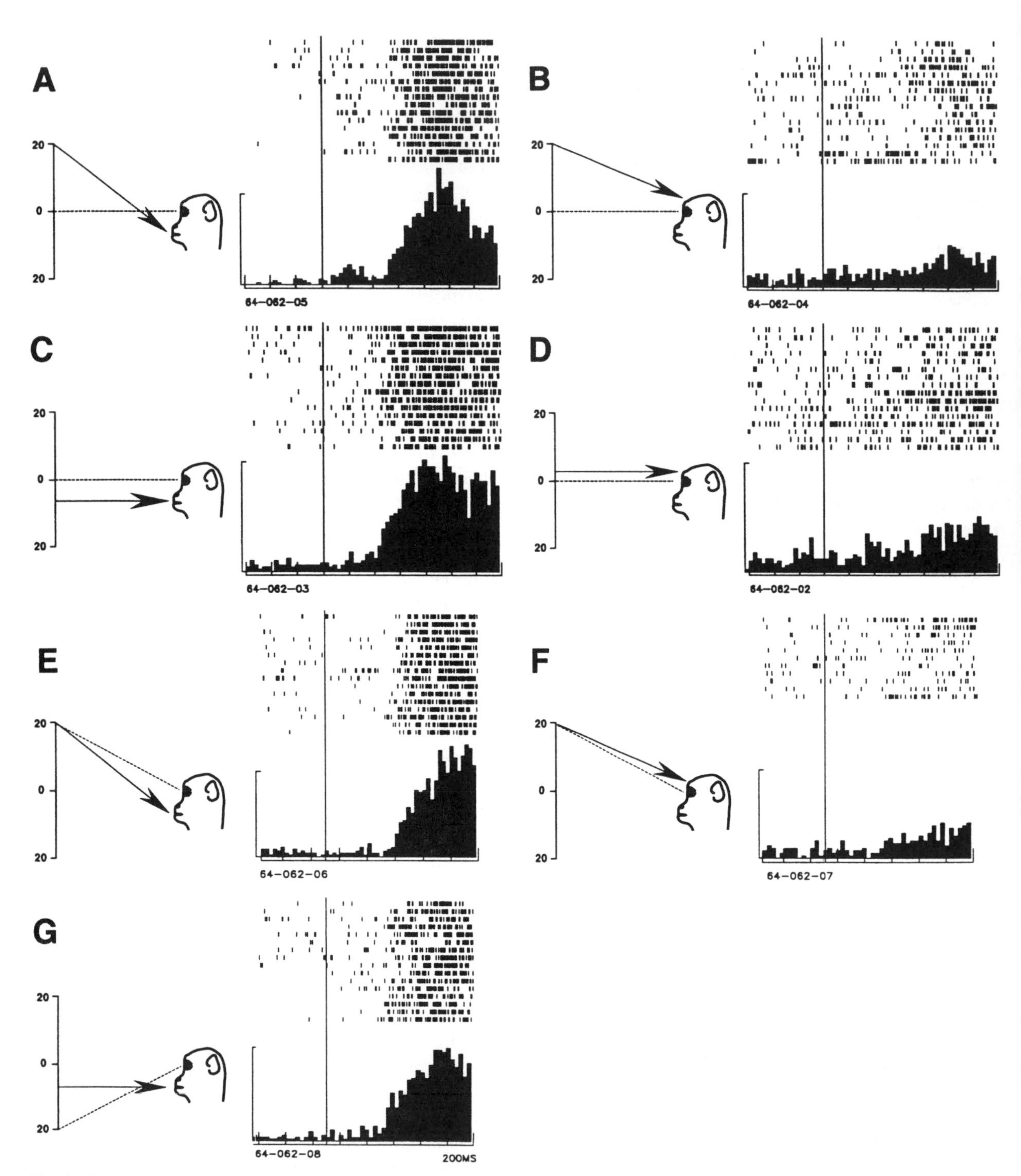

Fig. 2. Head-centered spatial representation in area VIP. Responses of a single VIP neuron to a visual stimulus approaching the mouth (left) or the brow (right). The neural response reflects the projected point of contact in a head-centered reference frame, rather than the absolute direction of motion (straight toward vs. down and toward, as in a world-centered frame) or the portion of the visual field stimulated (upper vs. lower, as in a retina-centered frame). Changes in eye position (E–G) do not affect the neuron's direction preference, indicating that the stimulus is coded in a head-centered reference frame. Adapted from Colby et al. (1993b).

can evoke saccades into a restricted zone in head-centered space, independent of the starting position of the eye (Thier and Andersen, 1996). On the other hand, some neurons have purely retinotopic receptive fields and presumably operate in retina-centered coordinates (Duhamel et al., 1997). Finally, some neurons are sensitive to vestibular stimuli, which raises the possibility that they encode motion of the head relative to an inertial, or world-based, reference frame (Bremmer et al., 1997). Taken together, these findings suggest that neurons in a single cortical area contribute to multiple representations of space, and could provide the spatial information for multiple kinds of action.

Oculocentric spatial representation

Neural activity in area LIP

We explore the world beyond our reach predominantly by moving our eyes. The contribution of parietal cortex to this exploration has been extensively investigated, especially in a subdivision of parietal cortex called the lateral intraparietal area. LIP neurons respond when a light flashes and a monkey looks at it. This response could represent a visual signal, a motor signal, an attentional signal, or an intentional signal. Introducing a delay between the visual stimulus and the motor response helps to distinguish among these possibilities (Hikosaka and Wurtz, 1983). Analysis of neural activity during the distinct time epochs of the delayed saccade task indicates that single neurons carry multiple signals (Barash, Bracewell, Fogassi et al., 1991; Colby, Duhamel and Goldberg, 1993a: Colby, Duhamel and Goldberg, 1996; Gnadt and Andersen, 1988). LIP neurons respond to the appearance of the stimulus, and may maintain activity during the delay and/or discharge around the time of the saccade. For some neurons in the LIP, delay period activity increases as a monkey chooses a target for a saccade, and the rate of increase correlates inversely with the difficulty of the decision (Gottlieb, Kusunoki and Goldberg, 1998; Shadlen and Newsome, 1996).

Area LIP neurons respond to the appearance of a visual stimulus in the receptive field in a fixation task (Robinson et al., 1978). These responses can be modulated by behavior: about two-thirds of LIP neurons are more strongly activated by the appearance of a stimulus to which the monkey must respond (Colby et al., 1996). The neuron illustrated in Fig. 3 shows that this enhanced visual activity is independent of the specific kind of response the animal will make. The amplitude of the visual response is increased in the saccade task (right panel) compared to the fixation task (left panel) because the visual stimulus has become relevant for the animal's behavior. The same kind of enhancement of the visual response also occurs in the peripheral attention task (center panel) in which the monkey must pay attention to the stimulus, without looking directly at it, in order to determine when it changes slightly in brightness. The monkey indicates that it has detected this luminance change by releasing a hand-held bar. The monkey is not permitted to make a saccade toward the stimulus at any time in this task. The observation that the amount of enhancement is similar for both the peripheral attention and the saccade tasks indicates that this response modulation must be due to attentional processes. This purely attentional response modulation is very different from the enhancement found in the frontal eye field (Goldberg and Bushnell, 1981) and the superior colliculus (Wurtz and Mohler, 1976), where cells give increased responses only to saccade targets. Because of this striking difference between the LIP and these more clearly oculomotor regions, we have proposed that enhancement in the LIP reflects visuospatial attention (Goldberg, Colby and Duhamel, 1990; Colby et al., 1996; Kusunoki, Colby, Duhamel and Goldberg, 1997).

The three tasks illustrated above all use an abruptly appearing stimulus to assess visual responsiveness. This procedure confounds the visual stimulus with an attentional event. Behavioral studies in humans indicate that an abrupt stimulus onset captures attention (Jonides and Yantis, 1988; Yantis and Jonides, 1984, 1990, 1996). The sudden appearance of a stimulus in any standard visual or oculomotor task may itself capture attention. This raises the possibility that neural activity evoked by the onset of the stimulus is primarily an attentional response rather than a purely visual one.

This idea was confirmed in an experiment in which responses to sudden onset stimuli were compared to responses to stable stimuli (Gottlieb et al., 1998). In this experiment, the monkey sees a sta-

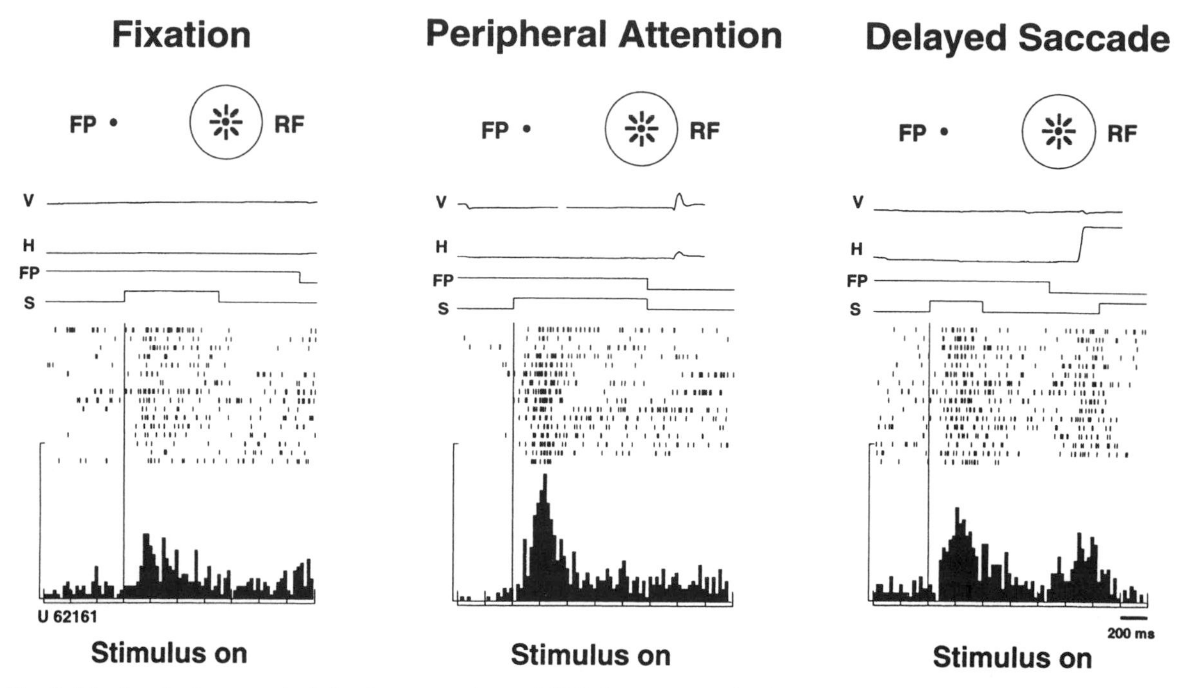

Fig. 3. Attentional enhancement of visual responses in area LIP. Left: responses of a single neuron to the onset of a light in the receptive field on 16 successive correctly performed trials. Raster and histogram are aligned on stimulus appearance. Center: the amplitude of response to stimulus onset is enhanced when the animal is required to attend to the brightness of the stimulus. Right: enhancement of the sensory response when the monkey is required to attend to the location of the stimulus and remember it in order to generate a subsequent saccade. FP, fixation point; RF, location of receptive field; S, stimulus; V, vertical eye position; H, horizontal eye position. Adapted from Goldberg et al. (1990).

ble array of symbols on a screen. The symbols do not change at all during the experiment, but remain constantly illuminated and immobile. As the monkey makes saccades across the stable array, stimuli are brought into and out of receptive fields. Strikingly, LIP neurons do not respond when a stable stimulus enters the receptive field. The neuron illustrated in Fig. 4 has a brisk response to the sudden onset of a stimulus in the receptive field while the monkey is fixating (left panel). In contrast, there is no response to a stimulus brought into the receptive field by a saccade to the center of the stable array (center panel). In this case, the stimulus is new only to the receptive field, and not to the visual environment as a whole. The response can be restored by flashing the stimulus briefly just before the saccade (right panel). This result indicates that the response to a visual stimulus in the fixation task reflects both attention, generated by the abrupt stimulus onset, as well as the visual properties of the stimulus. A similar observation has been made in the frontal eye field, where visual neurons respond to a stable stimulus brought into the receptive field only if that stimulus is behaviorally relevant (Burman and Segraves, 1994).

Stationary objects in the environment are irrelevant to behavior most of the time but they can be rendered relevant by the demands of the task. You can direct your attention to the clock on the wall when you want to know what the time is, even though it is not a new stimulus. In physiological experiments, attention can be directed to a stable object by requiring the monkey to use that stimulus to guide its behavior. The neuron illustrated in Fig. 5 fires strongly when the monkey is cued to make a saccade from the center of the array toward a stable target in the receptive field (top row). The first saccade brings the receptive field of the neuron onto the location of a stable, continuously present stimulus (the black square). The neuron fires because the cued stimulus is relevant for guiding the animal's behavior: the second saccade is directed to-

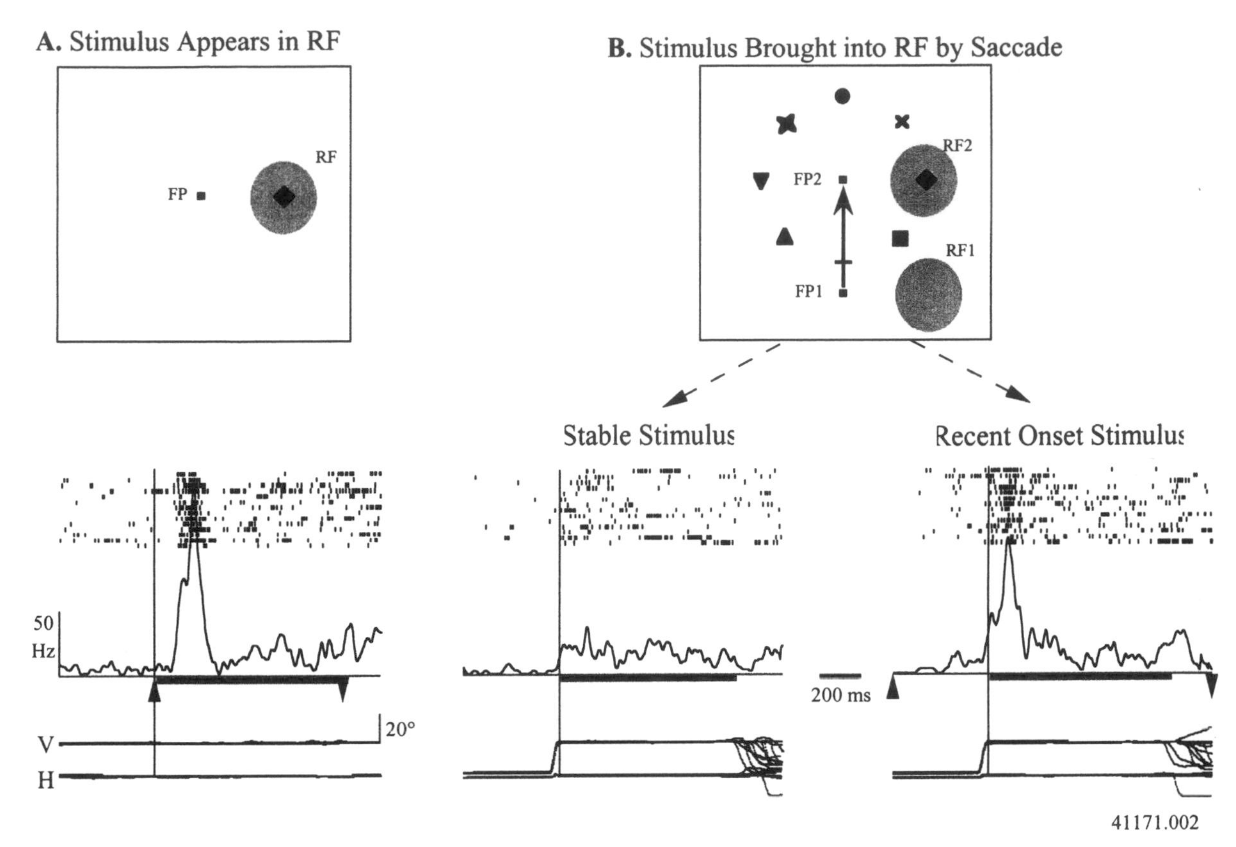

Fig. 4. Bottom-up effects of attention. (A) Responses of a single LIP neuron to the abrupt onset of a stimulus (diamond) in the receptive field. Raster and histogram are aligned on stimulus onset (up triangle). (B) Responses when the stimulus is brought into the receptive field by means of a saccade. The trial begins with fixation of FP1, at which time the receptive field (gray oval) is outside the array of stimuli. When the monkey makes a saccade from FP1 to FP2, the receptive field is moved onto the location of the diamond stimulus. When the diamond has been present continuously (left), there is little response to the entrance of the stimulus into the RF. But when the diamond stimulus appears immediately before the saccade (right, up triangle), the neuron fires almost as strongly as it did in the abrupt onset condition. Adapted from Gottlieb et al. (1998).

ward the stimulus in the receptive field. In contrast, this same neuron remains silent (bottom row) when the monkey is cued to look toward one of the other stimuli (the star), even though the same stable stimulus (black square) has entered the receptive field after the first saccade. The simplest interpretation of these data is that the black square became salient because it matches the cue. The neural response reflects the representation of a salient stimulus.

The activity of this neuron illustrates two ways that attention can be drawn to a stimulus. In the simple fixation task (Fig. 4, left panel), attention is drawn by the abrupt onset on the stimulus, a bottom-up process. In the stable target task (Fig. 5), attention is directed to the stimulus when it is matched to the cue by a top-down process. In both tasks, the visual response is strongly modulated by attention. An alternate interpretation of activity in area LIP is that it reflects a motor plan to make a saccade toward the receptive field (Andersen et al., 1997). It is well established that some LIP neurons exhibit presaccadic activity in delayed saccade tasks, and some of this activity is independent of visual stimulation (Colby et al., 1996; Colby, Duhamel and Goldberg, 1995). Some LIP neurons discharge before saccades even in the context of a learned saccade made without any recent visual stimulation, as do movement neurons in the frontal eye field (Bruce and Goldberg, 1985). However, across the population, presaccadic activity in LIP is less strong than visual activity.

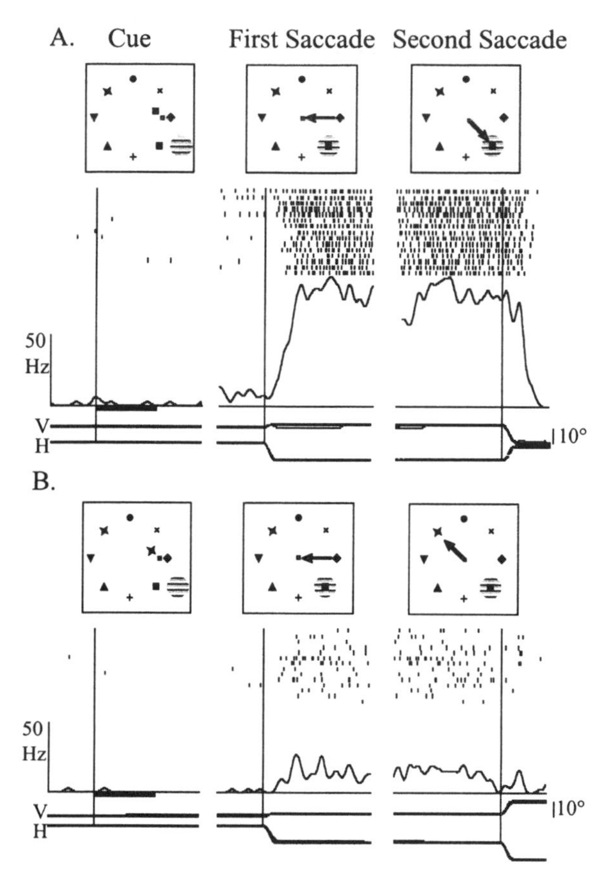

Fig. 5. Top-down effects of attention. (A) Responses of a single LIP neuron in the stable target task. Left: at the beginning of the trial, the monkey fixates the small open square. The receptive field (gray circle) is outside the array. A cue (the black square) appears near the fixation point to indicate which stimulus in the array will be the second saccade target. Center: the fixation point steps to the center of the array and the monkey makes a saccade to it. This saccade brings the receptive field onto the cued stimulus and the neuron responds. Right: the fixation point disappears and the monkey makes a second saccade to the stable stimulus matching the cue. (B) The same visual events fail to evoke a response when the monkey is instructed to make a saccade to a target outside the receptive field. Adapted from Kusunoki, Gottlieb and Goldberg, 2000.

This is markedly different from the frontal eye field, where an entire class of neurons, the movement neurons, exhibit little or no visual activity. These movement neurons provide the bulk of the projection from the frontal eye field (FEF) to the superior colliculus (Segraves and Goldberg, 1987) and pons (Segraves, 1992). The purely visual cells in the FEF do not project to the superior colliculus or pons at all. In contrast, the majority of collicular projection neurons in the LIP have significant visual responses (Pare and Wurtz, 1997). These observations suggest that the FEF has neurons appropriate for generating motor commands or intentions, while area LIP does not.

The function of area LIP is the representation of attended or salient spatial locations. The hallmark of neuronal activity in LIP is that, like spatial perception itself, it is not tied to any particular modality. Neurons in the LIP respond to salient visual stimuli, but they provide more than an exclusively visual representation because they also respond to attended auditory stimuli (Stricanne, Andersen and Mazzoni, 1996), respond weakly before saccades without visual targets, and respond even in anticipation of the appearance of a salient target (Colby et al., 1996). Their activity cannot be linked to the planning of particular movements. This combination of response properties suggests that the LIP represents the space that we explore best with our eyes — space not constrained to the immediate grasp of our arm or mouth. This representation is limited to attended objects and their locations, and damage to it may cause the neglect described in patients and monkeys with parietal lesions (Critchley, 1953; Duhamel, Goldberg, FitzGibbon et al., 1992b; Lynch and McLaren, 1989). The next critical problem is to understand the reference frame in which LIP represents attended space.

Spatial representation in area LIP

Receptive fields of neurons in area LIP are retinotopic. They carry visual, memory and saccade-related signals that encode stimuli in terms of the distance and direction of the stimulus or saccade location relative to the center of gaze. This retinotopic organization presents a paradox: how can accurate spatial information be derived from retinotopic input? Every time we move our eyes, each object in our surroundings activates a new set of retinal neurons. Despite these changes, we experience the world as stable and move accurately in it. This perceptual stability has long been understood to reflect the fact that what we see is not a direct impression of the external world, but a construction or representation of it. The brain must construct a representation that can compensate for changes in eye position.

This compensation for changes in eye position takes place in area LIP. Every time a monkey

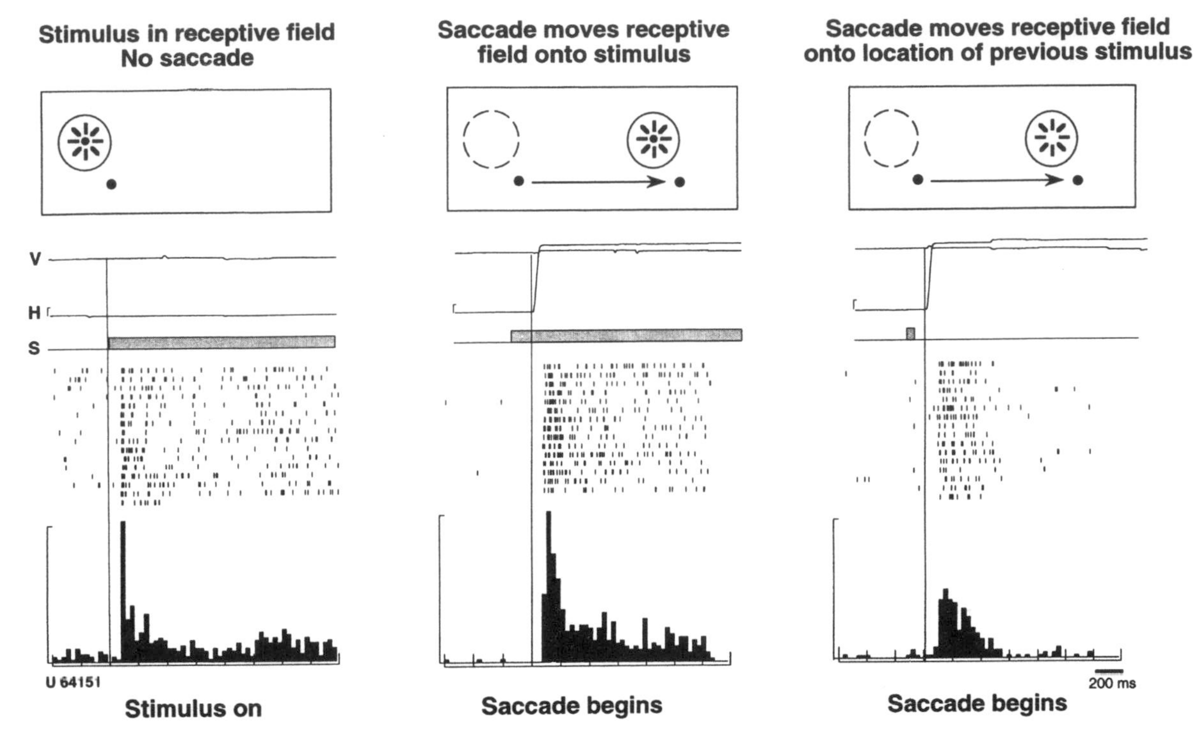

Fig. 6. Updating of a visual memory trace. Left: in a fixation task, the neuron responds to the abrupt onset of a stimulus in the receptive field. Center: the same neuron responds when a saccade moves the receptive field onto the location of a recent onset stimulus. Right: the neuron also responds when a saccade moves the receptive field onto a previously stimulated location. The stimulus is flashed on for only 50 ms and is extinguished before the saccade begins. The neural response is to a memory trace of the previous stimulus event. The memory trace has been updated in conjunction with the eye movement. Adapted from Duhamel et al. (1992a).

makes a saccade, the representation of the salient visual world in LIP shifts into a new coordinate system whose origin is the postsaccadic center of gaze (Duhamel, Colby and Goldberg, 1992a). The effect of saccades on the representation of remembered objects demonstrates this most dramatically. The experiment illustrated in Fig. 6 shows that the memory trace of a previous stimulus is updated when the eyes move. The activity of a single LIP neuron is shown in three conditions. In a standard fixation task (left panel), the neuron responds to the onset of a stimulus in the receptive field. In a saccade task (center), the neuron responds when an eye movement brings the receptive field onto a location containing a recent visual stimulus. The unexpected result is shown in the right panel. Here the monkey makes the same saccade, but the stimulus appeared for only 50 ms so that it was already extinguished before the saccade began. This means that no stimulus was ever physically present in the receptive field, yet the cell responds. The explanation for this surprising observation is that a memory trace of the stimulus was updated at the time of the saccade. This could occur in the following way. Before the saccade, while the monkey was looking straight ahead, the onset of the stimulus activates a set of LIP neurons whose receptive fields covered the stimulated screen location. Some of these neurons continue to fire after stimulus disappearance, encoding a memory trace of the location at which the stimulus occurred (Gnadt and Andersen, 1988). At the time of the saccade, a corollary discharge, or copy of the eye movement command, arrives in the parietal cortex containing information about the metrics of the eye movement. This corollary discharge causes the active LIP neurons to transmit their signals to the new set of LIP neurons whose receptive fields will encompass the stimulated screen location after the saccade. The representation of the salient location is thus updated from the coordinates of the initial eye position to the coordinates of the final eye position.

Remapping of stimulus memory traces occurs in nearly all LIP neurons. An important implication of this finding is that LIP neurons have access to visual information from the entire visual field and not just from the classically defined receptive field. LIP neurons must already have in place the connections that provide input from distant regions of the visual field. Additional experiments have shown that remapping takes place gradually in the epoch around the saccade. Some neurons actually begin to respond in advance, before the saccade begins, to stimuli that will enter the receptive field only after the saccade (Duhamel et al., 1992a). This predictive remapping is not unique to area LIP. It also occurs in the frontal eye field (Umeno and Goldberg, 1997), the intermediate layers of the superior colliculus (Walker, FitzGibbon and Goldberg, 1995) and even in extrastriate visual cortex (Nakamura and Colby, 1999, 2000).

The internal representation of salient spatial locations is updated in conjunction with eye movements so that it always matches the current eye position. Visual information is thereby maintained in eye-centered coordinates. Such a representation is necessary for the guidance of oculomotor responses directed toward the stimulated location. It is important to note, however, that remapping occurs automatically for salient stimuli. It does not depend on the monkey's intention to make a response to the remapped stimulus. In the task described above (Fig. 6), the monkey is not required to use the information provided by the remapped stimulus, and does not make a saccade toward its spatial location at any time (including the intertrial interval). Moreover, remapping is observed in purely visual neurons in area LIP that do not have any pre-saccadic burst. Conversely, the more motoric neurons in the FEF, those with presaccadic bursts, but not visual responses, do not exhibit remapping. In other words, remapping creates the appropriate spatial representation for a particular kind of action, but does not depend on the animal's intention to perform that action. An eye-centered representation has the advantage, compared to a head-centered or world-centered representation, that it is already in the coordinates of the effector system that will be used to acquire the target. Neurons in area LIP accomplish the sensory to motor coordinate transformation and generate the kind of representation needed for the guidance of eye movements.

If the parietal cortex in humans is the site of this sensory to motor coordinate transformation then a parietal lesion should manifest itself not as an absolute spatial deficit, but as a difficulty in compensating for a previous saccade. This prediction was verified in a case study of a patient who sustained a hemorrhage into the right frontoparietal cortex (Duhamel et al., 1992b). The patient had a mild left hemiparesis, mild left visual and somatosensory neglect and a left inferior quadrantanopsia that spared the central 6° of the visual field. With the head in a fixed position, she had a directional deficit for saccades between targets presented 5° to the left and to the right in a random walk: leftward saccades were hypometric and had a longer latency than rightward ones. These deficits did not vary with the starting position of the eye: the same spatial location acquired by an accurate rightward saccade would only be approached by a hypometric leftward saccade. Saccadic accuracy was measured in two versions of a double step saccade task. First, in the slow version of the double step task, the patient was instructed to make sequential saccades to the two targets in the order in which they appeared (Fig. 7, top). Each target stayed on for 500 ms, so both saccades were visually guided — no memory trace was needed to perform the task accurately. The order of the targets was likewise unimportant. Leftward saccades followed by rightward saccades were just as accurate as the reverse order, although all leftward saccades were somewhat inaccurate.

In the second condition, the targets were flashed so briefly that both were gone before any eye movement took place. In this case, the first saccade was still a visually guided saccade and the patient's performance was accurate for first targets in either the affected field or the good field (Fig. 7, bottom). The interesting case is performance of the second saccade. To make the correct saccade, the subject must know where the second target appeared relative to the new eye position. This requires taking into account the change in eye position resulting from the first saccade. The patient did this correctly when the first saccade was into the good field: an initial saccade to the right was followed by a reasonably accurate saccade to the left (bottom left panel). The deficit appeared only when the first saccade was di-

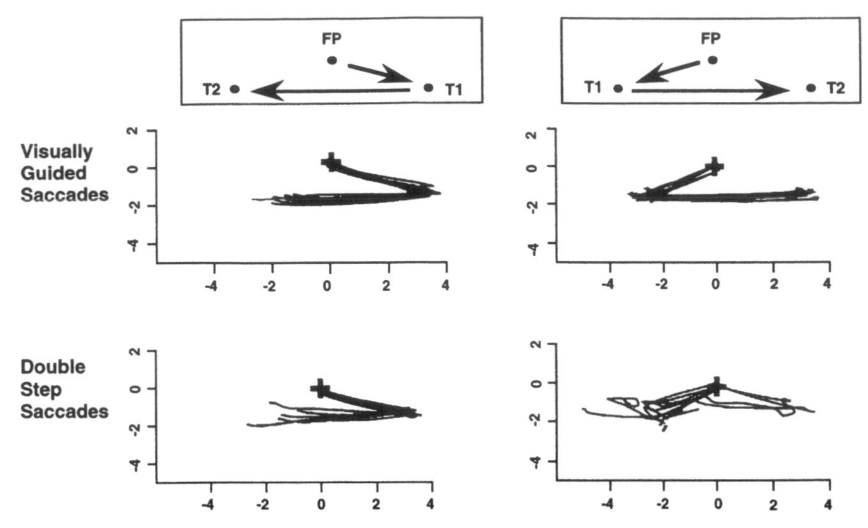

Fig. 7. Failure to update memory trace of stimulus location in a patient with a right frontoparietal lesion. Top: diagrams show the locations of targets and saccade directions. Middle: eye position in x/y coordinates for multiple trials. The patient begins by looking at the fixation point and then makes saccades to T1 and T2 in response to sequential flashes. The stimuli remain illuminated long enough (500 ms) for each saccade to be visually guided. The saccades into the ipsilesional, normal visual field are accurate, while those into the contralesional, affected field are hypometric. The order in which the saccades are made does not affect saccadic accuracy. Bottom: eye movements in the double step condition, with T1 presented for 100 ms and T2 for 80 ms. The first saccade is still visually guided, but the second saccade now depends on an updated internal representation of the second target location. When the first target appears in the normal field (left panel), the patient makes accurate saccades into the normal field and hypometric saccades into the affected field. But when the first target appears in the affected field, two alternative eye movement patterns occur. Either the patient makes a direct saccade to the second target, neglecting the target flashed in the affected field, or the patient makes a hypometric saccade into the contralesional field and then fails to make a saccade into the normal field. Adapted from Duhamel et al. (1992b).

rected into the affected field. An initial saccade to the left reached the first target location, but the patient was then completely unable to generate a saccade to the location of the second target (bottom right panel). Somewhat surprisingly, the patient failed on saccades in the good direction, to targets that appeared in the good field. Nevertheless, she clearly did not have a general spatial deficit for either field. On trials in which she neglected the first target (in the affected field) and went directly to the second target (in the good field) performance was accurate. Her specific deficit was an inability to calculate the change in target position relative to eye position. She could not compensate for the first saccade when it was in the direction of the affected field.

We conclude that this patient failed to update an internal representation of the stimulus: the memory trace was not remapped following leftward saccades. While this study was a single case report, the phenomenon has been replicated in a large number of patients and was exhibited only by patients whose lesion included the right posterior parietal cortex and not patients with damage limited to frontal cortex (Heide, Blankenburg, Zimmermann and Kompf, 1995). Two conclusions can be drawn from these experiments. First, these patients do not have a simple spatial deficit: they can make visually guided eye movements to all the targets perfectly well. Instead, they have a deficit that affects updating a spatial representation for use by a particular motor system. Second, updating depends on parietal cortex. The remapping of memory traces, demonstrated in single neurons in area LIP, presumably provides the substrate for the capacity to update an eye-centered spatial representation. Both the physiological and the neuropsychological results indicate that parietal cortex uses information about motor commands to transform visual input from retinal coordinates into an eye-centered representation suitable for the guidance of eye movements. The strong connections between area LIP and the frontal eye field and the discovery of remapped visual responses in the frontal eye field (Goldberg and Bruce, 1990; Umeno and Goldberg, 1997) suggest that these areas work together to construct an eye-centered representation of oculomotor space. Many questions remain as to how this representation is coordinated with the head, body, or world-centered reference frames that are called into play when the goal of foveating a target requires more than a saccade (Andersen et al., 1997; Brotchie, Andersen, Snyder and Goodman, 1995; Krauzlis, Basso and Wurtz, 1997).

Object-centered spatial representation

A component of neglect in many patients is object-centered. When presented with an image anywhere in the visual field, these patients tend to ignore the left side of the object. For example, when patients with left hemispatial neglect were required to maintain fixation on the center of a chimeric face, their reports of what they saw were based predominantly on the right halves of the images. This was true even when the entire composite face was presented within the right visual hemifield (Young, de Haan, Newcombe and Hay, 1990). Likewise, patients may neglect the leftmost portion of a word to be read, or fail to copy the left portion of a drawing (Marshall and Halligan, 1993). In monkeys, lesions of posterior parietal cortex interfere with processing of object-centered spatial information in the contralesional field (Olson and Gettner, 1998). Single neurons that encode object-centered locations have yet to be described in parietal cortex, but have been observed in frontal cortex in the supplementary eye field (SEF). Neurons here encode movement direction relative to the object itself (Olson and Gettner, 1995).

The SEF is a division of premotor cortex with attentional and oculomotor functions. Neurons here fire before and during saccadic eye movements directed toward particular regions of space. Certain response characteristics of SEF neurons indicate that its contribution to eye movement control occurs at a comparatively abstract level. Like neurons in area LIP, SEF neurons fire during the delay period while the monkey is waiting to make an eye movement in the preferred direction. Furthermore, some SEF neurons become especially active when the monkey is learning to associate arbitrary visual cues with particular directions of eye movements (Chen and Wise, 1995).

Neurons in the SEF exhibit a unique form of spatial selectivity: they encode the direction of an impending eye movement as defined relative to an object-centered reference frame. The neuron illustrated

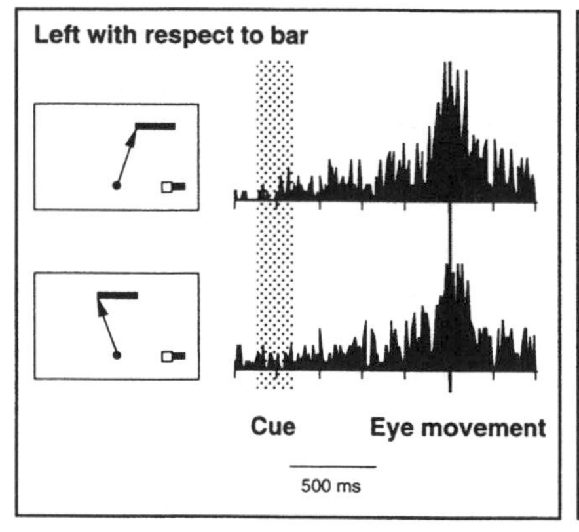

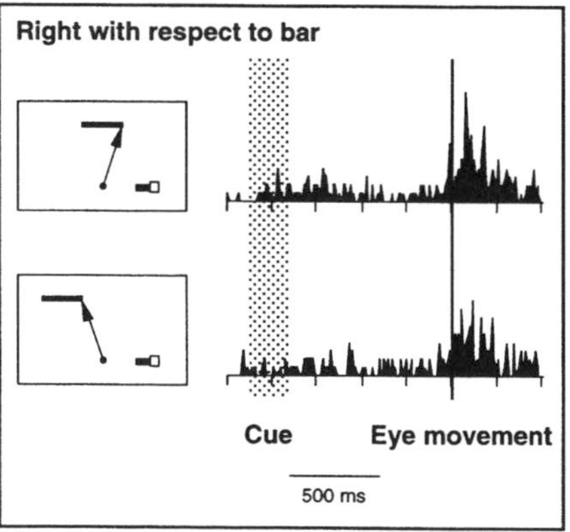

Fig. 8. Object-centered spatial representation in frontal cortex. Responses of a single supplementary eye field neuron in four conditions. On each trial, the monkey is instructed by a cue (the small bar with the white square at one end) to saccade to the left or right end of a subsequently appearing large target bar. The cue appears only briefly and is followed by a variable delay period in which the monkey maintains central fixation. At the end of the delay, the target bar appears at one of three locations above the fixation point and the monkey saccades to one end of it. Histograms are aligned on the onset of the saccade. The two panels on the left show strong activity during the delay period and the saccade to the left end of the bar, regardless of whether this response required a leftward or a rightward eye movement. The two panels on the right show that much less activity was evoked by the identical eye movements when they were directed toward the right end of the target bar. The firing rate depended on the object-centered direction of the response. Adapted from Olson and Gettner (1995).

in Fig. 8 is selective for the object-centered direction of an eye movement: the neuron is strongly active for eye movements directed to the left end of a bar (left column), but much less active for the same eye movements when they are directed to the right end of a bar (right column). This is true even though the physical direction of the eye movement is held constant. This neuron exhibited object-centered selectivity in the sense that it fired most strongly before and during movements to a certain location on a reference object. About half of the neurons in the SEF exhibit object-centered direction selectivity, each neuron favoring a particular location on the object.

This intriguing result indicates that single neurons can make use of quite abstract spatial reference frames. Although object-centered selectivity may at first seem hard to rationalize, it probably serves an important function in natural settings. In scanning the environment, we sometimes look toward locations where things are expected to appear but which, at the time, contain no visual detail — for example, the center of a blank screen or the center of an empty doorway. Our eyes are guided to these featureless locations by the surrounding visual details that define them indirectly. It is specifically in these cases that the SEF may contribute to the selection of the target for an eye movement. Object-centered spatial information could potentially guide arm movements as well as eye movements. And neuropsychological evidence indicates that an object-centered reference frame is used to direct attention: some patients exhibit object-centered neglect after parietal lobe damage (Behrmann and Moscovitch, 1994; Behrmann and Tipper, 1994; Tipper and Behrmann, 1996).

Conclusions

The studies reviewed above indicate that our unitary experience of space emerges from a diversity of spatial representations. Objects and locations are represented relative to multiple reference frames. Moreover, parietal and frontal cortex construct multiple spatial representations in order to serve distinct attentional and sensorimotor goals. These representations may be linked to specific spheres of action or to quite abstract and general reference frames.

Several general conclusions can be drawn from the studies reviewed above.

First, cortical spatial representations transform sensory information from the coordinates of specific receptor surfaces into the coordinates of particular motor effectors: the eye, head, arm, or hand. It is important to note, however, that parietal activity does not specify or command motor actions per se. Instead, neural activity, at least in area LIP, signifies the salience of a stimulus at a given spatial location. This representation of salience may contribute to the selection of a target for a saccade, but it also contributes to the processes of spatial attention and spatial memory, for which only salient objects are effective stimuli.

Second, particular spatial representations are tuned for specific regions of space, or spheres of action. The outputs of these parietal representations are presumably used by the specific frontal areas to which they are linked to plan and generate movements.

Third, neurons within a single cortical area may participate in multiple spatial representations. Receptive fields of single neurons in area VIP fall along a continuum from retina-centered to head-centered. The functions of these intermediate representations remain to be explored.

Fourth, egocentric spatial representations are dynamically updated in conjunction with self-generated movements, including eye movements (area LIP) and even tool use (area MIP). The mechanisms that underlie updating of spatial representations presumably reflect the influence of corollary discharge feedback from frontal cortex to parietal cortex.

Fifth, effector-centered representations, such as that in area AIP, can incorporate information about object shape and orientation, properties normally associated with ventral stream processing, so as to guide actions in space precisely.

Sixth, cortical representations of space are not limited to egocentric reference frames. Neurons in frontal cortex construct an allocentric spatial representation in which locations are coded relative to an object of interest. Object-centered representations are potentially useful for acting on, paying attention to or remembering particular locations as defined with respect to a salient object.

Neuropsychological studies tell us that we use multiple spatial reference frames to perceive and act on the world around us. Physiological studies of parietal and frontal cortex have begun to reveal how these representations are constructed.

Acknowledgements

Preparation of this article was supported by NIH (EY12032), the James S. McDonnell Foundation and the Whitehall Foundation.

References

Andersen RA, Snyder LH, Bradley DC, Xing J: Multimodal representation of space in the posterior parietal cortex and its use in planning movements. Annual Review of Neuroscience: 20; 303–330, 1997.

Barash S, Bracewell RM, Fogassi L, Gnadt JW, Andersen RA: Saccade-related activity in the lateral intraparietal area. I. Temporal properties. Journal of Neurophysiology: 66; 1095–1108, 1991.

Bartolomeo P, Chokron S: Levels of impairment in unilateral neglect. In Behrmann M (Ed), Disorders of Visual Behavior, Handbook of Neuropsychology, 2nd ed, Vol. 4. Amsterdam: Elsevier, pp. 67–98, 2001.

Batista AP, Buneo CA, Snyder LH, Andersen RA: Reach plans in eye-centered coordinates. Science: 285; 257–260.

Battaglia-Mayer A, Ferraina S, Mitsuda T, Marconi B, Genovesio A, Onorati P, Lacquaniti F, Caminiti R: Early coding of reaching in the parieto-occipital cortex. Journal of Neurophysiology: 83; 2374–2391, 2000.

Behrmann M: Spatial reference frames and hemispatial neglect. In Gazzaniga M (Ed), The New Cognitive Neurosciences. Cambridge, MA: MIT Press, pp. 651–666, 2000.

Behrmann M, Moscovitch M: Object-centered neglect in patients with unilateral neglect: effects of left–right coordinates of objects. Journal of Cognitive Neuroscience: 6; 1–16, 1994.

Behrmann M, Tipper SP: Object-based attentional mechanisms: evidence from patients with unilateral neglect. In Umilta C, Moscovitch M (Eds), Attention and Performance, Vol. 15. Cambridge, MA: MIT Press, pp. 351–375, 1994.

Berti A, Frassunatti F: When far becomes near: remapping of space by tool use. Journal of Cognitive Neuroscience: 12; 415–420, 2000.

Bisiach E, Perani D, Vallar G, Berti A: Unilateral neglect: Personal and extra-personal. Neuropsychologia: 24; 759–767, 1986.

Bisiach E, Vallar G: Unilateral neglect in humans. In Boller F, Grafman J (Eds) Handbook of Neuropsychology, 2nd edition, Vol. 1. Amsterdam: Elsevier, pp. 459–502, 2000.

Boussaoud D: Primate premotor cortex: modulation of preparatory neuronal activity by gaze angle. Journal of Neurophysiology: 73; 886–890.

Bremmer F, Duhamel J-R, Ben Hamed S, Graf W: The representation of movement in near extra-personal space in the macaque ventral intraparietal area (VIP). In Thier P, Karnath H-O (Eds), Parietal Lobe Contributions to Orientation in 3 D Space. Heidelberg: Springer, pp. 619–631, 1997.

Brotchie PR, Andersen, RA, Snyder LH, Goodman SJ: Head position signals used by parietal neurons to encode locations of visual stimuli. Nature: 375; 232–235, 1995.

Bruce CJ, Goldberg ME: Primate frontal eye fields: I. Single neurons discharging before saccades. Journal of Neurophysiology: 53; 603–635, 1985.

Burman DD, Segraves MA: Primate frontal eye field activity during natural scanning eye movements. Journal of Neurophysiology: 71; 1266–1271, 1994.

Caminiti R, Johnson PB, Galli C, Ferraina S, Burnod Y: Making arm movements within different parts of space: the premotor and motor cortical representations of a coordinate system for reaching to visual targets. Journal of Neuroscience: 11; 1182–1197, 1991.

Caminiti R, Ferraina S, Johnson PB: The sources of visual information to the primate frontal lobe: a novel role for the superior parietal lobule. Cerebral Cortex: 6; 319–328, 1996.

Carlson-Radvansky LA, Irwin DE: Reference frame activation during spatial term assignment. Journal of Memory and Language: 37; 411–437, 1994.

Chen LL, Wise SP: Neuronal activity in the supplementary eye field during acquisition of conditional oculomotor associations. Journal of Neurophysiology: 73; 1101–1121, 1995.

Colby CL, Duhamel, J-R: Heterogeneity of extrastriate visual areas and multiple parietal areas in the macaque monkey. Neuropsychologia: 29; 517–537, 1991.

Colby CL, Duhamel, J-R: Spatial representations for action in parietal cortex. Cognitive Brain Research: 5; 105–115, 1996.

Colby CL, Duhamel J-R, Goldberg ME: The analysis of visual space by the lateral intraparietal area of the monkey: the role of extraretinal signals. In Hicks TP, Molotchnikoff S, Ono T (Eds), Progress in Brain Research, Vol. 95. Amsterdam: Elsevier, pp. 307–316, 1993a.

Colby CL, Duhamel J-R, Goldberg ME Ventral intraparietal area of the macaque: anatomic location and visual response properties. Journal of Neurophysiology: 69; 902–914, 1993b.

Colby CL, Duhamel J-R, Goldberg ME: Oculocentric spatial representation in parietal cortex. Cerebral Cortex: 5; 470–481, 1995.

Colby CL, Duhamel J-R, Goldberg ME: Visual, presaccadic and cognitive activation of single neurons in monkey lateral intraparietal area. Journal of Neurophysiology: 76; 2841–2852, 1996.

Colby CL, Gattass R, Olson CR, Gross CG: Topographic organization of cortical afferents to extrastriate visual area PO in the macaque: a dual tracer study. Journal of Comparative Neurology: 269; 392–413, 1988.

Cowey A, Small M, Ellis S: Left visuo-spatial neglect can be worse in far than near space. Neuropsychologia: 32; 1059–1066, 1994.

Critchley M: The Parietal Lobes. London: Edward Arnold, 1953.

Driver J, Halligan PW: Can visual neglect operate in object-centered coordinates? An affirmative single case study. Cognitive Neuropsychology: 8; 475–496, 1991.

Duhamel J-R, Brouchon M: Sensorimotor aspects of unilateral

neglect: a single case analysis. Cognitive Neuropsychology: 7; 57–74, 1990.

Duhamel J-R, Colby CL, Goldberg ME: Congruent representation of visual and somatosensory space in single neurons of monkey ventral intraparietal cortex area (area VIP). In Paillard J (Ed), Brain and Space. Oxford: Oxford University Press, pp. 223–236, 1991.

Duhamel J-R, Colby CL, Goldberg ME: The updating of the representation of visual space in parietal cortex by intended eye movements. Science: 255; 90–92, 1992a.

Duhamel J-R, Goldberg ME, FitzGibbon EJ, Sirigu A, Grafman J Saccadic dysmetria in a patient with a right frontoparietal lesion: the importance of corollary discharge for accurate spatial behavior. Brain: 115; 1387–1402, 1992b.

Duhamel J-R, Bremmer F, BenHamed S, Graf W: Spatial invariance of visual receptive fields in parietal cortex neurons. Nature: 389; 845–848, 1997.

Duhamel J-R, Colby CL, Goldberg ME: Ventral intraparietal area of the macaque: convergent visual and somatic response properties. Journal of Neurophysiology: 79; 126–136, 1998.

Eskandar EN, Assad JA: Dissociation of visual, motor and predictive signals in parietal cortex during visual guidance. Nature Neuroscience: 2; 88-93, 1999.

Farah MJ, Brunn JL, Wong AB, Wallace MA, Carpenter PA: Frames of reference for allocating attention to space. Cognitive Neuropsychology: 28; 335–347, 1990.

Fogassi L, Gallese V, di Pellegrino G, Fadiga L, Gentilucci M, Luppino G, Matelli M, Pedotti A, Rizzolatti G: Space coding by premotor cortex. Experimental Brain Research: 89; 686-690, 1992.

Fogassi L, Gallese V, Fadiga L, Luppino G, Matelli M, Rizzolatti G: Coding of peripersonal space in inferior premotor cortex (area F4). Journal of Neurophysiology: 76; 141–157, 1996.

Funahashi S, Bruce CJ, Goldman-Rakic PS: Dorsolateral prefrontal lesions and oculomotor delayed-response performance: evidence for mnemonic 'scotomas'. Journal of Neuroscience: 13; 1479–1497, 1993.

Gallese V, Fadiga L, Fogassi L Luppino G, Murata A: A parietofrontal circuit for hand grasping movements in the monkey: evidence from reversible inactivation experiments. In Thier P, Karnath, H-O (Eds), Parietal Lobe Contributions to Orientation in 3 D Space. Heidelberg: Springer, pp. 619–631, 1997.

Gallese V, Murata A, Kaseda M, Niki N, Sakata H: Deficit of hand preshaping after muscimol injection in monkey parietal cortex. Neuroreport: 5; 1525–1529, 1994.

Galletti C, Fattori P, Kutz DF, Battaglini PP: Arm movement-related neurons in the visual area V6A of the macaque superior parietal lobule. European Journal of Neuroscience: 9; 410–413, 1997.

Gazzaniga M, Ladavas E: Disturbances in spatial attention following lesion or disconnection of the right parietal lobe. In Jeannerod M (Ed), Neurophysiological and Neuropsychological Aspects of Spatial Neglect. Amsterdam: Elsevier, pp. 203–213, 1987.

Gentilucci M, Fogassi L, Luppino G, Matelli M, Camarda R, Rizzolatti G: Functional organization of inferior area 6 in the macaque monkey: I. Somatotopy and the control of proximal movements. Experimental Brain Research: 71; 475–490, 1988.

Gentilucci M, Scandolara C, Pigarev IN, Rizzolatti G: Visual responses in the postarcuate cortex (area 6) of the monkey that are independent of eye position. Experimental Brain Research: 50; 464–468, 1983.

Gnadt JW, Andersen RA: Memory related motor planning activity in posterior parietal cortex of macaque. Experimental Brain Research: 70; 216–220, 1988.

Goldberg ME, Bruce CJ: Primate frontal eye fields. III. Maintenance of a spatially accurate saccade signal. Journal of Neurophysiology: 64; 489–508, 1990.

Goldberg ME, Bushnell MC: Behavioral enhancement of visual responses in monkey cerebral cortex. II. Modulation in frontal eye fields specifically related to saccades. Journal of Neurophysiology: 46; 773–787, 1981.

Goldberg ME, Colby CL, Duhamel, J-R: The representation of visuomotor space in the parietal lobe of the monkey. Cold Spring Harbor Symposium in Quantitative Biology: 60; 729–739, 1990.

Goldman-Rakic PS: Topography of cognition: parallel distributed networks in primate association cortex. Annual Review of Neuroscience: 11; 137–156, 1988.

Gottlieb JP, Kusunoki M, Goldberg ME: The representation of visual salience in monkey parietal cortex. Nature: 391; 481–484, 1998.

Graziano MS, Hu XT, Gross CG: Visuospatial properties of ventral premotor cortex. Journal of Neurophysiology: 77; 2268–2292, 1997.

Graziano MSA, Yap GS, Gross CG: Coding of visual space by premotor neurons. Science: 266; 1054–1056, 1994.

Gross CG, Graziano MSA: Multiple representations of space in the brain. Neuroscientist: 1; 43–50, 1995.

Habib M, Sirigu A: Pure topographical disorientation: a definition and anatomical basis. Cortex: 23; 73–85, 1987.

Halligan PW, Marshall JC: Left neglect for near but not far space in man. Nature: 350; 498–500, 1991.

Heide W, Blankenburg M, Zimmermann E, Kompf D: Cortical control of double-step saccades: implications for spatial orientation. Annals of Neurology: 38; 739–748, 1995.

Henriques DY, Klier EM, Smith MA, Lowy D, Crawford JD: Gaze-centered remapping of remembered visual space in an open-loop pointing task. Journal of Neuroscience: 18; 1583–1594, 1998.

Hikosaka O, Wurtz RH: Visual and oculomotor functions of monkey substantia nigra pars reticulata. III. Memory-contingent visual and saccade responses. Journal of Neurophysiology: 49; 1268–1284, 1983.

Hyvarinen J, Poranen A: Function of the parietal associative area 7 as revealed from cellular discharges in alert monkeys. Brain: 97; 673–692, 1974.

Iriki A, Tanaka M, Iwamura Y: Coding of modified body schema during tool use by macaque postcentral neurones. Neuroreport: 7; 2325–2330, 1996.

Jeannerod M, Arbib MA, Rizzolatti G, Sakata H: Grasping objects: the cortical mechanisms of visuomotor transformation. Trends in Neuroscience: 18; 314–320, 1995.

Johnson PB, Ferraina S, Bianchi L, Caminiti R: Cortical networks for visual reaching: physiological and anatomical organization of frontal and parietal lobe arm regions. Cerebral Cortex: 6; 102–119, 1996.

Johnson PB, Ferraina S, Caminiti R: Cortical networks for visual reaching. Experimental Brain Research: 97; 361–365, 1993.

Jonides J, Yantis S: Uniqueness of abrupt visual onset in capturing attention (published erratum appears in Perception and Psychophysics 47(4): 405, 1990). Perception and Psychophysics: 43; 346–354, 1988.

Karnath HO, Schenkel P, Fischer B: Trunk orientation as the determining factor of the 'contralateral' deficit in the neglect syndrome and as the physical anchor of the internal representation of body orientation in space. Brain: 114; 1997–2014, 1991.

Krauzlis RJ, Basso MA, Wurtz RH: Shared motor error for multiple movements. Science: 276; 1693–1695, 1997.

Kusunoki M, Colby CL, Duhamel J-R, Goldberg ME: The role of the lateral intraparietal area in the control of visuospatial attention. In Sakata H, Fuster J, Mikami A (Eds), The Association Cortex — Structure and Function, pp. 191–206. Harwood Academic Publishers, 1997.

Kusunoki M, Gottlieb J, Goldberg ME: The lateral intraparietal area as a salience map: the representation of abrupt onset, stimulus motion, and task relevance. Vision Research: 40; 1459–1468, 2000.

Lacquaniti F, Guigon E, Bianchi L, Ferraina S, Caminiti R: Representing spatial information for limb movement: role of area 5 in the monkey. Cerebral Cortex: 5; 391–409, 1995.

Lewis JW, Van Essen DC: Connections of visual area VIP with somatosensory and motor areas of the macaque monkey. Society for Neuroscience Abstracts: 22; 398, 1996.

Lynch JC, McLaren JW: Deficits of visual attention and saccadic eye movements after lesions of parieto-occipital cortex in monkeys. Journal of Neurophysiology: 61; 74–90, 1989.

Marshall JC, Halligan PW Visuo-spatial neglect: a new copying test to assess perceptual parsing. Journal of Neurology: 240; 37–40, 1993.

Matelli M, Luppino G, Murata A, Sakata H: Independent anatomical circuits for reaching and grasping linking the inferior parietal sulcus and inferior area 6 in macaque monkey. Society for Neuroscience Abstracts: 20; 984, 1994.

Milner AD, Goodale MA: The Visual Brain in Action. Oxford, Oxford University Press, 1995.

Moscovitch M, Behrmann M: Coding of spatial information in the somatosensory system: evidence from patients with neglect following parietal lobe damage. Journal of Cognitive Neuroscience: 6; 151–155, 1994.

Mountcastle VB, Lynch JC, Georgopoulos A, Sakata H, Acuna C: Posterior parietal association cortex of the monkey: command functions for operations within extrapersonal space. Journal of Neurophysiology: 38; 871–908, 1975.

Murata A, Fadiga L, Fogassi L, Gallese V, Raos V, Rizzolatti G: Object representation in the ventral premotor cortex (area F5) of the monkey. Journal of Neurophysiology: 78; 2226–2230, 1997.

Murata A, Gallese V, Kaseda M, Sakata H: Parietal neurons related to memory-guided hand manipulation. Journal of Neurophysiology: 75; 2180–2186, 1996.

Nakamura K, Colby CL: Updating of the visual representation in monkey striate and extrastriate cortex during saccades. Society for Neuroscience Abstracts: 25; 1163, 1999.

Nakamura K, Colby CL: Visual, saccade-related and cognitive activation of single neurons in monkey extrastriate area V3A. Journal of Neurophysiology: 84; 677–692, 2000.

Olson CR, Gettner SN: Object-centered direction selectivity in the macaque supplementary eye field. Science: 269; 985–988, 1995.

Olson CR, Gettner SN: Representation of object-centered space in the primate frontal lobe. Cognitive Brain Research: 5; 147–156, 1996.

Olson CR, Gettner SN: Impairment of object-centered vision following lesions of macaque posterior parietal cortex. Society for Neuroscience Abstracts: 24; 1140, 1998.

Pandya DN, Yeterian EH: Architecture and connections of cortical association areas. In Peters A, Jones EG (Eds), Cerebral Cortex, Vol. 4. New York: Plenum Press, pp. 3–61, 1985.

Pare M, Wurtz RH: Monkey posterior parietal cortex neurons antidromically activated from superior colliculus. Journal of Neurophysiology: 78; 3493–3497, 1997.

Perenin MT, Vighetto A: Optic ataxia: a specific disruption in visuomotor mechanisms. I. Different aspects of the deficit in reaching for objects. Brain: 111; 643–674.

Pizzamiglio L, Cappa S, Vallar G, Zoccolotti P, Bottini G, Clurll P, Guargia C, Antonucci G: Visual neglect for far and near extra-personal space in humans. Cortex: 25; 471–477, 1989.

Rizzolatti G, Fogassi L, Gallese V: Parietal cortex: from sight to action. Current Opinion in Neurobiology: 4; 562–567, 1997.

Rizzolatti G, Riggio L, Sheliga BM: Space and selective attention. In Umilta C, Moscovitch M (Eds), Attention and Performance, Vol. 15. Cambridge, MA: MIT Press, pp. 231–265, 1994.

Rizzolatti G, Scandolara C, Matelli M, Gentilucci M: Afferent properties of periarcuate neurons in macaque monkeys. I. Somato-sensory responses. Behavioral Brain Research: 2; 125–146, 1981a.

Rizzolatti G, Scandolara C, Matelli M, Gentilucci M: Afferent properties of periarcuate neurons in macaque monkeys. II. Visual responses. Behavioral Brain Research: 2; 147–163, 1981b.

Robinson DL, Goldberg ME, Stanton GB: Parietal association cortex in the primate: sensory mechanisms and behavioral modulation. Journal of Neurophysiology: 41; 910–932, 1978.

Sakata H., Taira M, Kusunoki M, Murata A, Tanaka Y, Tsutsui K: Neural coding of 3D features of objects for hand action in the parietal cortex of the monkey. Philosophical Transactions of the Royal Society London B, Biological Sciences: 353; 1363–1373, 1998.

Sakata H, Taira M, Murata A, Mine S: Neural mechanisms of visual guidance of hand action in the parietal cortex of the monkey. Cerebral Cortex: 5; 429–438, 1995.

Segraves MA: Activity of monkey frontal eye field neurons projecting to oculomotor regions of the pons. Journal of Neurophysiology: 68; 1967–1985, 1992.

Segraves MA, Goldberg ME: Functional properties of corticotectal neurons in the monkey's frontal eye field. Journal of Neurophysiology: 58; 1387–1419, 1987.

Sereno AB, Maunsell JH: Shape selectivity in primate lateral intraparietal cortex. Nature: 395; 500–503, 1998.

Shadlen MN, Newsome WT: Motion perception: seeing and deciding. Proceedings of the National Academy of Sciences USA: 93; 628–633, 1996.

Shikata E, Tanaka Y, Nakamura H, Taira M, Sakata H: Selectivity of the parietal visual neurons in 3D orientation of surface of stereoscopic stimuli. Neuroreport: 7; 2389–2394, 1996.

Sirigu A, Duhamel JR, Cohen L, Pillon B, Dubois B, Agid Y: The mental representation of hand movements after parietal cortex damage. Science: 273; 1564–1568, 1996.

Snyder LH, Batista AP, Andersen RA: Change in motor plan without a change in the spatial locus of attention, modulates activity in posterior parietal cortex. Journal of Neurophysiology: 79; 2814–2819, 1998.

Stein JF: The representation of egocentric space in the posterior parietal cortex. Behavioral Brain Science: 15; 691–700, 1992.

Stricanne B, Andersen RA, Mazzoni P: Eye-centered, head-centered, and intermediate coding of remembered sound locations in area LIP. Journal of Neurophysiology: 76; 2071–2076, 1996.

Thier P, Andersen RA: Electrical stimulation suggests two different forms of representation of head-centered space in the intraparietal sulcus of rhesus monkeys. Proceedings of the National Academy of Sciences: 93; 4962–4967, 1996.

Tipper SP, Behrmann M: Object-centered not scene-based visual neglect. Journal of Experimental Psychology: Human Perception and Performance: 22; 1261–1278, 1996.

Tipper SP, Lortie C, Baylis GC: Selective reaching: evidence for action-centered attention. Journal of Experimental Psychology: Human Perception and Performance: 18; 891–905, 1992.

Umeno MM, Goldberg ME: Spatial processing in the monkey frontal eye field. I. Predictive visual responses. Journal of Neurophysiology: 78; 1373–1383, 1997.

Ungerleider LG, Mishkin M: Two cortical visual systems. In Ingle DJ, Goodale MA, Mansfield, RJW (Eds), Analysis of Visual Behavior. Cambridge, MA: MIT Press, pp. 549–586, 1982.

Walker MF, FitzGibbon EJ, Goldberg ME: Neurons in the monkey superior colliculus predict the result of impending saccadic eye movements. Journal of Neurophysiology: 73; 1988–2003, 1995.

Wurtz RH, Mohler CW: Enhancement of visual response in monkey striate cortex and frontal eye fields. Journal of Neurophysiology: 39; 766–772, 1976.

Yantis S, Jonides J: Abrupt visual onsets and selective attention: evidence from visual search. Journal of Experimental Psychology: Human Perception and Performance: 10; 601–621, 1984.

Yantis S, Jonides J: Abrupt visual onsets and selective attention: voluntary versus automatic allocation. Journal of Experimental Psychology: Human Perception and Performance: 16; 121–134, 1990.

Yantis S, Jonides J: Attentional capture by abrupt onsets: new perceptual objects or visual masking? Journal of Experimental Psychology: Human Perception and Performance: 22; 1505–1513, 1996.

Young AW, de Haan EH, Newcombe F, Hay DC: Facial neglect. Neuropsychologia: 28; 391–415.

Handbook of Neuropsychology, 2nd Edition, Vol. 4
M. Behrmann (Ed)

CHAPTER 4

Levels of impairment in unilateral neglect

Paolo Bartolomeo [a,b,*] and Sylvie Chokron [c,d]

[a] *INSERM Unit 324, Centre Paul Broca, 2 ter rue d'Alesia, Paris F-65014, France*
[b] *Neuropsychology Unit, Henri-Mondor Hospital, Créteil, France*
[c] *Laboratoire de Psychologie Expérimentale, CNRS ep 617, Grenoble, France*
[d] *Fondation Opthalmologique Rothschild, Paris, France*

Introduction

Unilateral brain lesions may induce signs of lateralized spatial bias, whereby patients show a preference for responding to events occurring on the side of space ipsilateral to the lesion, as compared to events occurring on the other, contralesional side. This bias can range from a mild asymmetry of response latencies to lateralized events to situations in which patients seem to act as if the contralesional half of the world did not exist anymore. The resulting peculiar patterns of performance in everyday life and in paper-and-pencil tests are collectively described as unilateral neglect (Jeannerod, 1987; Robertson and Marshall, 1993; Weinstein and Friedland, 1977). It is now generally accepted that unilateral neglect is more common, severe and long-lasting after lesions in the right hemisphere than after left brain damage; in this chapter, we will thereby primarily focus on neglect for left-sided events after right-hemisphere lesions. Left neglect is often dramatic enough as to constitute a major handicap for neurological patients, who may repeatedly bump into objects on their left side, hurt themselves and get lost in familiar environments.

'Peripheral' sensory or motor processing is usually preserved in unilateral neglect; hence, neglect might stem from an impairment situated at one of the many levels of processing that go from primary sensory processing to action. In this chapter, we describe the most common behavioral signs of neglect and the neuropsychological tasks used to determine its presence and severity; we then review some of the putative levels of impairment involved in neglect, with the functional mechanisms that have been proposed to account for neglect. The chapter is concluded by a short overview of rehabilitation techniques.

* Corresponding author. E-mail: paolo@broca.inserm.fr

Clinical description

Signs of left neglect usually emerge after large lesions involving the temporo-parietal junction of the right hemisphere. In the acute phase, patients lie in bed with their head and eyes turned toward the right. They typically do not answer if questioned from the left side, and cannot pay attention to the left even if summoned to do so. The tendency to rightward orienting is so compulsive and pervasive in this stage, that it is usually impossible to administer neuropsychological tests.

After a few days, patients usually recover the ability to maintain head and eyes straight. However, the mere appearance of any visual object either on the right side or bilaterally induces an immediate orientation of the head and the eyes toward the right-sided object. For example, in testing the visual fields by means of the confrontation technique, as soon as the examiner outstretches his or her hands, patients may look at the hand on their right, before the actual administration of the stimuli ('magnetic attraction' of gaze, see Gainotti, D'Erme and Bartolomeo, 1991). At this stage, when questioned from the left side patients may answer to another person standing on their right. Other behavioral signs of left neglect include eating from only the right side of the dish, shaving or making up only the right half of the face, and reading only the right extremity of newspaper titles. Patients may forget to wear the left sleeve or slipper and leave hanging the left earpiece of their spectacles. Neuropsychological tests (see below for an overview) reveal the presence of a severe left unilateral neglect, with patients' performance often confined to a restricted region of the right hemispace, without reaching the sagittal midline.

Subsequently, patients may recover from gross behavioral signs of neglect in everyday life. In this phase, diagnosis of neglect rests on appropriate neuropsychological testing, in which patients may be able to attend to information from the right half of the display sheet, but still show defective performance on the left side.

After a period ranging from weeks to months since lesion onset, patients may learn to compensate for neglect both in everyday life and in paper-and-pencil tasks. Even in this phase, however, subtler signs of spatial bias can be demonstrated. Patients continue to begin their exploration from the right side (Mattingley, Bradshaw and Bradshaw, 1994b), whereas most normal individuals use a left-to-right scanning technique, possibly on account of their reading habits (Chokron and Imbert, 1993). When producing a manual or vocal response to lateralized visual targets, patients respond more slowly to left than to right targets, especially at the beginning of the test (Bartolomeo, 1997), as if a residual initial attraction for right-sided objects were at work (Mattingley et al., 1994b).

A number of patients do not recover from behavioral signs of neglect. For these patients, the presence of neglect may negatively affect motor recovery (Denes, Semenza, Stoppa and Lis, 1982). Thus, neglect does not only have important implications for understanding the brain mechanisms of space processing; it also constitutes a major clinical problem.

Diagnostic tests

Several neuropsychological tasks can be used to demonstrate the presence and the amount of unilateral neglect. Here we briefly describe three visuomotor procedures simple enough as to be administered at the bedside. Other tasks that can be used for the assessment of particular aspects of neglect will be discussed in *Unilateral neglect: from sensation to action*. Care should be taken in the proper positioning of the test sheet; in the usual clinical conditions, the midline of the sheet should correspond to the trunk midline of the patient.

Drawing tasks

In drawing figures, whether from memory or by copying them, neglect patients omit or distort the details on the left side (Gainotti, Messerli and Tissot, 1972) (Fig. 1).

When copying patterns composed of several elements aligned horizontally, some patients neglect the whole left part of the model, while others copy all the items, but leave unfinished the left part of each (Gainotti et al., 1972; Marshall and Halligan, 1993) (Fig. 2). These different patterns of performance have been respectively defined as scene- (or viewer-)based and object-based neglect (see Walker, 1995, for review).

In copying drawings, patients may sometimes displace to the right side of their copy details situated on the left side of the model (Fig. 3) (Halligan, Marshall and Wade, 1992). These transposition errors are often referred to as allochiria or allesthesia, by analogy with the behavior of patients who report as occurring on the good side of their body a tactile stimulus given to the affected side (Critchley, 1953).

Cancellation tasks

In cancellation tasks, patients are asked to cross out items scattered on a paper sheet, such as lines (Albert, 1973), letters (Mesulam, 1985) or shapes (Gauthier, Dehaut and Joanette, 1989; Halligan, Cockburn and Wilson, 1991). Patients typically begin to scan the sheet from the right side, unlike normal left-to-right readers, who start from the left side (Bartolomeo, D'Erme and Gainotti, 1994). Patients omit a number of left-sided targets, sometimes without even crossing the midline; they may continue to

Fig. 1. Copy of a linear drawing by a left neglect patient.

Fig. 2. 'Piecemeal' copy of the same drawing as in Fig. 1 by another patient with left neglect.

cancel the same rightmost items over and over again (Fig. 4).

A monetary reward for each canceled item can dramatically reduce neglect on cancellation tasks (Mesulam, 1985); this finding underlies the importance of motivational factors in neglect behavior, and the possibility of circumventing neglect by manipulating task conditions apparently unrelated to space.

Line bisection

In line bisection tasks, patients have to mark the midpoint of a horizontal line; neglect patients deviate the subjective midpoint to the right of the true center of the line (Schenkenberg, Bradford and Ajax, 1980). The amount of deviation depends on several factors. The longer the line, the more rightward the bisection point; for the shortest lines there may be a paradoxical leftward deviation (the 'crossover effect', Marshall and Halligan, 1989b). The location in space of the line with respect to the patient's trunk midline also influences performance; rightward deviation increases when lines are located in the left hemispace and decreases when they are in the right hemispace (Heilman and Valenstein, 1979; Schenkenberg

Fig. 3. Copy of a linear drawing of a face, with transposition to the right side of the eye on the patient's left side.

et al., 1980). Another factor that influences line bisection performance is the direction of exploration of the line. In a passive version of the task, in which patients had to observe a dot or pen moving along the line and to say 'stop' when it crossed the perceived middle, neglect patients' rightward error decreased when the pen traveled from the left to the right, as opposed to the right-to-left condition, which increased the amount of rightward shift (Chokron, Bartolomeo, Perenin et al., 1998; Mattingley, Bradshaw and Bradshaw, 1994a; Reuter-Lorenz and Posner, 1990). Reading habits also seem to influence line bisection, presumably through the induction of preferential exploratory strategies. Chokron and Imbert (1993) demonstrated that whereas left-to-right French readers deviated toward the left in a visuomotor line bisection task, right to left Israeli readers shifted the subjective middle toward the right. This effect of reading habits on line bisection performance occurs not only for school-children (8 years old) and adults, but also for pre-school children, indicating that reading habits may influence the visual exploration of non-linguistic stimuli even before formal reading begins (Chokron and De Agostini, 1995).

How many neglects?

The peculiar issues that unilateral neglect raises concerning space processing and consciousness, together with the puzzling fact that neglect occurs preferentially after right-hemisphere lesions, have stimulated a large body of research in the last decades. A number of theories have been advanced to explain neglect, but a unitary explanation has up to now proved elusive, and there is no consensus about its causal mechanisms (see Halligan and Marshall, 1994).

The shift in neuropsychological research from group studies to single-case studies has led to the description of several dissociations in neglect. Thus, patients have been described who neglect left-sided events in near (peripersonal), but not far space (Halligan and Marshall, 1991a), or vice versa (Cowey et al., 1994), or who show neglect on some tests, but not others (Halligan and Marshall, 1992), or even opposite patterns of neglect (left vs. right) depending on the task administered (Costello and Warrington, 1987; Halligan and Marshall, 1998; Humphreys and Riddoch, 1994). This apparently "unmanageable explosion of dissociations" (Vallar, 1994) has understandably led to the consideration of neglect as a highly heterogeneous disorder (see, e.g. Chatterjee, 1998; Stone, Halligan, Marshall and Greenwood, 1998), if not "a meaningless entity" (Halligan and Marshall, 1992).

It is certainly possible that different causes lead to similar neglect behavior through different routes (see, e.g. Barton, Behrmann and Black, 1998). However, it must be noted that the status of some neglect dissociations as diagnostic of qualitatively different impairments has been questioned. Neglect has a unique position in neuropsychology, in that the same event can elicit different behaviors depending on which side of space it occurs. But the left/right border, and consequently the border between attended and neglected objects, is not a fixed border, but a dynamic one (Gainotti, 1994), and can be influenced by several factors, including patients' exploratory strategies and compensatory mechanisms.

Spatial exploratory tasks, such as those used to investigate neglect, are particularly sensitive to

Fig. 4. Performance of a patient with left neglect on a line cancellation test. Note the perseverations of response on right-sided lines.

changes in strategy. For example, changing the direction of exploration of a horizontal line can reverse the direction of the bisection error, both in normals and in neglect patients (Chokron et al., 1998). In a similar vein, although the dissociation of scene- and object-based neglect does suggest that they reflect different underlying impairments (see Walker, 1995), any firm conclusion in this sense is rendered difficult by the finding that the same patients can show scene- or object-based neglect depending on the nature of the task (see below, *Object-based attentional deficits*). Analogous considerations can be made for the distinction between visual and imaginal neglect (see *Imaginal neglect in isolation*) for the dissociation between perceptual and premotor forms of neglect (*Directional arm movements*). Moreover, the well-established evidence that lesions determining neglect tend to cluster over the temporo-parietal junction of the right hemisphere seems to suggest that some core deficit, or some peculiar association of deficits (as suggested by the generally large size of the lesions, which may indicate damage to several functional systems), is at work in a large majority of neglect patients. Thus, at this stage, any conclusion about the heterogeneity or a (relative) homogeneity of the neglect syndrome seems premature. In view of these considerations, multiple single-case studies, in which individual performance of several patients are explored in detail, seem at present the best way to constrain theoretical models of neglect, and to determine the real clinical importance of the deficits at issue.

The peculiarities of neglect behavior have fostered several explanations of neglect. These hypotheses were often inspired by a particular aspect or symptom, that was isolated and considered to account for the other manifestations of the syndrome. Thus, one hypothesis may consider one aspect as the cause and the other aspects as its consequences; another explanation may revert the putative cause–consequence relationship in a chicken-and-egg fashion. For example, a rightward deviation in line bisection has always been seen as a consequence of left neglect, but a rightward deviation in judging the position of the 'straight ahead' has been interpreted as a shift of the egocentric reference leading to neglect (see below, *Shift of the egocentric frame of reference*). It is thus perhaps no wonder that the explanatory value of the existing theories of neglect has been considered to be very low, if not "essentially zero" (Marshall and Halligan, cited by Bisiach, Cornacchia, Sterzi and Vallar, 1994).

Unilateral neglect: from sensation to action

Various levels of impairment from primary sensory processing to motor programs have been invoked to explain neglect. Acting in the environment continuously demands visuomotor transformations. Perceptual representations and motor plans mutually update each other as action changes the perceived environment (action–perception cycles; Arbib, 1981). For example, the mere fact of crossing out lines in a cancellation task modifies the visual scene, so that patients' performance in this task may differ from performance in an equivalent task where lines are to be erased rather than crossed (Mark, Kooistra and Heilman, 1988) (see *A rightward attentional bias in left neglect*).

One could thus conceive that patients show left neglect signs as illustrated in Figs. 1–4 because: (1) they do not see the left part of the test sheet; (2) their representation of the space array is amputated, distorted or deviated; (3) they suffer from an attentional bias favoring the right side or penalizing the left side; (4) their exploration of space is biased toward the right; and (5) they have problems in programming movements of the arm or the hand toward the left. It is also possible that any combination between these impairments determines neglect. In the following sections, we will review and discuss the possible contribution of each of these putative levels of spatial bias to neglect.

Elementary sensory processing

The first possible level of spatial bias in neglect could logically be an elementary sensory impairment. For example, patients could neglect the left side of their world just because they do not see it, possibly in the context of altered mental functioning (Battersby, Bender, Pollack and Kahn, 1956). This hypothesis has long been falsified by the reports of double dissociations between hemianopia and neglect (Gainotti, 1968; McFie, Piercy and Zangwill, 1950). Importantly, hemianopic patients without neglect try to compensate for their deficit, often to the point of a paradoxical contralesional deviation in line bisection (Barton and Black, 1998), whereas patients with hemianopia and neglect deviate ipsilesionally [1]. Moreover, neglect has been shown not only in the visual space, but also in auditory (Bisiach et al., 1984; De Renzi, Gentilini and Barbieri, 1989a), tactile (Bisiach, Capitani and Porta, 1985b; Chedru, 1976) and imagined space (Bisiach, Capitani, Luzzatti and Perani, 1981; Bisiach and Luzzatti, 1978). Thus, unilateral neglect can be a supramodal disorder. A third argument that challenges the hypothesis of an important role of primary sensory impairment in neglect is that the early stages of visual perception, such as figure-ground segregation, can be preserved in neglect (Driver, Baylis and Rafal, 1992). These considerations call for a more abstract of a level of impairment than primary sensory representations. For example, Denny-Brown, Meyer and Horenstein (1952) surmised that the parietal cortex is concerned with the perceptual synthesis of multiple sensory data (morphosynthesis), achieved through spatial summation. The loss of visual and tactile components of this integrative process would result in neglect behavior (amorphosynthesis). This putative level of sensory integration is still close to perceptual processes. Levels of impairment further away from perception have also been hypothesized, such as a difficulty in building or in exploring an internal representation of space.

Space representation

Neglecting mental images

Accounts of neglect based on a disturbed mental representation of space stem from the observation that

[1] The hypothesis of a primary sensory impairment as the origin of neglect has been somewhat reversed by the demonstration that neglect can be so profound as to simulate a non-existent hemianopia (Kooistra and Heilman, 1989; Walker, Findlay, Young and Welch, 1991) or hemianesthesia (Vallar, Sandroni, Rusconi and Barbieri, 1991).

neglect may not only occur during activities requiring the processing of sensory input, but also during tasks less directly involved with perception, such as the description from memory of places. Brain (1941) reported on a patient who, "when asked to describe how she would find her way from the tube station to her flat, she described this in detail correctly and apparently visualizing the landmarks, but she consistently said right instead of left for the turning except on one occasion" (p. 259). McFie et al. (1950), commenting upon Brain's study, observed that "not uncommonly, loss of topographical orientation can be traced to massive neglect of the left half of visual space ... This symptom (...) undoubtedly accounts for the greater part of the topographical disability observed by Russell Brain" (p. 170, note 1). These authors described a patient with topographical disorientation who showed "no evidence of neglect of left half of space apart from his own admission that he thought most of the turnings which he missed when he became lost were on his left" (McFie et al., 1950, p. 176). When the patient reported by Denny-Brown et al. (1952) was asked to describe the ward 2 months after discharge from hospital, she "began by describing all the patients and the windows which had been on her right, mentioning them from right to left. She made no mention of the patients on the left until pressed and then was able to recall 2 out of 5" (Denny-Brown et al., 1952, p. 438–439).

The issue of mental representation of space in neglect assumed theoretical significance in the work of Bisiach and his associates (see Bisiach, 1993, for review). In their seminal paper, Bisiach and Luzzatti (1978) reported two left neglect patients who, when asked to imagine and describe from memory familiar surroundings (the Piazza del Duomo in Milan), omitted to mention left-sided details regardless of the imaginary vantage point that they assumed, thus showing representational, or imaginal, neglect. Bisiach et al. (1981) replicated this finding in a group study with 28 neglect patients, of which 13 had to be excluded from analysis because they misplaced the imagined details (e.g. they said that a left-sided detail was on the right side); the remaining 15 patients showed a bias toward mentioning more right-sided than left-sided details of the Piazza del Duomo. Bisiach and coworkers interpreted these findings as evidence that neglect patients suffer from "a representational map reduced to one half" (Bisiach et al., 1981, p. 549).

Bartolomeo et al. (1994) reasoned that, if such a representational deficit were at the base of neglect, patients should show comparable neglect signs in imaginal (i.e. description from memory of known places) and visuospatial tasks. They assessed quantitatively the amount of neglect in 30 right-brain-damaged (RBD) and 30 left-brain-damaged (LBD) patients, tested consecutively. RBD patients showed a significant ipsilesional (rightward) bias in both sets of tasks, while LBD patients, taken as a group, performed not differently from controls. For RBD patients, the amount of spatial bias in imaginal tasks correlated with that in visuospatial tasks, thus supporting the idea of a relationship between the two impairments. However, analysis of individual performance revealed that only five of the 17 RBD patients with visuospatial neglect also showed neglect in the imaginal domain, contrary to the predictions of the representational hypothesis. Furthermore, only in the visuospatial tasks, and not in the imaginal tasks, RBD patients consistently showed the right-to-left scanning procedure typical of left neglect. The greater frequency of left neglect in visuospatial than imaginal tasks may thus result from the fact that visual objects are more likely than imagined details to attract RBD patients' attention toward the right (see *A right attentional bias in left neglect*). Of the 30 LBD patients, two showed signs of right visuospatial neglect, none of right imaginal neglect. That left visuospatial neglect often stands unaccompanied by imaginal neglect was also confirmed by another group study (Halsband, Gruhn and Ettlinger, 1985), by the detailed report of two cases (Anderson, 1993), and by a study conducted during intracarotid injection of amobarbital (Manoach, O'Connor and Weintraub, 1996).

A problem with the description from memory of known places is that abilities other than visual imagery might be used to perform this task. In the study of Bartolomeo et al. (1994), patients were invited to imagine the places "as if they were before their eyes". Despite these instructions, some of them might simply have produced a list of details from verbal semantic memory. If so, imaginal neglect would be underestimated in these tasks, and might thus ultimately appear to be less common than visuospatial neglect (although it is unlikely that the two-thirds of left neglect patients of the Bartolomeo et al.'s series did not comply with the test instructions). A different paradigm to study lateralized defects of mental representation was devised by Bisiach, Luzzatti and Perani (1979), who had 19 RBD patients with left neglect perform same/different judgements over pairs of cloud-like shapes that moved horizontally and could only be seen while passing behind a narrow slit. Performance was particularly impaired when the shapes differed on the left side. Because the overall shape had to be mentally reconstructed to perform the same/different judgement, Bisiach et al. (1979) concluded that a representational disorder was of primary importance in neglect. However, since patients without neglect were not examined in this study, the results simply indicated that an imaginal defect could be present in neglect. In a similar task, Ogden (1985) also found impaired accuracy for contralesional details in four RBD (of whom three had left visuospatial neglect) and five LBD patients (of whom two had right visuospatial neglect; five other RBD and four LBD patients could not complete the task). The status of the slit experiment as a test of imaginal neglect was, however, later questioned by Bisiach and Rusconi (1990), who found that the left part of a drawing may continue to be neglected even when patients correctly follow the contour of the drawing with their finger. This finding suggested to Bisiach and Rusconi a reinterpretation of the slit experiment results, as "a defective pick-up of information from the leftmost part of the stimuli in the short lapse of time in which this part was shown in central vision" (p. 647).

The interpretation of imaginal neglect depends on the development of theories of mental imagery. The possibility that patients who neglect visual objects could also neglect visual mental images was easily explained within the general framework theories considering mental images as functionally similar to visual percepts. If visual perception and visual imagery share a number of mental operations (Kosslyn, 1994), and rely upon common neural structures, including early visual cortices (Damasio, 1989; Kosslyn, 1994), then an association of visual and imaginal neglect is indeed to be expected. However, there is now robust evidence that patients with severe perceptual impairment can conjure up vivid mental images of the very items that they cannot perceive (Bartolomeo, Bachoud-Lévi, de Gelder et al., 1998a; Behrmann, Winocur and Moscovitch, 1992). This evidence calls into question the hypothesis of too strict an equivalency between the act of perceiving and that of imagining, and seems to relate imagery to more abstract abilities than perception. If so, imaginal neglect is an even more striking phenomenon, perhaps akin to forms of 'conceptual' bias, such as the one demonstrated by occasional neglect patients who seem unwilling even to utter the word 'left'.

Imaginal neglect in isolation

Neglect for the left part of mental images has been described in the absence of neglect for visual objects (Beschin, Cocchini, Della Sala and Logie, 1997; Coslett, 1989, 1997; Guariglia, Padovani, Pantano and Pizzamiglio, 1993). The most straightforward interpretation of this dissociation is that different mechanisms mediate visuospatial and imaginal neglect. A more parsimonious account would be that these patients have learned with time (and possibly the help of people around them) to compensate for their neglect in the visuospatial domain, but not in the less ecological imaginal domain. As a matter of fact, neglect patients are often reminded by relatives and hospital staff to explore the visual scene thoroughly, and could learn to appreciate the consequences of their omissions (e.g. while eating or reading a newspaper), but this cannot happen in the imaginal space. The follow up of a patient with a severe visuospatial and imaginal neglect seems to support this idea. Eight months after the first testing, this patient had recovered from visuospatial neglect, but still showed imaginal neglect (Bartolomeo et al., 1994). Patient M.N. described by Coslett (1989, 1997) also showed a similar pattern of selective recovery from visuospatial, but not from imaginal, neglect. Another patient (D'Erme, Bartolomeo and Gainotti, 1994) did not show clinical signs of neglect 8 days after the stroke; he had, however, mild but definite left neglect signs on visuospatial testing and on imaginal tasks. Two weeks after the stroke, visuospatial neglect had resolved, leaving an isolated imaginal neglect, which disappeared in turn 22 days after onset (Fig. 5). In this patient, visuospatial neglect at the initial assessment was so mild, that it would have probably passed undetected with-

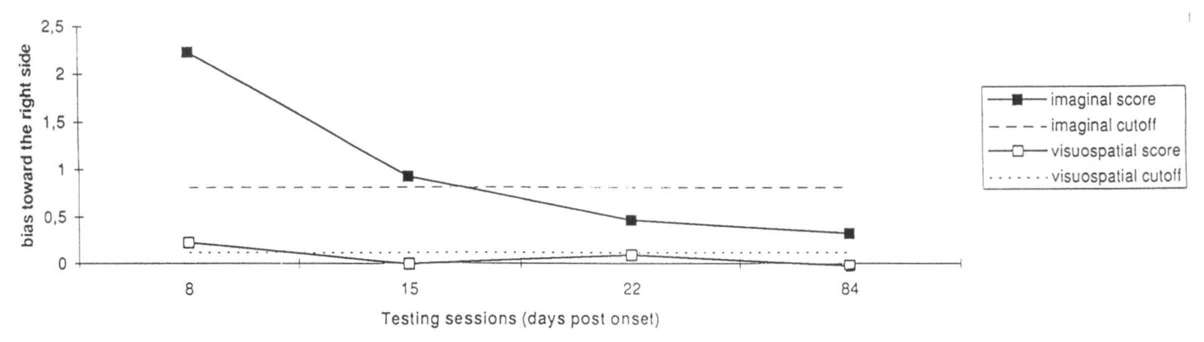

Fig. 5. Follow-up study of a left neglect patient. His performance on imaginal and visuospatial tasks is measured by a laterality score (described in Bartolomeo et al., 1994). Cutoff scores are based on performance of normal individuals.

out proper testing, thus leaving the impression that neglect was exclusive for visual imagery from the beginning.

Thus, follow-up studies can disentangle residual deficits from compensatory mechanisms, and they can possibly contribute to reduce the confusing variety of neglect dissociations to a number of component mechanisms [2].

Anisometry of mental coordinates

Other explanatory accounts of neglect focus on a dysfunction of the left part of a mental representation of space in neglect. These accounts, however, propose that this part of the representation is not destroyed, but distorted. Evidence relevant to this issue was collected by Gainotti and Tiacci, 1971 (Experiment 2), who had 75 RBD patients (of which 31 with left neglect) compare the size of two geometrical figures presented on the left and the right sides of a sheet. Neglect patients tended to overestimate right-sided as compared to left-sided figures. Also seven right neglect patients (out of a group of 62 LBD patients) showed a similar, albeit less marked tendency to overestimate the size of ipsilesional figures. Drawing on evidence showing that normal individuals overvalue the dimensions of those items on which their gaze is mostly fixed (Piaget, 1961), Gainotti and Tiacci (1971) attributed the perceptual bias of neglect patients to an asymmetrical exploration of space favoring ipsilesional over contralesional objects (see *A rightward attentional bias in left neglect* below). More recently, a similar experimental paradigm was employed by Milner and Harvey (1995), who reasoned that a 'shrinkage' in object size perception in the left hemispace could explain neglect patients' rightward error in line bisection. They asked 15 RBD patients (of whom three had left neglect) to compare pairs of horizontally arranged shapes (horizontal rectangles, vertical rectangles, or nonsense shapes). Neglect patients consistently underestimated items presented on the left side, with the exception of the vertical rectangles, for which they were accurate. Milner and Harvey (1995) concluded that horizontal size is miscomputed in the left parts of the visual array. Bisiach, Pizzamiglio, Nico and Antonucci (1996) had neglect patients mark the left and right endpoints of a virtual horizontal line on the basis of a given midpoint. Patients misplaced the left endpoint leftwards, as if mimicking their biased performance in line bisection. Bisiach et al. (1996) concluded that space representation in neglect is characterized by a horizontal anisometry, with spatial coordinates progressively relaxing from the right to the left side (Fig. 6).

When placing the endpoints of a virtual line, patients should travel further leftward than rightward to equalize the amount of perceived spatial extent. It has also been shown, however, that only patients with an association of neglect and complete left hemianopia seem to show this peculiar behavior, whereas neglect patients without visual field defect do not demonstrate consistent asymmetries in placing the endpoints (Doricchi and Angelelli, 1999); this finding limits the generality of the anisometry account. Moreover, performance of one left neglect patient would rather suggest a *compression* of left-sided

[2] By this account, it remains of course to be elucidated why some patients develop effective strategies for certain domains, whereas other patients do not.

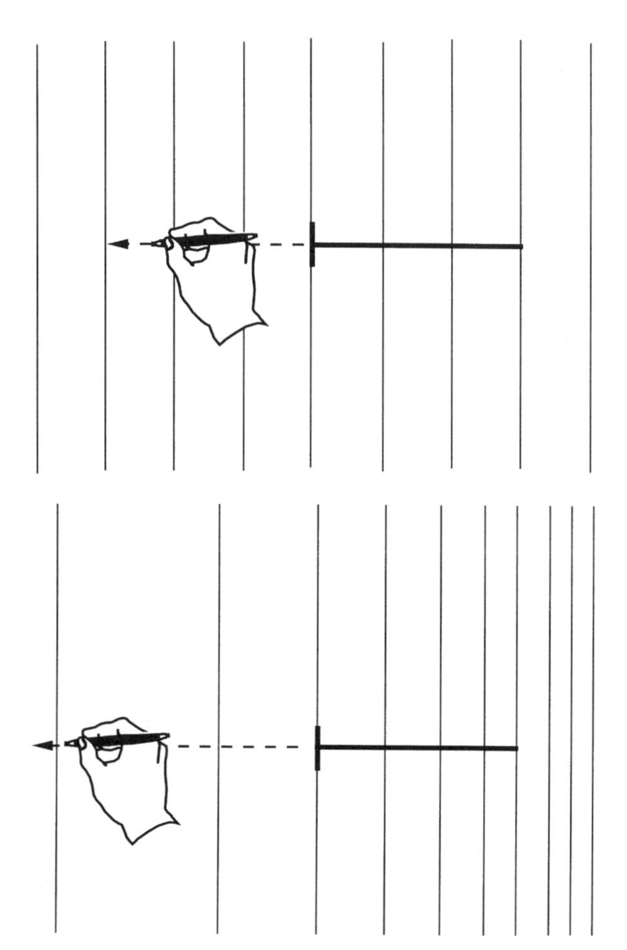

Fig. 6. The hypothetical anisometry of space representation in left neglect, as assessed by a line extension task (discussed in *Directional arm movements*). Vertical lines represent the coordinates of represented space. The continuous horizontal line depicts the given half-line (model); the dashed line represents subjects' performance. In normal conditions (upper part of the figure), spatial coordinates are evenly distributed; as a result, the leftward extension accurately reproduces the length of the model. In left neglect (lower part of the figure), spatial coordinates progressively relax from the right side to the left; as a consequence, the line must be further extended toward the left in order to cross the same amount of spatial coordinates as the model. This results in a pathological overextension. A similar mechanism would explain patients' performance on Bisiach et al. (1996) endpoint-placing task (see text).

spatial coordinates (Halligan and Marshall, 1991b). When this patient saw rows of numbers (from 1 to 15), and had to identify the number aligned with an arrow presented either at the top or bottom of the monitor, she often indicated a number to the right of the target. The more the target was on the left, the more the response was shifted rightward. Halligan and Marshall (1991b) concluded that in this patient points in left space were compressed rightward [3].

While the accounts based on a horizontal anisometry of space representation may explain relatively easily the patients' behavior in line bisection and related tasks, they fare less well for visual search paradigms, in which it is not clear why neglect patients should *omit* left-sided targets. Moreover, further assumptions are necessary for the model to explain why neglect patients deviate much more when bisecting a line than when bisecting an empty space between two points (see Bisiach et al., 1996). More generally, models of neglect based on a dysfunction of space representation are not able to account for the dramatic effect exerted on neglect signs by variables such as the presence or absence of visual guidance (see *Orienting of attention*). For example, when two horizontally arranged LEDs are presented in otherwise complete darkness, neglect patients can accurately adjust their position to a prespecified distance, independent of the hemispace of presentation (Karnath and Ferber, 1999). In this case, the absence of other visual stimuli or of a visual background seems to nullify the error of horizontal length estimation induced by neglect. This appears in turn to underline the importance of the presence of competing visual events to elicit neglect.

Shift of the egocentric frame of reference

On the basis of the observation of asymmetric compensatory eye movements after lesions in the cat parietal cortex and superior colliculus, Ventre and colleagues (Ventre and Faugier-Grimaud, 1986; Ventre, Flandrin and Jeannerod, 1984) hypothesized that a body reference frame that allows a reconstruction of body position in space with respect to external objects is built as an internal representation of body midline or longitudinal axis. This internal representation was assumed to be a result of symmetrical activity of associative neural structures. Unilateral lesions of these structures would produce permanent

[3] Another possible explanation of these results is that patient's attention was attracted by the digits to the right of the target digit (see below, *A rightward attentional bias in left neglect*), thus biasing her responses toward right-sided digits.

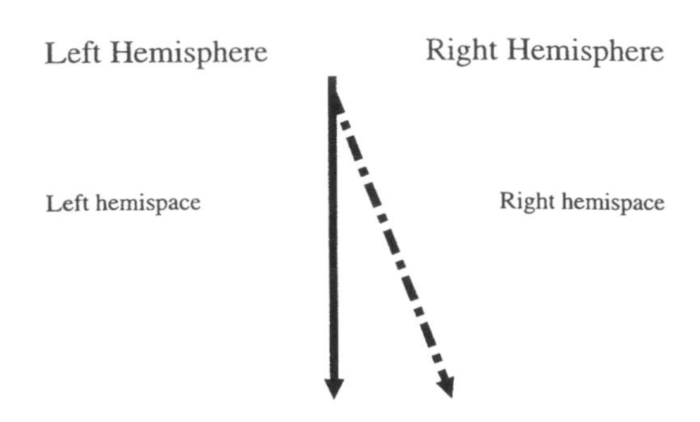

Fig. 7. The reference shift hypothesis of left neglect. Solid arrow, position of the egocentric reference in normal subjects, superimposed to the midsagittal plane; dashed arrow, hypothesized ipsilesional deviation of the egocentric reference in left neglect patients.

asymmetrical activity inducing a displacement of the egocentric coordinates to a new position located in the ipsilesional hemispace, thus inducing a contralesional neglect (Fig. 7).

One way of improving neglect patients would thus be to restore the position of their egocentric reference. Several authors assumed that this was indeed the reason explaining the positive, if temporary, effect on left neglect signs of a number of vestibular and proprioceptive experimental stimulations. Thus, caloric vestibular stimulation, optokinetic stimulation, vibration of neck muscles on the left side, leftward trunk rotation and transcutaneous electrical stimulation of the left hand would reduce left neglect signs by temporarily inducing a leftward deviation of the egocentric reference, thus counteracting the pathological ipsilesional deviation of this reference and replacing it at the mid-sagittal plane as observed in normals (Fig. 8) (Karnath, 1997; Karnath, Christ and Hartje, 1993; Karnath, Schenkel and Fischer, 1991; Rode, Charles, Perenin et al., 1992; Rode and Perenin, 1994; Vallar, Antonucci, Guariglia and Pizzamiglio, 1993a; Vallar, Bottini, Rusconi and Sterzi, 1993b; Vallar, Guariglia and Rusconi, 1997; Vallar, Rusconi, Barozzi et al., 1995; Vallar, Sterzi, Bottini and Rusconi, 1990).

Patients would then become temporarily aware of otherwise neglected stimuli delivered to the affected side.

This theoretical set implies three distinct assertions. First, it takes for granted the existence of an ipsilesional deviation of the egocentric reference in left neglect patients. Second, this deviation is considered as the cause of the neglect behavior. Third, the above-cited stimulations are seen as a means to restore the position of the reference. If some physiological and clinical evidence seem to support these assertions, other experimental findings challenge them.

The vestibular system is a component part of cerebral circuits including cortical and sub-cortical structures. Its main cortical projections are on the parietal cortex (Fredrickson, Scheid, Figge and Kornhuber, 1966), which in turn projects to the vestibular nuclei in the brainstem (Ventre and Faugier-Grimaud, 1986). According to these anatomical data, the vestibular system could be involved in maintaining orientation in egocentric space. Other neurophysiological studies (reviewed by Stein, 1992) suggest that the vestibular system project to the posterior–superior temporal region. This area is adjacent to the infero-posterior parietal cortex, which is frequently damaged in patients with contralateral neglect.

In neglect patients, a constant 'directional' error, which would fit the hypothesis of an ipsilesional deviation of the egocentric reference, has been repeatedly described. The usual way of testing the perceived direction of the egocentric reference is to

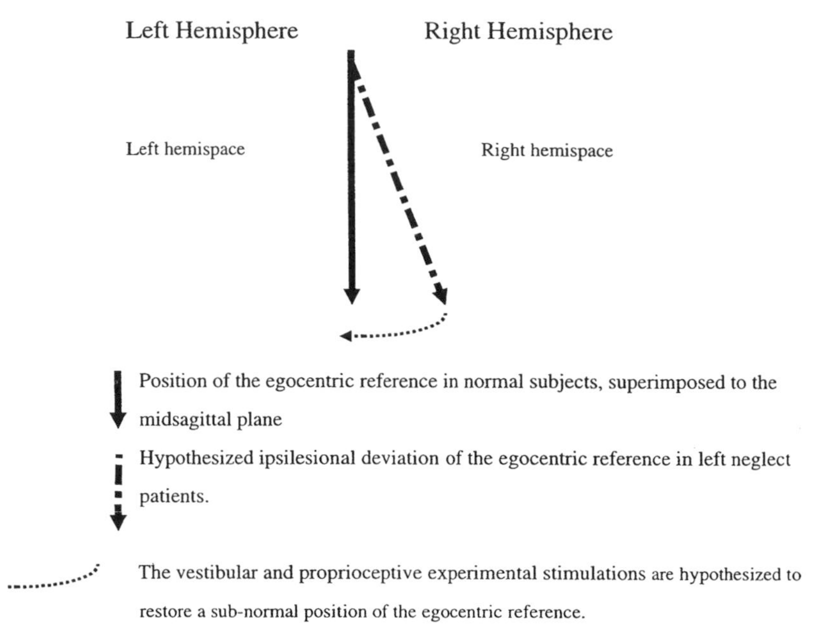

Fig. 8. The putative effect of vestibular and proprioceptive stimulations on the position of the egocentric reference. Solid arrow, position of the egocentric reference in normals subjects, superimposed to the midsagittal plane; dashed arrow, hypothesized ipsilesional deviation of the egocentric reference in left neglect patients; dotted curved arrow, the vestibular and proprioceptive experimental stimulations are hypothesized to restore a sub-normal position of the egocentric reference.

ask subjects to point straight ahead while blindfolded and to record this subjective position (Jeannerod and Biguer, 1987). Heilman, Bowers and Watson (1983) reported in five left neglect patients a large deviation of the subjective straight-ahead to the right ipsilesional hemispace. Heilman and coworkers interpreted their results in neglect patients in terms of a directional motor disorder ('hemispatial akinesia'; see *Directional arm movements* below). The finding of an ipsilesional shift of the subjective sagittal middle in left neglect was replicated in one patient with a proprioceptive straight-ahead pointing task (Chokron and Imbert, 1995) and in three patients with a visual straight-ahead pointing task (Karnath et al., 1993). Perenin (1997) found a mean rightward deviation of about 9° in a group of 25 left neglect patients using a straight-ahead pointing task performed in darkness (see Perenin, 1997, Fig. 5). It was also recently suggested that the presence of an extensive right parietal lesion correlated with a rightward shift of the egocentric reference (Chokron and Bartolomeo, 1999; Hasselbach and Butter, 1997).

However, others have found no correlation between left neglect signs and either the presence or the side of a deviation of the egocentric reference position recorded during a straight-ahead pointing task (Bartolomeo and Chokron, 1999a; Chokron and Bartolomeo, 1997, 1998; Farnè, Ponti and Làdavas, 1998; Hasselbach and Butter, 1997; Perenin, 1997). The absence of a direct causal link between the position of the egocentric reference and the presence of neglect signs is confirmed by several experimental data. First, there is evidence for a significant deviation of the egocentric reference in patients with hemianopia (Fuchs, 1920), ataxia (Perenin, 1997) or primary motor deficit (Chokron and Bartolomeo, 1997), but without any signs of neglect. Second, neglect signs may arise in frames of reference other than the egocentric one (e.g., object-based: see *Object-based attentional bias* below). Third, visual guidance seems to exacerbate the neglect behavior with respect to conditions in which visual control is minimized (see *Orienting of attention*). The reference shift hypothesis would on the contrary predict that the absence of visual control worsened patients' performance, because the egocentric reference is not defined in retinotopic coordinates, but in body-centered ones (Jeannerod and Biguer, 1987; Karnath et al., 1991).

It follows from these considerations that the positive effect of the experimental stimulations mentioned above cannot come from a restoration of a normal egocentric frame of reference. This notion was confirmed by evidence showing that optokinetic stimulation may not always restore normal performance in neglect (Bisiach et al., 1996). As reported in *Anisometry of mental coordinates*, when required to set the endpoints of an imaginary horizontal line of a given length on the basis of its midpoint, left neglect patients can misplace endpoints leftwards, thus reproducing the usual rightward deviation of the subjective middle found in line bisection. When the task was executed during leftward optokinetic stimulation (known to temporarily improve left neglect), the disproportion increased instead of vanishing. Bisiach et al. (1996) concluded that manipulations such as optokinetic stimulation may remove neglect without normalizing the representational medium itself. In a similar vein, imposing a left-to-right scanning of a to-be-bisected line may induce a pathological leftward deviation of the subjective middle in neglect patients, thus reversing left neglect behavior without reducing it (Chokron et al., 1998). Several data suggest that these stimulations could act by allowing an orientation of attention to the left hemispace (see section below). These considerations strongly suggest an important role of attentional processes in the determinism of left neglect.

Orienting of attention

The basic fact of left neglect is that an event on the right side is more likely to attract patient's attention than an event occurring on the left. This is particularly true when the two events are in competition, for example when they appear at the same time. The phenomenon of omitting to report a contralesional stimulus only when a concurrent ipsilesional stimulus is presented is called *extinction*. Left visual stimuli are usually extinguished in neglect patients (Gainotti et al., 1991); extinction may persist after clinical signs of neglect have subsided (Kaplan, Cohen, Rosengart et al., 1995; Karnath, 1988). Thus, the fact of putting stimuli in competition is a powerful means of eliciting signs of spatial bias (Di Pellegrino and De Renzi, 1995). This observation naturally leads to explanations of neglect based on an attentional bias, because attention is considered the basic mechanism used to deal with multiple competing stimuli.

The concept of attention refers to a heterogeneous set of phenomena, whose goal is to maintain coherent behavior in the face of irrelevant distractions. William James (1890) already observed that "my experience is what I agree to attend to ... Without selective interest, experience is an utter chaos" (James, 1890, p. 402). James distinguished among different "varieties of attention"; for example, he separated "passive, reflex, non-voluntary, effortless" attention from "active and voluntary" attention (James, 1890, p. 416). In a recent review, Parasuraman (1998) identified at least three independent but interacting components of attention: (1) *selection*, that is, systems determining more extensive processing of some input rather than another; (2) *vigilance*, or the capacity of sustaining attention over time; and (3) *control*, the ability of planning and coordinating different activities. Most attentional accounts of neglect postulate a problem of spatial selective attention. Spatial selective attention refers operationally to the advantage in speed and accuracy of processing for objects lying in attended regions of space as compared to objects located in non-attended regions (Posner, 1980; Umiltà, 1988). The scope of attentional selection need not be confined to perception, but can be functional to coherent control of action (Allport, 1989). Goal-directed behavior results from an orderly sequence of a limited number of actions; sensory information irrelevant to current behavioral scopes has to be filtered out to prevent interferences.

Attention can be oriented in space *overtly*, when eye and head movements align the fovea with the attended region, or *covertly*, in the absence of such movements. Posner and coworkers (see Posner, 1980, for review) developed a manual reaction time (RT) paradigm to study the covert orienting of attention. Subjects are presented with three horizontally arranged boxes. They fixate the central box and respond by pressing a key to a target (an asterisk) appearing in one of two lateral boxes. The target is preceded by a cue indicating one of the two lateral boxes. The cue can be either an arrow presented in the central box, or a brief brightening of one peripheral box. *Valid* cues correctly predict the box in which the target will appear, whereas *invalid* cues indicate the wrong box. Often, a large majority (usually 80%) of cues is valid; in this case, cues are said to be *informative* of the future emplacement of the target. The experimental paradigm may require the cue to be *non-informative*; in this case, the target will appear with equal probabilities in the cued or in the uncued location. For informative cues, normal subjects usually show an advantage of valid cue-target trials as compared to invalid trials. This suggests that the cue prompts an attentional orienting toward the cued location, which speeds up the processing of targets appearing in that region and slows down responses to targets appearing in other locations.

Other studies highlighted the fact that attention can not only be directed to a region of space, but also (and perhaps more importantly) to visual objects in space. For example, when normal subjects see a rectangle with a line struck through it, they can more easily report two attributes if they belong to the same object (e.g. if the line is dashed and tilted), than if they belong to two different objects (e.g. if the rectangle has a gap and the line is dotted), notwithstanding the fact that the two objects appear in the same spatial region (Duncan, 1984). In such a view, objects would be preattentively defined in the space array, and attention would then prompt selection of an entire object, and not of its spatial location. The demonstration that attention is directed to objects in space has since been confirmed by many studies (see Egeth and Yantis, 1997, for review). As a matter of fact, normal observers find it extremely difficult, if not impossible, to covertly attend to a 'blank' region of space, where no object is present (see Nakayama and Mackeben, 1989, Experiment 2).

Before proceeding with an overview of attentional accounts of neglect, it is worth examining some of the reasons why attentional processes can be considered more relevant than others for explaining unilateral neglect. Consideration of the sensory modalities of expression of neglect may prove useful. For example, costs and benefits provided by cues are maximal for visual targets and decrease for tactile and even more for acoustic targets (Posner, 1978). This is perhaps related to the topographical organization of the visual system, which might emphasize the spatial aspects of cueing (see Reuter-Lorenz, Jha and Rosenquist, 1996). Moreover, the organization of the oculomotor system, with the possibility of rapidly bringing into foveal vision objects to be identified, calls for an efficient interface with the perceptual system. Seeing an object 'out of the corner of the eye' typically induces movements of the eyes and of the head to align the object with the retinal fovea, the region with the highest spatial definition for visual identification. Attentional orienting is often triggered by the sudden appearance of an object in the retinal periphery (Yantis, 1995). As we have seen, orienting one's attention toward a visual object means being able to process it with increased speed and accuracy. This clearly represents an advantage when a quick decision is to be taken about which objects are to be approached (e.g. food) and which to be avoided (e.g. dangers). Thus, the anisometry of the sensory surface, with a region (the fovea) much more sensitive than others, prompts the need for orienting movements to align the sensory input with this region. These characteristics are much less evident in other sensory systems.

If neglect, then, can be shown to occur more in the visual modality than in other domains, it would parallel an important characteristic of visual attention. As mentioned before, neglect is not exclusive to visually presented material, but can be apparent in auditory, tactile and imagined space. However, when patients' performance in tactile or imagery tests is directly compared with their performance in visuospatial tests, neglect often results more common and severe for visual than for nonvisual stimuli (see Bartolomeo et al., 1994, for imagined space; Fujii, Fukatsu, Kimura et al., 1991; Gentilini, Barbieri, De Renzi and Faglioni, 1989; Hjaltason, Caneman and Tegnér, 1993 for tactile space). Also for auditory neglect, it has been shown that blindfolding improves the ability of neglect patients to localize correctly sound stimuli originating on the left (Soroker, Calamaro, Glicksohn and Myslobodsky, 1997). Thus, one can conclude that visually presented stimuli exacerbate neglect (Hjaltason and Tegnér, 1992), as Fig. 9 dramatically demonstrates.

These considerations are strong arguments in favor of the role of attentional processes in the determinism of neglect. For example, a defective conceptualization of an hemispace (see *Neglecting mental images*), or a shift of the egocentric frame of reference (see *Shift of the egocentric frame of reference*),

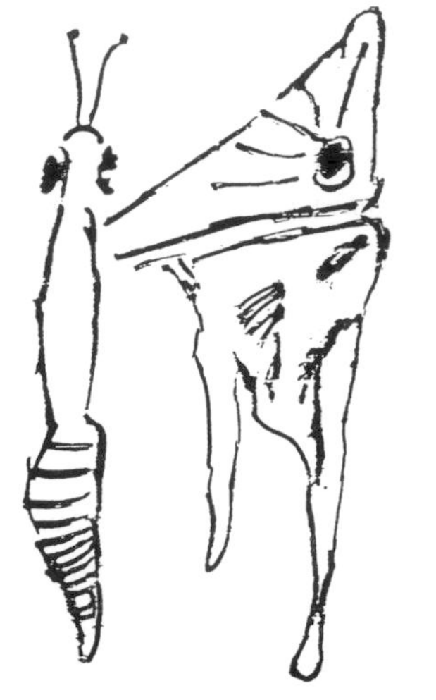

Fig. 9. Drawing from memory of a butterfly by a left neglect patient. Left side of the figure: drawing in free vision; right side of the figure: without the aid of vision.

would have little reason to express themselves more in the visual than in the tactile or in the acoustic space.

A rightward attentional bias in left neglect

A well articulated account of neglect based on orienting of attention is the opponent processor model (Kinsbourne, 1970, 1977, 1987, 1993). This model draws upon the very general biological evidence that reciprocally inhibiting opponent systems are an evolutionary advantageous way of solving the problem of deciding whether to turn right or left. The dominant system would achieve its goal of turning the organism by progressively inhibiting its contralateral counterpart. A first assumption of the opponent processor model is that each hemisphere shifts attention toward the contralateral hemispace by inhibiting the other hemisphere. A second assumption is that, in the normal brain, there is a tendency to rightward orienting supported by the left hemisphere, which has a stronger orienting tendency than the right hemisphere. Right hemisphere lesions, by disinhibiting the left hemisphere, exaggerate this physiological rightward bias, thus giving rise to left neglect. Left neglect does not reflect an attentional deficit, but an attentional bias consisting of enhanced attention to the right. The verbal interaction between patient and examiner would further enhance left neglect by further activating the already disinhibited left hemisphere. Furthermore, left neglect patients would suffer from an abnormally tight focus of attention, which would deprive them of the possibility of a more general overview of the visual scene (Kinsbourne, 1993). Right neglect would rarely be observed because much larger lesions of the left hemisphere are needed to overcome its stronger tendency to rightward orienting, and because the verbal exchanges with the examiner would now work in the opposite direction, thus minimizing right neglect. This latter aspect of the model seems at variance with the common observation of neglect signs in everyday situations, when no verbal exchange takes place. Moreover, a task of visual matching of letters to auditorily presented samples has been shown to disclose right neglect in LBD patients, but it was not able to elicit left neglect in RBD patients (Leicester, Sidman, Stoddard and Mohr, 1969). This finding is contrary to the predictions of opponent processor model; it is, however, consistent with the idea that verbal tasks may induce a left-to-right exploratory strategy (see Chokron et al., 1998), and that attention is thus preliminarily driven to the leftmost stimulus, thereby increasing right, but not left, neglect.

Despite these problems, other aspects of the opponent processor model appeared to be confirmed by subsequent empirical evidence. For example, a patient who showed a severe left neglect following a first right-sided parietal infarct abruptly recovered from neglect 10 days later, when he suffered from a second, left side infarct in the dorsolateral frontal cortex (Vuilleumier, Hester, Assal and Regli, 1996). However, inferences from this case report must be prudent. All the case history took place in the acute phase of the disease, when transient phenomena of neural depression in areas remote from the lesion (diaschisis: see Meyer, Obara and Muramatsu, 1993) render difficult any firm conclusions about the effect of anatomical damage. As the authors reported, the second stroke induced a tonic leftward deviation of head and gaze; this occurrence might have contributed to minimizing left neglect signs, similarly to the effects of vestibular or optokinetic stimulations (see *Shift of the egocentric frame of reference*).

Also the basic assumptions of the opponent processing model about the functional organization of the brain hemispheres have been questioned. First, while the concept of mutually inhibitory lateral structures appears adequate to describe the mode of functioning of subcortical structures, like the superior colliculi, it looks as an excessive simplification of the relationship of structures much more complex as the cerebral hemispheres (among other considerations, callosal connections seem prevalently excitatory, and not inhibitory, in nature, see Berlucchi, 1983). Second, the assumption of a left hemispheric dominance for attentional orienting seems challenged by PET data showing a preferential involvement of the right parietal lobe for both left- and right-sided attentional shifts, whereas the left parietal lobe is only activated by shifts in the right hemifield (Corbetta, Miezin, Schulman and Petersen, 1993), and by ERP results suggesting that the right hemisphere is activated earlier than the left in visual perception (Compton, Grossenbacher, Posner and Tucker, 1991).

The crucial mechanisms of left neglect according to the opponent processor model is a rightward attentional bias. That patients do not simply neglect left objects, but are attracted by right ones has been repeatedly shown. In an ingenious variant of the line cancellation task, Mark et al. (1988) had ten patients with left neglect erase lines or draw over them by a pencil mark, and found lesser neglect in the 'erase' than in the 'draw' condition. Mark et al. concluded that right-sided lines attracted patients' attention when they were crossed by a pencil mark; rendering these lines invisible by erasing them obviously nullified this effect, thus decreasing neglect. Similarly, Marshall and Halligan (1989a) reported that targets could be omitted in a shape cancellation task independently of their position with respect of the midsagittal plane, and concluded that 'right attentional capture' might be a better description of patients' performance than 'left neglect'.

An important marker of the direction of attention is the position of gaze. While attention can be shifted while maintaining fixation (Posner, 1980), a gaze shift usually correspond to an analogous shift in visual attention (Hoffman and Subramaniam, 1995; Kowler, Anderson, Dosher and Blaser, 1995; Shepherd, Findlay and Hockey, 1986). Brain lesions often induce a conjugated shift of gaze toward the side of the lesion. De Renzi, Colombo, Faglioni and Gibertoni (1982) importantly demonstrated that gaze deviation does not occur with equal frequency after left- and right-hemisphere lesions, but preferentially occurs after posterior lesions of the right hemisphere, and is often associated with left neglect, again suggesting that a rightward attentional bias is an important component of left neglect. Neglect patients are indeed prone to orient their gaze toward the rightmost stimulus as soon as the visual scene unfolds (De Renzi, Gentilini, Faglioni and Barbieri, 1989b). This observation is reminiscent of the 'magnetic attraction' of gaze, originally described by Cohn (1972) in hemianopic patients. This phenomenon can be observed during the clinical test of the visual fields by the confrontation method; as soon as the examiner outstretches her arms in the patient's visual fields, before the actual administration of stimuli, the patient compulsively looks at the hand on the right. Also this phenomenon, which can be considered as a lesser degree of tonic gaze paresis, is strictly associated with right hemisphere lesions and left neglect (Gainotti et al., 1991, Experiment 1). Moreover, RBD patients typically begin from the right side their exploration of a complex stimulus array (Gainotti et al., 1991, Experiment 2), again suggesting an initial rightward attentional orienting, whereas normal controls and LBD patients start from the left. This set of phenomena may easily explain why neglect, even if it is not exclusive for visually presented material, is nevertheless exacerbated by the presence of visual stimuli. Under visual control, attention might be captured and maintained in the right hemispace by visual objects, thus increasing neglect for the left side. The absence of visual control would improve performance by eliminating this attentional capture exerted by right-sided visual stimuli. In this sense, right-sided external percepts might be more 'sticky' than, for example, internal images (Anderson, 1993).

An important question raised by these findings is: does the rightward bias reflect enhanced attention to the right (resulting from a left hemisphere released from right-hemisphere inhibition), as postulated by the opponent processor model? Làdavas, Petronio and Umiltà (1990) found that patients with left neglect responded faster to right-sided than to left-sided targets, even when all the stimuli were presented in the right visual field. RBD patients without neglect, on the contrary, were faster for left-sided than for right-sided stimuli, probably because left targets appeared closer to the fovea. This finding is consistent with the opponent processor model, which holds that there is no special status for the patient's sagittal midline for dividing the attended from the neglected parts of space; independent of its absolute position, any object is likely to be neglected if it is 'left of' some other object that attract patients' attention (see also Marshall and Halligan, 1989a). Of particular interest was the finding by Làdavas et al. (1990) that neglect patients' response times for right targets were faster than those of RBD patients without neglect. Neglect patients' attention for right targets seemed thus enhanced with respect to RBD control patients, consistent with the opponent processor model. As Làdavas et al. (1990) pointed out, according to this model neglect patients should be faster for right-sided stimuli even with respect to normal individuals without brain damage; this, however, would be an unlikely result, given that right brain lesions cause a deficit in arousal (Howes and Boller, 1975). Indeed, subsequent RT studies (Bartolomeo, 1997; Bartolomeo, D'Erme, Perri and Gainotti, 1998b; D'Erme, Robertson, Bartolomeo and Daniele, 1992; Smania, Martini, Gambina et al., 1998) invariably found that left neglect patients were slower than normal controls when responding to right (ipsilesional) stimuli. Recent evidence (Bartolomeo and Chokron, 1999b) indicates that this slowing for ipsilesional targets does not simply reflect a nonspecific arousal deficit, but is strictly related to the severity of left neglect. The manual response times to lateralized visual stimuli of 24 left neglect patients were plotted against a laterality score measuring their neglect independent of the overall level of performance. That is, for example, right-sided omissions in cancellation tests with equal number of left omissions would decrease the amount of the score; thus, a non-lateralized pattern of omissions in paper-and-pencil tests, such as the one expected with a nonspecific arousal deficit, would not inflate the score.

Results (Fig. 10) showed that not only RTs to left targets, but also RTs to right targets increased with increasing neglect, contrary to the predictions of the opponent processor model. The two regression lines were not, however, parallel. With increasing neglect, responses to left targets increased more steeply than those to right targets did, suggesting that a rightward attentional bias participates in left neglect. However, this rightward bias seems one of defective, and not enhanced, attention.

That left neglect does not result from a hyperactive left hemisphere is also suggested by functional brain imaging studies of diaschisis in left neglect (Fiorelli, Blin, Bachine et al., 1991; Pantano, Di Piero, Fieschi et al., 1992; Perani, Vallar, Paulesu et al., 1993), which demonstrated a widespread hypometabolism in both the lesioned and the intact hemisphere. Recovery from neglect seems to correlate with restoration of normal metabolism not only in the unaffected regions of the right hemisphere, but also in the left hemisphere (Pantano et al., 1992; Perani et al., 1993). An increase of neural activity, metabolism and perfusion in the unaffected hemisphere seems indeed a general mechanism of prolonged recovery from neurological and neuropsychological impairments after unilateral strokes (Meyer et al., 1993).

A deficit of disengagement

Posner, Walker, Friedrich and Rafal (1984) had six RBD and seven LBD patients with predominantly parietal lesions perform the cued detection task described on p. 80. Patients were disproportionally slow when a contralesional target was preceded by an ipsilesional (invalid) cue. This RT pattern was present in both RBD and LBD patients, but considerably larger in RBD patients, and evident with both central cues (arrow) and peripheral cues (brightening of the box). Posner et al. (1984) argued that this effect, reminiscent of extinction of contralesional stimuli in double visual stimulation, resulted from an impaired disengagement of attention from the ipsilesional side. The amount of the observed RT effect correlated significantly with the extension of lesion in the superior parietal lobe [4]. Because control patients with frontal or temporal lesions did not present this pattern of performance, the authors concluded that an important role of each parietal lobe was one

[4] In a subsequent study, Friedrich et al. (1998) compared patients with chronic lesions of the superior parietal lobe with patients with lesions of the temporal–parietal junction (involving the superior temporal gyrus), all without clinical signs of neglect or extinction, and found an extinction-like RT pattern only for the temporal–parietal group.

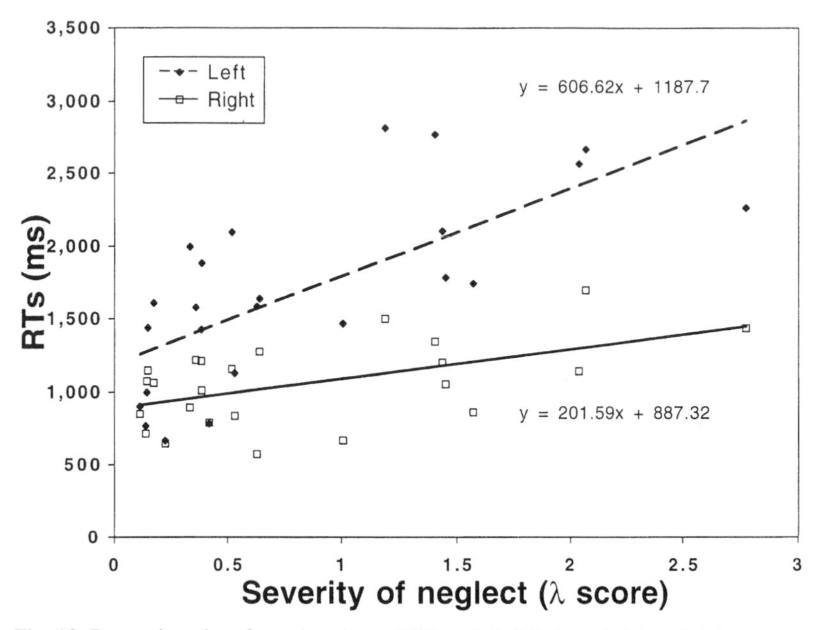

Fig. 10. Regression plot of reaction times (RTs) to left (filled symbols) and right (open symbols) targets as a function of the severity of left neglect (assessed by a laterality score) in 24 right brain-damaged patients (based on data in Bartolomeo and Chokron, 1999).

of disengaging attention from previously attended locations in the ipsilateral hemispace. A problem of disengagement from ipsilesional stimuli could, in principle, explain some aspects of neglect, such as the failure to explore the contralesional parts of a cancellation test. However, the parietal patients in the study by Posner et al. (1984) showed little or no contralesional neglect (no neglect in five patients, minimal neglect in two, mild in five and moderate in one). Thus, in this study, there was no direct evidence for a relationship between the observed extinction-like RT pattern and neglect.

This issue was addressed more directly by Morrow and Ratcliff (1988), who tested 12 RBD and ten LBD patients using a RT paradigm with peripheral cues. All patients had lesions including the parietal lobe, contralesional neglect, or both. Only RBD patients showed a significant extinction-like RT pattern (though LBD patients' results did go in the same direction, see Morrow and Ratcliff, 1988, Fig. 1). For RBD patients, the cost for invalid contralesional targets correlated with a measure of left neglect, thus suggesting a causal relationship between the two phenomena.

However, for such a right-disengagement deficit to produce clinical left neglect, attention must logically have been engaged to the right *before* the occurrence of the disengagement problem (see Gainotti et al., 1991; Karnath, 1988). D'Erme et al. (1992) produced evidence for such an early rightward engagement by manipulating the Posner RT paradigm. In this paradigm, targets appear in boxes displayed to facilitate position expectancy. D'Erme et al. (1992) reasoned that, by analogy with the magnetic attraction phenomenon (see above, p. 80), the mere appearance on the computer screen of the placeholder boxes should elicit a shift of patients' attention toward the rightmost box. D'Erme et al. (1992) contrasted the traditional RT paradigm in which targets appeared in boxes with a condition in which targets appeared in a blank screen, not surrounded by boxes. The presence of the boxes considerably increased the left/right RT difference for neglect patients, as if the right-sided box acted as an invalid cue for left targets (the boxes were indeed more powerful than actual right-sided cues to induce an extinction-like RT pattern, Fig. 11).

Because the boxes were not informative about the future location of the targets, the type of orienting elicited by the boxes could best be characterized as reflexive, or exogenous, as opposed to the voluntary, or endogenous orienting elicited by central cues or

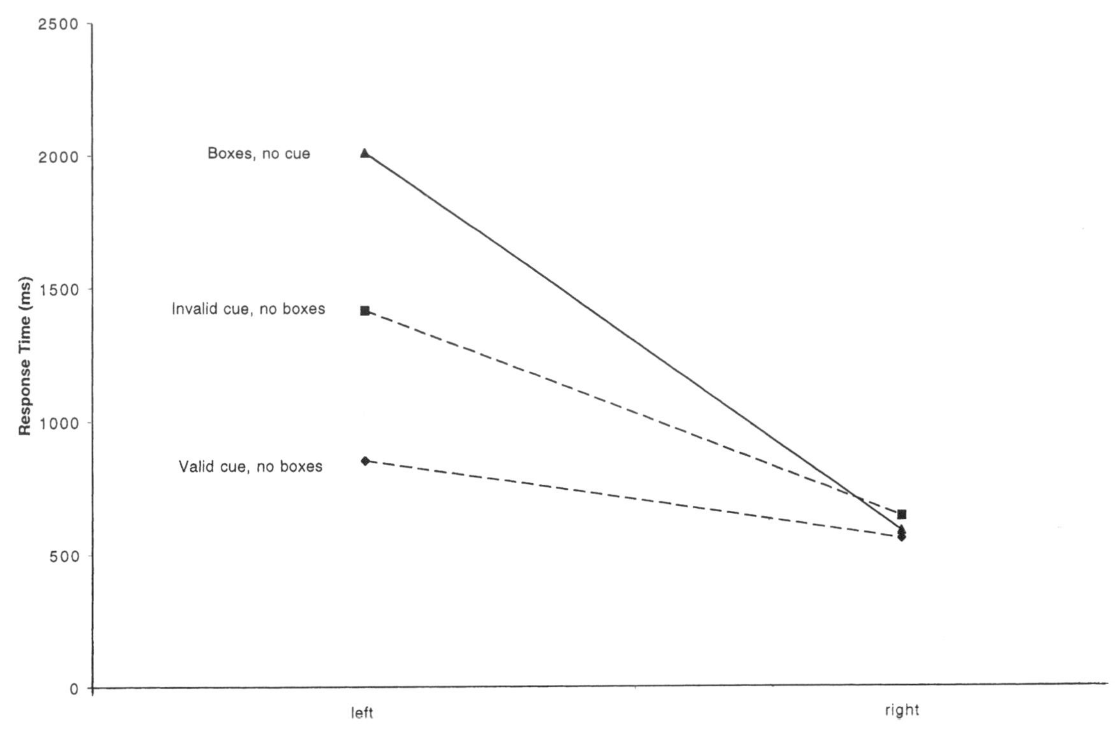

Fig. 11. Left neglect patients' cued response times to left and right targets, framed or not by placeholder boxes (based on data in D'Erme et al., 1992).

by peripheral informative cues[5] (Müller and Rabbitt, 1989). Thus, D'Erme et al. (1992) proposed that the attentional imbalance in neglect was primarily one of exogenous attention, in keeping with previous similar suggestions based on the apparent 'automaticity' of rightward attentional attraction in left neglect (Gainotti et al., 1991).

The early rightward orientation of attention may be observed as a residual sign of spatial bias in patients who had recovered from left neglect (Bartolomeo, 1997; Karnath, 1988; Mattingley et al., 1994b). Thus, to produce clinical neglect, either the initial rightward orienting must be present in a certain critical amount, or it must be accompanied by other component deficits. Concerning this last possibility, the disengagement problem (Morrow and Ratcliff, 1988; Posner et al., 1984), subsequent to the early ipsilesional engagement, would seem a good candidate. Patients would be initially attracted by a right-sided object, and would subsequently be unable to rapidly remobilize their attention from that location (see D'Erme et al., 1992; Gainotti et al., 1991). However, the disengagement problem has been demonstrated in patients without clinical signs of neglect (Friedrich, Egly, Rafal and Beck, 1998). It remains to be understood, therefore, under which conditions these impairments do or do not produce clinical neglect. Perhaps it is a matter of quantitative amount of deficit, as suggested by the correlation between the amount of extinction-like RT pattern and the severity of neglect (Morrow and Ratcliff, 1988). Alternatively or in addition, other deficits could add to those described in order to produce a clinically evident spatial bias. For example, preliminary results seem to suggest that a mechanism which purportedly promotes the exploration of the visual scene by inhibiting repeated orientations towards the same locations (Posner and Cohen, 1984) does not work properly in neglect. Left neglect patients seem to show facilitation, instead of nor-

[5] A distinction reminiscent of that, proposed by James (1890), between 'passive' and 'voluntary' attention, see p. 79.

mal inhibition, for repeated events occurring on the right side (Bartolomeo, Chokron and Siéroff, 1999). A persisting, unopposed attentional facilitation for right-sided items could explain why neglect patients cannot explore the remaining portions of space once their attention has been captured by a right-sided object.

Accounts of neglect based on orienting of attention seem thus consistent with several neglect phenomena, provided that these accounts are articulated as an association of a number of concurrent deficits. However, on some occasions, neglect patients do seem to orient toward neglected stimuli, yet fail all the same to produce the correct response. For example, Bisiach et al. (1994) observed neglect patients who occasionally followed with their index finger the complete contour of a drawing, but failed to notice the details on its left side. When bisecting lines, some patients with left neglect and hemianopia can look at the left part of the line, but this leftward search does not influence the final bisection decision, which remains rightward-biased (Barton et al., 1998; Ishiai, Seki, Koyama and Gono, 1996). Similarly, neglect patients may fail to produce the appropriate manual response to left-sided stimuli despite having looked at them (Làdavas, Zeloni, Zaccara and Gangemi, 1997). These puzzling patterns of behavior are reminiscent of the possibility that some patients may show an implicit (or 'covert') knowledge of otherwise neglected details (see, e.g. D'Erme, Robertson, Bartolomeo and Daniele, 1993; Marshall and Halligan, 1988; Volpe, Ledoux and Gazzaniga, 1979). Future research should compare more closely the characteristics of ineffective exploratory behavior with those of orienting behavior associated with 'normal' responses.

Object-based attentional bias

As mentioned above, spatial attention can perhaps be better conceived as orienting towards objects in space than towards 'blank' regions of space. If neglect results from an attentional bias, then, it should be possible to observe instances of neglect of the left part of objects, independent of the absolute location of these objects in space. The 'piecemeal' copy of complex drawings shown in Fig. 2 is an example of such an object-based neglect (Gainotti et al., 1972). Consistent with the possibility of an object-based, and not solely space-based, neglect, a patient was found to be impaired in reporting the left-sided details of a vertically elongated shape both when the shape was upright, but also when it was tilted by 45° toward the right, so that these details were now on the right with respect to the patient's sagittal midline (Driver and Halligan, 1991). Three other patients showed similar effects when reporting gaps on one side of triangles whose perceived principal axis was manipulated by context (Driver, Baylis, Goodrich and Rafal, 1994). Also, a left-handed patient with left-hemisphere damage and right neglect produced errors on the final part of words, irrespective of whether the words were presented in a horizontal, vertical, or mirror-reversed format (Caramazza and Hillis, 1990). However, Farah, Brunn, Wong et al. (1990) found no evidence of object-based neglect in a group of ten left neglect patients. When identifying single letters scattered over drawings of familiar objects, patients failed to report left-sided letters when the objects were upright, but they correctly reported these same letters when the objects were tilted[6]. Behrmann and Moscovitch (1994) reasoned that object-based neglect might emerge only for those objects which have an intrinsic handedness, where a vertical reference axis allows the definition of left and right with respect to the object itself (see Driver and Halligan, 1991). Consistent with this prediction, they demonstrated object-based neglect with upper-case letters presenting a left–right asymmetry (e.g. B, E), but not with symmetrical letters (A, X).

Using another paradigm to demonstrate object-based effects, Behrmann and Tipper (1999) had left neglect patients respond to targets appearing inside one of two horizontally aligned circles of different colors. As expected, patients responded faster to right than to left targets (space-based neglect). However, this effect was reversed when the two circles were connected by a line, like a barbell (thus forming a single perceptual object), and the barbell rotated by 180° just before the target appeared. In this case, RTs for the targets now on the left side,

[6] A subsequent reanalysis of Farah et al.'s data examined individual performances and indicated that three patients did omit more letters printed on the left side of the object, even when the object was rotated, thus showing evidence of object-based neglect (Hillis and Rapp, 1998).

but appearing in a previously right-sided circle, were faster than RTs for the targets appearing on the right, thus suggesting object-based neglect. In other words, the *same* neglect patients could show either space- or object-based neglect depending on the experimental conditions. The implication of these findings is that, once again, a dissociation in performance of neglect patients do not necessarily indicate different impairments, but perhaps different strategies evoked by the experimental conditions. Although not suitable to explain the Behrmann and Tipper (1999) findings, the results of a study by Buxbaum, Coslett, Montgomery and Farah (1996) provide some hint about what these different strategies might look like. These authors described a patient who showed object-based neglect with tilted shapes and asymmetrical letters only when he mentally rotated the stimuli to restore their canonical, upright position; when instructed to refrain from mental rotation, neglect was only relative to his sagittal midline.

Non-lateralized attentional impairments

Other component deficits of neglect might not necessarily be lateralized or directional problems. For example, it has been suggested that neglect results not only from a bias in selective spatial attention, but also from impairments in other, non-lateralized attentional components (see the taxonomy on p. 79), such as arousal or vigilance (Robertson, 1993). Such non-lateralized deficits may be invoked to explain the fact that neglect patients are slower than normal individuals when responding to visual targets even in the ipsilesional, non-neglected space. Indeed, this ipsilesional slowing might disappear with recovery of neglect (Bartolomeo, 1997). The normal timing of attentional events also seems to be disrupted in neglect for centrally presented visual stimuli. When normal individuals have to identify two visual events appearing one shortly after another in the same spatial location, the second event goes undetected if presented in a time window of 100–450 ms after the first event ('attentional blink': Raymond, Shapiro and Arnell, 1992). Husain, Shapiro, Martin and Kennard (1997) had eight left neglect patients perform this dual identification task, and found that neglect patients needed about 1.5 s of interstimulus interval to detect the second target, thus showing an important slowing of the time to select visual information. Non-lateralized impairments interact with lateralized spatial bias in neglect, as demonstrated by the fact that a warning 'beep', which arouses vigilance, is able to decrease visuospatial bias in neglect patients (Robertson, Mattingley, Rorden and Driver, 1998). Phenomena of transcallosal diaschisis (Feeney and Baron, 1986; Meyer et al., 1993) might constitute the anatomo-functional basis for such non-lateralized impairments.

Space exploration

When patients with neglect search for a target in a cluttered environment, they explore asymmetrically the visual scene, favoring the ipsilesional side (Chedru, Leblanc and Lhermitte, 1973). The objective correlate of this tendency is an increased number of saccades (with increased fixation times) to the ipsilesional side. As discussed in the previous section, this could depend on the fact that patients' attention is attracted by the visual objects lying in the ipsilesional part of space. However, an alternative view might be that this asymmetry of exploratory movements reflects in fact an ipsilesional shift of the whole frame for exploratory behavior. If so, patients should explore the visual space in a symmetrical way around a new center, which would be deviated in the ipsilesional space by a given angle.

Hornak (1992) had five neglect patients search for a (non-existent) visual target in darkness. The frequency of patients' eye fixations peaked about 15° right of objective midline. Karnath and Fetter (1995) subsequently replicated this finding with five other neglect patients. These authors concluded that in neglect patients, the represented spatial frame of reference used for exploratory behavior is shifted toward the right side, due to a corresponding deviation of the egocentric frame of reference (see *Shift of the egocentric frame of reference*). However, a potential confounding factor could have influenced these results. During the calibration phase of the eye movement recording, patients were asked to detect a series of light spots presented individually in each visual field. The experimental phase began when, unknown to the patient, no spots were presented, but the patient was anyway asked to detect a spot. It is reasonable to assume that patients were biased to explore those regions of space where they had most easily detected a spot during the calibration phase. For left neglect patients, the most likely localization of these regions was in the right hemispace. A deficit of visual short-term memory for left-sided stimuli (D'Erme and Bartolomeo, 1997) might also have added to patients' unwillingness to explore the left hemispace, by decreasing the possibility of exploring around space locations in which the presentation of calibration spots was soon forgotten.

Karnath, Niemeier and Dichgans (1998) recorded the gaze and head positions of neglect patients exploring an array of letters to search for a non-existent target. In these conditions, the maximal exploration time occurred around 30° to the right of the objective midline (see Karnath et al., 1998, Fig. 2). That is, the mere presence of visual stimuli led to a twice stronger shift of the center of visual exploration with respect to the condition in darkness, where it shifted by about 15° (see Hornak, 1992; Karnath and Fetter, 1995), as if patients' attention were attracted by right-sided letters. Moreover, if, as the authors propose, the distribution of gaze and head exploration time was just shifted rightward in neglect patients compared to controls, one could expect that the neglect patients behave at their center of exploration as controls do at their mid-sagittal plane. In fact, it appears that whereas controls showed a flat distribution of gaze positions up to 130° left and right of the body's sagittal middle, without spending more time to explore the midsagittal plane, neglect patients exhibited a narrow peak of their exploring time at their so-called "centre of exploration" that is at a position around 30° in the right hemispace (see Karnath et al., 1998, Fig. 2). Also, neglect patients seemed to spend about the same time around their actual sagittal midline than controls did.

Therefore, instead of exhibiting a shift of their center of exploration, neglect patients in the study by Karnath et al. (1998) showed a peak of exploration in the right hemispace. By contrast, controls were neither particularly biased towards a specific location, nor around their midsagittal plane, where they actually spent less time than in the more lateral parts of the display.

Thus, rather than confirming a general deviation of the exploratory behavior as the authors propose, the results of Karnath et al. (1998) strongly suggest that right-sided stimuli exerted a 'magnetic attraction' on neglect patients' attention (see *A rightward attentional bias in left neglect*).

Directional arm movements

The last possible level of impairment in the action–perception cycle is the programming of arm movements in or towards the neglected hemispace. This pre-motor deficit would express itself as a reluctance or a slowing in performing movements towards left-sided targets. It is important to distinguish directional motor disorders of limbs, which involve left-directed movements independent of which arm (left or right) perform the movement, from motor neglect (Laplane and Degos, 1983), the unwillingness of moving the contralesional limbs in the absence of primary motor deficit.

Drawing on previous work on monkeys with lesions in the frontal lobe or in the brainstem reticular formation (Watson, Miller and Heilman, 1978), Heilman and Valenstein (1979) proposed that left neglect patients have a deficit in programming movements in the right hemispace (hemispatial hypokinesia). Such a 'pre-motor' deficit was proposed because rightward error in line bisection was not ameliorated by forcing patients to explore the leftmost extremity of the line. As an alternative explanation, however, Heilman and Valenstein (1979) argued that patients could have 'forgotten' the left part of the line when placing the bisection mark, because of a lateralized deficit of short-term visual memory (see also D'Erme and Bartolomeo, 1997). In subsequent work, Heilman, Bowers, Coslett et al. (1985) asked six left neglect patients to move a handle as quickly as possible along a fixed horizontal pathway in the frontal plane, either rightward or leftward. Patients were slower to initiate hand movements towards the left side of space than rightward-directed movements. Once the movement was initiated, its speed did not vary, regardless of the direction. Heilman et al. termed the described impairment 'directional hypokinesia'. The possibly related concept of directional hypometria, i.e. insufficient amplitude of contralesionally directed movements, was originally introduced to define hypometric leftward saccades in a patient with right frontal lesion (Butter, Rapcsak, Watson and Heilman, 1988), and subsequently used to describe the performance of a patient showing rightward line bisection errors in the absence of other signs of left neglect (Marshall and Halligan, 1995). Mesulam (1981) proposed that the motor aspect of neglect reflects involvement of the frontal component of an attentional network including the posterior parietal and cingulate cortices and the brainstem reticular formation.

Bisiach, Berti and Vallar (1985a) recorded the accuracy of 16 left neglect patients when pressing left- or right-sided buttons in response to lateralized visual stimuli. Crossed and uncrossed conditions were performed, in which the side of stimulation and the side of motor response were respectively the opposite or the same. Most errors concerned left-sided responses, irrespective of the side of stimulation. Bisiach et al. concluded that an "output neglect" was present in their patients. However, in the right stimulus/left response condition, crucial for demonstrating the output component, the ipsilesional stimulation could have captured patients' attention (see *A rightward attentional bias in left neglect*, above), thus decreasing accuracy on contralesional responses.

Other attempts to isolate the motor aspects of neglect include a line bisection test, in which a pointer could be moved by a pulley in the direction opposite to the hand movement (Bisiach, Geminiani, Berti and Rusconi, 1990), and a line cancellation test where left and right sides could be reversed using a mirror (Bisiach, Tegnér, Làdavas et al., 1995; Tegnér and Levander, 1991), an epidiascope (Nico, 1996) or a TV monitor (Coslett et al., 1990; Na, Adair, Williamson et al., 1998). These studies demonstrated instances of 'motor' and 'perceptual' forms of neglect. While perceptual factors prevailed in most neglect patients, motor factors seemed more pronounced in patients with lesions involving the frontal lobes, which appeared consistent with evidence coming from case reports (Bottini, Sterzi and Vallar, 1992; Coslett et al., 1990; Daffner, Ahern, Weintraub and Mesulam, 1990; Liu, Bolton, Price and Weintraub, 1992). However, Na et al. (1998) found that the patterns of performance on line bisection and line cancellation were not always coherent; three out of their 10 patients showed a 'perceptual' pattern on cancellation and a 'motor' pattern on line bisection. This finding casts doubt on the capacity of paradigms which contrast a perceptually congruent with a perceptually incongruent condition to reliably distinguish between 'motor' and 'perceptual' forms of neglect. As Na et al. (1998) note, these paradigms frequently disclose a decrease of accuracy in the incongruent condition with respect to the congruent condition. This seems to underline the particularly demanding situation faced by patients asked to perform a motor task with visual feedback being artificially reversed with respect to the proprioceptive feedback. These characteristics could render the task particularly difficult for patients with frontal lobe damage, thus explaining their impaired performance in the non-congruent condition (Mattingley and Driver, 1997).

More 'ecological' paradigms devised to study directional motor disorders have sometimes produced negative results. Mijovic' (1991) asked 40 RBD patients to find a target among distractors by moving the stimulus display board under a panel until the target appeared in a window (e.g. to bring a right-sided target into view, the board was to be moved towards the left). Patients were fast and accurate in this task, thus not showing any evidence of directional hypokinesia. Ishiai and colleagues (Ishiai, Sugushita, Watabiki et al., 1994a; Ishiai, Watabiki, Lee et al., 1994b) asked neglect patients to extend a line leftwards to double its original length. The presence of a directional motor disorder should have shortened the left part of the line, but this was neither observed in patients with parietal lesions, nor in patients with frontal lesions. Patients as a group performed in the range of controls, with occasional patients showing a tendency to overextend lines. Chokron, Bernard and Imbert (1997) presented two neglect patients with either the left half or the right half of a line on a computer screen. The line could be extended by pressing a key, and patients were asked to complete the half-line to obtain a whole line with two equal halves (there was always a mark indicating where the midpoint should be). Thus, no directional motor component was present in this task. Both patients showed a significant underconstruction of the right half with respect to the left one and a significant overconstruction of the left half from the right one. The final midpoint was deviated to the right, thus mimicking the usual performance of neglect patients in line bisection. It might then be that the overall accuracy of leftward line extension found by Ishiai et al. (1994a,b) resulted from a trade-off between directional hypokinesia, leading to reduced leftward extension, and perceptual bias, determining a tendency to overconstruct the left half of the line. Bisiach, Ricci and Neppi Mòdona (1998b) examined 91 left neglect patients and 43 RBD patients without neglect on a line extension task similar to that of Ishiai et al. (1994a), but with an additional condition consisting in the rightward extension of the line. The principal findings of this large-scale study were as follows. First, 27 neglect patients out of 91 showed a tendency to leftward overextension, but 14 other neglect patients showed an opposite rightward overextension. Second, the tendency to a relative leftward overextension was greater in RBD patients without neglect than in those with neglect. Third, the severity of neglect was higher in patients showing a relative right overextension than in those showing a relative left overextension.

In a similar vein, Perri, Bartolomeo and Gainotti (2000) compared line bisection with paper-and-pencil extension either toward the left or toward the right side. Perri and her coworkers reasoned that a predominant role of motor factors in neglect should determine a reduced leftward extension with normal rightward extension, whereas a predominant left perceptual underestimation should produce the opposite pattern, namely normal (or excessive) leftward extension with reduced rightward extension. They studied 25 RBD patients (of whom 16 had left neglect) and 11 controls. Neglect patients deviated rightward on line bisection, but they performed no differently from controls or patients without neglect when extending lines in either direction. Inspection of individual performances revealed that two neglect patients performed as predicted by the hypothesis of a directional motor disorder (reduced leftward with normal rightward extension). One patient without signs of neglect presented the opposite pattern of performance (normal leftward with reduced rightward extension), as if left perceptual underestimation were at work. Other patients performed abnormally in an unpredictable manner, more often in the sense of an overextension. One tentative explanation of these contrasting pattern of results obtained with line extension tasks is that line extension evokes different attentional mechanisms than the perceptual evaluation of a visual scene or of a to-be-bisected line. As Ishiai et al. (1994a,b) note, neglect patients rarely look at the left end of a line when bisecting it; on the other hand, when extending a line patients' attention may follow the leftward movement of the pencil tip. Thus, line extension could be a spatial task which forces neglect patients to continuously monitor their spatially oriented activities, thereby reducing or eliminating signs of neglect.

In the *landmark test* (Harvey, Milner and Roberts, 1995), subjects have to point to either of the ends of a mid-transected line which they judge closer to the transection, under the (perhaps unwarranted) assumption that leftward hypokinesia would force patients to point predominantly to the right extremity, independent of their perceptual judgement. Of eight patients tested by Harvey et al. (1995), seven pointed consistently leftward, thus showing perceptual forms of neglect. Only one patient pointed predominantly rightward, a pattern suggestive of directional motor deficit. Bisiach, Ricci, Lualdi and Colombo (1998a) tested 121 neglect patients on a similar task. Patients had either to manually point to the shorter segment of a black pre-bisected line, or to name the color of the shorter segment of lines composed of two segments, one black and the other red. Instances were found of 'perceptual bias' (i.e. patients pointing to or defining the left segment as shorter) and of 'response bias' (the opposite pattern of performance). Both forms of bias correlated with each other across the two task conditions (pointing vs. verbal responses). However, perceptual bias was mainly associated with anterior brain lesions, whereas response bias was more frequently associated with subcortical damage, contrary to the prevalent theoretical framework. In some cases, the authors found the two type of bias to be present in the same patients.

Mattingley, Bradshaw and Phillips (1992) requested brain-damaged patients to press buttons which were horizontally arranged and illuminated in sequence from left to right or in the opposite direction. RBD neglect patients were slower when executing leftward movements than when moving rightward. In particular, patients with retro-rolandic lesions were slowed when initiating movements toward a button illuminated on the left side, whereas patients with anterior or subcortical lesions showed a decreased speed of leftward movements. Nevertheless, in Mattingley et al.'s paradigm the slowing of the initiation time exhibited by neglect patients with posterior lesions is not unambiguously interpretable in terms of directional hypokinesia, since patients had to detect the occurrence (lighting) of a left-sided stimulus before moving to reach it. The confounding effect of this perceptual–attentional component might thus have added to the motor component in slowing down patients' performance. In a subsequent study, Mattingley, Husain, Rorden et al. (1998b) tried to clarify this potential confound. They asked six left neglect patients (three with lesions centered on the inferior parietal lobe, three with inferior frontal lobe lesions) to reach for lights appearing right or left of fixation with their hand starting at the body midline (i.e. between the targets) or left or right of both targets. Results showed that all patients responded slower to left than to right targets. Parietal, but not frontal, patients showed an effect of the hand start position; starting from the extreme left position, so that left targets now required a rightward movement, reduced the disadvantage for left targets. Somewhat surprisingly, initiation of these rightward movements to attain left targets was ~600 ms faster than responses to the same targets with the hand already positioned below them, without the need of any reaching movements (compare Figs. 3 and 4 in Mattingley et al., 1998b). This finding led the authors to conclude that the advantage for rightward reaching movements to left targets was not due to a cueing effect of visual or proprioceptive inputs from the hand situated in the left hemispace. When the hand started from the extreme right, left targets were again responded to more slowly than right targets, thus suggesting that the impairment did not concern leftward movements per se, but leftward movements directed to left-sided targets. In other words, a perceptual component seemed again to play a role in directional motor disorders. More specifically, the position of the effector (in this case the hand) could contribute to the patients' perception of right (non-neglected) and left (neglected) sides, perhaps by affecting the coding of 'right' vs. 'left'. If so, one could indeed expect a decrease of the disadvantage for left targets when the hand is positioned at their left, thus rendering the targets more 'righty'. Another study by Mattingley, Corben, Bradshaw et al. (1998a) further strengthens the conclusion that at least some instances of directional motor disorder in neglect do not stem from a purely output mechanism. Using a procedure similar to that of Mattingley et al. (1992), they found that leftward movements were slowed in neglect patients only in the following conditions: (1) when the movement path could not be predicted in advance; and (2) in the presence of a concurrent right distractor.

Bartolomeo et al. (1998b) tried to disentangle the perceptual from the directional motor aspects of unilateral neglect by contrasting patients' performance on two RT tasks. The 'perceptual' task consisted of lateralized visual stimuli and central motor responses, whereas the 'motor' task consisted of the same visual stimuli presented on the vertical midline (like a traffic light) and hand responses to be produced in either hemispace. Thirty-four RBD patients (of whom 14 showed signs of left neglect) and 15 controls participated in the study. Results showed that patients showed a clear spatial bias (in the sense of a right over left target advantage) when responding centrally to lateralized targets. However, neither the neglect nor the non-neglect group of patients showed any evidence of directional slowing of performance with lateralized responses. Inspection of individual performance revealed that only two RBD patients (showing no signs of severe neglect) were consistently slowed in producing leftward motor responses. Thus, the results of this study suggest again that, when lateralized visual feedback is minimized, a slowing of leftward arm movements does not play a crucial role in left unilateral neglect.

Conclusions and perspectives on rehabilitation

Although we are still far from understanding the precise mechanisms leading to neglect, the evidence reviewed thus far seems to suggest that a large majority of neglect patients suffer from an association of lateralized and non-lateralized attentional problems. These could include an early orientation of attention towards objects (or object attributes) lying in the ipsilesional side of space, a deficit in reorienting attention toward the contralesional side, and a non-lateralized deficit in rapidly dealing with sensory events. Impairments at other levels of space processing might add to these problems in individual patients. Follow-up studies of recovery from neglect support the idea of a multi-component syndrome, in that they show the apparent recovery of some component deficits and the persistence of others (Bartolomeo, 1997; Mattingley et al., 1994b).

Insight on the nature of neglect is also offered by the study of the effects of the various rehabilitation techniques that have been devised for its treatment. Interestingly, very different approaches appear to decrease neglect, regardless of the theoretical background they stem from. The diverse sort of maneuvers that have been shown to improve neglect include: training visual (Pizzamiglio, Antonucci, Judica et al., 1992; Seron, Deloche and Coyette, 1989; Weinberg, Diller, Gordon et al., 1977; Wiart, Bon Saint Come, Debelleix et al., 1997) or tactile (Weinberg, Diller, Gordon et al., 1979) exploration, actively or passively moving the contralesional arm (Robertson and Hawkins, 1999), imagining mental scenes (Smania, Bazoli, Piva and Guidetti, 1997), wearing optical prisms shifting the visual scene toward the right (Rossetti, Rode, Pisella et al., 1998), receiving appropriate vestibular, optokinetic, somatosensory or proprioceptive stimulation (see *Shift of the egocentric frame of reference* above).

From a clinical point of view, the notion of the success of such disparate techniques in reducing neglect seems reassuring and suggests that an effective strategy for rehabilitating neglect might be to vary the techniques used. From a theoretical standpoint, this multiplicity of apparently successful maneuvers suggests two conclusions. First, this evidence may be considered as another, if indirect, proof that neglect is a multi-component syndrome. Second, one could hypothesize that far from acting at different levels, all of these techniques are in fact attentional in nature. For example, visual exploration training implies an explicit orientation of attention (recall that directing the eyes to a specific location usually triggers an attentional orientation in the same direction). Also mental imagery training might reduce left neglect by training patients to mentally orient their attention to the neglected part of space. Even in the domain of vestibular and proprioceptive stimulations, one could surmise that what is at work is not a restoration of the position of the egocentric reference (see *Shift of the egocentric frame of reference*), but an orientation of attention to the left neglected hemispace by the way of the induced optokinetic nystagmus or of the stimulation itself. Indeed, not only a shift in gaze direction, but also head or trunk turning could be involved in orienting of attention (Gainotti, 1993). These arguments need of course empirical confirmation. Nevertheless, elucidating at which level these different rehabilitation techniques operate, as well as exploring the possibilities of transiently created neglect signs by applying experimental stimulations to normal individuals, could offer important insight into the mechanisms leading to neglect behavior.

References

Albert ML: A simple test of visual neglect. Neurology: 23; 658–664, 1973.

Allport DA: Visual attention. In Posner MI (Ed), Foundations of Cognitive Science. Cambridge, MA: MIT Press, pp. 631–68, 1989.

Anderson B: Spared awareness for the left side of internal visual images in patients with left-sided extrapersonal neglect. Neurology: 43; 213–216, 1993.

Arbib MA: Perceptual structures and distributed motor control. In Brooks VB (Ed), Handbook of Physiology: The Nervous System II. Motor Control. Bethesda, MD: American Physiological Society, pp. 1449–1480, 1981.

Bartolomeo P: The novelty effect in recovered hemineglect. Cortex: 33; 323–332, 1997.

Bartolomeo P, Bachoud-Lévi AC, de Gelder B, Denes G, Dalla Barba G, Brugières P, Degos JD: Multiple-domain dissociation between impaired visual perception and preserved mental imagery in a patient with bilateral extrastriate lesions. Neuropsychologia: 36; 239–249, 1998a.

Bartolomeo P, Chokron S: Egocentric frame of reference: its role in spatial bias after right hemisphere lesions. Neuropsychologia: 37; 881–894, 1999a.

Bartolomeo P, Chokron S: Left unilateral neglect or right hyperattention? Neurology: 53; 2023–2027, 1999b.

Bartolomeo P, Chokron S, Siéroff E: Facilitation instead of inhibition for repeated right-sided events in left neglect. NeuroReport: 10; 3353–3357, 1999.

Bartolomeo P, D'Erme P, Gainotti G: The relationship between visuospatial and representational neglect. Neurology: 44; 1710–1714, 1994.

Bartolomeo P, D'Erme P, Perri R, Gainotti G: Perception and action in hemispatial neglect. Neuropsychologia: 36; 227–237, 1998b.

Barton JJ, Behrmann M, Black S: Ocular search during line bisection. The effects of hemi-neglect and hemianopia. Brain: 121; 1117–1131, 1998.

Barton JJ, Black SE: Line bisection in hemianopia. Journal of Neurology, Neurosurgery and Psychiatry: 64; 660–662, 1998.

Battersby WS, Bender MB, Pollack M, Kahn RL: Unilateral 'spatial agnosia' ('inattention') in patients with cerebral lesions. Brain: 79; 68–93, 1956.

Behrmann M, Moscovitch M: Object-centered neglect in patients with unilateral neglect: effects of left-right coordinates of objects. Journal of Cognitive Neuroscience: 6; 1–16, 1994.

Behrmann M, Tipper SP: Attention accesses multiple reference frames: evidence from visual neglect. Journal of Experimental Psychology: Human Perception and Performance: 25; 83–101, 1999.

Behrmann M, Winocur G, Moscovitch M: Dissociation between mental imagery and object recognition in a brain-damaged patient. Nature: 359; 636–637, 1992.

Berlucchi G: Two hemispheres but one brain. Behavioral and Brain Sciences: 6; 171–172, 1983.

Beschin N, Cocchini G, Della Sala S, Logie R: What the eyes perceive, the brain ignores: a case of pure unilateral representational neglect. Cortex: 33; 3–26, 1997.

Bisiach E: Mental representation in unilateral neglect and related disorders. The Quarterly Journal of Experimental Psychology: 46A; 435–461, 1993.

Bisiach E, Berti A, Vallar G: Analogical and logical disorders underlying unilateral neglect of space. In Posner MI, Marin OS (Eds), Attention and Performance XI. Hillsdale, NJ: Lawrence Erlbaum Associates, pp. 239–249, 1985a.

Bisiach E, Capitani E, Luzzatti C, Perani D: Brain and conscious representation of outside reality. Neuropsychologia: 19; 543–551, 1981.

Bisiach E, Capitani E, Porta E: Two basic properties of space representation in the brain: evidence from unilateral neglect. Journal of Neurology, Neurosurgery and Psychiatry: 48; 141–144, 1985b.

Bisiach E, Cornacchia L, Sterzi R, Vallar G: Disorders of perceived auditory lateralization after lesions of the right hemisphere. Brain: 107; 37–52, 1984.

Bisiach E, Geminiani G, Berti A, Rusconi ML: Perceptual and premotor factors of unilateral neglect. Neurology: 40; 1278–1281, 1990.

Bisiach E, Luzzatti C: Unilateral neglect of representational space. Cortex: 14; 129–133, 1978.

Bisiach E, Luzzatti C, Perani D: Unilateral neglect, representational schema and consciousness. Brain: 102; 609–618, 1979.

Bisiach E, Pizzamiglio L, Nico D, Antonucci G: Beyond unilateral neglect. Brain: 119; 851–857, 1996.

Bisiach E, Ricci R, Lualdi M, Colombo MR: Perceptual and response bias in unilateral neglect: two modified versions of the Milner landmark task. Brain and Cognition: 37; 369–386, 1998a.

Bisiach E, Ricci R, Neppi Mòdona M: Visual awareness and anisometry of space representation in unilateral neglect: a panoramic investigation by means of a line extension task. Consciousness and Cognition: 7; 327–355, 1998b.

Bisiach E, Rusconi ML: Break-down of perceptual awareness in unilateral neglect. Cortex: 26; 643–649, 1990.

Bisiach E, Rusconi ML, Peretti VA, Vallar G: Challenging current accounts of unilateral neglect. Neuropsychologia: 32; 1431–1434, 1994.

Bisiach E, Tegnér R, Làdavas E, Rusconi ML, Mijović D, Hjaltason H: Dissociation of ophthalmokinetic and melokinetic attention in unilateral neglect. Cerebral Cortex: 5; 439–447, 1995.

Bottini G, Sterzi R, Vallar G: Directional hypokinesia in spatial hemineglect: a case study. Journal of Neurology, Neurosurgery and Psychiatry: 55; 562–565, 1992.

Brain RW: Visual disorientation with special reference to lesion of the right brain hemisphere. Brain: 64; 244–272, 1941.

Butter CM, Rapcsak S, Watson RT, Heilman KM: Changes in sensory inattention, directional motor neglect and 'release' of the fixation reflex following a unilateral frontal lesion: A case report. Neuropsychologia: 26; 533–545, 1988.

Buxbaum LJ, Coslett HB, Montgomery MW, Farah MJ: Mental rotation may underlie apparent object-based neglect. Neuropsychologia: 34; 113–126, 1996.

Caramazza A, Hillis AE: Spatial representation of words in the brain implied by studies of a unilateral neglect patient. Nature: 346; 267–269, 1990.

Chatterjee A: Motor minds and mental models in neglect [Review]. Brain and Cognition: 37; 339–349, 1998.

Chedru F: Space representation in unilateral spatial neglect. Journal of Neurology, Neurosurgery and Psychiatry: 39; 1057–1061, 1976.

Chedru F, Leblanc M, Lhermitte F: Visual searching in normal and brain-damaged subjects (contribution to the study of unilateral inattention). Cortex: 9; 94–111, 1973.

Chokron S, Bartolomeo P: Patterns of dissociation between left hemineglect and deviation of the egocentric reference. Neuropsychologia: 35; 1503–1508, 1997.

Chokron S, Bartolomeo P: Position of the egocentric reference and directional arm movements in right brain-damaged patients. Brain and Cognition: 37; 405–418, 1998.

Chokron S, Bartolomeo P: Pointing straight-ahead: reversed patterns of performance in right brain-damaged patients with or without extensive parietal lesion. Brain and Cognition: 40; 79–84, 1999.

Chokron S, Bartolomeo P, Perenin MT, Helft G, Imbert M: Scanning direction and line bisection: a study of normal subjects and unilateral neglect patients with opposite reading habits. Cognitive Brain Research: 7; 173–178, 1998.

Chokron S, Bernard JM, Imbert M: Length representation in normal and neglect subjects with opposite reading habits studied through a line extension task. Cortex: 33; 47–64, 1997.

Chokron S, De Agostini M: Reading habits and line bisection: a developmental approach. Cognitive Brain Research: 3; 51–58, 1995.

Chokron S, Imbert M: Influence of reading habits on line bisection. Cognitive Brain Research: 1; 219–222, 1993.

Chokron S, Imbert M: Variations of the egocentric reference among normal subjects and a patient with unilateral neglect. Neuropsychologia: 33; 703–711, 1995.

Cohn R: Eyeball movements in homonymous hemianopia following simultaneous bitemporal object presentation. Neurology: 22; 12–14, 1972.

Compton PE, Grossenbacher P, Posner MI, Tucker DM: A cognitive–anatomical approach to attention in lexical access. Journal of Cognitive Neuroscience: 3; 304–312, 1991.

Corbetta M, Miezin FM, Shulman GL, Petersen SE: A PET study of visuospatial attention. The Journal of Neuroscience: 13; 1202–1226, 1993.

Coslett HB: Dissociation of attentional mechanisms in vision: evidence from neglect (abstract). Journal of Clinical and Experimental Neuropsychology: 11; 80, 1989.

Coslett HB: Neglect in vision and visual imagery: a double dissociation. Brain: 120; 1163–1171, 1997.

Coslett HB, Bowers D, Fitzpatrick E, Haws B, Heilman KM: Directional hypokinesia and hemispatial inattention in neglect. Brain: 113; 475–486, 1990.

Costello AD, Warrington EK: The dissociation of visuospatial neglect and neglect dyslexia. Journal of Neurology, Neurosurgery and Psychiatry: 50; 1110–1116, 1987.

Cowey A, Small M, Ellis S: Left visuo-spatial neglect can be worse in far than in near space. Neuropsychologia: 32; 1059–1066, 1994.

Critchley M: The Parietal Lobes. New York: Hafner, 1953.

D'Erme P, Bartolomeo P: A unilateral defect of short-term visual memory in left hemineglect. European Journal of Neurology: 4; 382–386, 1997.

D'Erme P, Bartolomeo P, Gainotti G: Difference in recovering rate between visuospatial and representational neglect (abstract). International Neuropsychological Society, 17th Annual European Conference, 49, 1994.

D'Erme P, Robertson I, Bartolomeo P, Daniele A: Unilateral neglect: The fate of the extinguished visual stimuli. Behavioural Neurology: 6; 143–150, 1993.

D'Erme P, Robertson I, Bartolomeo P, Daniele A, Gainotti G: Early rightwards orienting of attention on simple reaction time performance in patients with left-sided neglect. Neuropsychologia: 30; 989–1000, 1992.

Daffner KR, Ahern GL, Weintraub S, Mesulam M-M: Dissociated neglect behaviour following sequential strokes in the right hemisphere. Annals of Neurology: 28; 97–101, 1990.

Damasio A: Time-locked multiregional retroactivation: a system-level proposal for the neuronal substrates of recall and recognition. Cognition: 33; 25–62, 1989.

De Renzi E, Colombo A, Faglioni P, Gibertoni M: Conjugate gaze paresis in stroke patients with unilateral damage: an unexpected instance of hemispheric asymmetry. Archives of Neurology: 39; 482–486, 1982.

De Renzi E, Gentilini M, Barbieri C: Auditory neglect. Journal of Neurology, Neurosurgery and Psychiatry: 52; 613–617, 1989a.

De Renzi E, Gentilini M, Faglioni P, Barbieri C: Attentional shifts toward the rightmost stimuli in patients with left visual neglect. Cortex: 25; 231–237, 1989b.

Denes G, Semenze C, Stoppa E, Lis A: Unilateral spatial neglect and recovery from hemiplegia: a follow-up study. Brain: 105; 543–552, 1982.

Denny-Brown D, Meyer JS, Horenstein S: The significance of perceptual rivalry resulting from parietal lesion. Brain: 75; 433–471, 1952.

Di Pellegrino G, De Renzi E: An experimental investigation on the nature of extinction. Neuropsychologia: 33; 153–170, 1995.

Doricchi F, Angelelli P: Misrepresentation of horizontal space in left unilateral neglect: role of hemianopia. Neurology: 52; 1845–1852, 1999.

Driver J, Baylis GC, Goodrich SJ, Rafal RD: Axis-based neglect of visual shapes. Neuropsychologia: 32; 1353–1365, 1994.

Driver J, Baylis GC, Rafal RD: Preserved figure-ground segregation and symmetry perception in visual neglect. Nature: 360; 73–75, 1992.

Driver J, Halligan PW: Can visual neglect operate in object-centered co-ordinates? An affirmative single-case study. Cognitive Neuropsychology: 8; 475–496, 1991.

Duncan J: Selective attention and the organization of visual information. Journal of Experimental Psychology: General: 113; 501–517, 1984.

Egeth H, Yantis S: Visual attention: control, representation, and time course. Annual Review in Psychology: 48; 269–297, 1997.

Farah MJ, Brunn JL, Wong AB, Wallace MA, Carpenter PA: Frames of reference for allocating attention to space: evidence from the neglect syndrome. Neuropsychologia: 28; 335–347, 1990.

Farnè A, Ponti F, Làdavas E: In search for biased egocentric reference frames in neglect. Neuropsychologia: 36; 611–623, 1998.

Feeney DM, Baron JC: Diaschisis. Stroke: 17; 817–30, 1986.

Fiorelli M, Blin J, Bakchine S, Laplane D, Baron JC: PET studies of cortical diaschisis in patients with motor hemineglect. Journal of the Neurological Sciences: 104; 135–142, 1991.

Fredrickson JM, Scheid P, Figge U, Kornhuber HH: Vestibular nerve projection to the cerebral cortex of the rhesus monkey. Experimental Brain Research: 2; 318–317, 1966.

Friedrich FJ, Egly R, Rafal RD, Beck D: Spatial attention deficits in humans: a comparison of superior parietal and temporal-parietal junction lesions. Neuropsychology: 12; 193–207, 1998.

Fuchs W: Untersuchung über das sehen der hemianopiker und hemiamblyopiker. Zeitschrift für Psychologie und Physiologie der Sinnersorgane, 84, 67–169, 1920.

Fujii T, Fukatsu R, Kimura I, Saso S, Kogure K: Unilateral spatial neglect in visual and tactile modalities. Cortex: 27; 339–343, 1991.

Gainotti G: Les manifestations de négligence et d'inattention pour l'hémi-espace. Cortex: 4; 64–91, 1968.

Gainotti G: The role of spontaneous eye movements in orienting attention and in unilateral neglect. In Robertson IH, Marshall JC (Eds), Unilateral Neglect: Clinical and Experimental Studies. Hove: Lawrence Erlbaum Associates, pp. 107–122, 1993.

Gainotti G: The dilemma of unilateral spatial neglect. Neuropsychological Rehabilitation: 4; 127–132, 1994.

Gainotti G, D'Erme P, Bartolomeo P: Early orientation of attention toward the half space ipsilateral to the lesion in patients with unilateral brain damage. Journal of Neurology, Neurosurgery and Psychiatry: 54; 1082–1089, 1991.

Gainotti G, Messerli P, Tissot R: Qualitative analysis of unilateral spatial neglect in relation to the laterality of cerebral lesions. Journal of Neurology, Neurosurgery and Psychiatry: 35; 545–550, 1972.

Gainotti G, Tiacci C: The relationships between disorders of visual perception and unilateral spatial neglect. Neuropsychologia: 9; 451–458, 1971.

Gauthier L, Dehaut F, Joanette Y: The bells test: a quantitative and qualitative test for visual neglect. International Journal of Clinical Neuropsychology: 11; 49–53, 1989.

Gentilini M, Barbieri C, De Renzi E, Faglioni P: Space exploration with and without the aid of vision in hemisphere-damaged patients. Cortex: 25; 643–651, 1989.

Guariglia C, Padovani A, Pantano P, Pizzamiglio L: Unilateral neglect restricted to visual imagery. Nature: 364; 235–237, 1993.

Halligan P, Marshall JC: Left visuospatial neglect: a meaningless entity? Cortex: 28; 525–535, 1992.

Halligan P, Marshall JC: Spatial neglect: position papers on theory and practice. Neuropsychological Rehabilitation: 4; 99–240, 1994.

Halligan PW, Cockburn J, Wilson B: The behavioural assessment of visual neglect. Neuropsychological Rehabilitation: 1; 5–32, 1991.

Halligan PW, Marshall JC: Left neglect for near but not far space in man [see comments]. Nature: 350; 498–500, 1991a.

Halligan PW, Marshall JC: Spatial compression in visual neglect: a case study. Cortex: 27; 623–629, 1991b.

Halligan PW, Marshall JC: Visuospatial neglect: the ultimate deconstruction? Brain and Cognition: 37; 419–438, 1998.

Halligan PW, Marshall JC, Wade DT: Left on the right: allochiria in a case of left visuo-spatial neglect. Journal of Neurology, Neurosurgery and Psychiatry: 55; 717–719, 1992.

Halsband U, Gruhn S, Ettlinger G: Unilateral spatial neglect and defective performance in one half of space. International Journal of Neurosciences: 28; 173–195, 1985.

Harvey M, Milner AD, Roberts RC: An investigation of hemispatial neglect using the landmark task. Brain and Cognition: 27; 59–78, 1995.

Hasselbach M, Butter CM: Ipsilesional displacement of egocentric midline in neglect patients with, but not in those without, extensive right parietal damage. In Thier P, Karnath HO (Eds), Parietal Lobe Contributions to Orientation in 3D-Space. Heidelberg: Springer, pp. 579–595, 1997.

Heilman KM, Bowers D, Coslett HB, Whelan H, Watson RT: Directional hypokinesia: prolonged reaction times for leftward movements in patients with right hemisphere lesions and neglect. Neurology: 35; 855–859, 1985.

Heilman KM, Bowers D, Watson RT: Performance on hemispatial pointing task by patients with neglect syndrome. Neurology: 33; 661–664, 1983.

Heilman KM, Valenstein E: Mechanisms underlying hemispatial neglect. Annals of Neurology: 5; 166–170, 1979.

Hillis AE, Rapp B: Unilateral spatial neglect in dissociable frames of reference: a comment on Farah, Brunn, Wong, Wallace, and Carpenter (1990). Neuropsychologia: 36; 1257–1262, 1998.

Hjaltason H, Caneman G, Tegner R: Visual and tactile rod bisection in unilateral neglect. Cortex, 583–588, 1993.

Hjaltason H, Tegnér R: Darkness improves line bisection in unilateral spatial neglect. Cortex: 28; 353–358, 1992.

Hoffman JE, Subramaniam B: The role of visual attention in saccadic eye movements. Perception and Psychophysics: 57; 787–795, 1995.

Hornak J: Ocular exploration in the dark by patients with visual neglect. Neuropsychologia: 30; 547–552, 1992.

Howes D, Boller F: Simple reaction time: evidence for focal impairment from lesions of the right hemisphere. Brain: 98; 317–332, 1975.

Humphreys GW, Riddoch MJ: Attention to within-object and between-object spatial representations: multiple sites for visual selection. Cognitive Neuropsychology: 11; 207–241, 1994.

Husain M, Shapiro K, Martin J, Kennard C: Abnormal temporal dynamics of visual attention in spatial neglect patients. Nature: 385; 154–156, 1997.

Ishiai S, Seki K, Koyama Y, Gono S: Ineffective leftward search in line bisection and mechanisms of left unilateral spatial neglect. Journal of Neurology: 243; 381–387, 1996.

Ishiai S, Sugushita M, Watabiki S, Nakayama T, Kotera M, Gono S: Improvement of left unilateral spatial neglect in a line extension task. Neurology: 44; 294–298, 1994a.

Ishiai S, Watabiki S, Lee E, Kanouchi T, Odajima N: Preserved leftward movement in left unilateral spatial neglect due to frontal lesions. Journal of Neurology, Neurosurgery and Psychiatry: 57; 1085–1090, 1994b.

James W: The Principles of Psychology. New York: Henry Holt, 1890.

Jeannerod, M (Ed): Neurophysiological and Neuropsychological Aspects of Spatial Neglect, Vol 45. Amsterdam: Elsevier Science, 1987.

Jeannerod M, Biguer B: The directional coding of reaching movements. A visuomotor conception of visuospatial neglect. In Jeannerod M (Ed), Neurophysiological and Neuropsychological Aspects of Spatial Neglect. Amsterdam: Elsevier Science, pp. 87–113, 1987.

Kaplan RF, Cohen RA, Rosengart A, Elsner AE, Hedges TR, Caplan LR: Extinction during time controlled direct retinal stimulation after recovery from right hemispheric stroke. Journal of Neurology, Neurosurgery and Psychiatry: 59; 534–536, 1995.

Karnath H-O: Deficits of attention in acute and recovered hemi-neglect. Neuropsychologia: 20; 27–45, 1988.

Karnath H-O: Neural encoding of space in egocentric coordinates? Evidence for and limits of a hypothesis derived from patients with parietal lesions and neglect. In Thier P, Karnath HO (Eds), Parietal lobe contributions to orientation in 3D space. Heidelberg: Springer, pp. 497–520, 1997.

Karnath H-O, Christ K, Hartje W: Decrease of contralateral neglect by neck muscle vibration and spatial orientation of trunk midline. Brain: 116; 383–396, 1993.

Karnath H-O, Fetter M: Ocular space exploration in the dark and its relation to subjective and objective body orientation in neglect patients with parietal lesions. Neuropsychologia: 33; 371–377, 1995.

Karnath H-O, Schenkel P, Fischer B: Trunk orientation as the determining factor of the contralateral deficit in the neglect syndrome and as the physical anchor of the internal representation of body orientation in space. Brain: 114; 1997–2014, 1991.

Karnath HO, Ferber S: Is space representation distorted in neglect? Neuropsychologia: 37; 7–15, 1999.

Karnath HO, Niemeier M, Dichgans J: Space exploration in neglect. Brain: 121; 2357–2367, 1998.
Kinsbourne M: A model for the mechanism of unilateral neglect of space. Transactions of the American Neurological Association: 95; 143–146, 1970.
Kinsbourne M: Hemi-neglect and hemisphere rivalry. In Weinstein EA, Friedland RP (Eds), Hemi-Inattention and Hemisphere Specialization. New York: Raven Press, pp. 41–49, 1977.
Kinsbourne M: Mechanisms of unilateral neglect. In Jeannerod M (Ed), Neurophysiological and Neuropsychological Aspects of Spatial Neglect. Amsterdam: Elsevier Science, pp. 69–86, 1987.
Kinsbourne M: Orientational bias model of unilateral neglect: evidence from attentional gradients within hemispace. In Robertson IH, Marshall JC (Eds), Unilateral Neglect: Clinical and Experimental Studies. Hove: Lawrence Erlbaum Associates, pp. 63–86, 1993.
Kooistra CA, Heilman KM: Hemispatial visual inattention masquerading as hemianopia. Neurology: 39; 1125–1127, 1989.
Kosslyn SM: Image and Brain: The Resolution of the Imagery Debate. Cambridge, MA: MIT Press, 1994.
Kowler E, Anderson E, Dosher B, Blaser E: The role of attention in the programming of saccades. Vision Research: 35; 1897–1916, 1995.
Làdavas E, Petronio A, Umiltà C: The deployment of visual attention in the intact field of hemineglect patients. Cortex: 26; 307–317, 1990.
Làdavas E, Zeloni G, Zaccara G, Gangemi P: Eye movements and orienting of attention in patients with visual neglect. Journal of Cognitive Neuroscience: 9; 67–74, 1997.
Laplane D, Degos JD: Motor neglect. Journal of Neurology, Neurosurgery and Psychiatry: 46; 152–158, 1983.
Leicester J, Sidman M, Stoddard LT, Mohr JP: Some determinants of visual neglect. Journal of Neurology, Neurosurgery and Psychiatry: 32; 580–587, 1969.
Liu GT, Bolton AR, Price BH, Weintraub S: Dissociated perceptual-sensory and exploratory-motor neglect. Journal of Neurology, Neurosurgery and Psychiatry: 55; 701–706, 1992.
Manoach DS, O'Connor M, Weintraub S: Absence of neglect for mental representations during the intracarotid amobarbital procedure. Archives of Neurology: 53; 333–336, 1996.
Mark VW, Kooistra CA, Heilman KM: Hemispatial neglect affected by non-neglected stimuli. Neurology: 38; 640–643, 1988.
Marshall JC, Halligan P: Within- and between-task dissociations in visuo-spatial neglect: a case study. Cortex: 31; 367–376, 1995.
Marshall JC, Halligan PW: Blindsight and insight into visuo-spatial neglect. Nature: 336; 766–767, 1988.
Marshall JC, Halligan PW: Does the midsagittal plane play any privileged role in 'left' neglect? Cognitive Neuropsychology: 6; 403–422, 1989a.
Marshall JC, Halligan PW: When right goes left: an investigation of line bisection in a case of visual neglect. Cortex: 25; 503–515, 1989b.
Marshall JC, Halligan PW: Visuo-spatial neglect: a new copying test to assess perceptual parsing. Journal of Neurology: 240; 37–40, 1993.
Mattingley JB, Bradshaw JL, Bradshaw JA: Horizontal visual motion modulates focal attention in left unilateral spatial neglect. Journal of Neurology, Neurosurgery and Psychiatry: 57; 1228–1235, 1994a.
Mattingley JB, Bradshaw JL, Bradshaw JA, Nettleton NC: Residual rightward attentional bias after apparent recovery from right hemisphere damage: implications for a multicomponent model of neglect. Journal of Neurology, Neurosurgery and Psychiatry: 57; 597–604, 1994b.
Mattingley JB, Bradshaw JL, Phillips JG: Impairments of movement initiation and execution in unilateral neglect. Brain: 115; 1849–1874, 1992.
Mattingley JB, Corben LA, Bradshaw JL, Bradshaw JA, Phillips JG, Horne MK: The effects of competition and motor reprogramming on visuomotor selection in unilateral neglect. Experimental Brain Research: 120; 243–256, 1998a.
Mattingley JB, Driver J: Distinguishing sensory and motor deficits after parietal damage: an evaluation of response selection biases in unilateral neglect. In Thier P, Karnath HO (Eds), Parietal Lobe Contributions to Orientation in 3D-Space. Heidelberg: Springer, pp. 309–337, 1997.
Mattingley JB, Husain M, Rorden C, Kennard C, Driver J: Motor role of human inferior parietal lobe revealed in unilateral neglect patients. Nature: 392; 179–182, 1998b.
McFie J, Piercy MF, Zangwill OL: Visual spatial agnosia associated with lesions of the right hemisphere. Brain: 73; 167–190, 1950.
Mesulam MM: A cortical network for directed attention and unilateral neglect. Annals of Neurology: 10; 309–325, 1981.
Mesulam MM: Attention, confusional states and neglect. In Mesulam MM (Ed), Principles of Behavioral Neurology. Philadelphia, PA: Davis, pp. 125–168, 1985.
Meyer JS, Obara K, Muramatsu K: Diaschisis. Neurological Research: 15; 362–366, 1993.
Mijovic' D: Mechanisms of visual spatial neglect: absence of directional hypokinesia in spatial exploration. Brain: 114; 1575–1593, 1991.
Milner AD, Harvey M: Distortion of size perception in visuospatial neglect. Current Biology: 5; 85–89, 1995.
Morrow LA, Ratcliff G: The disengagement of covert attention and the neglect syndrome. Psychobiology: 16; 261–269, 1988.
Müller HJ, Rabbitt PM: Reflexive and voluntary orienting of visual attention: time course of activation and resistance to interruption. Journal of Experimental Psychology: Human Perception and Performance: 15; 315–330, 1989.
Na DL, Adair JC, Williamson DJ, Schwartz RL, Haws B, Heilman KM: Dissociation of sensory-attentional from motor-intentional neglect. Journal of Neurology, Neurosurgery and Psychiatry: 64; 331–338, 1998.
Nakayama K, Mackeben M: Sustained and transient components of focal visual attention. Vision Research: 29; 1631–1647, 1989.
Nico D: Detecting directional hypokinesia: the epidiascope technique. Neuropsychologia: 34; 471–474, 1996.
Ogden JA: Contralesional neglect of constructed visual images in

right and left brain-damaged patients. Neuropsychologia: 23; 273–277, 1985.

Pantano P, Di Piero V, Fieschi C, Judica A, Guariglia C, Pizzamiglio L: Pattern of CBF in the rehabilitation of visual spatial neglect. International Journal of Neurosciences: 66; 153–161, 1992.

Parasuraman R: The attentive brain: issues and prospects. In Parasuraman R (Ed), The Attentive Brain. Cambridge, MA: MIT Press, pp. 3–15, 1998.

Perani D, Vallar G, Paulesu E, Alberoni M, Fazio F: Left and right hemisphere contribution to recovery from neglect after right hemisphere damage — an [^{18}F]FDG PET study of two cases. Neuropsychologia: 31; 115–125, 1993.

Perenin MT: Optic ataxia and unilateral neglect: clinical evidence for dissociable spatial fonctions in posterior parietal cortex. In Thier P, Karnath HO (Eds), Parietal Lobe Contributions to Orientation in 3D-Space. Heidelberg: Springer, pp. 289–308, 1997.

Perri R, Bartolomeo P, Gainotti G: Lack of impairments on leftward and rightward line extension tasks in neglect patients. International Journal of Neurosciences: 103; 101–113, 2000.

Piaget J: Les Mécanismes Perceptifs. Paris: P.U.F., 1961.

Pizzamiglio L, Antonucci G, Judica A, Montenero P, Razzano C, Zoccolotti P: Cognitive rehabilitation of the hemineglect disorder in chronic patients with unilateral right brain damage. Journal of Clinical and Experimental Neuropsychology: 14; 901–923, 1992.

Posner MI: Chronometric Explorations of Mind. New York: Oxford University Press, 1978/1986.

Posner MI: Orienting of attention. The Quarterly Journal of Experimental Psychology: 32; 3–25, 1980.

Posner MI, Cohen Y: Components of visual orienting. In Bouma H, Bouwhuis D (Eds), Attention and Performance X. London: Lawrence Erlbaum, pp. 531–556, 1984.

Posner MI, Walker JA, Friedrich FJ, Rafal RD: Effects of parietal injury on covert orienting of attention. Journal of Neuroscience: 4; 1863–1874, 1984.

Raymond JE, Shapiro KL, Arnell KM: Temporary suppression of visual processing in an RSVP task: An attentional blink? Journal of Experimental Psychology: Human Perception and Performance: 18; 849–860, 1992.

Reuter-Lorenz PA, Jha AP, Rosenquist JN: What is inhibited in inhibition of return? Journal of Experimental Psychology: Human Perception and Performance: 22; 367–378, 1996.

Reuter-Lorenz PA, Posner MI: Components of neglect from right-hemisphere damage: an analysis of line bisection. Neuropsychologia: 28; 327–333, 1990.

Robertson IH: The relationship between lateralised and non-lateralised attentional deficits in unilateral neglect. In Robertson IH, Marshall JC (Eds), Unilateral Neglect: Clinical and Experimental Studies. Hove: Lawrence Erlbaum Associates, pp. 257–275, 1993.

Robertson IH, Hawkins K: Limb activation and unilateral neglect. Neurocase: 5; 153–160, 1999.

Robertson IH, Marshall JC (Eds): Unilateral Neglect: Clinical and Experimental Studies. Hove: Lawrence Erlbaum Associates, 1993.

Robertson IH, Mattingley JB, Rorden C, Driver J: Phasic alerting of neglect patients overcomes their spatial deficit in visual awareness. Nature: 395; 169–172, 1998.

Rode G, Charles N, Perenin MT, Vighetto A, Trillet M, Aymard G: Partial remission of hemiplegia and somatoparaphrenia through vestibular stimulation in a case of unilateral neglect. Cortex: 28; 203–208, 1992.

Rode G, Perenin MT: Temporary remission of representational hemineglect through vestibular stimulation. NeuroReport: 5; 869–872, 1994.

Rossetti Y, Rode G, Pisella L, Farnè A, Li L, Boisson D, Perenin MT: Prism adaptation to a rightward optical deviation rehabilitates left hemispatial neglect. Nature: 395; 166–169, 1998.

Schenkenberg T, Bradford DC, Ajax ET: Line bisection and unilateral visual neglect in patients with neurologic impairment. Neurology: 30; 509–517, 1980.

Seron X, Deloche G, Coyette F: A retrospective analysis of a single case neglect therapy: a point of theory. In Seron X, Deloche G (Eds), Cognitive Approaches in Neuropsychological Rehabilitation. Hillsdale: Lawrence Erlbaum Associates, pp. 289–316, 1989.

Shepherd M, Findlay JM, Hockey RJ: The relationship between eye movements and spatial attention. The Quarterly Journal of Experimental Psychology, 38A, 475–791, 1986.

Smania N, Bazoli F, Piva D, Guidetti G: Visuomotor imagery and rehabilitation of neglect. Archives of Physical Medicine and Rehabilitation: 78; 430–436, 1997.

Smania N, Martini MC, Gambina G, Tomelleri G, Palamara A, Natale E, Marzi CA: The spatial distribution of visual attention in hemineglect and extinction patients. Brain: 121; 1759–1770, 1998.

Soroker N, Calamaro N, Glicksohn J, Myslobodsky MS: Auditory inattention in right-hemisphere-damaged patients with and without visual neglect. Neuropsychologia: 35; 249–256, 1997.

Stein JF: The representation of egocentric space in the posterior parietal cortex. Behavioral and Brain Sciences: 15; 691–700, 1992.

Stone SP, Halligan PW, Marshall JC, Greenwood RJ: Unilateral neglect: a common but heterogeneous syndrome. Neurology: 50; 1902–1905, 1998.

Tegnér R, Levander M: Through a looking glass. A new technique to demonstrate directional hypokinesia in unilateral neglect. Brain: 114; 1943–1951, 1991.

Umiltà C: Orienting of attention. In Boller F, Grafman J (Eds), Handbook of Neuropsychology, Vol. 1. Amsterdam: Elsevier Science, pp. 175–193, 1988.

Vallar G: Left spatial hemineglect: an unmanageable explosion of dissociations? No. Neuropsychological Rehabilitation: 4; 209–212, 1994.

Vallar G, Antonucci G, Guariglia C, Pizzamiglio L: Deficits of position sense, unilateral neglect and optokinetic stimulation. Neuropsychologia: 31; 1191–1200, 1993a.

Vallar G, Bottini G, Rusconi ML, Sterzi R: Exploring somatosensory neglect by vestibular stimulation. Brain: 116; 71–86, 1993b.

Vallar G, Guariglia C, Rusconi ML: Modulation of the neglect syndrome by sensory stimulation. In Thier P, Karnath HO (Eds), Parietal Lobe Contributions to Orientation in 3D-Space. Heidelberg: Springer, pp. 555–578, 1997.

Vallar G, Rusconi ML, Barozzi S, Bernardini B, Ovadia D, Papagno C, Cesarini A: Improvement of left visuo-spatial hemineglect by left-sided transcutaneous electrical stimulation. Neuropsychologia: 33; 73–82, 1995.

Vallar G, Sandroni P, Rusconi ML, Barbieri S: Hemianopia, hemianesthesia, and spatial neglect: a study with evoked potentials. Neurology: 41; 1918–1922, 1991.

Vallar G, Sterzi R, Bottini G, Rusconi ML: Temporary remission of left hemianesthesia after vestibular stimulation. A sensory neglect phenomenon. Cortex: 26; 123–131, 1990.

Ventre J, Faugier-Grimaud S: Effects of posterior parietal lesions (area 7) on VOR in monkeys. Experimental Brain Research: 62; 654–658, 1986.

Ventre J, Flandrin JM, Jeannerod M: In search for the egocentric reference. A neuropsychological hypothesis. Neuropsychologia: 22; 797–806, 1984.

Volpe BT, Ledoux JE, Gazzaniga MS: Information processing of visual stimuli in an 'extinguished' field. Nature: 282; 722–724, 1979.

Vuilleumier P, Hester D, Assal G, Regli F: Unilateral spatial neglect recovery after sequential strokes. Neurology: 46; 184–189, 1996.

Walker R: Spatial and object-based neglect. Neurocase: 1; 371–383, 1995.

Walker R, Findlay JM, Young AW, Welch J: Disentangling neglect and hemianopia. Neuropsychologia: 29; 1019–1027, 1991.

Watson RT, Miller BD, Heilman KM: Nonsensory neglect. Annals of Neurology: 3; 505–508, 1978.

Weinberg J, Diller J, Gordon W, Gerstman L, Lieberman A, Lakin P et al.: Visual scanning training effect on reading-related tasks in acquired right-brain damage. Archives of Physical Medicine and Rehabilitation: 58; 479–486, 1977.

Weinberg J, Diller J, Gordon W, Gerstman L, Lieberman A, Lakin P et al.: Training sensory awareness and spatial organization in people with brain damage. Archives of Physical Medicine and Rehabilitation: 60; 491–496, 1979.

Weinstein EA, Friedland RP (Eds), Hemi-Inattention and Hemisphere Specialization, Vol. 18. New York: Raven Press, 1977.

Wiart L, Bon Saint Come A, Debelleix X, Petit H, Joseph PA, Mazaux JM, Barat M: Unilateral neglect syndrome rehabilitation by trunk rotation and scanning training. Archives of Physical Medicine and Rehabilitation: 78; 424–429, 1997.

Yantis S: Attentional capture in vision. In Kramer AF, Coles GH, Logan GD (Eds), Converging Operations in the Study of Visual Selective Attention. Washington, DC: American Psychological Association, pp. 45–76, 1995.

Handbook of Neuropsychology, 2nd Edition, Vol. 4
M. Behrmann (Ed)

CHAPTER 5

Constructional and visuospatial disorders

Dario Grossi [a,*] and Luigi Trojano [b]

[a] *Second Neurologic Department, School of Medicine, Federico II University, Nuovo Policlinico, Ed. 17, Via S. Pansini 5, 80131 Naples, Italy*
[b] *Salvatore Maugeri Foundation, Rehabilitation Center of Telese (BN), I.R.C.C.S., Via Bagni Vecchi, 82037 Telese Terme (BN), Italy*

Introduction

Visuospatial abilities are those non-verbal cognitive abilities which operate upon perceptual stimuli and mental images in order to allow individuals to interact with the environment. The knowledge of spatial coordinates of one's own body and of the surrounding space is the prerequisite of any action: to get around through city streets, to do any manual job, to play any sport would be impossible without a spatial processing system.

It is quite difficult to single out 'pure' visuospatial processes due to the lack of generally accepted definitions and theoretical frameworks. Several visuospatial cognitive defects may be variably associated in single patients after a brain lesion. The co-occurrence of two visuospatial disturbances might be based on a common cognitive defect, while some clinical pictures conceived of as unitary syndromes in the past (such as Balint–Holmes syndrome and unilateral spatial neglect, that are described in detail elsewhere in this book), have been shown to fractionate in different ways.

Faced with this complex situation, in recent years many authors have tried to develop a new approach to visuospatial disturbances, following the same cognitive methodology applied to the linguistic domain. According to this approach, any cognitive process is based upon a modular functional architecture. By formulating a cognitive model of a certain mental process it is possible to identify its different functional components, to interpret normal subjects' performances and to foresee consequences of lesions to different components of the model. From such a viewpoint, cognitive disturbances are thought of as the result of a lesion to one or more subcomponents.

The main focus of the present chapter is on constructional apraxia. We will describe some clinical and experimental issues regarding constructional disorders, and some theoretical facets. We will also briefly review visuospatial disturbances and discuss their possible relationships with constructional apraxia.

Constructional disturbances

Definition

The inability to construct a complex object, arranging its component elements in their correct spatial relationships, was observed as early as the beginning of the century (Rieger, 1909). Even so, it was not until years later that the specific nature of this disability was recognised, thanks to the work of Kleist (1934), who coined the term 'constructional apraxia' (CA). According to Kleist, the syndrome comprised "a disturbance in the activities of drawing, assembling and building, in which the spatial form of the product proves to be unsuccessful without there being an apraxia for single movements" (1934). Kleist

* Corresponding author. Tel./Fax: +39 (081) 7462672;
E-mail: dagrossi@unina.it

set out to differentiate constructional–apraxic disabilities from other motor programme disorders (e.g. ideomotor apraxia) and elementary visuoperceptual deficits, proposing that they derived from "an alteration in the connections between visual functions, that is visuospatial, and the kinetic engrams that control manual activity" (Kleist, 1934).

In spite of Kleist's specific definition, and of other researchers' precise formulations (e.g. CA denotes "an impairment in combinatory or organising activity in which the details must be clearly perceived and in which the relationship among the component parts of the entity must be apprehended if the desired synthesis of them is to be achieved"; Benton, 1967), in subsequent years theoretical interpretation of CA fell into two main camps. Some authors saw CA as an executive disorder, on the basis of observations of performance on complex cognitive tasks, whilst others considered it the consequence of a visuoperceptual disorder (see Gainotti, 1985, for a full review of the literature). The existence of divergent opinions gave rise to a terminological confusion, and it gradually became customary to use the term CA to refer to any anomaly observed during the performance of a constructional task. In other words, there was a general tendency to ignore Kleist's original definition and to use CA as an umbrella term for any 'constructional disability' (Gainotti, 1985), irrespective of the presence or absence of a visuoperceptual deficit.

The legacy of this theoretical debate is a single diagnostic category which fails to acknowledge the various hypotheses put forward to account for different types of constructional disability. The only reference to theory has been in the definition of 'constructional skills' as those identified by Kleist through his clinical research. In reality, however, drawing, assembling and building (Kleist's 'constructional skills') cannot be considered equivalent because they rely on various cognitive mechanisms (sustained attention, reasoning, motor, perceptual and visuospatial skills) to different extents. Even though some researchers have noted a significant correlation between drawing, three-dimensional object construction and visuospatial tasks (e.g. replication of spatial arrangements of counters, Arrigoni and De Renzi, 1964) in right and left hemisphere lesion patients, numerous studies have yielded contrasting data. Benton and Fogel (1962), for example, observed low inter-correlations between two- and three-dimensional constructional tasks, a copying task and the block design subtest of the WAIS in a group of 100 brain-damaged patients. Furthermore, cases of patients who fail at graphomotor tasks, but not at three-dimensional constructional tasks and vice-versa (Dee, 1970) have also been reported.

Despite these observations, most CA researchers adhere to the traditional approach, and it is for this reason that it is useful to briefly summarise the tasks which explore 'constructional abilities' before moving on to discuss the threads of clinical and experimental research.

Assessment of constructional abilities

The presence of a constructional disability is tested by asking the patient to assemble or draw a simple two-dimensional model. Studies of CA have most often employed tasks which require the produced shape to have component lines of equal length and arranged in their given spatial relationships. An example of this type of test is that compiled, standardised and normed by Benson and Barton (1970). The block design subtest of the WAIS (Wechsler, 1981) — where the person has to reconstruct a two-dimensional pattern using multicoloured cube faces, is used for the same purpose, yet it is perhaps the clearest example of how a so-called test of constructional skills taps different cognitive mechanisms, i.e. attentional, perceptual, motor and visuospatial.

Other tests investigate three-dimensional constructional abilities, beginning with simple shapes. One such test has been standardised by Benton and Fogel (1962); another assessing constructional abilities in an 'ecological' context has been recently developed by Trojano, Angelini, Gallo and Grossi (1997). It has been posited that there could be differences between the mechanisms involved in two- and three-dimensional constructional tasks, for which reason some researchers recommend testing both competencies (Benton, 1989); others, however, consider this an unnecessary procedure (De Renzi, 1980).

Drawing tasks are those most widely used to tap constructional abilities, although it should be underlined that unlike the above-mentioned tests, they rely on the presence of intact graphomotor skills. In fact, a dissociation between drawing and constructional tasks has recently been reported amongst aphasic patients (Kashiwagi, Kashiwagi, Kunimori et al., 1994). However, not even copying and free drawing (traditional constructional tasks) can be considered completely equivalent.

Free drawing — in which the patient is asked to draw a named object (e.g. a clock, a face and so on) — is perhaps the most immediate test of constructional skills. It reveals information about the patient's ability to draw complete shapes or a tendency to omit parts; his ability to organise the figure as a whole, with its component parts in their correct spatial relationships and the features of the lines drawn (see Freedman, Leach, Kaplan et al., 1994 for a detailed analysis of clock drawing). Even so, this kind of assessment does not easily lend itself to standardisation and relies on the presence of intact non-constructional cognitive abilities. Regarding the latter point, Gainotti, Silveri, Villa and Caltagirone (1983) demonstrated that drawing abilities were more compromised in aphasics than in non-aphasic left hemisphere and right hemisphere brain-damaged patients; in other words, the resulting damage seemed to be more significantly related to a lexical–semantic deficit than to a visual–constructional disorder. Similarly, Grossman (1988) observed that in many cases, brain-damaged patients made errors in associating shape with appropriate size when drawing single objects, revealing a disorder that was not purely constructional in nature. In the assessment of constructional skills then, the complexity of free drawing tasks should be recognised, in terms of the role played by lexical–semantic mechanisms and imagery abilities (see Trojano and Grossi, 1994, for a more detailed discussion).

The above considerations are not relevant to copying tasks, which more directly assess the patient's ability to reproduce a figure (Figs. 1–5). However, there has not always been consistency in the selection of stimuli for tests (simple shapes, e.g. circles and squares, or complex designs, e.g. the Rey figure and the Taylor figure — see Figs. 4 and 5), and above all in the formulation of diagnostic criteria for CA. Confirming the need for standardisation, Arrigoni and De Renzi (1964) have highlighted that although it is easier to classify patients with an obvious disorder at a clinical level, there may be substantial differences amongst those who present with milder disabilities. It therefore seems clear that a diagnosis of CA should be based on the administration of copying, drawing or constructional tasks (remembering that, in the opinion of some researchers, both graphomotor and constructional skills should be tested; Benton, 1967, 1989) which incorporate stimuli of gradually increasing complexity, do not draw on general intellectual resources to a great extent, and above all, have been tested on a sample of normal subjects (De Renzi, 1982).

Prevalence and hemispheric localization

The terminological uncertainty outlined above, the use of non-standardised tests and the selection of non-homogeneous patient groups have all contributed to a lack of consensus regarding the anatomical and functional aetiology of CA. In the first instance, there is inconsistency between estimates of the incidence of CA following left and right hemisphere damage; most studies report incidence rates of 30–40% for right-brain-damaged patients although the figures for left-lesioned patients vary considerably. Kleist's original work drew attention to a link between CA and dominant parietal lesions, but early studies of broader samples of patients with focal lesions indicated that CA was less prevalent and less severe following damage to the left hemisphere (see Piercy, Hécaen and Ajuriaguerra, 1960; Piercy and Smyth, 1962), suggesting a right hemisphere dominance for constructional–praxic abilities. Other studies, however, attribute the higher incidence of CA in right hemisphere patients to greater severity of the lesion (Arrigoni and De Renzi, 1964) and to neglect errors, which are more prevalent in this group (Gainotti and Tiacci, 1970). In fact, more recent studies, which have controlled these variables, demonstrate a similar prevalence of CA following lesions to either hemisphere (Carlesimo, Fadda and Caltagirone, 1993; Kirk and Kertesz, 1989; Villa, Gainotti and De Bonis, 1986), giving less weight tout-court to the 'dominant right hemisphere' hypothesis and reinforcing the idea that there could be qualitative differences between the mechanisms responsible for CA in the two groups of brain-damaged patients.

The first writer to explicitly propose an interhemispheric distinction was Duensing (1953), who main-

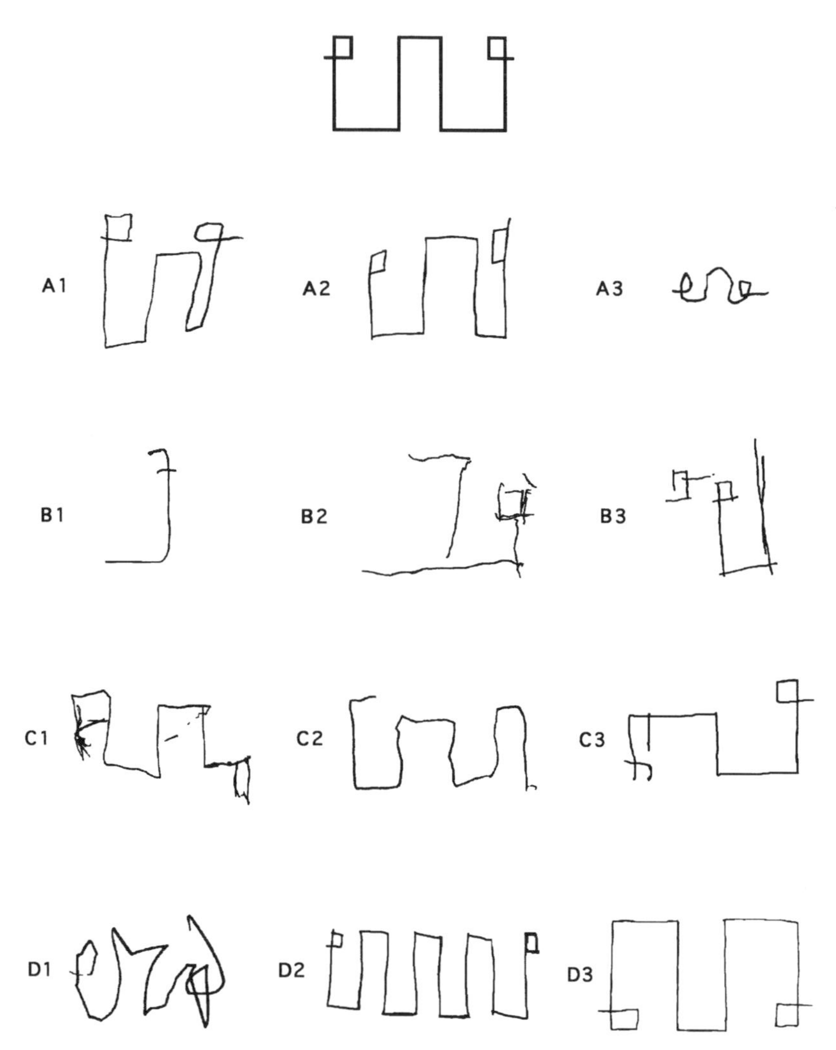

Fig. 1. Copying of geometrical drawings: novel figure (model on the top). (A) Drawings by left-brain-damaged patients — spatial relationships appear to be relatively spared. (B) Drawings by right-brain-damaged patients with hemineglect. (C) Drawings by right-brain-damaged patients with visuospatial defects, but without hemineglect; note the good reproduction of the right part with respect to the left in C3. (D) Drawings by demented patients: examples of gross spatial distortions, perseveration and rotation.

tained that right hemisphere patients failed at copying tasks because of defective visuospatial mechanisms (a spatial agnosic form of CA), whilst left hemisphere patients were affected by an ideational form of apraxia. This hypothesis was triggered by the observation that right-brain-damaged patients tend to produce drawings with the wrong orientation and disorganised spatial relationships between component parts, whilst patients with left-sided lesions tend to simplify the model, omitting some details, but preserving the original spatial relationships (see Figs. 1–4). Numerous studies have confirmed the presence of these characteristics in the drawings of brain-damaged patients (see Gainotti and Tiacci, 1970).

Several noteworthy studies seem to acknowledge the presence of a specific executive disorder (Piercy, Hécaen and Ajuriaguerra, 1960) or motor programming deficit (Warrington, James and Kinsbourne, 1966) in left hemisphere apraxic patients. Experimental proof of the latter hypothesis has been provided by Hécaen and Assal (1970) who devised a

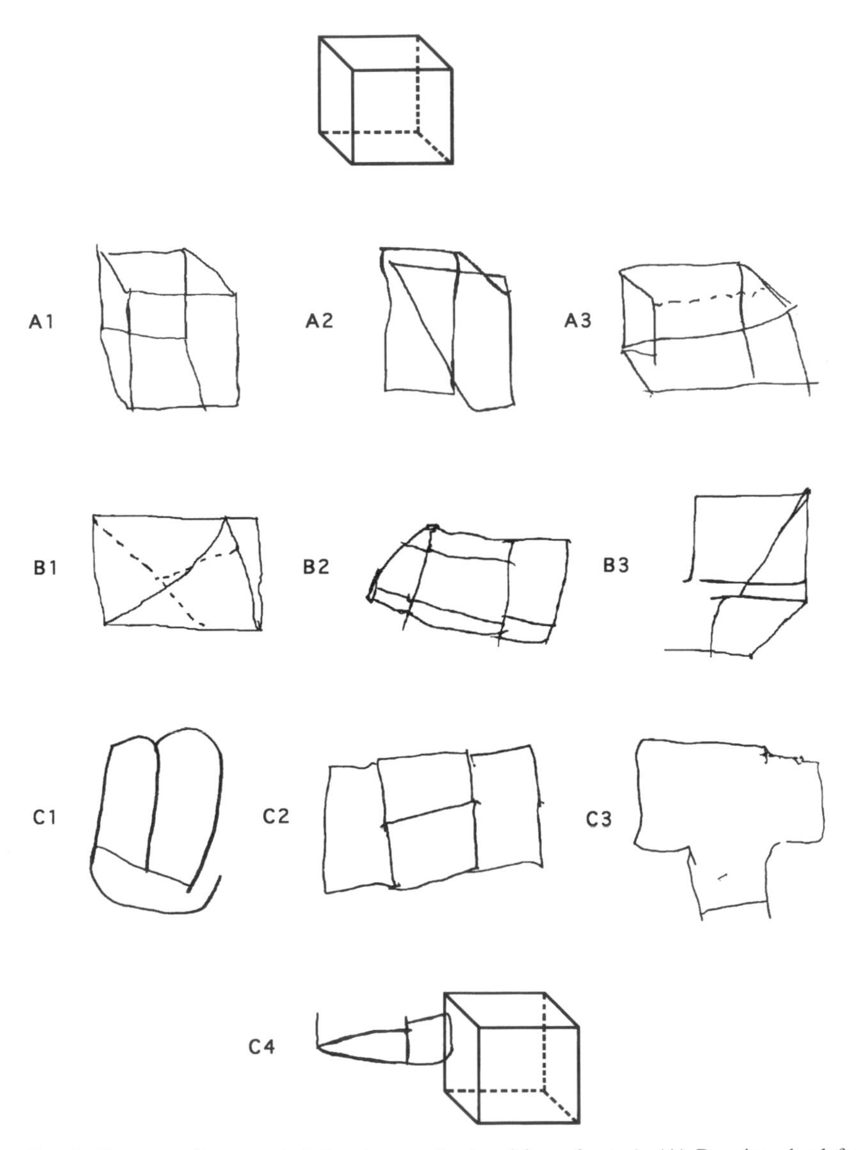

Fig. 2. Copying of geometrical drawings: cube (model on the top). (A) Drawings by left-brain-damaged patients. (B) Drawings by right-brain-damaged patients, one of whom with hemineglect (B3). (C) Drawings by demented patients: three severely distorted drawings and one example of closing-in (C4).

copying task with 'planning' tokens, in the form of geometric shapes which guided the reproduction of the stimulus. In this study, left hemisphere patients (as opposed to their right hemisphere counterparts) benefitted from the availability of an explicit planning strategy, confirming the presence of a planning deficit. Gainotti, Miceli and Caltagirone (1977) later tried to replicate these results, comparing the copying performance of a series of right and left hemisphere patients with performance on an analogous task which made use of 'planning' tokens. The results were inconsistent with those of Hécaen and Assal (1970) after the effects of general intellectual deterioration and spatial hemineglect were equally weighted.

The existence of a specific visuoperceptual deficit in right hemisphere apraxic patients has been confirmed by some studies (see Mack and Levine, 1981),

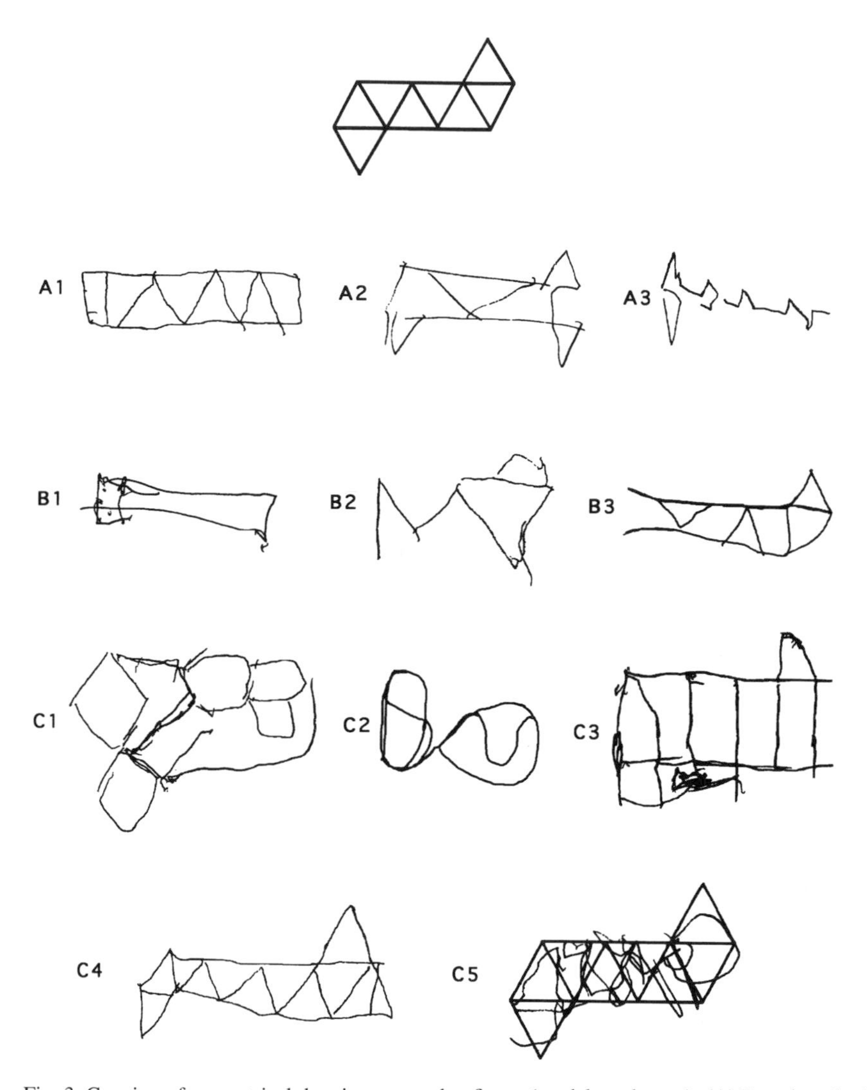

Fig. 3. Copying of geometrical drawings: complex figure (model on the top). (A) Drawings by left-brain-damaged patients. (B) Drawings by right-brain-damaged patients, one of whom with hemineglect (B3). (C) Drawings by demented patients: examples of gross spatial distortions (C1 and C2), simplification (C3), perseveration (C4) and closing-in (C5).

although the majority of studies reveal comparable visuospatial disorders in patients with right- and left-sided lesions (Gainotti, 1985).

Given the data for and against a distinction between apraxias of right and left lesion origin, it is only possible to retain the lateralization hypothesis in a 'weak' version. In right-brain-damaged patients, a deficit in visuospatial analysis appears to predominate, whilst in left-lesioned patients, visuoconstructional disabilities probably have more complex origins — in movement planning disorders, but also in general intellectual deficits or disorders of visuospatial analysis (De Renzi, 1980).

This greatly researched interhemispheric difference in the mechanisms underlying CA can only be demonstrated by experiments in which certain skills are seen to correlate with constructional performance in one patient group, but not in the other, whilst other abilities exhibit the opposite tendency. A study of this nature has been published by Kirk and Kertesz (1989), who noted that drawing disabil-

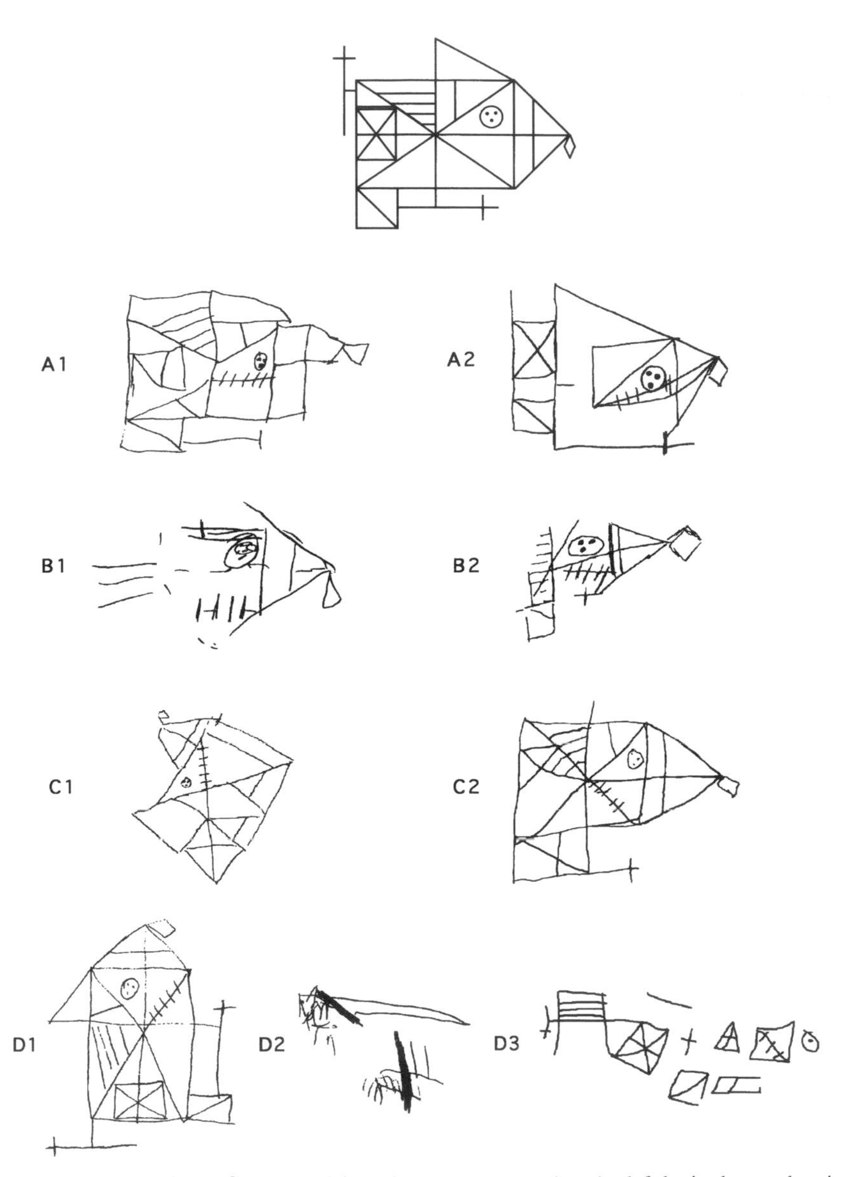

Fig. 4. Copying of Rey figure (model on the top). (A) Drawings by left-brain-damaged patients. (B) Drawings by right-brain-damaged patients with hemineglect. (C) Drawings by right-brain-damaged patients without hemineglect, but with gross visuospatial defects; note the good reproduction of the right part with respect to the left in C2. (D) Drawings by demented patients: examples of rotation and gross spatial distortions; in D3 the reproduction of the single subcomponents of the figure is relatively spared, but spatial relationships among them are lost.

ities correlated strongly with performance on a visuoperceptual task in patients with right hemisphere lesions whilst correlating more strongly with tests of verbal comprehension and severity of hemiparesis in the left hemisphere group. Kirk and Kertesz (1989) concluded that CA can originate from a visuoperceptual deficit other than hemineglect in right-brain-damaged patients, whilst it could be linked to disorders at the semantic or elementary motor level in patients with left-sided lesions. It should, however, be highlighted that since Kirk and Kertesz employed a free-drawing task in their study, their conclusions may not be replicated with a simple copying task. Furthermore, the visuospatial deficit in

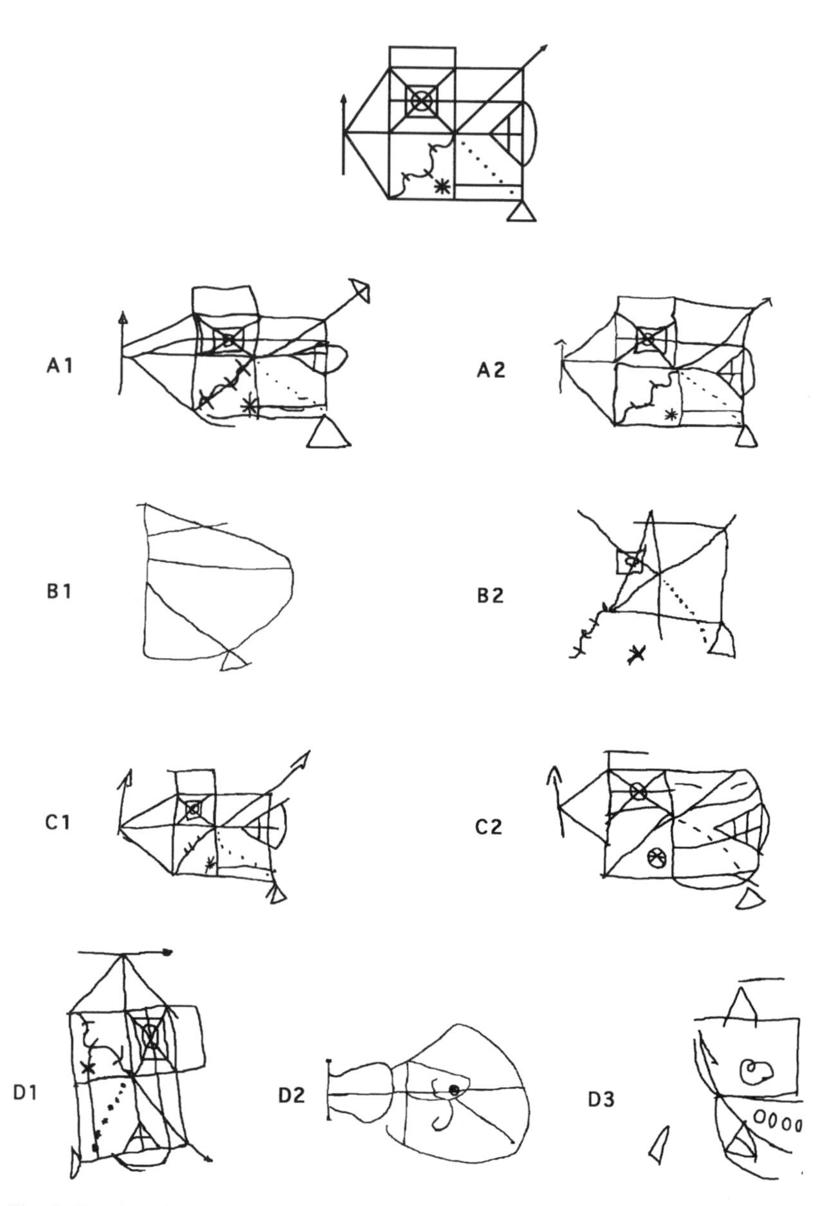

Fig. 5. Copying of Taylor figure (model on the top). (A) Drawings by left-brain-damaged patients. (B) Drawings by right-brain-damaged patients with hemineglect. (C) Drawings by right-brain-damaged patients without hemineglect. (D) Drawings by demented patients: examples of rotation and gross spatial distortions with simplifications.

right-lesioned patients was identified using Raven's Progressive Matrices, which tap not only perceptual mechanisms, but also general intellectual ability.

A more recent study with a similar experimental design (Carlesimo et al., 1993) used copying performance as an index of constructional ability and judgement of line orientation, comparison of distorted geometric figures, a 'tapping' test (elementary motor skills) and a 'tracking' test (spatially guided motor skills: to follow a track with a pencil) to explore the various subskills involved in the process of construction. To complete the battery, Raven's Progressive Matrices were incorporated as a measure of intellectual ability. Carlesimo et al. (1993) observed that tracking performance significantly correlated with drawing ability in right-brain-damaged patients. On the other hand, constructional performance correlated strongly with the results of the tapping test in left hemisphere patients. The authors concluded that the basic disturbance in right hemisphere apraxics is more likely to be an alteration in their ability to carry out spatial manipulations than a visuospatial deficit per se (in this group, judgement of line orientation correlated only marginally with drawing performance) whilst in left hemisphere patients, a disorder at the elementary motor level could play a more crucial role — in accordance with the hypothesis of Kirk and Kertesz (1989). Though once again, note how two more or less similar studies reach conclusions which are at least partially inconsistent.

With regard to the intrahemispheric locus of CA, it is generally accepted that CA is more frequently associated with parieto-occipital lesions (De Renzi, 1982), although it can also be observed in patients with frontal lesions. Severity of constructional disturbances does not seem to differ in patients with anterior or posterior lesions (Black and Bernard, 1984). As in the case of the left–right issue, it has been argued that lesions with different intrahemispheric loci give rise to qualitatively different types of constructional disabilities. Luria and Tsvetkova (1964), for example, proposed that CA in patients with posterior lesions (parieto-occipital) is caused by a defect in the analysis of spatial relations whilst a deficit in movement planning could underlie apraxia of frontal lesion origin. A series of studies seems to confirm on the one hand, the role of caudal regions (predominantly right hemisphere) in visuospatial analysis and on the other hand, the role of the frontal lobes in the programming of drawing (see Gainotti, 1985, for a review).

The first study which simultaneously verified both hypotheses and demonstrated a double dissociation between the behaviour of patients with anterior and posterior lesions was that of Pillon (1981). Pillon observed that patients with posterior lesions, whether left- or right-sided, performed better on copying tasks when provided with visuospatial reference points. On the other hand, the copying performance of patients with anterior lesions was facilitated by the provision of a copying plan. It should be noted that the guided copying task in this study is extremely similar to the copying task of Hécaen and Ajuriaguerra (1954) although the goal here is different (to facilitate the processing of an executive plan); yet Pillon's study does not support the interhemispheric theory.

More recent data fail to support the crucial role of intrahemispheric localisation in determining the nature of CA. Kirk and Kertesz (1989) observed no difference between the performances of patients with anterior and posterior lesions in free-drawing tasks. However, a peculiar constructional disorder may be observed in some patients with lesions involving frontal cerebral cortex: the tendency to reproduce drawings in a rotated orientation. Solms, Turnbull, Kaplan-Solms et al. (1998) identified 16 patients, from a consecutive unselected series of 240 neurological patients, who reproduced Rey's or Taylor's complex figures, with their major axis usually rotated vertically rather than horizontally. In these cases, the model may be reproduced with correct inner spatial relationships, but the whole copy was rotated. This finding could suggest that the ability to reproduce the correct spatial disposition of a model is functionally distinct from the ability to correctly organize reciprocal relationships among model's constitutive elements. Seven of these patients had diffuse cerebral involvement, but all remaining cases showed a lesion involving frontal regions. The authors suggest that this behaviour could reflect the lack of planning and verification abilities of frontal patients (Solms et al., 1998). In rare cases, like in the patient with a right temporoparietal lesion described by Turnbull, Laws and McCarthy (1995), rotated drawing may be related to a deficit in perceptual processing of object orientation.

Subcortical structures do contribute to the drawing process and it is possible to observe selective constructional defects after a single right subcortical lesion (Grossi, Correra, Calise et al., 1996). No distinctive features seem to characterize constructional disorders of subcortical origin (Kirk and Kertesz, 1993), but Marshall, Lazar, Binder et al. (1994) observed in a series of patients with focal right hemisphere damage that subcortical anterior lesions gave rise to a disability regardless of the presence or absence of neglect while constructional disabilities were, as a rule, associated with neglect in the case of posterior lesions.

Constructional apraxia and visuospatial disturbances

Many early studies hypothesized that, at least in right focal brain-damaged patients, constructional disturbances are related to visuospatial disorders. However, as summarized above, most recent literature failed to demonstrate such a strong association (see for example Carlesimo et al., 1993). Therefore, the relationships between constructional disorders and spatial perception remain open to debate.

Spatial perception is a term which refers to the analysis of spatial relationships of objects to each other and to the observer (De Renzi, 1982). This label is quite loose and may embrace elementary (e.g. location of points in the space, appreciation of dimensions, orientation or distance of an object) and complex (e.g. recognition of shapes, maze learning, mental rotation) processing abilities. For this reason, De Renzi (1982) suggested using the term 'spatial perception' in reference to elementary processing stages, while using the term 'spatial cognition' to designate more complex mental abilities requiring the use of mental ('internal') representations.

The disorders of spatial perception have been presumed to occur at a relatively early stage of visuospatial processing. However, sensory loss is not a sufficient condition for the emergence of 'higher-order' perceptual and visuospatial defects (Ratcliffe and Ross, 1981). Although some recent evidence shows how elementary visual sensory defects may impair performances on several visual tasks (Kempen, Krichevsky and Feldman, 1994), it remains well-established that at least some visuospatial abilities (e.g. location and orientation senses) rely on specialized neural structures (Westheimer, 1996).

Several aspects of the so-called elementary visuospatial analysis processes (location of points in bidimensional space, line orientation, depth perception) have been extensively studied in the literature (for comprehensive reviews see De Renzi, 1982; Newcombe and Ratcliffe, 1989; see also the chapter on Balint's syndrome in this book) with the main aim of establishing hemispheric dominance and identifying cortical areas specialized for these cognitive abilities. While there is increasing evidence that posterior, occipitoparietal, cortical areas are responsible for spatial processing of visual input (Ungerleider and Mishkin, 1982), the issue of hemispheric dominance is less well understood, at least as regards elementary visuospatial processes like the ability to identify point location or line orientation.

The elementary visuospatial processes are likely aimed to identify and to integrate simultaneous or successive stimuli in a spatial schema, in order to elaborate a body-centered spatial coordinate system, that can guide motor actions and behaviour (Andersen, Essick and Siegel, 1985; Hyvarinen, 1982; Stein, 1992). The mental representation of the external environment with respect to egocentric coordinates can be conceived of as a mental map of surrounding space. The ability to elaborate such a map can be selectively impaired even in the absence of disorders of space exploration, as has been recently demonstrated in a patient with progressive visuospatial disorders due to a degenerative lesion (Stark, Coslett and Saffran, 1996).

In the body-centered mental representation of the external world, it is then possible that the representation of horizontal, vertical and radial axes is based upon dissociable cognitive processes. In a patient with primary degenerative dementia, we have actually demonstrated a selective inability to code spatial relationships along the horizontal axis, with the appreciation of vertical and radial dimensions being spared (e.g. the patient was able to copy vertical, but not horizontal, segments correctly), independently from visual exploration or eye movement disorders (Grossi, Fragassi, Giani and Trojano, 1998). Such a dissociation could occur because the mental representation of spatial relationships along horizontal, vertical and radial axes is likely dependent on the integration of information from different sensorial modalities (Gold, Adair, Jacobs and Heilman, 1990).

One of the most important features of the spatial representation system would therefore consist in the construction of a 'coherent' mental map (a sort of continuum) of points in space. A 'coherent' mental representation of space allows one to assign a location to surrounding objects and to define spatial relationships among themselves and with the subject; two or more simultaneous stimuli can thus be perceived as physically distinct and coexistent localized in different locations of visual field, provided that they occupy different sites of the same mental representation of space, viz. because they are embedded in the same cognitive map.

Such a mental spatial representation is computed by a 'spatiotopic' representation system in the comprehensive model of visual processing by Kosslyn and coworkers (Kosslyn, Flynn, Amsterdam and Wang, 1990; Kosslyn and Koenig, 1992); this system integrates information about position of head, eyes and body of the observer with visual retinotopic information and allows the localization of an object in the surrounding space. The model foresees that two parallel processors can analyze non-retinotopic spatial properties of the object perceived on the basis of the 'spatiotopic' representation. The former processor is able to identify categorial spatial relationships (that may be expressed as topological relationships — under/below, or right/left — without metric evaluations), while the latter processes coordinate relationships (expressed as absolute metric evaluations).

In a recent paper on cognitive processes involved in drawing, Guérin, Ska and Belleville (1999) underline that the model of Kosslyn et al. (1990) provides a good conceptualization of visuospatial perceptual processes involved in drawing, but the problem remains to what extent perceptual visuospatial abilities are correlated with constructional performances and whether the cognitive 'spatiotopic' map is used to solve constructional problems. Stated in different words, further specifically designed studies have to be conducted to demonstrate relationships of elementary visuospatial disorders with constructional apraxia.

Constructional apraxia and unilateral spatial neglect

As discussed above, recent studies on the prevalence of CA in focal brain-damaged patients have taken care not to include patients affected by unilateral spatial neglect (USN), since this syndrome may affect performances at copying and spontaneous drawing tasks. In the present chapter, we do not want to address general issues regarding USN (that is treated elsewhere in this book), but we will discuss some points relevant to constructional abilities.

In the absence of gross constructional disorders, which are indeed often associated with USN, neglect patients typically show unilateral omissions in reproducing elements of a perceived or imagined model (Figs. 1–4). In a copying task, the model is given by the examiner, and omissions may derive from a faulty perceptual appreciation of its figural components. In other words, the most intuitive explanation of lateralized omissions in copying is that defective visual exploration and analysis of the model induces subjects to reproduce only the perceived elements. However, such an explanation cannot account for a range of phenomena; for example, a recent study by Ishiai, Seki, Koyama and Yokota (1996) has demonstrated that neglect patients were able to detect the absence of left-sided leaves on a sunflower, despite failing to draw them in a subsequent copying task. These findings are not consistent with the presence of a visuoperceptual defect and might suggest an interaction between attentional mechanisms and the process of drawing.

Moreover, it must be noted that omissions can become evident in copying complex drawings (e.g. Rey or Taylor figure) even when patients do not show signs of USN at traditional tasks for visual exploration. This finding could be explained by the heavy attentional load imposed by the processing of complex spatial structures or also by hypothesizing that specific interactions may exist between space representation, and the drawing processes.

Typically, omissions occur during spontaneous drawing too, when no visually presented model is available and subjects have to resort to their long-term memory representations. In this case, exploratory visuoperceptual defects are not viable explanatory tools. It could be expected that the tendency to omit part of drawings in tasks like spontaneous drawing, due to impaired exploratory or attentional mechanisms, would be compensated for by information stored in semantic knowledge or in a procedural memory that could be specific for constructional processes. It can be hypothesized that patients' mental representations are impaired in the neglected hemifield (as foreseen by several interpretative accounts of neglect; see Bisiach, Luzzatti and Perani, 1979) and that the patients' reproductions are the direct by-product of these defects. Alternatively, it can be hypothesized that unilateral omissions in spontaneous drawing are specifically due to a defect in the patient's dealing with the 'drawing space', intended as that part of the paper in which subjects decide to draw and which is identified as a bidimensional frame originating from (or in relation to) the starting point of the drawing. Neglect patients could be unable to operate within or to fully represent such a 'drawing space', and tend to reproduce only some parts of items that they can entirely represent in their mind. For instance, Anderson (1993) demonstrated that a neglect patient who made omissions in copying and spontaneous drawing of a clock face, could draw it correctly if she was instructed to close her eyes, see the clock in her mind and draw what she saw with her eyes shut. These data would confirm that omissions may reflect faulty reproduction of intact mental representations.

This alternative hypothesis could be compatible with a phenomenon which is frequently observed in USN patients, the so-called allochiria (also referred to as 'spatial transposition'): patients tend to report on the ipsilesional side stimuli occurring in the neglected, contralesional side. This phenomenon has been described in several modalities (tactile, auditory, olfactive, visual), but it is particularly striking in copying and spontaneous drawing (Fig. 5B), where patients can check their reproductions for accuracy and still fail to notice their mistakes (see Halligan, Marshall and Wade, 1992, for a brilliant example of allochiria in copying). The mechanisms through which allochiria realizes in drawings of USN patients still remain matter of debate (see Di Pellegrino, 1995, for a discussion), but the phenomenon suggests that internal representations may be spared, although representing only a subset of geometrical relationships. It is worth mentioning that, according to Mijovic (1991), transposition of contralesional elements of a drawing onto the ipsilesional side suggests that the representations of both contralesional and ipsilesional space are distorted, and that this latter has become more compliant. The possibility that a defect in the representation of two-dimensional space associated with USN can be well revealed by drawing tasks has received some support by a recent study on a group of neglect patients (Grossi, Lepore, Esposito et al., 1999). Three patients, although producing the expected rightward displacement of the subjective midline in a rectangle bisection task, copied bisected rectangles overrepresenting rectangles' ipsilesional sides, and underrepresenting the contralesional sides. Such data suggest that the representation of space had lost its structural integrity and was no longer organized analogously with Euclidean space in these neglect patients (see also Irving-Bell, Small and Cowey, 1999, for a demonstration of non-Euclidean distortion of visually perceived space in neglect patients).

Another drawing feature of USN patients, which has been somewhat underestimated, is the occurrence of constructional disorders, typically spatial distortions, *only* on the contralesional side. This unilateral drawing impairment may be found also in patients who do not show, or do not longer show, symptoms of USN: they do not make omissions in copying drawings, and yet produce drawing with altered spatial relationships on the contralesional side *only* (see Fig. 1C3 and Fig. 4C2). This constructional disorder might suggest the existence of an impairment specific to one constructional hemispace, as if two-dimensional frames necessary for drawing were distorted only on the contralesional side. In a sense, this disorder, which could be referred to as 'constructional hemiapraxia', requires explanations different from those put forward for omissions (both in the attentional and in representational explanatory frameworks of USN). Here, the disorder would not consist in a loss of information, but in the impairment of the processes through which two-dimensional frames are generated and operated upon. More clinical and experimental work-up is necessary to verify whether this unilateral disorder of the constructional space is related to or is simply associated with USN, since it can be found even in patients with no other manifestation of neglect.

All the phenomena we have briefly summarized are part of the USN syndrome, and as such they have been studied to obtain clues about the nature and the mechanisms of USN. However, theoretical interpretations of unilateral omissions, allochiria and 'constructional hemiapraxia' point to close relationships between attentional mechanisms, space representation, and the drawing processes, and can provide new insight on theory of constructional disorders.

The problem of constructional strategies

Omissions and distortions made by neglect patients in drawing are likely due to different causal mechanisms, which reveal complex relationships among attention, mental representation and the drawing process. The analysis of constructional errors, however, is not a straightforward procedure. The amount and the type of errors may greatly vary within the same subject and only a few attempts have been made at a systematic analysis of single patients' drawings errors, at variance with common neuropsychological practice in the verbal domain. The analysis of constructional errors has to take into account the effect of constructional strategies; one can plan to reproduce a figure through different procedures; for example, it is possible to reproduce first the main rectangle of Rey figure or to draw the model by mentally segmenting it in small subunits. Such a decision will have a great impact on the process of drawing and also influence type and number of errors. A clear example of the influence of constructional strategies on the performance comes from neglect literature: Ishiai, Seki, Koyama and Izumi (1997) recently demonstrated that the choice of different constructional strategies may even induce neglect phenomena in drawing (omissions) to disappear.

No systematic study is available about consistency of constructional strategies: common observation, however, suggests that the same subject can use different constructional strategies in different tasks, and even in two successive attempts at reproducing the same drawing. Only in some cases, the choice of a specific strategy seems to be forced by other cognitive defects, as in the case of visual agnosic patients who are not able to visually recognize known figures and resort to slavish line-by-line drawing procedures (Trojano and Grossi, 1992; Wapner, Judd and Gardner, 1978).

Several studies have aimed to establish whether focal brain lesions may alter constructional strategies. The first formalised observations of copying performance were those of Osterreith (1944) who presented brain-damaged patients with the Rey figure. It has been asserted that observation of copying strategies in certain patients reveals the presence of a constructional disability more effectively and accurately than analysis of the final result (Kaplan, 1983, 1988). Semenza, Denes, D'Urso et al. (1978) noted that right and non-aphasic left hemisphere patients tended to use a global strategy, similar to that adopted by 'normal' subjects in copying tasks whereas left hemisphere aphasics, in the absence of an adequate self-generated plan, used a more analytical strategy, copying the model piecemeal. A study by Binder (1982), in which the Rey figure was used as a model, contradicts these observations. Binder demonstrated that control subjects tended to use a global strategy whilst those with right- and left-sided lesions broke the task down into successive steps. Analogous results have been obtained by Trojano, De Cicco and Grossi (1993) who asked a group of patients without severe constructional disabilities to copy the Rey complex figure. This study confirmed that regardless of the lesion locus, brain-damaged patients adopt a line-by-line copying strategy, in response to the difficulties posed by the task. An alteration in drawing strategies (i.e. in planning the copy) is therefore not sufficient to induce a constructional disability; other cognitive anomalies have to be present to determine a clinical picture of CA.

Constructional apraxia and dementia

Studies of the link between CA and diffuse cognitive deficits also merit discussion. Some clinical and experimental studies attributed a causal role in the aetiology of constructional disabilities to general intellectual deterioration in patients with focal brain damage, because apraxic patients often show intellectual abilities which are inferior to those of non-apraxic patients with focal lesions (Arrigoni and De Renzi, 1964). Adding weight to the argument, other studies have noted that constructional disorders represent an index for diffuse cognitive deterioration, both in left (Borod, Carper and Goodglass, 1982) and right (Benowitz, Moya and Levine, 1990) brain-damaged patients.

On the other hand, CA is considered one of the most common behavioural alterations in Alzheimer's disease (see Figs. 1–7). Dementia of whichever aetiology, conceived of as a general intellectual impairment, may cause difficulties in assembling single elements in correct reciprocal spatial relationships to reproduce a model. Constructional operations, particularly those new or complex, can be considered as a sort of problem solving tasks, in which abstractive logical abilities play a role. For a long time it has been noted that constructional disabilities are present in the early stages of Alzheimer's disease

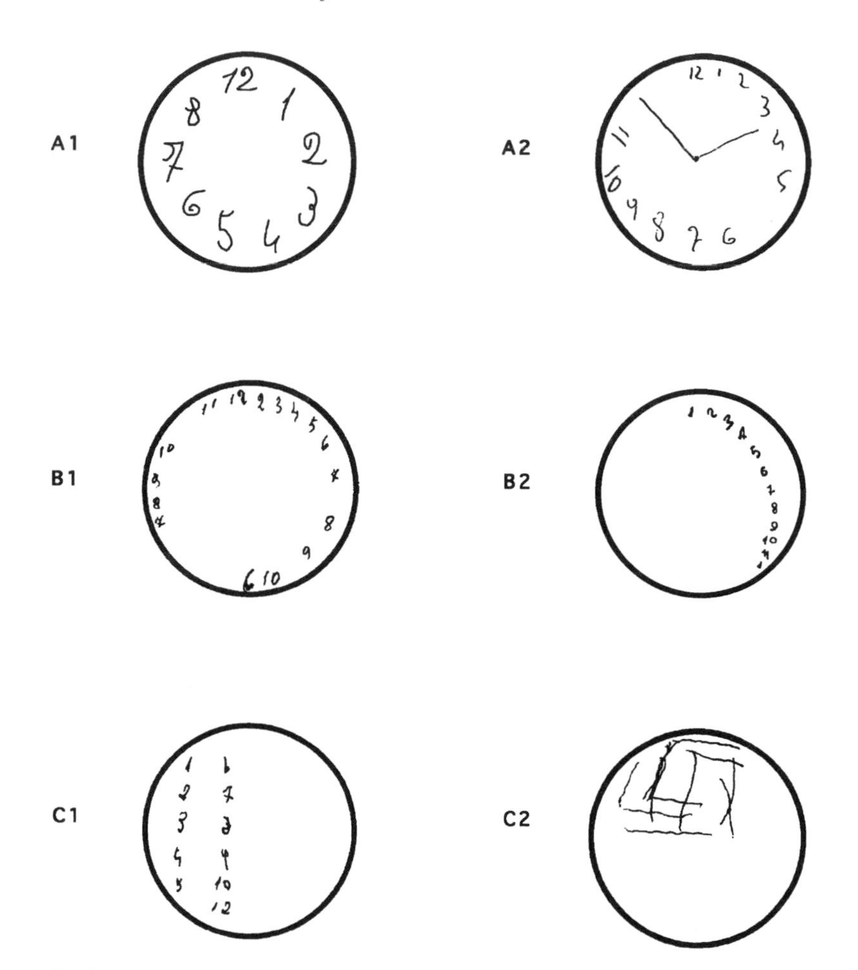

Fig. 6. Writing numbers in the face of a clock. (A) Left (A1) and right focal brain-damaged patients. (B) Hemineglect patients showing the phenomenon of allochiria. (C) Demented patients; note in C1 the loss of semantic knowledge about hour position.

and become more prominent as the illness progresses (Ajuriaguerra, Muller and Tissot, 1960).

An attempt to systematically describe drawing errors of Alzheimer's patients (Kirk and Kertesz, 1991) has demonstrated that the drawings contain simplifications, fewer angles, spatial alterations and a lack of perspective; together, these characteristics do not constitute the type of drawings typically produced by left or right hemisphere patients. Furthermore, patients' scores on this task do not correlate with performance on language or memory tests, suggesting that constructional disabilities develop relatively independently during the course of the illness; individual patients may not show constructional disabilities even in the advanced stages of Alzheimer's disease (Denes and Semenza, 1982). This observation ties in with the finding that in some patients with Alzheimer's dementia, CA may be the prominent cognitive disorder, more severe than disturbances in the verbal domain (Martin, 1990). This is not surprising if we consider that parietal and temporal regions are the first to be involved by the dementing process.

However, it must be kept in mind that spontaneous drawing is a task with a heavy load on semantic memory, and that, for example, simplifications in drawing a house may derive from impaired access to semantic knowledge or to impaired visuoperceptual processing (Grossman, Mickanin, Onishi et al., 1996; see Fig. 5C1).

The role of semantic memory in spontaneous drawing gives rise to more impaired performance in

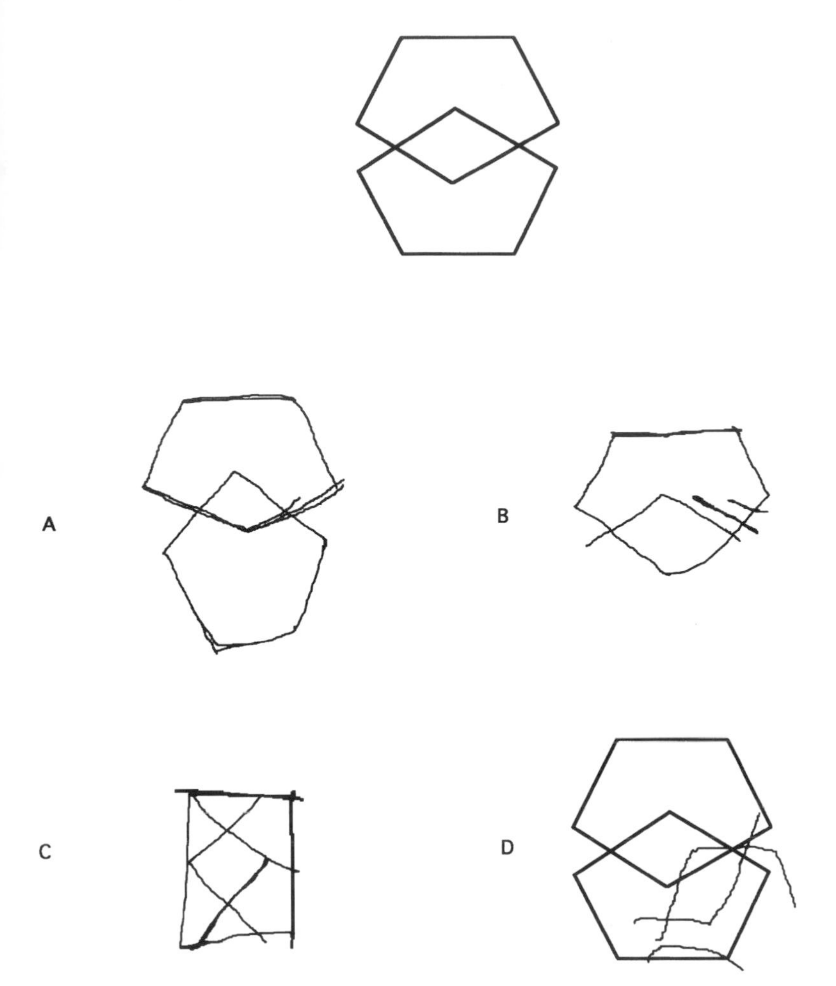

Fig. 7. Follow-up of copying a complex geometrical figure in a demented patient (model on the top). (A) One year post-onset: copying is relatively spared. (B) Two years post-onset: only a single figure is well reproduced. C) Three years post-onset: the patient produced a simplified figure, poorly related to the stimulus. (D) Closing-in phenomenon at 5 years post-onset: the patient overlapped the copy with the model, taking the original as a reference point.

Alzheimer's disease patients with respect to copying, at variance with what found in Huntington's disease (Rouleau, Salmon, Butters et al., 1992) and in Lewy body dementia (Gnanalingham, Byrne and Thornton, 1996; but see Swanwick, Coen, Maguire et al., 1996). Longitudinal studies have confirmed that spontaneous drawing is impaired in the early stages of the disease and that copying deteriorates successively (Rouleau, Salmon and Butters, 1996).

In early demented patients, the copy of simple geometrical figures may be relatively spared while the copy of complex figures is particularly sensitive to the progression of the disease (Binetti, Cappa, Magni et al., 1998). For example the Rey's figure may be reproduced in a simplified way, with single constitutive elements put one after the other (see Fig. 4D3). In these cases, patients seem to be able to recognize and to reproduce single well-known elements (likely by the activation of motor subroutines which are stored in a specialized long-term memory store — a sort of constructional lexicon), but are unable to reproduce complex spatial relationships correctly. Another 'simplification' error may consist in the reproduction of more familiar or simpler figures instead of more complex ones (e.g. a square instead of a diamond).

As the disease progresses, patients usually become unable even to draw simple figures correctly, as they no longer have access to well-consolidated motor subroutines (Fig. 6).

In advanced stages of dementia (Ober, Jagust, Koss et al., 1991; Rouleau et al., 1996), the tendency either to overlap the copy with the model, reproducing the original using its parts as a reference point, or to trace the pencil over the lines of the model, producing a scrawl (see Figs. 2, 3 and 6) may become evident. This phenomenon, termed 'closing-in', was first described by Mayer-Gross (1935) and since then has often been reported in demented patients (Ajuriaguerra et al., 1960; Gainotti, 1972). Some writers regard this phenomenon as a primitive trigger reflex in patients with diffuse cognitive deterioration (Gainotti, 1972); patients might be strongly attracted by the model and be unable to detach from it (as in a sort of echopraxia). In some cases, however, a simple verbal instruction may suffice to avoid this constructional error. Other authors suggest that closing-in occurs when patients who are unable to structure an empty space look for a reference point to solve difficult constructional dilemmas (De Renzi, 1959). In these cases, patients might be unable to generate a bidimensional frame in the copying paper (i.e. they cannot identify a 'constructional space'), and try to use already existing frames, for example, the border of the model or, in other cases, the edge of the paper ('margination' of the copy, seen also in children). In the course of dementia syndromes, the presence of this phenomenon seems consistent with a diagnosis of 'primary degenerative type' (Gainotti, Parlato, Monteleone and Carlomagno, 1992). Rarely, closing-in may be observed in patients with focal lesions. Gainotti (1972) observed closing-in in only 15 of a series of 200 patients with focal lesions. A recent study on a patient with a focal cerebral lesion seems to confirm that the closing-in phenomenon can be related to a deficit in localizing points in space (Grossi et al., 1996).

Severely demented patients may also show the tendency to perseverate (Rouleau et al., 1996), which would suggest a lesion of frontal regions. In particular, patients with frontotemporal dementia would frequently show perseveration errors (Snowden, Neary and Mann, 1996), while specific disturbances in reproducing spatial relationships are less common.

Toward a cognitive model of drawing

Available cognitive models for drawing

Three points emerge from this review of the literature. Firstly, even though CA is a symptom which is recognisable by the administration of simple tests — even at the patient's bedside, clinical and experimental studies have nonetheless failed to generate a homogeneous picture of its various facets. One thing which seems certain is that the incidence of CA in patients with left and right hemisphere lesions is more or less similar, while the nature of CA and the presence of qualitative inter- and intra-hemispheric differences are issues which remain open to discussion.

The second point is that several cognitive disorders (e.g. visual recognition impairments, neglect, visuoperceptual and general intellectual deficits) can interfere with the execution of a constructional task.

Third, the study of CA is becoming more directed towards an analysis of drawing processes. Almost all the studies cited in this review have employed graphomotor tasks, probably borne out by the fact that they are versatile, easy to carry out and to score, although it is also plausible that the heterogeneity of constructional disabilities (and the theory's lack of defining power) have urged various researchers to focus their attention on one constructional skill in particular. As a result, drawing disabilities have become considered constructional disabilities per se. This implicit decision has paved the way for substantial changes in approaches to the study of constructional disorders. Rather than proceeding from an operational definition of constructional abilities, a specific cognitive skill — drawing — has been taken as a starting point and researchers have tried to identify the individual processes which contribute to its execution.

The traditional approach proceeded from an analysis of the correlations between various visuoperceptual, executive and constructional tasks without looking for clear relationships between the performance of subjects on specific tests and their constructional abilities. This has been superseded by attempts to apply cognitive neuropsychological principles to drawing, as in other cognitive domains, i.e. reading, writing, visual recognition and so on.

One of the first cognitive models of drawing was proposed by Roncato, Sartori, Masterson and Rumiati (1987). According to them, the copying of a figure comprises four basic stages: two preparatory stages (exploration of the model and preparation of the drawing plan), execution and checking. These operations are probably hierarchically organised and each stage in turn consists of a series of substages. The preparatory phase involves the processing of an internal representation of the model, which guides copying. This representation contains specifications of global form, the constituent parts of the stimulus, its details and their spatial relationships. The preparation of a drawing plan implicates decisions concerning the scale and the positioning of the copy. The executive stage starts with decisions about the initial shape of the drawing and proceeds in accordance with the drawing plan. Checking processes perform comparisons between the copy and the stimulus, allowing the copying process to proceed whilst making corrections if necessary.

Roncato et al. (1987) have also designed a series of tests which provide insight into the various stages of copying and therefore permit identification of the defective cognitive process in a particular patient. The test battery assesses only categorical spatial relationships and uses two simple geometric forms as stimuli in a series of tasks: copying, drawing from verbal description, assembly of a requested shape, visual comparison and comparison of a picture with a sentence which describes it. The final test requires the patient to decide if two sentences describe the same spatial arrangement of shapes (e.g. the circle is on the left of the square; the square is on the right of the circle). Using this battery, Roncato et al. (1987) have identified a patient with a specific deficit at the level of internal representation and a patient with a specific disorder at the executive level.

Another cognitive model of drawing has been proposed by Van Sommers (1989). This model sees the internal representation of a percept or mental image as the starting point for its graphic representation. The planning of a drawing starts with depiction decisions and processes, where a person decides how to draw the object represented in short-term visual memory; decisions at this stage include: variety of object (e.g. an open or closed umbrella), two- or three-dimensionality, orientation, level of detail and so on. Having made these decisions, the drawing is planned (a drawing strategy is selected, i.e. which parts will be drawn first and which later) taking into account the individual's drawing ability and properties of the graphic motor system (the greater ease with which certain movements, motor routines etc. are carried out).

One of the most interesting aspects of this model is the links between the imagery system and the semantic system. Van Sommers (1989) underlines that some forms of constructional apraxia can be limited to free-drawing and related to alterations at the level of mental representation (so-called 'visuoimaginative apraxia', Grossi et al., 1986, 1989) or specific defects at the depiction decisions and processes stage. The latter clinical picture, characterised by an intact ability to generate mental images and a selective inability to carry out spontaneous drawing, was reported in Van Sommer's (1989) patient.

A third model of the mental processes involved in drawing has been described by Grossi and Angelini (Grossi, 1991). They also distinguish four sequential steps in copying tasks: preliminary analysis, central processing, execution and checking. Preliminary analysis consists of a search for an interpretative hypothesis of the model: on the one hand, the individual tries to identify in the stimulus objects that have already been drawn in the past and at the same time, he analyses the spatial relationships between elements of the picture and those between the picture and the paper on which it is drawn (orientation, size etc.). In this initial phase, there is an interaction with long-term memory because in interpreting the picture, the individual activates visual, spatial and constructional knowledge (there may also be a long-term store for familiar constructional schema, a so-called 'constructional lexicon'). The elements identified by preliminary analysis, are then processed in order to formulate a drawing plan (the complex of instructions which are subsequently transformed into graphics). The drawing plan, the fruit of central processing, results from a series of procedural decisions concerning what to draw first, where to start, the order in which successive parts are drawn and so on. The plan is preserved in a short-term memory buffer for as long as is necessary to complete its translation onto paper via the activation of motor programmes.

Grossi and Angelini propose two copying procedures: a 'lexical' route which predominantly involves activation of familiar visual or constructional schema (for example in the drawing of a square or a face) and a second 'line-by-line' procedure, based on a spatial analysis which does not use constructional representations (activated when copying a doodle, for example). Both procedures may be adopted for copying complex pictures, but some patients might be constrained to use either one or the other. Here, the reader is reminded of the slow, slavish 'line-by-line' copying procedure adopted by visual agnosic patients (Wapner, Judd and Gardner, 1978), who perhaps cannot access the lexical route for familiar objects. On the contrary, a patient has recently been described who successfully uses the lexical route in simple drawing tasks, but is unable to activate spatial analysis for more complex tasks, producing pictures with distorted spatial relationships. The diagnosis of a cognitive defect at the heart of a constructional disorder is, therefore, possible via a specific test battery which has recently normed and published (Angelini and Grossi, 1993) and which explores the various stages involved in copying.

Some (provisional) conclusions

The aforementioned models distinguish some fundamental stages in the process of drawing. There are certain parallels between them (Grossi and Trojano, 1999), although they are differentiated in terms of their formal characteristics, depth of analysis and in certain theoretical aspects. None of them have, at present, received general acceptance, in the absence of adequate clinical and experimental evidence. In particular, the heuristic value of each model (its ability to interpret the errors made by patients and to predict the various symptomological permutations which are classed as drawing disabilities) has yet to be demonstrated.

In a recent theoretical review, Guérin et al. (1999) argue that drawing is a multicomponential process that relies on at least three cognitive systems: visual perception, visual imagery and graphic production. As mentioned above, the authors suggest that visual perception abilities related to drawing are best described in terms of the model of Kosslyn and Koenig (1992), but we have already underlined that the specific consequences of elementary visuospatial disturbances on constructional performances have not been fully identified. Moreover, Guérin et al. (1999) suggest that visual imagery would be involved in drawing unfamiliar objects, while drawing familiar objects (which are strictly related to the drawer's premorbid abilities) may proceed by the activation of motor procedural memory, and this could correspond to what we have called a sort of constructional lexicon. Therefore, Guérin et al. (1999) suggest that producing familiar drawings would not need planning abilities, while a kind of planning (similar to that required by other problem-solving tasks) would be necessary to produce novel or unfamiliar drawings. The authors suggest that this planning component would be not specific to drawing and, similarly, maintain that damage to an action programming subsystem could result in the associated picture of CA and gestural apraxia. In summary, reviewing available cognitive models, Guérin et al. (1999) agree that model-based neuropsychological studies may provide new insights on CA, but also cast some doubts about the specificity of the cognitive abilities thought to be necessary to draw spontaneously or to copy.

In some sense, this position might undermine the validity of the concept of CA as a specific cognitive disorder, originally put forward by Kleist. However, some cognitively oriented studies are now available that would demonstrate selective impairments in patients with constructional disabilities. Trojano and Grossi (1998) reported on a patient with a bilateral ischemic lesion of posterior cerebral areas who could copy and draw to command only simple geometrical figures. The combined use of assessment batteries by Roncato et al. (1987) and Angelini and Grossi (1993) allowed then to explore cognitive processes devoted to drawing from two complementary points of view and demonstrated that the patient did not show any elementary impairment of visuospatial or executive processes; on the other hand, the patient did not show defects of general intellectual abilities. Therefore, his gross distortions in copying complex geometrical figures had to be accounted for by a selective defect at a planning component specific for drawing. Similar observations, albeit at a lower detail, have been reported in two other patients with right cerebral lesions (Angelini and Grossi, 1993; Roncato et al., 1987, Case 1).

On this basis, it could be possible to argue that at least one intermediate step exists between visuoperceptual analysis and realization of graphic productions. This intermediate 'central', cognitive step would consist of the elaboration of information obtained from visual input analysis in order to prepare and guide motor processes. A defect at this stage, identified by specific test batteries, could thus be caused by focal cerebral lesions and would reveal itself through the inability to reproduce complex figures (Trojano and Grossi, 1998).

This study also confirms that to draw simple figures in canonical perspective can proceed via the sole activation of well-learned motor subroutines. This observation would tie in with another case report on a patient with a subcortical right ischemic lesion (Grossi et al., 1996), in which it was argued that such motor subroutines could be part of a procedural memory (a sort of 'constructional lexicon') which develops as a result of formal education and personal aptitudes.

From these considerations it would be possible to implement the definition of the 'central' elaboration of the drawing plan as that cognitive process through which simple motor subroutines are selected, integrated in a spatial relationship system and sequentially activated to draw novel or complex structures. If no available motor routine appears to be useful for reproducing a certain model (say a scrawl, for example), it would be possible to solve the constructional problem by means of a line-by-line strategy relying predominantly on visuoperceptual analysis, as visual agnosic patients usually do (Trojano and Grossi, 1992). In this case, the drawing plan would consist of the sequential activation of the most simple motor routines (those allowing to reproduce straight or curve lines), under the continuous guidance of visual analysis.

In conclusion, the cognitive approach seems to offer new tools for investigating and conceptualizing drawing disorders. The recent cognitive models allow us to formulate in modern terms the original clinical observations of Kleist (1934), according to which (true forms of) CA can be ascribed to specific programming impairments independent of elementary visuoperceptual or executive defects.

Many aspects remain unclear. For example, one regards the possible generalization of these models to the other 'constructional skills' identified by Kleist (1934), for example the ability to reproduce tri-dimensional structures. Does it imply the same visuoperceptual, representational and executive processes as drawing? By means of systematic, theoretically driven, assessment tools, it will possible to improve the defining power of interpretative hypotheses and address open questions.

At the moment, to draw some (provisional) conclusions, we would argue that constructional disorders are multicomponential in nature, but also that some of them can derive from impairments of cognitive abilities specific to drawing. It would be perhaps premature to put forward a comprehensive cognitive model for drawing, but it is possible to provide an overview of cognitive abilities necessary in copying a complex geometrical figure. Drawing likely includes the following steps.

(1) The stimulus to be copied has to be perceived. Severe visuoperceptual disturbances, such as cortical blindness and apperceptive agnosia, impair perceptual appreciation of the stimulus and its reproduction.

(2) The stimulus has to be fully explored. Unilateral spatial neglect may induce different types of impairment in copying a figure:

- USN can damage exploration (producing omissions in the reproduction);
- USN can damage bidimensional spatiotopic processing of the drawing (giving rise to distortions or hemidistortions in the reproduction).

(3) The stimulus has to be recognized. In visual associative agnosia the impaired access to previous visual knowledge may impair the activation of motor sub-routines in the constructional lexicon while copying well-known figures. Visual associative agnosic patients may also experience difficulties in copying a novel figure, which proceeds through the assimilation to, or the decomposition of, well-known figures. For these reasons agnosic patients often resort to slavish line-by-line copying procedures.

(4) The stimulus has to be spatially analyzed. Both simple and complex figures have to undergo bidimensional spatiotopic analysis and the relationships among simple constituents of the figure have to be coded in terms of bidimensional spatial coordinates; this step may be impaired in patients with Balint syndrome, USN or frontal lesions.

(5) The reproduction must be planned. Information gathered through visuoperceptual processes

have to be integrated in an executive plan, and this step could be conceived of as a form of problem solving. Therefore, defects of sustained attention and of general planning abilities, like those found in patients with frontal lesions or dementia, or in patients with dysexecutive syndrome may determine an alteration of planning strategies or several subsequent changes in planning decisions. However, at least some stages of this planning process are specific to drawing and can be selectively impaired after brain lesions, giving rise to ('pure' forms of) CA.

(6) The reproduction must be executed. A first step of the execution phase is the identification of the constructional space on the drawing sheet, choosing the starting point: this means that bidimensional spatiotopic coordinates have to be projected on the sheet. The constructional space is the external rendering of the 'inner' space representation and is affected by the same cognitive disorders (neglect, Balint syndrome) that can disrupt the latter. However, a patient might process the mental spatial representation accurately, but fail in structuring the constructional space, as has been demonstrated in neglect patients. Do the two spaces share the same coordinate frames? Or do the motor requirements of the drawing task elicit specific attentional or representational processes?

In the past, it was said that the study of CA, in view of its great complexity, could not contribute to an understanding of the organisation of spatial abilities in the brain (De Renzi, 1982). Nonetheless, having abandoned the traditional operational definition of CA — leaving room for diverse interpretations of constructional tasks and disabilities — the cognitive approach seems to offer new hopes for an improved theory.

References

Ajuriaguerra J, Muller M, Tissot R: A propos de quelques problèmes posés par l'apraxie dans les démences. Encéphale: 49; 275–401, 1960.

Andersen RA, Essick GK, Siegel RM: The encoding of spatial location by posterior parietal cortex. Science: 230; 56–58, 1985.

Anderson B: Spared awareness for the left side of internal images in patients with left-sided extrapersonal neglect. Neurology: 43; 213–216, 1993.

Angelini R, Grossi D: La Terapia Razionale dei Disordini Costruttivi. Rome: Centro di Riabilitazione S. Lucia, 1993.

Arrigoni C, De Renzi E: Constructional apraxia and hemispheric locus of lesion. Cortex: 1; 170–197, 1964.

Benowitz LI, Moya KL, Levine DN: Impaired verbal reasoning and constructional apraxia in subjects with right hemisphere damage. Neuropsychologia: 28; 231–241, 1990.

Benson DF, Barton M: Disturbances in constructional ability. Cortex: 6; 19–46, 1970.

Benton AL: Constructional apraxia and the minor hemisphere. Confinia Neurologica: 29; 1–16, 1967.

Benton AL: Constructional apraxia. In Boller F, Grafman J (Eds), Handbook of Neuropsychology, 1st edn., Vol. 2. Amsterdam: Elsevier, pp. 387–394, 1989.

Benton AL, Fogel ML: Three-dimensional constructional praxis: a clinical test. Archives of Neurology (Chicago): 7; 347–354, 1962.

Binder LM: Constructional strategies of complex figure drawings after unilateral brain damage. Journal of Clinical Neuropsychology: 4; 51–58, 1982.

Binetti G, Cappa S, Magni E, Padovani A, Bianchetti A, Trabucchi M: Visual and spatial perception in the early phase of Alzheimer's disease. Neuropsychology: 12; 29–33, 1998.

Bisiach E, Luzzatti C, Perani D: Unilateral neglect, representational space. Cortex: 14; 129–133, 1979.

Black FW, Bernard BA: Constructional apraxia as a function of lesion locus and size in patients with focal brain damage. Cortex: 20; 111–120, 1984.

Borod JC, Carper M, Goodglass H: WAIS performance IQ in aphasia as a function of auditory comprehension and constructional apraxia. Cortex: 18; 212–220, 1982.

Carlesimo GA, Fadda L, Caltagirone C: Basic mechanisms of constructional apraxia in unilateral brain-damaged patients: role of visuo-perceptual and executive disorders. Journal of Clinical and Experimental Neuropsychology: 15; 342–358, 1993.

De Renzi E: Osservazioni semeiogenetiche in tema di aprassia costruttiva. Rivista Sperimentale di Freniatria: 58; 231–256, 1959.

De Renzi E: L'aprassia costruttiva. In Bisiach F et al. (Eds), Neuropsicologia Clinica. Milan: Franco Angeli Ed., 1980.

De Renzi E: Disorders of Space Exploration and Cognition. New York: Wiley and Sons, 1982.

Dee HL: Visuoconstructive and visuoperceptive deficits in patients with unilateral cerebral lesions. Neuropsychologia: 8; 305–314, 1970.

Denes G, Semenza C: Sparing of constructional abilities in severe dementia. European Neurology: 21; 161–164, 1982.

Di Pellegrino G: Clock-drawing in a case of left visuo-spatial neglect: a deficit of disengagement? Neuropsychologia: 33; 353–358, 1995.

Duensing F: Raumagnostische und ideatorische-apraktische Storung des gestalten den Handelns. Deutsche Zeitschrift fur Nervenheilkunde: 170; 191–204, 1953.

Freedman M, Leach L, Kaplan E, Winocur G, Shulman KI, Delis DC: Clock Drawing: a Neuropsychological Analysis. New York: Oxford, 1994.

Gainotti G: A quantitative study of the 'closing-in' symptom

in normal children and in brain-damaged patients. Neuropsychologia: 10; 429–436, 1972.
Gainotti G: Constructional apraxia. In Fredericks JAM (Ed), Handbook of Clinical Neurology, Vol. 45. Amsterdam: Elsevier, pp. 491–506, 1985.
Gainotti G, Miceli G, Caltagirone C: Constructional apraxia in left brain-damaged patients: a planning disorder? Cortex: 13; 109–18, 1977.
Gainotti G, Parlato V, Monteleone D, Carlomagno S: Neuropsychological markers of dementia on visuospatial tasks: a comparison between Alzheimer's type and vascular forms of dementia. Journal of Clinical and Experimental Neuropsychology: 14; 239–252, 1992.
Gainotti G, Silveri MC, Villa G, Caltagirone C: Drawing from memory in aphasia. Brain: 106; 613–622, 1983.
Gainotti G, Tiacci C: Patterns of drawing disability in right and left hemispheric patients. Neuropsychologia: 8; 379–384, 1970.
Gold M, Adair JC, Jacobs DH, Heilman KM: Right–left confusion in Gertsmann's syndrome: a model of body centered spatial orientation. Cortex: 31; 267–83, 1990.
Gnanalingham KK, Byrne EJ, Thornton A: Clock-face drawing to differentiate Lewy body and Alzheimer type dementia. Lancet: 347; 696–697, 1996.
Grossi D: La Riabilitazione dei Disturbi della Cognizione Spaziale. Milan: Masson, 1991.
Grossi D, Correra G, Calise C, Trojano L: Selective constructional disorders after right subcortical stroke. A neuropsychological premorbid and follow-up study. Italian Journal of Neurological Sciences: 14, 23–33, 1996.
Grossi D, Fragassi NA, Giani E, Trojano L: The selective inability to draw horizontal lines: on a peculiar constructional disorder. Journal of Neurology, Neurosurgery and Psychiatry: 64; 795–798, 1998.
Grossi D, Lepore M, Esposito A, Napolitano A, Serino M, Trojano L: Neglect-associated constructional disorders: a paradoxical phenomenon? Neuropsychologia: 37; 589–594, 1999.
Grossi D, Modafferi A, Pelosi L, Trojano L: On the different roles of the cerebral hemispheres in Mental Imagery. The 'o' clock' test in two clinical cases. Brain and Cognition: 10; 18–27, 1989.
Grossi D, Orsini A, Modafferi A, Liotti M: Visuoimaginal constructional apraxia: on a case of selective deficit of imagery. Brain and Cognition: 5; 255–267, 1986.
Grossi D, Trojano L: Constructional apraxia. In Denes F, Pizzamiglio L (Eds), Handbook of Clinical and Experimental Neuropsychology. Hove: Psychology Press, pp. 441–450, 1999.
Grossman M: Drawing deficits in brain-damaged patients' freehands pictures. Brain and Cognition: 8; 189–205, 1988.
Grossman M, Mickanin J, Onishi K, Robinson KM, D'Esposito M: Freehand drawing impairments in probable Alzheimer's disease. Journal of the International Neuropsychological Society: 2; 226–235, 1996.
Guérin F, Ska B, Belleville S: Cognitive processing of drawing abilities. Brain and Cognition: 40; 464–478, 1999.
Halligan PW, Marshall JC, Wade DT: Left on the right: allochiria in a case of left visuo-spatial neglect. Journal of Neurology, Neurosurgery and Psychiatry: 55; 717–719, 1992.
Hécaen H, Ajuriaguerra J: Brain, 77: 373–400, 1954.
Hécaen H, Assal G: A comparison of constructive deficits following right and left hemispheric lesion. Neuropsychologia: 8; 289–303, 1970.
Hyvarinen J: The Parietal Cortex of Monkey and Man. Berlin: Springer-Verlag, 1982.
Irving-Bell L, Small M, Cowey A: A distortion of perceived space in patients with right-hemisphere lesions and visual hemineglect. Neuropsychologia: 37; 919–925, 1999.
Ishiai S, Seki K, Koyama Y, Yokota T: Mechanisms of unilateral spatial neglect in copying a single object. Neuropsychologia: 34; 965–971, 1996.
Ishiai S, Seki K, Koyama Y, Izumi Y: Disappearance of unilateral spatial neglect following a simple instruction. Journal of Neurology, Neurosurgery and Psychiatry: 63; 23–27, 1997.
Kaplan E: A process approach to neuropsychological assessment. In Boll T, Bryant BK (Eds), Clinical Neuropsychology and Brain Function: Research, Measurement and Practice. Washington: APA, pp. 129–167, 1983.
Kaplan E: Process and achievement revisited. In Wapner S, Kaplan B (Eds), Toward a Holistic Developmental Psychology. Hillsdale: Erlbaum, pp. 143–156, 1988.
Kashiwagi T, Kashiwagi A, Kunimori Y, Yamadori A, Tanabe H, Okuda D: Preserved capacity to copy drawings in severe aphasics with little premorbid experience. Aphasiology: 8; 427–442, 1994.
Kempen JH, Krichevsky M, Feldman ST: Effect of visual impairment on neuropsychological test performance. Journal of Clinical and Experimental Neuropsychology: 16; 223–231, 1994.
Kirk A, Kertesz A: Hemispheric contributions to drawing. Neuropsychologia: 27; 881–886, 1989.
Kirk A, Kertesz A: On drawing impairment in Alzheimer's disease. Archives of Neurology: 48; 73–77, 1991.
Kirk A, Kertesz A: Subcortical contributions to drawing. Brain and Cognition: 21; 57–70, 1993.
Kleist K: Gehirnpathologie. Leipzig: Barth, 1934.
Kosslyn SM, Flynn RA, Amsterdam JB, Wang G: Components of high-level vision: a cognitive neuroscience analysis and accounts of neurological syndromes. Cognition: 34; 203–277, 1990.
Kosslyn SM, Koenig O: Wet Mind: The New Cognitive Neuroscience. New York: The Free Press, 1992.
Luria AR, Tsvetkova LS: The programming of constructive activity in local brain injuries. Neuropsychologia: 2; 95–108, 1964.
Mack JL, Levine RN: The basis of visual constructional disability in patients with unilateral cerebral lesions. Cortex: 17; 515–532, 1981.
Marshall RS, Lazar RM, Binder JR, Desmond DW, Drucker PM, Mohr JP: Intrahemispheric localization of drawing dysfunction. Neuropsychologia: 32; 493–501, 1994.
Martin A: Neuropsychology of Alzheimer's disease: the case for subgroups. In Schwartz MF (Ed), Modular Deficits in

Alzheimer Type Dementia. Cambridge, MA: MIT Press, pp. 143–176, 1990.

Mayer-Gross W: Some observations on apraxia. Proceedings of Royal Society of Medicine: 28; 1203–1212, 1935.

Mijovic D: Mechanisms of visual spatial neglect. Absence of directional hypokinesia in spatial exploration. Brain: 114; 1575–1593, 1991.

Newcombe F, Ratcliffe G: Disorders of visuospatial analysis. In Boller F, Grafman J (Eds), Handbook of Neuropsychology, 1st edn., Vol 2. Amsterdam: Elsevier, pp. 333–356, 1989.

Ober BA, Jagust WJ, Koss E, Delis DC, Friedland RP: Visuoconstructive performance and regional cerebral glucose metabolism in Alzheimer's disease. Journal of Clinical and Experimental Neuropsychology: 13; 752–772, 1991.

Osterreith P: Le test de copie d' une figure complexe. Archives de Psychologie: 30; 206–356, 1944.

Piercy M, Hecaen H, Ajuriaguerra J: Constructional apraxia associated with unilateral cerebral lesions. Left and right sided cases compared. Brain: 83; 225–242, 1960.

Piercy M, Smyth VOG: Right hemisphere dominance for certain nonverbal intellectual skills. Brain: 85; 775–790, 1962.

Pillon B: Troubles visuo-constructifs et methodes de compensation: resultats de 85 patients atteints de lesions cerebrales. Neuropsychologia: 19; 375–383, 1981.

Ratcliffe G, Ross J: Visual perception and perceptual disorders. British Medical Bullettin: 37; 181–186, 1981.

Rieger C: Ueber Apparate in dem Hirn. Arbeiten aus der Psychiatrischen Klinik zu Wuerzburg, Heft 5. Jena: Gustav Fischer, 1909.

Roncato S, Sartori G, Masterson J, Rumiati R: Constructional apraxia: an information processing analysis. Cognitive Neuropsychology: 4; 113–129, 1987.

Rouleau I, Salmon DP, Butters N, Kennedy C, McGuire K: Quantitative and qualitative analyses of clock drawing in Alzheimer's and Huntington's disease. Brain and Cognition: 18; 70–87, 1992.

Rouleau I, Salmon DP, Butters N: Longitudinal analysis of clock drawing in Alzheimer's disease patients. Brain and Cognition: 31; 17–34, 1996.

Semenza C, Denes G, D'Urso V, Romano O, Montorsi T: Analytical and global strategies in copying designs by unilaterally brain-damaged patients. Cortex: 14; 404–410, 1978.

Snowden JS, Neary D, Mann DM: Fronto-temporal Lobar Degeneration: Fronto-temporal Dementia, Progressive Aphasia, Semantic Dementia. New York: Churchill Livingstone, pp. 49–50, 1996.

Solms M, Turnbull OH, Kaplan-Solms K, Miller P: Rotated drawing: the range of performance and anatomical correlates in a series of 16 patients. Brain and Cognition: 38; 358–368, 1998.

Stark M, Coslett B, Saffran EM: Impairment of an egocentric map of locations: implications for perception and action. Cognitive Neuropsychology: 13; 481–523, 1996.

Stein JF: The representation of egocentric space in the posterior parietal cortex. Behavioral Brain Science: 15; 691–700, 1992.

Swanwick GRJ, Coen RF, Maguire CP, Coakley D, Lawlor BA: Clock-face drawing to differentiate dementia syndrome. Lancet: 347; 1115, 1996.

Trojano L, Angelini R, Gallo P, Grossi D: An 'ecological' constructional task. Perceptual and Motor Skills: 85; 51–57, 1997.

Trojano L, De Cicco G, Grossi D: Copying procedures of Rey complex figure in normal subjects and brain-damaged patients. Italian Journal of Neurological Sciences: 14; 23–33, 1993.

Trojano L, Grossi D: Impaired drawing from memory in a patient with visual associative agnosia. Brain and Cognition: 20; 327–344, 1992.

Trojano L, Grossi D: A critical review of mental imagery defects. Brain and Cognition: 24; 213–243, 1994.

Trojano L, Grossi D: 'Pure' constructional apraxia. A cognitive analysis of a single case. Behavioral Neurology: 11; 43–49, 1998.

Turnbull OH, Laws KR, McCarthy RA: Object recognition without knowledge of object orientation. Cortex: 31; 387–395, 1995.

Ungerleider LG, Mishkin M: Two cortical visual systems. In Ingle DJ, Goodale MA, Mansfield RJW (Eds), Analysis of Visual Behaviour. Cambridge, MA: MIT Press, pp. 549–586, 1982.

van Sommers P: A system for drawing-related neuropsychology. Cognitive Neuropsychology: 6; 117–164, 1989.

Villa G, Gainotti G, De Bonis C: Constructive disabilities in focal brain-damaged patients: influence of hemispheric side, locus of lesion and coexistent mental deterioration. Neuropsychologia: 24; 497–510, 1986.

Wapner W, Judd T, Gardner H: Visual agnosia in an artist. Cortex: 14; 343–364, 1978.

Warrington EK, James M, Kinsbourne M: Drawing disability in relation to laterality. Brain: 89; 530–582, 1966.

Wechsler D: Wechsler Adult Intelligence Scale – Revised. New York: Harcourt Brace Jovanovic, 1981.

Westheimer G: Location and line orientation as distinguishable primitives in spatial vision. Proceedings of Royal Society of London: B Biological Sciences: 263; 503–508, 1996.

Handbook of Neuropsychology, 2nd Edition, Vol. 4
M. Behrmann (Ed)

CHAPTER 6

Bálint's syndrome

Robert Rafal *

School of Psychology, University of Wales, Bangor LL57 2AS, UK

Introduction

Rezso Bálint first described a remarkable syndrome caused by bilateral lesions of the parieto-occipital junction that rendered its victims functionally blind (Bálint, 1909). While visual acuity is preserved and patients are able to recognize objects placed directly in front of them, they are unable to interact with, or make sense of, their visual environment. They are lost in space. Fleeting objects that they can recognize, but which they cannot localize or grasp, appear and disappear, and their features jumble together. They are helpless in a visually chaotic world.

Contemporary developments in neuroscience and cognitive science are providing a better understanding of the experience of these patients. This chapter will summarize some of the critical clues that their plight provides in helping us understand the neural basis of visual attention and perception, and how they operate together normally to provide a coherence and continuity of perceptual experience.

A good place to start is to compare Bálint's syndrome with hemispatial neglect. Other chapters on hemispatial neglect in this volume describe the syndrome resulting from unilateral lesions of the posterior association cortex that causes a derangement of spatial attention. Patients with this syndrome do not attend to information that is contralateral to the lesion. 'Contralateral', however, does not necessarily refer to the opposite visual field. Patient with this syndrome can exhibit 'object-centered' neglect: that is, neglect of the contralesional side of an object independent of its location in the retinotopic frame of reference. Nevertheless, even when hemispatial neglect operates in an object-centered reference frame, the deficit is still inherently spatial; that is, it is the contralesional side of the object which is neglected. By contrast, the bilateral lesions that result in Bálint's syndrome result in a simultaneous agnosia — a constriction of visual attention that allows the patient to see only one object at a time — that is entirely object-based and independent of any spatial representation. The patient perceives whole objects, but can only see one object at a time and neglects all other objects — *even another object sharing the same retinotopic coordinates.*

Fig. 1 illustrates simultaneous agnosia in patient RX. He is shown a ruler and identifies it. Immediately, the ruler is removed and he is shown a comb that he had seen a few moments earlier. He promptly reports that the "comb reappeared". Immediately thereafter, while he is still looking at the comb, the ruler is brought again into view just behind the comb and he is asked, again, to report what he sees. He reports only the comb. When he is asked, "What happened to the ruler?", he seems bemused and responds, "I see the comb. It reappeared. What happened to the ruler? I don't know if I can answer that."

Patients with simultaneous agnosia have their attention fixed on a single object or detail in the scene and neglect all other objects. This is not due to a constriction of the visual field (tunnel vision). The visual fields may be shown to be intact when a single object is presented in the periphery of an otherwise empty

* Tel.: +44 (1248) 383603; Fax: +44 (1248) 382599;
E-mail: r.rafal@bangor.ac.uk

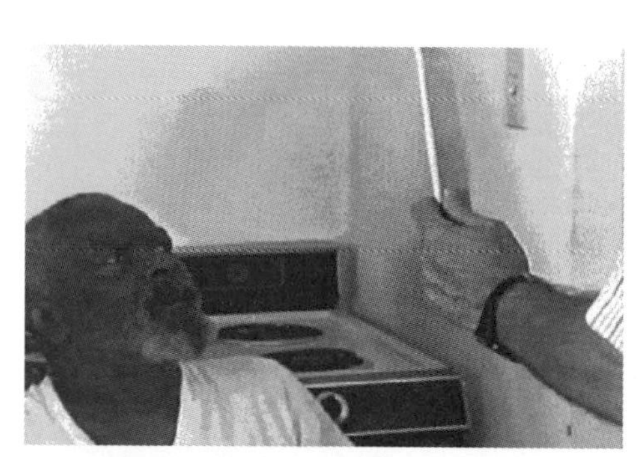

RX "I see a ruler"

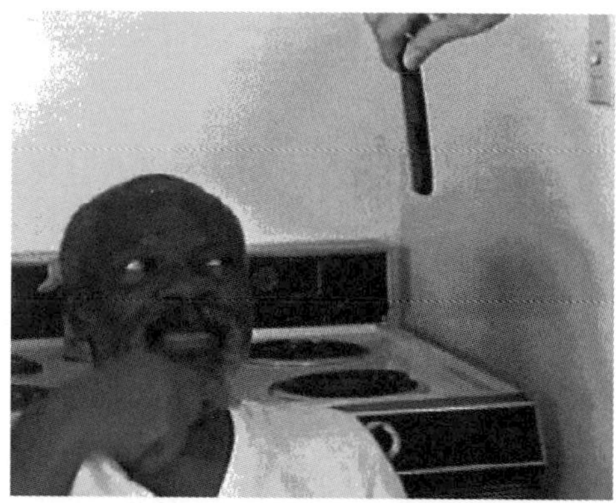

RX "The comb."

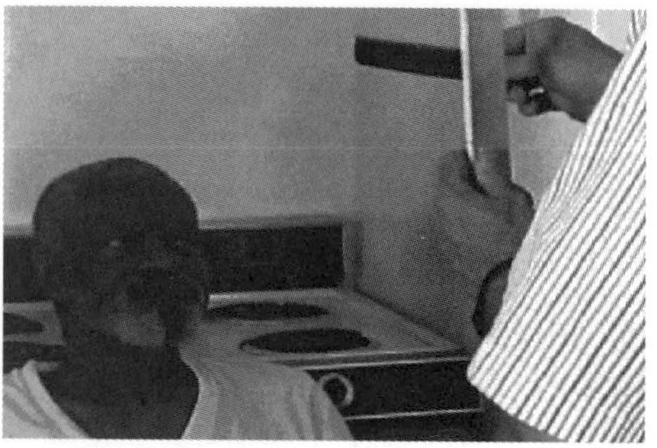

RR "How about now? What do you see?"
RX "I see the comb. The comb reappeared."

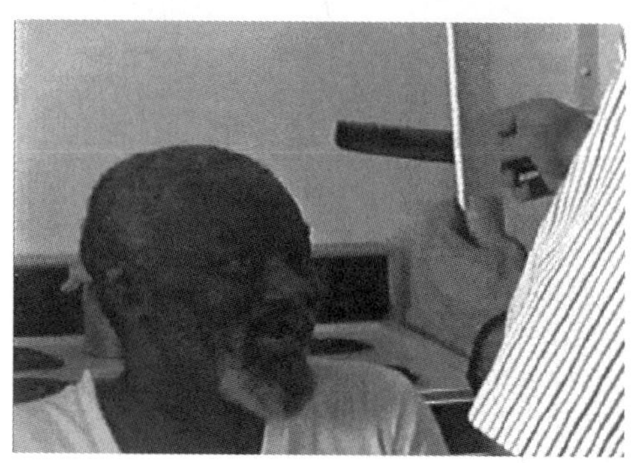

RR "What happened to the ruler?"

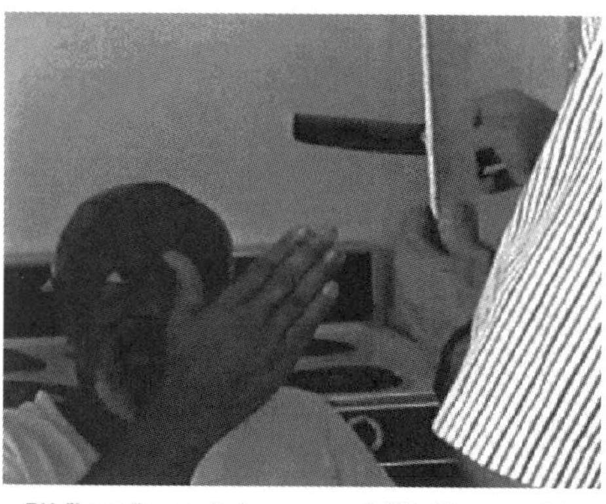

RX "I see the comb. It reappeared. What happened to the ruler? I don't know if I can answer that".

Fig. 1. Simultaneous agnosia. RX could see the ruler or the comb, but not both. From video (see text).

visual field. Moreover, the simultaneous agnosia is independent of the size of the object, or the extent to which the object includes the visual periphery. These patients can see an ant or an elephant — but only one object at a time.

When the woman shown in Fig. 2 was asked whether she could see my face, she reported that she could. When asked to look at my face and "tell me if I'm wearing glasses", she could not. She could not see the glasses and my face at the

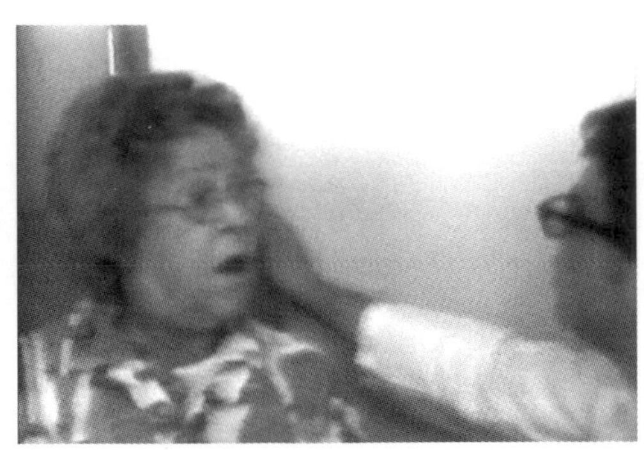

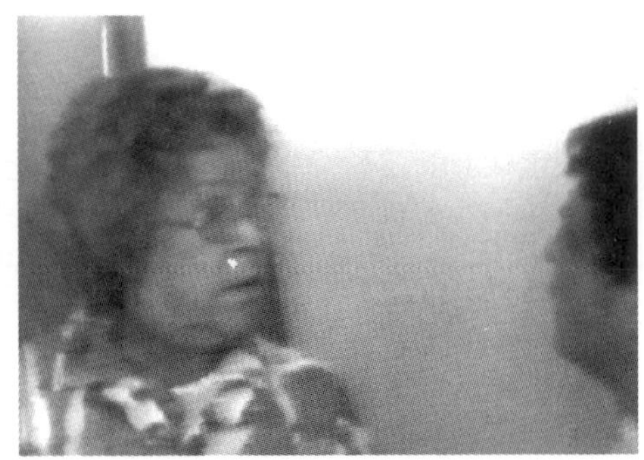

Fig. 2. Simultaneous agnosia. TX could not see, simultaneously, my glasses and my face, and could not say whether or not I was wearing glasses. From video.

same time, and could not tell me if I were wearing glasses.

The biparietal syndrome of Bálint is, thus, distinguished from hemispatial neglect by a distinctive form of object-based neglect that is independent of spatial location. This constriction of visual attention is accompanied by spatial disorientation that causes disabling impairments of spatial memory, reaching, eye movement control and depth perception. This chapter will review the clinical and neuropsychological aspects of this intriguing syndrome. It reviews its anatomical basis and some of the diseases that cause it. It then details the independent component symptoms of Bálint's syndrome. This analysis starts with simultaneous agnosia, the symptom illustrated in Figs. 1 and 2. A distinction is emphasized between object-centered neglect, as occurs in hemispatial neglect, on the one hand and an object-based deficit, that occurs in Bálint's syndrome, on the other. Spatial disorientation, the other cardinal symptom of the syndrome, is then considered as well as the related symptoms of optic ataxia, oculomotor impairment and impaired depth perception. The chapter ends with a synthesis that attempts to summarize what Bálint's syndrome tells us about the role attention and spatial representation in perception and action.

The morbid anatomy and etiology of Bálint's syndrome

The anatomical substrate for Bálint's syndrome is distinguished from that which causes hemispatial

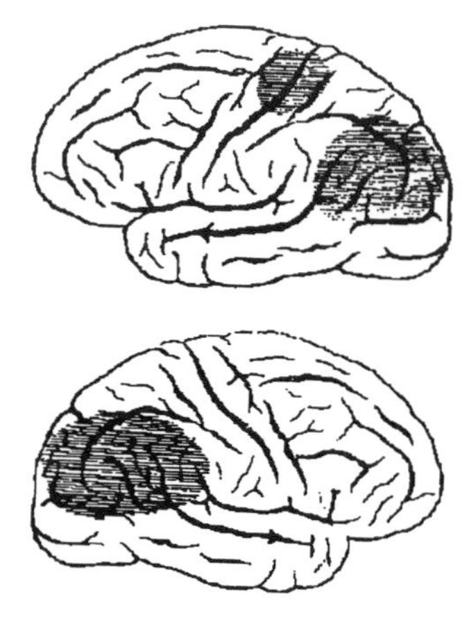

Fig. 3. Bálint's drawing of the brain of the patient he described.

neglect not only because the lesions which cause Bálint's syndrome are bilateral, but also because the lesions involve different areas of posterior association cortex. Whereas lesions of the temporo-parietal junction seem most critical for producing hemispatial neglect (Vallar, 1993), Bálint's syndrome is produced by bilateral lesions of the parieto-occipital junction. The lesions characteristically involve the dorso-rostral occipital lobe (area 19), and often — but not invariably (Karnath, Ferber, Rorden and Driver, 2000) in — the angular gyrus, but may spare the supramarginal gyrus and the superior temporal gyrus. Fig. 3 shows a drawing of the lesions in the patient reported by Bálint's in 1909 (Husain and Stein, 1988). The supramarginal gyrus and the posterior part of the superior temporal gyrus are affected in the right hemisphere, but spared on the left. The superior parietal lobule is only minimally involved in either hemisphere.

Fig. 4 (Friedman-Hill, Robertson and Treisman, 1995) shows the reconstructed magnetic resonance brain image of one of my patients with Bálint's syndrome. The lesion involves the parieto-occipital junction and part of the angular gyrus of both hemispheres, but spares the supramarginal and superior temporal gyri. Review of other recent cases of Bálint's syndrome emphasizes the consistent involvement of the posterior parietal lobe and parieto-occipital junction as critical in producing the syndrome (Coslett and Saffran, 1991; Pierrot-Deseillgny, Gray and Brunet, 1986; Verfaellie, Rapcsak and Heilman, 1990).

Thus, Bálint's syndrome is most commonly caused by diseases which typically involve the parieto-occipital junctions bilaterally. Penetrating missile wounds from projectiles entering laterally and traversing in the coronal plane through the parieto-occipital regions have been reported by Luria (1958) and by Holmes and Horax (1919). Strokes successively injuring both hemispheres in the distribution of posterior parietal branches of the middle cerebral artery are another common cause (Coslett and Saffran, 1991; Friedman-Hill et al., 1995; Pierrot-Deseillgny et al., 1986). Because the parieto-occipital junction lies in the watershed between the middle and the posterior cerebral arteries, Bálint's syndrome is a common sequelae of watershed infarction due to global cerebral hypoperfusion caused by cardiac arrest or other conditions, like cardiogenic shock, in which hypotension is accompanied by hypoxia. Another symmetric pathology is the 'butterfly' glioma — a malignant tumor originating in one parietal lobe and spreading across the corpus callosum to the other side. Radiation necrosis may develop after radiation of a parietal lobe tumor in the opposite hemisphere in the tract of the radiation port. Cerebral degenerative disease, prototypically Alzheimer disease, may begin in the parieto-occipital regions, and there is now a growing literature reporting cases of classic Bálint's syndrome due to degenerative diseases (Benson, Davis and Snyder, 1988; Hof, Bouras, Constantinidis and Morrison, 1989, 1990; Mendez, Turner, Gilmore et al., 1990).

The symptom complex of Bálint's syndrome

The Hungarian physician, Rezsö Bálint first described the syndrome in 1909 (Bálint, 1909; Harvey, 1995; Harvey and Milner, 1995; Husain and Stein, 1988). He emphasized, in his patient, the constriction of visual attention resulting in an inability to perceive more than one object at a time, and 'optic ataxia', the inability to reach accurately toward an object. Bálint intended the term, 'optic ataxia', to contrast it with tabetic ataxia from neurosyphilis. Tabetic ataxia refers to an inability to coordinate movements based on proprioceptive input, whereas 'optic ataxia' describes an inability to coordinate movements based on visual input. Many similar patients have since been reported (Coslett and Saf-

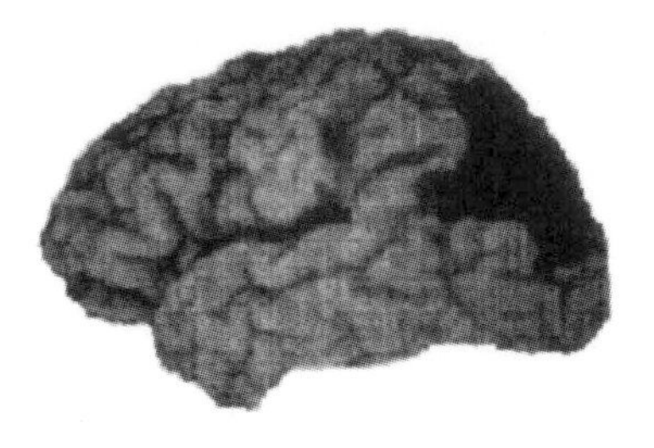
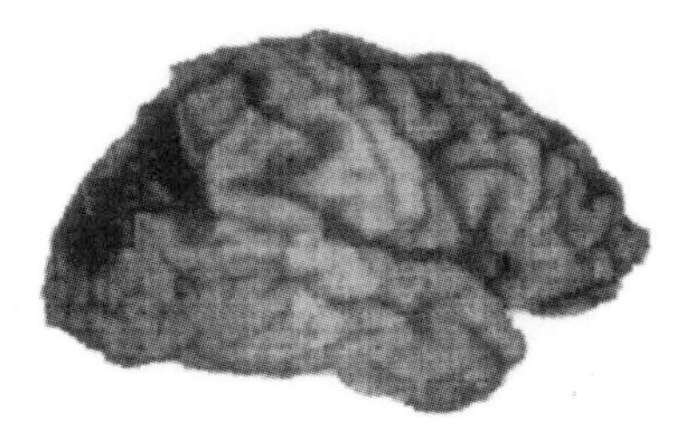

Fig. 4. Neuroimage reconstruction of the lesions of patient RM showing symmetrical lesions of the parieto-occipital junction (adapted from Friedman-Hill et al., 1995).

fran, 1991; Girotti, Milanese, Casazza et al., 1982; Godwin-Austen, 1965; Kase, Troncoso, Court et al., 1977; Luria, 1958; Luria, Pravdina-Vinarskaya, and Yarbuss, 1963; Pierrot-Deseillgny et al., 1986; Tyler, 1968; Williams, 1970).

The paper of Holmes and Horax (1919) stands as definitive in detailing the syndrome and specifying its component signs and symptoms. In addition to noting the simultaneous agnosia and optic ataxia reported by Bálint, their analysis emphasized 'spatial disorientation' as the cardinal feature of the syndrome. Holmes and Horax offered their case: "for the record ... as an excellent example of a type of special disturbance of vision ... which sheds considerable light on ... those processes which are concerned in the integration and association of sensation" (p. 385). I shall review each of the component symptoms identified by Holmes and Horax in 1919, and attempt a contemporary synthesis.

Constriction of visual attention: simultaneous agnosia

In their 1919 report of a 30-year-old First World War veteran who had a gunshot wound through the parieto-occipital regions, Holmes and Horax observed that: "the essential feature was his inability to direct attention to, and to take cognizance of, two or more objects ... ." (p. 402). They argued that this difficulty "must be attributed to a special disturbance or limitation of attention ... " (p. 402). Because of this constriction of visual attention (what Bálint referred to as the psychic field of gaze), the patient could attend to only one object at a time regardless of the size of the object. In this report, Holmes and Horax observed that the constriction of visual attention was not location-based, but object-based: "In one test, for instance, a large square was drawn on a sheet of paper and he recognized it immediately, but when it was again shown to him after a cross had been drawn in its center he saw the cross, but identified the surrounding figure only after considerable hesitation; his attention seemed to be absorbed by the first object on which his eyes fell" (p. 390).

Fig. 5 shows an example in which a small and more distant item captured JX's attention and caused objects closer to him, which he had just perceived, to disappear. When I first showed two superimposed objects to this gentleman he reported seeing the comb; and when asked about the spoon, he denied seeing it. I then set down these objects for a few seconds. When I picked them up and showed them to the patient again asking him "What do you see now?", he reported seeing only the comb. After setting them down a second time and showing them to the patient a few seconds later, he seemed perplexed and could not seem to make out what he was seeing. When asked if he still saw either the comb or the spoon, he shook his head and said, "I think I see a blackboard with a bunch of writing on it." I might have thought his response to be confabulatory, but when I looked over my shoulder there was, in fact, a blackboard with writing in chalk behind me. He was looking through the comb and the spoon and his attention had become locked on the chalk marks. All other objects, comb and spoon included, were excluded from his awareness.

The degree to which local detail can capture the patient's attention and exclude all other objects from her ken can be quite astonishing. I was testing a patient one day, drawing shapes on a piece of paper and asking her to tell me what she saw. She was

RR "What do you see here?"
JX "A comb"

RR "What do you see now?"
JX "A comb"

RR Moves spoon and asks,
"What do you see now?"
JX "A spoon"
RR "Do you see the comb?"
JX "No."

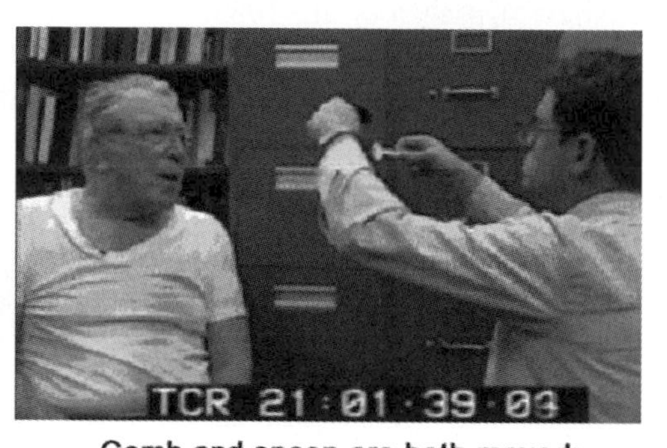

Comb and spoon are both moved;
the patient then seems not to see
either of them and is asked:
RR "Just tell me what you see".
JX "I see what looks like a blackboard
with some writing on it".

There was, in fact, a blackboard with
writing in chalk behind the examiner.

Fig. 5. Simultaneous agnosia with attentional capture by distant stimuli. From video (see text). Video by Perpetua Productions.

doing well at reporting simple shapes until, at one point, she shook her head, perplexed, and told me, "I can't see any of those shapes now, doctor, the watermark on the paper is so distracting."

Object-centered and object-based attention

Fig. 6 shows an excerpt from an examination of a patient (WX) with hemispatial neglect. It should

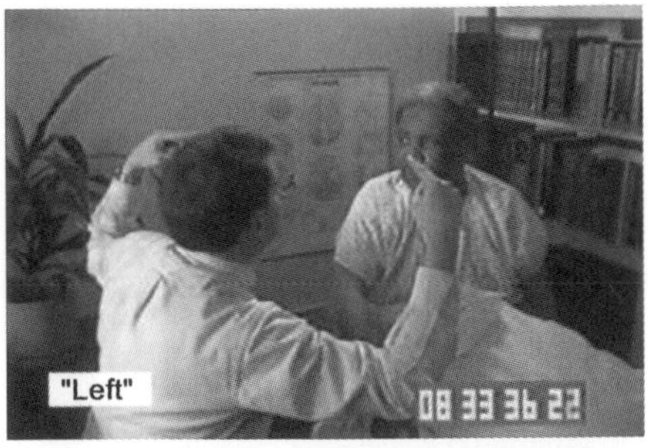

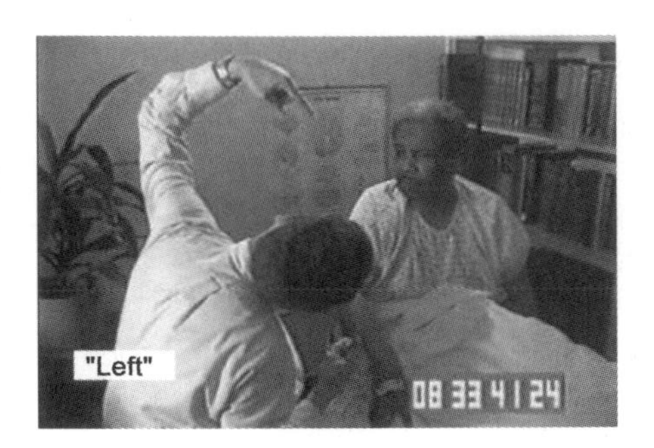

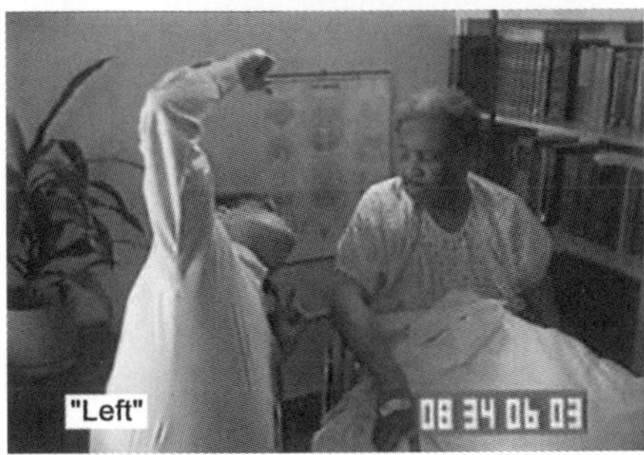

Fig. 6. Object-centered visual extinction in hemispatial neglect. From video (see text). Video by Perpetua Productions.

help to clarify what is meant by *object-centered* neglect and to distinguish it from *object-based* neglect as manifest by simultaneous agnosia in Bálint's syndrome. In Fig. 6, WX is being examined for a sign called visual extinction, used to test patients for hemispatial neglect. I wiggled a finger in either the right (ipsilesional) field, the left (contralesional) field, or both simultaneously. WX reported seeing a finger wiggled in either the left or right field when presented alone; but when they were wiggled simultaneously he reported only seeing "your left hand" (first frame of Fig. 6), that is, the hand in his right visual field. His awareness of the wiggling finger in his contralesional, left visual field is extinguished by the competing stimulus in his ipsilesional, right visual field.

Next WX, was tested with a variant of this bedside confrontation test for visual extinction that Lynn Robertson introduced to demonstrate object-centered neglect (Rafal and Robertson, 1995). I rotated my body by 90° either to the right (such that the previously extinguished hand that had been in the patient's left visual field is now in his upper visual field), or to the left (such that it is now his lower visual field). (See middle and right frame of Fig. 6). In both cases, WX continues to extinguish my hand that had been in his contralesional left visual field, and reports seeing only "your left hand." This kind of demonstration is often cited to indicate that extinction can be 'object-centered', and has been rigorously documented under more controlled conditions than can be achieved by bedside testing in an elegant series of experiments by Behrmann and Tipper (1994, 1999).

However, 'object-centered' is sometimes construed to mean being based on a reference frame that is defined by the object allocentrically and independent of the viewer. This is clearly not the case in the example shown in Fig. 6. The object (me) to which WX is responding has a right side and a left side. If WX were neglecting the left side of the object from the viewpoint/reference frame of the object, he would be extinguishing *my left hand*. But if you look again at Fig. 6, you will note, as Patti Reuter-Lorenz pointed out to me, that what he reports is seeing "your left hand" and he extinguishes *my right hand*. So he is not neglecting 'left' from the frame of reference of the object, but from his point of view. It is clear that even in such examples of 'object-centered' neglect, it is the left side of space that is neglected. 'Space' in this context, is defined by a grouped array (Vecera and Farah, 1994) determined by the object, but it is still a spatial frame of reference and it is still viewer based, not object-based.

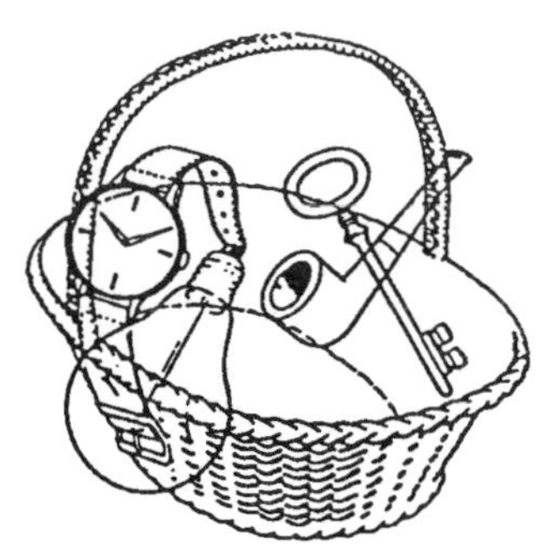

Fig. 7. Overlapping line drawings used to test for simultaneous agnosia.

Contrast this object-centered neglect with the simultaneous agnosia that is observed in Bálint's syndrome as depicted in Figs. 1 and 2. In these examples, the neglect is entirely non-spatial. The man in Fig. 1 sees the whole comb or the whole ruler, but only one or the other. The lady in Fig. 2 sees my face or my glasses, but not both. In these cases, attention is locked on an object, not a region of space, and the reference frame that determines what is neglected is based on the object, not centered on it in terms of any spatial coordinates.

In contrast to hemispatial neglect, simultaneous agnosia in Bálint's syndrome is a neglect of whole objects totally independent of spatial coordinates. It is whole objects that are neglected, not spatially determined parts of objects; and the objects that are neglected may occupy the same spatial coordinates as an object that is seen. A useful clinical test uses overlapping figures such as those of Poppelreuter (Fig. 7).

The perplexing world of simultaneous agnosia

The visual experience of the patient with Bálint's syndrome is a chaotic one of isolated snapshots with no coherence in space or time. Coslett and Saffran report a patient for whom: "television programs bewildered her because she could only 'see' one person or object at a time and, therefore, could not determine who was speaking or being spoken to: she reported watching a movie in which, after a heated argument, she noted to her surprise and consternation that the character she had been watching was suddenly sent reeling across the room, apparently as a consequence of a punch thrown by a character she had never seen" (Coslett and Saffran, 1991, p. 1525).

Coslett and Saffran's patient also illustrated how patients with Bálint's syndrome are confounded in their efforts to read: "Although she read single words effortlessly, she stopped reading because the 'competing words' confused her" (p. 1525). Luria's (1958) patient reported that he, "discerned objects around him with difficulty, that they flashed before his eyes and sometimes disappeared from his field of vision. This [was] particularly pronounced in reading: the words and lines flashed before his eyes and now one, now another, extraneous word suddenly intruded itself into the text (p. 440)." The same occurred in writing: "the patient was unable to bring the letters into correlation with his lines or to follow visually what he was writing down: letters disappeared from the field of vision, overlapped with one another and did not coincide with the limits of the lines" (p. 440). The patient of Coslett and Saffran (1991) "was unable to write as she claimed to be able to see only a single letter; thus when creating a letter she saw only the tip of the pencil and the letter under construction and 'lost' the previously constructed letter" (p. 1525). Fig. 8 shows the attempts of one of Luria's patients to draw familiar objects. As the patient's attention was focused on the attempt to draw a part of the object, the orientation of that part with regard to the rest of the object was lost, and the rendering reduced to piecemeal fragments.

Patients with Bálint's syndrome are unable to perform the simplest everyday tasks involving the comparison of two objects. They cannot tell which of two lines is longer, nor which of two coins is bigger. The patient of Holmes and Horax (1919) could not tell, visually, which of two pencils was bigger, although he had no difficulty doing so if he touched them. Holmes and Horax made the important observation that, although their patient could not explicitly compare the lengths of two lines or angles of a quadrilateral shape, he had no difficulty distinguishing shapes whose identity is implicitly dependent upon such comparisons: "Though he failed to distinguish any difference in the length of lines, even if it was as great as 50 percent, he could always recognize whether a quadrilateral rectangular figure was a square or not ... he did not compare the lengths of its sides but 'on the first glance I see the

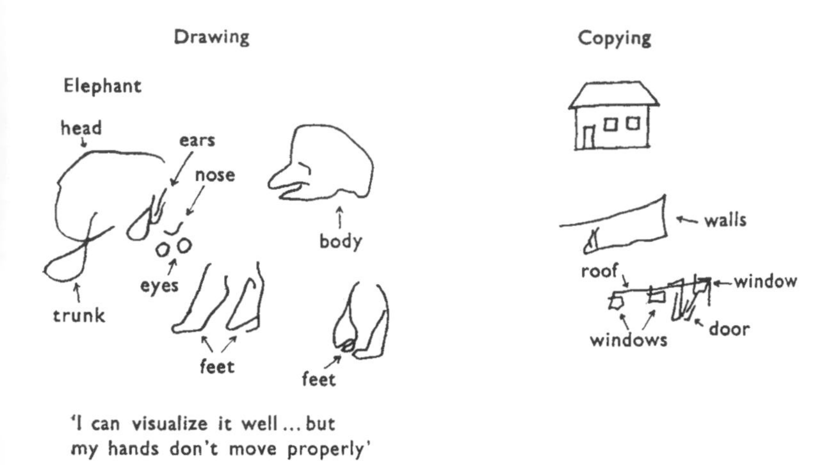

Fig. 8. Drawings by the patient described by Luria, 1958.

whole figure and know whether it is a square or not' ... He could also appreciate ... the size of angles; a rhomboid even when its sides stood at almost right angles was 'a square shoved out of shape' " (p. 394). Holmes and Horax appreciated the importance of their observations for the understanding of normal vision: "It is therefore obvious that though he could not compare or estimate linear extensions he preserved the faculty of appreciating the shape of bidimensional figures. It was on this that his ability to identify familiar objects depended" (p. 394).

What is a visual object?

Patients with Bálint's syndrome can only be aware of one object at a time. But in the visual world of everyday life, objects are often made up of other objects: faces are made up of a nose, mouth, eyes, etc; houses have windows and doors, and doors have handles. So what does a patient with Bálint's syndrome see when confronted with this type of hierarchical stimulus? Little systematic work has been done on this question. My experience is that patients usually, but not always, perceive entire objects rather than a feature or a constituent part. Thus, the patient of Holmes and Horax was able to see a 'square' when shown four dots (::): " ... this is due to the rule that the mind when possible takes cognizance of unities" (Holmes and Horax (1919), p. 400).

Karnath et al. (2000) showed a patient with Bálint's syndrome hierarchical stimuli with both a global and local level, of the type employed by Navon (1977), in which, for example, a large letter is constructed from small letters. The patient consistently reported seeing only the local element. Similarly, Lynn Robertson and Marcia Grabowecky (unpublished observations) showed RM hierarchical stimuli, a large letter H constructed from small S's, and asked him to report what he saw. Regardless of the size of the global letter H, he only reported the local S. On repeated testing over several months, only twice did he also report the global element ('H') at all. When the global letter was made up of several different letters, he reported seeing "the alphabet" (Rafal, 1996). This propensity of patients to get perceptually sucked into local details is reminiscent of the difficulties of JX (Fig. 5) getting stuck on the distant chalk marks, and that of the lady whose attention got stuck on the watermark.

Luria (1958) systematically explored the question of what constitutes an object for a patient with Bálint's syndrome. Shown a six pointed star drawn in a single color, Luria's patient saw a star. When the two triangles were drawn in different colors, the patient saw only one triangle. When shown two adjacent circles, the patient only saw one of them; yet, when the two circles were connected by a line, the patient saw a single object (a dumbbell or spectacles.)

Applying a similar approach, Humphreys and Riddoch (1991) have provided elegant experimental evidence that demonstrates the object-based restriction of attention in Bálint's syndrome, and the principles operating in early vision for generating objects for attentional selection. Two patients were shown 32 circles which were all red, all green, or half red and half green. The task was simply to report whether each display contained one or two colors. The critical test was when the displays contained two colors. In one condition, the spaces between the circles contained randomly placed black lines. In two further conditions, the lines connected either pairs of same-colored circles or pairs of different-colored circles. Both patients were better at correctly reporting the presence of two colors when the lines connected different-colored pairs of circles. Circles connected by a line were perceived as a single object (e.g. as a dumbbell). When each object contained both red and green, the patients could report the presence of the two colors. When the lines connected circles of the same color such that each object contained only a single color, only one color was perceived.

Spatial disorientation

Holmes and Horax (1919) considered spatial disorientation to be a symptom independent from simultaneous agnosia, and to be the cardinal feature of the syndrome: "The most prominent symptom, ... was his inability to orient and localize correctly objects which he saw" (pp. 390–391). Patients with Bálint's syndrome cannot indicate the location of objects, verbally or by pointing (optic ataxia, to be discussed later). Holmes and Horax emphasized that the defect in visual localization was not restricted to visual objects in the outside world, but also extended to a defect in spatial memory: " ... he described as a visualist does his house, his family, a hospital ward in which he had previously been, etc. But, on the other hand, he had complete loss of memory of topography; he was unable to describe the route between the house in a provincial town in which he had lived all his life and the railway station a short distance away, explaining 'I used to be able to see the way but I can't see it now ... .' He was similarly unable to say how he could find his room in a barracks in which he had been stationed for some months, or describe the geography of trenches in which he had served" (p. 389).

This gentleman was clearly lost in space: "On one occasion, for instance, he was led a few yards from his bed and then told to return to it; after searching with his eyes for a few moments he identified the bed, but immediately started off in a wrong direction" (p. 395). This patient showed, then, no recollection of spatial relationships of places he knew well before his injury, and no ability to learn new routes: "He was never able to give even an approximately correct description of the way he had taken, or should take, and though he passed along it several times a day he never 'learned his way' as a blind man would" (p. 395). Holmes and Horax concluded that: "The fact that he did not retain any memory of routes and topographical relations that were familiar to him before he received his injury and could no longer recall them, suggests that the cerebral mechanisms concerned with spatial memory, as well as those that subserve the perception of spatial relations, must have been involved" (p. 404).

Holmes and Horax (1919) considered spatial disorientation to be the salient feature of the syndrome, and that "The disturbances we have interpreted as a local and special affection of attention [simultaneous agnosia] ... do not form an essential part of that complex of symptoms which is of greatest interest in our case, and often occurs apart from and independently of it" (p. 399). Nevertheless, they appreciated that the interaction of simultaneous agnosia with spatial disorientation combined in contributing to the severe disability in simple, daily tasks like reading and counting. Their patient complained that, " ... When I move my eye from a word I cannot get back to the right place". Later, when he became able to read a few words in sequence he could rarely bring his eyes to the left of the succeeding line —"That's when I'm done, I can't get my eyes down to the next line" (p. 397) " ... when asked to count a row of coins he became hopelessly confused, went from one end to the other and back again, and often passed over some of the series; but he succeeded in enumerating them correctly when he was allowed to run his fingers over them" (p. 461) " ... he generally stared fixedly for a time at one and then moved his eyes about the surface irregularly and unmethodically without making a systematic attempt to explore the whole. When four or five coins were place irregularly he generally failed to see them all, frequently included one or more a second time in his count, and eventually became so confused that he gave up the attempt. That this was due to his inability to form a clear picture or idea of the spatial relations of those he perceived was made probable by his own explanation, 'I seem to lose myself when I look from one to the other' " (p. 396).

Ocular behavior

Oculomotor behavior is also chaotic in Bálint's syndrome, with striking disturbances of fixation, saccade initiation and accuracy, and smooth pursuit eye movements. The patient may be unable to maintain fixation, may generate apparently random saccadic eye movements (Luria et al., 1963), and may seem unable to execute smooth pursuit eye movements. The disorder of eye movement in Bálint's syndrome is restricted to visually guided eye movements. The patient can program accurate eye movements when they are guided by sound or touch: "When, however, requested to look at his own finger or to any point of his body which was touched he did so promptly and accurately" (Holmes and Horax, 1919, p. 387).

Holmes and Horax (1919) suggested that the oculomotor disturbances seen in Bálint's syndrome were secondary to spatial disorientation: "Some influence might be attributed to the abnormalities of the movements of his eyes, but ... these were an effect and not the cause" (p. 401). "All these symptoms were secondary to and dependent upon the loss of spatial orientation by vision" (p. 405). The oculomotor behavior of Bálint's syndrome patients is chiefly caused by the failure to see what they are to look at, or by uncertainty about the target's location — not necessarily due to deficient oculomotor programming per se. Eye movements are chaotic because perceptual experience is chaotic.

Holmes and Horax (1919) described the typical behavior of a patient with Bálint's syndrome when tested for smooth pursuit eye movements: "When an object at which he was staring was moved at a slow and uniform rate he could keep his eyes on it, but if it was jerked or moved abruptly it quickly disappeared ... " (p. 387).

Fig. 9 shows eye movements and visual search in patient TX, taken from a video. She does not, initially, see the pipe, even though it is almost right in front of her. Its movement then captures her attention, and she makes a fast and accurate saccade to it. When I move it to her left visual field, she makes an eye movement to it. I put the pipe down for a few seconds and then presented it again in her right visual field. Without looking at it, she reports seeing "a pipe". Then I put the pipe down once more and presented a pen in her right visual field. She seems to see something there and, although obviously puzzled and unable to recognize it, she fails spontaneously to look at it, finally saying, "I think that's still a pipe." When the pen was then briskly moved in front of her she immediately identified it, "oh, that's a pen." When the pen was abruptly removed from fixation, it vanished. When I asked her to look at it, she responded, "I can't see it, doctor", and began moving her eyes, searching for it.

Optic ataxia

Fig. 10 shows misreaching in Bálint's syndrome. Even though RX seems to be looking at the screwdriver, his reaching is inaccurate in depth as well as being off to the side. Given a pencil and asked to mark the center of a circle, the patient with Bálint's syndrome typically will not even get the mark within the circle, and may not be able to even hit the paper. In part this may be because the patient cannot take cognizance, simultaneously, of both the circle and the pencil point; but it is also clear that the patient does not know where the circle is. Holmes and Horax (1919) considered optic ataxia, like the oculomotor impairment, to be secondary to "his inability to orient and localize correctly in space objects which he saw. When ... asked to take hold of or point to any object, he projected his hand out vaguely, generally in a wrong direction, and had obviously no accurate idea of its distance from him" (p. 391).

Holmes and Horax (1919) again observed that the lack of access to a representation of space was specific to vision. Their patient was able to localize sounds and he did have a representation of peri-personal space based on kinesthetic input: "The contrast between the defective spatial guidance he received from vision and the accurate knowledge of space that contact gave him, was excellently illustrated when he attempted to take soup from a small bowl with a spoon; if he held the bowl in his own hand he always succeeded in placing the spoon accurately in it, ... but when it was held by a observer or placed

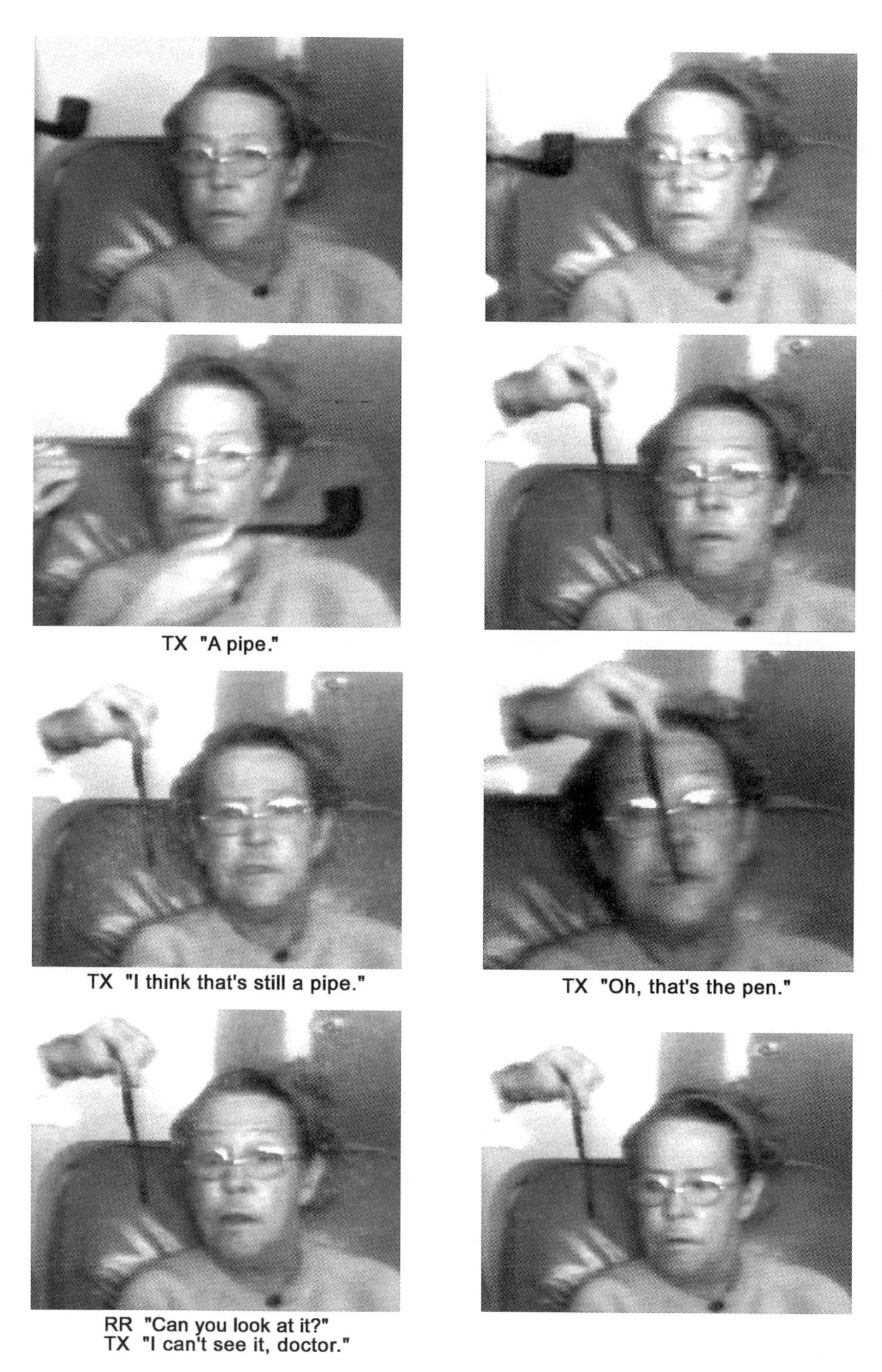

Fig. 9. Eye movements and visual search. From video (see text).

Fig. 10. Optic ataxia. From video.

on a table in front of him he could rarely bring his spoon to it at once, but had to grope for it till he had located it by touch." (pp. 391 and 393).

Impaired depth perception

Holmes and Horax (1919) also attributed impaired depth perception to spatial disorientation. Although the patient in their 1919 report did have deficient stereoscopic vision, they considered his astereopsis as an incidental association and not typical of Bálint's syndrome, since Holmes (1918) had reported six different patients with the same syndrome, but with preserved stereoscopic fusion. They viewed the loss of depth perception in Bálint's syndrome as a consequence of the loss of topographic perception, and as a failure to have any appreciation of distance.

The loss of blink to visual threat they attributed to his inability to "recognized the nearness of the threatening object". The problem in judging distances also causes another serious problem for patients: collision with objects when they walk about.

The impairment of depth perception in Bálint's syndrome seems to be due to a failure to appreciate the relative location of two objects — or of the patient and the object he or she is looking at. Size cues seem not to help the patient judge the distance to an object. However, Holmes and Horax (1919) commented that their patient's lack of a sense of distance did not indicate a lack of appreciation of metrics in general since he could: "... indicate by his two hands the extension of ordinary standards of linear measurement, as an inch, a foot, or a yard ... and he could indicate the lengths of familiar objects, as his rifle, bayonet, etc." (p. 393).

Nosological consideration: Bálint's syndrome, its neighbors and relatives

The clinical picture described above is that of Bálint's syndrome when it is quite dense, and in its pure form. It reflects the typical presentation of a patient with bilateral lesions restricted to the parieto-occipital junction. While strokes and head trauma may occasionally cause discretely restricted and symmetric lesions (such as those shown in Fig. 4), it is more commonly the case that lesions will not respect these territories, and cause more extensive damage to occipital, parietal and temporal lobes. Coexisting visual field deficits, hemispatial neglect, apperceptive or associative agnosia, prosopagnosia, alexia and other cognitive deficits are often present in association with Bálint's syndrome or some of its constituent elements. The patient reported by Bálint (1909) for example, also had left hemispatial neglect, possibly due to extension of the lesion into the right temporo-parietal junction (Fig. 3): "... the attention of the patient is always directed [by approximately 35 or 40 degrees] to the right-hand side of space when he is asked to direct his attention to another object after having fixed his gaze on a first one, he tends to the right-hand rather than the left-hand side" (cited by Husain and Stein, 1988, p. 90). In other cases in which a constriction of visual attention is also associated with object agnosia, the tendency of the patient to become locked on parts of objects may contribute to observed agnosic errors; and it may result in diagnostic confusion with 'integrative agnosia' (Riddoch and Humphreys, 1987).

It is also the case that a given patient may have optic ataxia, spatial disorientation, or simultaneous agnosia without other elements of Bálint's syndrome. Thus, spatial disorientation may occur without simultaneous agnosia (Stark, Coslett and Saffran, 1996); optic ataxia may occur without simultaneous agnosia or spatial disorientation (Perenin and Vighetto, 1988); and simultaneous agnosia may occur without spatial disorientation (Kinsbourne and Warrington, 1962, 1963; Rizzo and Robin, 1990). It should be borne in mind that, in such cases, the observed symptoms may result from very different mechanisms than those that produce them in Bálint's syndrome. Thus, while optic ataxia and oculomotor impairment may be attributable to a loss of spatial representation in patients with Bálint's syndrome due to bilateral parieto-occipital lesions, optic ataxia from superior parietal lesions may reflect disruption of the neural substrates mediating visuomotor transformations (Milner and Goodale, 1995).

Similarly, simultaneous agnosia may be caused by very different kinds of lesions and for different reasons. The term 'simultanagnosia' was originated specifically to describe a defect in integrating complex visual scenes. As defined by Wolpert, the term includes, but is more general than, the constriction of attention seen in Bálint's syndrome. It is seen in conditions other than Bálint's syndrome and may result from unilateral lesions. Hécaen and de Ajuriaguerra (1956) describe the difficulties of one of their patients (case 1) on being offered a light for a cigarette: "... when the flame was offered to him an inch or two away from the cigarette held between his lips, he was unable to see the flame because his eyes were fixed on the cigarette" (p. 374). However, the mechanism underlying simultaneous agnosia in such cases may be different than that which causes simultaneous agnosia in Bálint's syndrome. Unlike the simultaneous agnosia present in Bálint's syndrome, that due to left temporo-parietal lesions appears to be due to a perceptual bottleneck caused by slowing of visual processing as measured, for example, by the ability to recognize a series of individual pictures flashed briefly in a rapid, serial, visual presentation (RSVP) test (Kinsbourne and Warrington, 1962, 1963). In contrast, patients with Bálint's syndrome may be able to identify individual pictures flashed briefly in an RSVP stream (Coslett and Saffran, 1991).

Implications of Bálint's syndrome for understanding visual cognition

Bálint's syndrome holds valuable lessons for understanding the neural processes involved in controlling attention, representing space and providing coherence and continuity to conscious visual experience:

- Attention selects from object-based representations of space.
- There are independent neural mechanisms, which operate in parallel, for orienting attention within objects and between objects.
- The candidate objects on which attention operates are generated preattentively by early vision in the absence of explicit awareness.
- Attention is involved in affording explicit (conscious) access to spatial representations needed for goal-directed action and for binding features of objects.

Object and space based attention

An appreciation of simultaneous agnosia in Bálint's syndrome has proven influential in helping to resolve one of the major theoretical controversies in visual attention research. The issue at stake was whether visual attention acts by selecting locations or objects. Work by Michael Posner and others (Posner, 1980; Posner, Snyder and Davidson, 1980) showed that allocating attention to a location in the visual field enhanced the processing of visual signals that appeared at the attended location. Some models of visual attention have characterized attention as something like a spot light or 'zoom lens' (Eriksen and St. James, 1986) that enhances processing of all information at the locus on which it is focused.

Object-based models of attention, in contrast, postulate that preattentive processes parse the visual scene to generate candidate objects (more on this later) and that attention then acts by selecting one such object for further processing that can guide goal-directed action. These models are supported by experiments in normal individuals that show better discrimination of two features belonging to the same object, than of features belonging to two different objects (Duncan, 1984); and that these object-based effects are independent of the spatial location of their features (Baylis and Driver, 1995; Vecera and Farah, 1994). Physiological recordings in monkey have shown that attention can be oriented to a location within an object independent of its location in the visual field (Olson and Gettner, 1995), and that object-based attentional set can modulate processing in extrastriate visual cortex (Chelazzi, Duncan, Miller and Desimone, 1998). Recent neuroimaging studies have confirmed that attentional selection of one of two objects results in activation of brain regions representing other unattended features of that object (O'Craven, Downing and Kanwisher, 1999).

Object-based models predict that brain lesions could produce an object-based simultaneous agnosia that is independent of location — of precisely the kind that had been observed in patients with Bálint's syndrome decades before this debate was joined by psychologists and physiologists. Moreover, recent experimental work by Humphreys and colleagues has shown that simultaneous agnosia can be manifest in non-spatial domains. In two patients with parietal lobe lesions and poor spatial localization, they observed that pictures extinguished words and closed shapes extinguished open shapes (Humphreys, Romani, Olson, Riddoch, and Duncan, 1994). Thus, the object-based attention deficit in this syndrome cannot be attributed simply to the effects of parietal lobe lesions in disrupting access to spatial representation.

Not surprisingly, a debate predicated upon a dichotomy that attention must be either object-based or location-based was ill conceived. Emerging evidence in both normal individuals (Lavie and Driver, 1996), and those based on neuropsychological observations (Humphreys and Riddoch, 1991), indicate that both location-based and object-based attentional processes may interact in determining visual selection. Bottom up processes may summon attention to regions of space with candidate objects while, in parallel, activated object representations may operate top-down such that spatial attention affects object selection at the same time that object properties bias spatial selection to engage on objects (Duncan, 1996).

An interactive model has also been supported by neuropsychological observations in patients with hemispatial neglect. Behrmann and Tipper (1999) have shown recently that neglect may occur in either location or object-centered reference frames; and that the reference frame in which neglect is manifest is determined by whether the attentional set of the patients is tuned to select locations or objects. Moreover, under conditions of rapid serial visual presentation, patients with hemispatial neglect exhibit a pathologically prolonged 'attentional dwell time' even for stimuli presented at fixation (Husain, Shapiro, Martin and Kennard, 1997). However, this prolongation of attentional dwell time interacts with spatial location, being more prolonged in the contralesional field (di Pellegrino, Basso and Frassinetti, 1998).

Shifting attention within and between objects

The spatial representations upon which attention operates are determined, not simple by Cartesian coordinates of empty space centered on the observer (Humphreys, 1998), but by objects, or 'candidate' objects, derived from an array of features grouped by early vision (Vecera and Farah, 1994). Neuropsychological evidence indicates, for example, that when patients with unilateral lesions of the temporo-parietal junction have their attention summoned to objects in the ipsilesional field, they are slow to disengage attention in order to move it to detect a new target in the contralesional field (Friedrich, Egly, Rafal and Beck, 1998). The same patients, however, may not show this deficit when attention is summoned to the ipsilesional visual field if there is no object at the cued location (e.g. a permanent marker box on the screen of a video display) from which to disengage (Marangolo, Di Pace, Rafal and Scabini, 1998).

Humphreys has recently posited that attention operates on spatial representations determined by objects, and that there are separate mechanisms, operating in parallel, for shifting attention within objects and for shifting attention between objects (Humphreys, 1998). This framework is supported by converging neuropsychological evidence from several sources.

Fig. 11 shows stimuli that Cooper and Humphreys (2000) used to study shifts of attention within and between objects in patient GK with Bálint's syndrome. In Fig. 11, conditions 1 and 2, GK's task was to report whether the upright segments were the same or different length. For the stimuli in condition 1, in which the comparison was between two parts of the same object, GK was correct on 84% of trials; whereas, in condition 2, in which the judgement required comparison to two separate objects, performance was at chance (54%).

Egly and his coworkers showed in normal individuals that greater time was required to shift attention between two points in different objects (two different rectangles) than to shift attention an equal distance between two points in the same object (Egly, Driver and Rafal, 1994). In neuropsychological studies using this approach, they also showed, in patients with unilateral parietal lesions (Egly, Driver

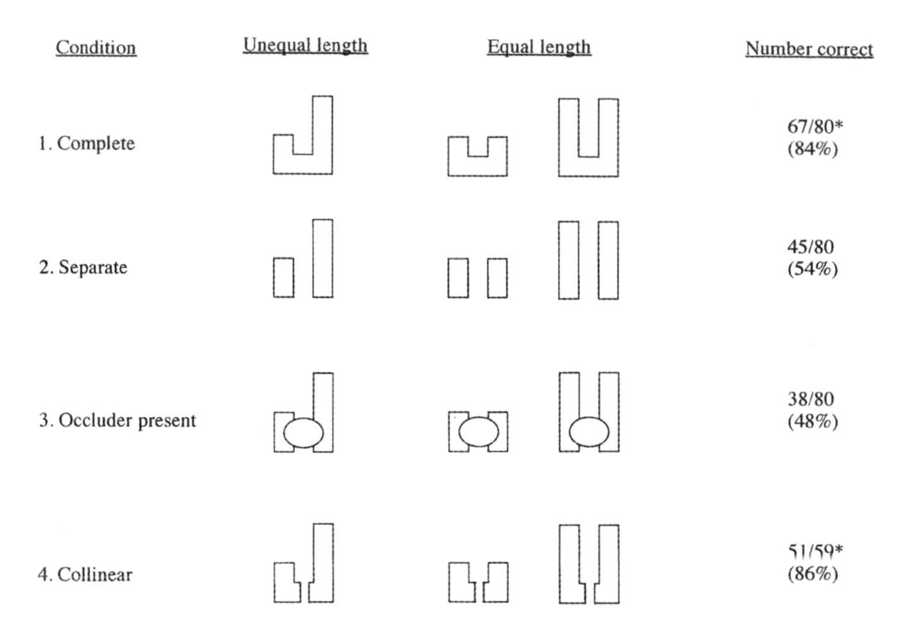

Fig. 11. Figures used by Cooper and Humphreys (2000) to demonstrate grouping in Bálint's syndrome.

and Rafal, 1994) and in a split brain patient (Egly, Rafal, Driver and Starreveld, 1994), that the left hemisphere plays a special role in shifting attention between objects.

Humphreys and Riddoch (1994) demonstrated the dissociation between within and between object attention mechanisms in an elegant case study. Patient JR, who had sustained lesions in both the left parieto-occipital and right fronto-parietal regions, was shown words and asked to either read the word, or to report each of the letters. In the within object task (reading the word), the patient manifested left neglect (e.g. reading 'night' instead of 'light'). By contrast, in the between object task (reporting individual letters) he neglected letters on the right side of the string (e.g. reported ligh_ and missed the t).

Visual processing outside of conscious awareness

The interactions between spatial and object representations, which have been discussed as determining the allocation of attention, require that candidate objects are first provided by preattentive processes that proceed in the absence of awareness. Cumulative observations in patients with hemispatial neglect have indeed provided evidence that early vision does segregate figure from ground, group features, assign primary axes and even extract semantic information that can determine attentional priorities for subsequent processing. Here some examples are considered in which implicit measures of processing in Bálint's syndrome have provided strong evidence for extensive processing of visual information outside of awareness.

Preattentive representation of space

Spatial disorientation is a cardinal feature of Bálint's syndrome, and one view of the constriction of visual attention posits that it, too, is due to a loss of a neural representation of space on which attention may act (Friedman-Hill et al., 1995). However, as we have seen from the work of Humphreys et al. (1994), simultaneous agnosia may also occur for non-spatial information, such as shifting between words and pictures. Moreover, recent observations in patients with both hemispatial neglect (Danziger, Kingstone and Rafal, 1998), and Bálint's syndrome (Robertson, Treisman, Friedman-Hill and Grabowecky, 1997) have shown that parietal damage does not eliminate representations of spatial information, but rather prevents explicit access to this information. Robertson et al. (1997) showed that, although patient RM could not explicitly report the relative location of two objects, he nevertheless exhibited a spatial Stroop interference effect. That is, although he could not report whether the word 'up' was in the upper or lower visual field, he was, nevertheless, slower to read 'up' if it appeared in the lower visual field than in the upper visual field.

Preattentive grouping of features and alignment of principal axis

As described earlier, observations by Luria (1958), and by Humphreys and Riddoch (1993) have revealed that there is less simultaneous agnosia when shapes in the visual field are connected. It would thus seem that grouping of shapes by connectedness proceeds preattentively to generate candidate objects on which attention may operate. Uniform connectedness has been suggested, however, to operate at earlier levels of processing than other grouping principles (Palmer and Rock, 1994). Other recent observations by Humphreys and his colleagues in patient GK with Bálint's syndrome have confirmed that grouping based on brightness, collinearity, surroundedness and familiarity are also generated preattentively, as is grouping based on alignment of a principle axis. Fig. 12 shows GK's performance in reporting two items, and demonstrates better performance when the items are grouped on the basis of brightness, collinearity, surroundness and familiarity (Humphreys, 1998). The benefit of colinearity is also evident in condition 4 at the bottom of Fig. 11.

Boutsen and Humphreys (1999) asked patient GK to report whether groups of equilateral triangles, like those shown in Fig. 13, were oriented vertically or obliquely. Note that the axis of any individual triangle (i.e. which way it points) is ambiguous, and the correct response can only be arrived at by grouping the triangles. The groups on the top are axis-aligned, while those on the bottom are edge-aligned. GK was unable to report, explicitly, which arrays were axis-aligned and which were edge-aligned. Nevertheless, he was correct in reporting the orientation of the axis-aligned groups, but unable to do so with the edge-aligned groups. These observations confirm that grouping by axis-alignment proceeds preattentively in the absence of explicit awareness.

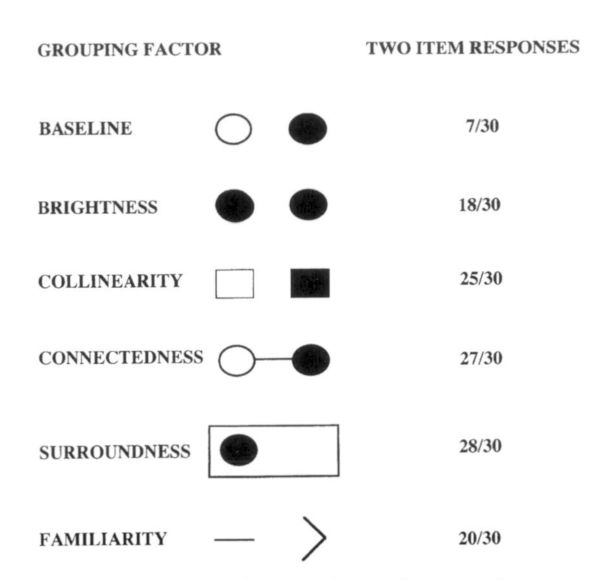

Fig. 12. Figures used by Humphreys (1998) to demonstrate grouping in Bálint's syndrome. Simultaneous agnosia is reduced by grouping based on brightness, collinearity, surroundness and familiarity.

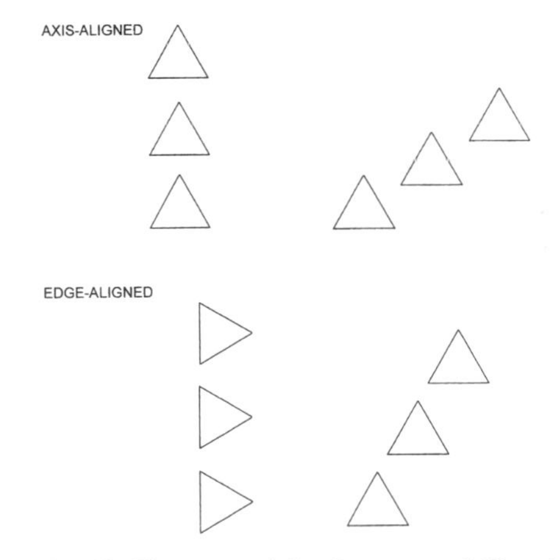

Fig. 13. Figures used by Boutsen and Humphreys (1999) to demonstrate axis alignment in Bálint's syndrome.

Preattentive processing of depth

Although patients with Bálint's syndrome are unable to report, explicitly, the distance of objects or whether one object is in front of or behind the other, it is clear that early processes of stereopsis are intact. RM, for example, was able to see shapes in random dot stereograms (Rafal, 1996). Figure–ground segregation based on symmetry is also preserved enabling

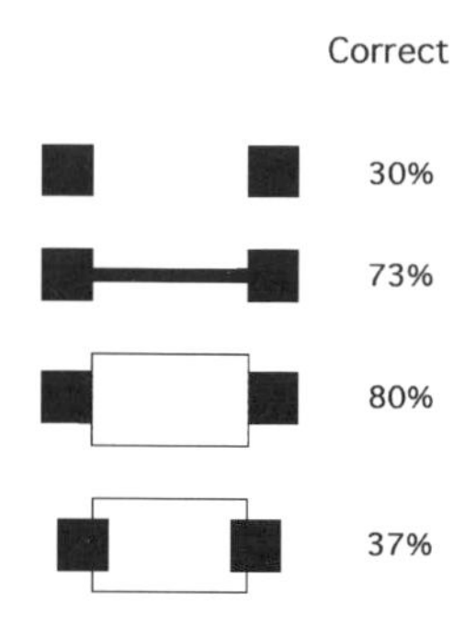

Fig. 14. Figures used by Humphreys (1998) showing segregation in depth based on occlusion cues. Simultaneous agnosia for the black squares is reduced by connecting items, but not when they occlude the connecting rectangle causing segregation of the squares and rectangles in depth.

RM to see symmetric forms as being 'in front of' the background (see unpublished observations by Diane Beck reported in Rafal, 1996, as well as those by VS Ramachandran demonstrating that depth information based on shading was intact in RM.)

Fig. 14, adapted from Humphreys (1998) shows implicit evidence for processing of depth information based on occlusion cues in patient GK. The numbers on the right of each row indicate the number of trials (out of 30) in which the patient correctly reported that there were two black squares. There is less simultaneous agnosia in the second and third rows in which the two black squares are better grouped because they are connected (by a line in the second row and by a rectangle in the third). In the bottom row, in which the two black squares are moved closer so as to occlude the rectangle (causing normal observers to perceive them in being in front of it), simultaneous agnosia is as severe as in the unconnected condition shown in the top row.

Hence, although GK might not be able to report explicitly that the black squares are in front of the oblong, it is clear that implicit depth information derived from implicit occlusion cues is encoded such that the two squares are not grouped with the rectangle. A similar effect is evident in the bottom row of Fig. 11.

Preattentive processing of global information from hierarchical objects

As discussed earlier, patients with Bálint's syndrome, when shown hierarchical figures, will usually only see the local level. Recently, however, Karnath et al. (2000) confirmed unpublished observations by Rob Egly and Lynn Robertson in patient RM (see Rafal, 1996) that patients with Bálint's syndrome do process the global information in hierarchical stimuli, even if they are not explicitly aware of it. Karnath et al. reported that patient KB, although unable to report the letter at the global level, was nevertheless slower to report the local letter when the global letter was not the same as the local letter.

Preattentive processing of meaning of words

The observations summarized in the preceding section demonstrate that, as is the case in hemispatial neglect, neglected objects do appear to be processed to a high level of semantic classification in patients with Bálint's syndrome. Furthermore, although this information is not consciously accessible to the patient, it does influence the perception of objects that are seen. Coslett and Saffran (1991) presented, simultaneously, pairs of words or pictures briefly to their patient, and asked her to read or name them. When the two stimuli were not related semantically, the patient usually saw only one of them, but when they were related she was more likely to see them both. Hence, both stimuli must have been processed to a semantic level of representation, and the meaning of the words or objects determined whether one or both would be perceived.

Words are an example of hierarchical stimuli in which letters are present at the local level and the word at the global level. We (Baylis, Driver, Baylis and Rafal, 1994) showed patient RM letter strings and asked him to report all the letters he could see. Since he could only see one letter at a time, he found this task difficult and, with the brief exposure durations used in the experiment, he usually only saw a few of the letters. However, when the letter string constituted a word, he was able to report more letters than when it did not. That is, even when the patient was naming letters and ignoring the word, the word was processed and helped bring the constituent letters to his awareness.

Attention, spatial representation and feature integration: gluing the world together

I discussed earlier how the single object seen by the patient is experientially mutable in time. It has no past or future. Any object that moves disappears. In addition, objects seen in the present can be perplexing to the patient, because other objects that the patient does not see, and their features, are processed and do impinge upon the experience of the attended object. Normally, the features of an object such as its color and its shape are correctly conjoined, because visual attention selects the location of the object and glues together all the features sharing that same location (Treisman and Gelade, 1980). For the patient with Bálint's syndrome, however, all locations are the same, and all the features which impinge on the patient's awareness are perceptually conjoined into that object.

Friedman-Hill et al. (1995) showed RM pairs of colored letters and asked him to report the letter he saw and its color. RM saw an exceptional number of illusory conjunction (Treisman and Schmidt, 1982), reporting the color of the letter which he did not see as being the color of the letter that he did report. Lacking access to a spatial representation in which co-located features could be co-registered by his constricted visual attention, visual features throughout the field are free floating and conjoined arbitrarily. Bernstein and Robertson (1998) also reported that RM made illusory conjunctions of shape, color and motion. Since a spatial Stroop effect was observed in patient RM (see above), Robertson et al. (1997) argued that spatial information did exist and that feature binding relies on a relatively late stage where implicit spatial information is made explicitly accessible.

Subsequent observations in patient RM showed, however, that feature binding did occur implicitly. Wojciulik and Kanwisher (1998) used a modification of a Stroop paradigm in which RM was shown two words, one of which was colored, and asked to report the color and ignore the words. Although he was not able to report, explicitly, which word was colored, there was, nevertheless, a larger Stroop interference effect (i.e. he was slower to name the color) when an incongruent color name word was colored. Thus, there was implicit evidence that the word and its color had been bound, even though RM had no explicit access to the conjunction of features.

Conclusion

Lost in space, and stuck in a perceptual present containing only one object which he or she cannot find or grasp, the patient with Bálint's syndrome is helpless in a visually chaotic world. Objects appear and disappear and their features jumble together. Contemporary theories of attention and perception help us to understand the experience of these patients; and their experience provides critical insights into the neural basis of visual attention and perception, and how they operate together normally to provide coherent perceptual experience and efficient goal-directed behavior.

References

Bálint R: Seelenlahhmung edes 'Schauens', optische Ataxie, raumliche Storung der Aufmerksamkeit. Montschrife Pscyhiatrie und Neurologie: 25; 51–81, 1909.

Baylis GC, Driver J: One-sided edge-assignment in vision: 1. Figure–ground segmentation and attention to objects. Current Directions in Psychological Science: 4; 201–206, 1995.

Baylis GC, Driver J, Baylis LL, Rafal RD: Perception of letters and words in Bálint's syndrome: evidence for the unity of words. Neuropsychologia: 32; 1273–1286, 1994.

Behrmann M, Tipper SP: Object-based visual attention: evidence from unilateral neglect. In Umilta C, Moscovitch M (Eds), Attention and Performance XIV: Conscious and Nonconscious Processing and Cognitive Functioning. Hillsdale, NJ: Lawrence Erlbaum, pp. 351–376, 1994.

Behrmann M, Tipper SP: Attention accesses multiple frames of reference: evidence from visual neglect. Journal of Experimental Psychology: Human Perception and Performance: 25; 83–101, 1999.

Benson DF, Davis RJ, Snyder BD: Posterior cortical atrophy. Archives of Neurology: 45; 789–793, 1988.

Bernstein LJ, Robertson LC: Illusory conjunctions of color and motion with shape following bilateral parietal lesions. Psychological Science: 9; 167–175, 1998.

Boutsen L, Humphreys GW: Axis-alignment affects perceptual grouping: evidence from simultaneous agnosia. Cognitive Neuropsychology: 16; 655–672, 1999.

Chelazzi L, Duncan J, Miller EK, Desimone R: Responses of neurons in inferior temporal cortex during memory-guided visual search. Journal of Neurophysiology: 80; 2918–2940, 1998.

Cooper CG, Humphreys GW: Coding space within but not between objects: evidence from Bálint's syndrome. Neuropsychologia: 38; 723–733, 2000.

Coslett HB, Saffran E: Simultaneous agnosia. To see but not two see. Brain: 113; 1523–1545, 1991.

Danziger S, Kingstone A, Rafal R: Reflexive orienting to signals in the neglected visual field. Psychological Science: 9; 119–123, 1998.

di Pellegrino G, Basso G, Frassinetti F: Visual extinction as a spatio-temporal disorder of selective attention. NeuroReport: 9; 835–839, 1998.

Duncan J: Selective attention and the organization of visual information. Journal of Experimental Psychology: General: 113; 501–517, 1984.

Duncan J: Cooperating brain systems in selective perception and action. In Inui T, McClelland JL (Eds), Attention and Performance XVI: Information Integration in Perception and Communication. Cambridge, MA: MIT Press, pp. 15–46, 1996.

Egly R, Driver J, Rafal, R. (1994). Shifting visual attention between objects and locations: Evidence from normal and parietal lesion subjects. Journal of Experimental Psychology: General: 123; 161–177.

Egly R, Rafal R, Driver J, Starreveld, Y. (1994). Hemispheric specialization for object-based attention in a split-brain patient. Psychological Science: 5; 380–383.

Eriksen CW, St. James JD: Visual attention within and around the field of focal attention: a zoom lens model. Perception and Psychophysics: 40; 225–240, 1986.

Friedman-Hill SR, Robertson LC, Treisman A: Parietal contributions to visual feature binding: Evidence from a patient with bilateral lesions. Science: 269; 853–855, 1995.

Friedrich FJ, Egly R, Rafal RD, Beck D: Spatial attention deficits in humans: a comparison of superior parietal and temporal-parietal junction lesions. Neuropsychology: 12; 193–207, 1998.

Girotti F, Milanese C, Casazza M, Allegranza A, Corridori F, Avanzini G: Oculomotor disturbances in Bálint's syndrome: anatomoclinical findings and electrooculographic analysis in a case. Cortex: 16; 603–614, 1982.

Godwin-Austen RB: A case of visual disorientation. Journal of Neurology, Neurosurgery and Psychiatry: 28; 453–458, 1965.

Hécaen H, de Ajuriaguerra J: Agnosie visuelle pour les objects inanimes par lesion unilaterle gauche. Review Neurologique: 94; 222–233, 1956.

Harvey M: Psychich paralysis of gaze, optic ataxia, spatial disorder of attention. Translated from Bálint (1909). Cognitive Neuropsychology: 12; 266–282, 1995.

Harvey M, Milner AD: Bálint's patient. Cognitive Neuropsychology: 12; 261–264, 1995.

Hof PR, Bouras C, Constantinidis J, Morrison JH: Bálint's syndrome in Alzheimer's disease: specific disruption of the occipito-parietal visual pathway. Brain Research: 493; 368–375, 1989.

Hof PR, Bouras C, Constantinidis J, Morrison JH: Selective disconnection of specific visual association pathways in cases of Alzheimer's disease presenting with Bálint's syndrome. Journal of Neuropathology and Experimental Neurology: 49; 168–184, 1990.

Holmes G: Disturbances of visual orientation. British Journal of Ophthalmology: 2; 449–468 and 506–518, 1918.

Holmes G, Horax G: Disturbances of spatial orientation and visual attention, with loss of stereoscopic vision. Archives of Neurology and Psychiatry: 1; 385–407, 1919.

Humphreys GW: Neural representation of objects in space: a dual coding account. Philosophical Transactions of the Royal Society of London Series B: Biological Sciences: 353; 1341–1351, 1998.

Humphreys GW, Riddoch MJ: Interactions between object and space systems revealed through neuropsychology. In Meyer DE, Kornblum S (Eds), Attention and Performance XIV. Hillsdale, NJ: Lawrence Erlbaum, 1991.

Humphreys GW, Riddoch MJ: Interactive attentional systems in unilateral visual neglect. In Robertson IH, Marshall JC (Eds), Unilateral Neglect: Clinical and Experimental Studies. Hillsdale, NJ: Lawrence Erlbaum, pp. 139–168, 1993.

Humphreys GW, Riddoch MJ: Attention to within-object and between-object spatial representations: multiple sites for visual selection. Cognitive Neuropsychology: 11; 207–242, 1994.

Humphreys GW, Romani C, Olson A, Riddoch MJ, Duncan J: Non-spatial extinction following lesions of the parietal lobe in humans. Nature: 372; 357–359, 1994.

Husain M, Shapiro K, Martin J, Kennard C: Abnormal temporal dynamics of visual attention in spatial neglect patients. Nature: 385; 154–156, 1997.

Husain M, Stein J: Rezso Bálint and his most celebrated case. Archives of Neurology: 45; 89–93, 1988.

Karnath H-O, Ferber S, Rorden C, Driver J: The fate of global information in dorsal simultaneous agnosia. NeuroCase; 6; 295–306, 2000.

Kase CS, Troncoso JF, Court JE, Tapia FJ, Mohr JP: Global spatial disorientation. Journal of the Neurological Sciences: 34; 267–278, 1977.

Kinsbourne M, Warrington EK: A disorder of simultaneous form perception. Brain: 85; 461–486, 1962.

Kinsbourne M, Warrington EK: The localizing significance of limited simultaneous visual form perception. Brain: 86; 697–702, 1963.

Lavie N, Driver J: On the spatial extent of attention in object-based visual selection. Perception and Psychophysics: 58; 1238–1251, 1996.

Luria AR: Disorders of 'simultaneous perception' in a case of bilateral occipito-parietal brain injury. Brain: 83; 437–449, 1958.

Luria AR, Pravdina-Vinarskaya EN, Yarbuss AL: Disorders of ocular movement in a case of simultaneous agnosia. Brain: 86; 219–228, 1963.

Marangolo P, Di Pace E, Rafal R, Scabini D: Effects of parietal lesions in humans on color and location priming. Journal of Cognitive Neuroscience: 10; 704–771, 1998.

Mendez MF, Turner J, Gilmore GC, Remler B, Tomsak RL: Bálint's syndrome in Alzheimer's disease: visuospatial functions. International Journal of Neuroscience: 54; 339–346, 1990.

Milner AD, Goodale MA: The Visual Brain in Action. Oxford: Oxford University Press, 1995.

Navon D: Forest before trees: the precedence of global features in visual perception. Cognitive Psychology: 9; 353–383, 1977.

O'Craven K, Downing P, Kanwisher N: fMRI evidence for objects as the units of attentional selection. Nature: 401; 584–587, 1999.

Olson CR, Gettner SN: Object-centered direction selectivity in the macaque supplementary eye field. Science: 269; 985–988, 1995.

Palmer S, Rock I: Rethinking perceptual organization: The role of uniform connectedness. Psychonomic Bulletin and Review: 1; 29–55, 1994.

Perenin, M-T, Vighetto A: Optic ataxia: a specific disruption in visuomotor mechanisms.I. Different aspects of the deficit in reaching for objects. Brain: 111; 643–674, 1988.

Pierrot-Deseillgny C, Gray F, Brunet P: Infarcts of both inferior parietal lobules with impairment of visually guided eye movements, peripheral visual inattention and optic ataxia. Brain: 109; 81–97, 1986.

Posner MI: Orienting of attention. Quarterly Journal of Experimental Psychology: 32; 3–25, 1980.

Posner MI, Snyder, CRR, Davidson B: Attention and the detection of signals. Journal of Experimental Psychology: General: 109; 160–174, 1980.

Rafal R, Robertson L: The neurology of visual attention. In Gazzaniga MS (Ed), The Cognitive Neurosciences. Cambridge, MA: MIT Press, pp. 625–648, 1995.

Rafal RD: Bálint's Syndrome. In Feinberg TE, Farah MJ (Eds), Behavioral Neurology and Neuropsychology. New York: McGraw-Hill, 1996.

Riddoch MJ, Humphreys GW: A case of integrative visual agnosia. Brain: 110; 1431–1462, 1987.

Rizzo M, Robin DA: Simultaneous agnosia: a defect of sustained attention yields insights on visual information processing. Neurology: 40; 447–455, 1990.

Robertson LC, Treisman A, Friedman-Hill SR, Grabowecky M: The interaction of spatial and object pathways: evidence from Bálint's syndrome. Journal of Cognitive Neuroscience: 9; 295–317, 1997.

Stark M, Coslett HB, Saffran E: Impairment of an egocentric map of locations: implications for perception and action. Cognitive Neuropsychology: 13; 481–523, 1996.

Treisman A, Gelade G: A feature integration theory of attention. Cognitive Psychology: 12; 97–136, 1980.

Treisman A, Schmidt N: Illusory conjunctions in the perception of objects. Cognitive Psychology: 14; 107–141, 1982.

Tyler HR: Abnormalities of perception with defective eye movements (Bálint's syndrome). Cortex: 3; 154–171, 1968.

Vallar G: The anatomical basis of spatial neglect in humans. In Robertson IH, Marshall JC (Eds), Unilateral Neglect: Clinical and Experimental Studies. Hillsdale, NJ: Lawrence Erlbaum, pp. 27–62, 1993.

Vecera SP, Farah MJ: Does visual attention select objects or locations? Journal of Experimental Psychology: General: 123; 146–160, 1994.

Verfaellie M, Rapcsak SZ, Heilman KM: Impaired shifting of attention in Bálint's syndrome. Brain and Cognition: 12; 195–204, 1990.

Williams M: Brain Damage and the Mind. Baltimore, MD: Penguin Books, 1970.

Wojciulik W, Kanwisher N: Implicit but not explicit feature binding in a Bálint's patient. Visual Cognition: 5; 157–182, 1998.

Handbook of Neuropsychology, 2nd Edition, Vol. 4
M. Behrmann (Ed)

CHAPTER 7

Visual aspects of anosognosia, confabulation and misidentification

Todd E. Feinberg [a,*] and David M. Roane [b]

[a] *Neurobehavior and Alzheimer's Disease Center, Beth Israel Medical Center, 317 East 17th Street, Fierman Hall, 9th Floor, New York, NY 10003, USA*

[b] *Department of Psychiatry, Beth Israel Medical Center, 317 East 17th Street, Fierman Hall, 9th Floor, New York, NY 10003, USA*

Introduction

In this chapter, we consider how three related conditions, anosognosia, confabulation, and misidentification, relate to visual processes. In the first section, we address unawareness of visual defects, and consider several conditions where there is an overlap between anosognosia and confabulation.

In the second section, we consider a broad group of disorders known as delusional misidentification syndromes (DMS). While DMS is not strictly speaking a disorder of visual identification, most forms of DMS involve visual misidentification. In this section, we also briefly consider the relationship between DMS and anosognosia.

Unawareness of visual defects

Anosognosia refers to the unawareness of neurological defects or illness. Patients may show anosognosia for a variety of defects including, but not restricted to, hemiplegia, amnesia, and visual disturbance. There are various theories as to the origin of anosognosia for neurological defects. Some have tried to account for unawareness seen in neurological patients on the basis of cognitive impairment or generalized confusion (Geschwind, 1965; Levine, Calvanio and Rinn, 1991; Nathanson, Bergman and Gordon, 1952; Redlich and Dorsey, 1945). Others have emphasized the importance of sensory loss (Babinski, 1918; Barkman, 1925; Barre, Morin and Kaiser, 1923; Critchley, 1953; Gerstmann, 1942; Levine et al., 1991). Head and Holmes (1911) attributed anosognosia to a disturbance of the body schema. Other factors implicated in the production of anosognosia include hemispatial neglect (Feinberg, 1997), disordered feedback, feedforward, and monitoring functions (Heilman, 1991), psychological denial (Weinstein and Kahn, 1955) cerebral disconnection (Geschwind, 1965), and impaired self-monitoring (Stuss, 1991).

We have suggested that a close relationship exists between unawareness of neurological defects and confabulation (Feinberg, 1997; Feinberg and Roane, 1997a; Feinberg, Roane, Kwan et al., 1994). Although no single definition exists, confabulation can be broadly characterized as an erroneous statement made without a conscious effort to deceive (Berlyne, 1972; Joseph, 1986b). While normally associated with amnesia, confabulation can occur in a variety of neurological conditions. This section will focus on those conditions that entail unawareness of visual defects, including the blind spot, scotomas, hemianopias, cerebral blindness, and issues of unaware-

* Corresponding author. Tel.: +1 (212) 420-4111; Fax: +1 (212) 420-2028; E-mail: tfeinberg@bethisraelny.org

ness after callosal disconnection. In all of these, the role of completion and confabulation in fashioning and sustaining the unawareness, will be considered. A discussion of anosognosia for defects other than visual impairment is outside the scope of this chapter. Contemporary reviews of anosognosia and major articles addressing other forms of anosognosia include the following: Feinberg, 1997; Giacino and Cicerone, 1998; Heilman, Barrett and Adair, 1998; Levine et al., 1991; McGlynn and Schacter, 1989; Prigatano and Schacter, 1991.

Unawareness of the blind spot, scotomata, and hemianopias

Mariotte, in 1668 (Finger, 1994), provided the first description of the physiological blind spot which appears in the temporal field of each eye. The blind spot is caused by the lack of retinal ganglia cells at the optic disk located 3–4 mm nasal to the fovea. That the blind spot was not described until the 17th century is due to the fact that, even with monocular viewing, we are not normally aware of its presence. It was Helmholtz's explanation that the blind spot was discovered *negatively* by careful observation of the absent aspects of the stimulus (Gassel and Williams, 1963). When these absences were recognized, the gap could be deduced.

Fuchs (1955a) invoked perceptual completion as the reason for unawareness of the blind spot. He pointed out that certain stimuli, such as evenly colored surfaces, printed pages and continuous lines and circles, were visually completed across the blind spot. However, not all stimuli are visually completed across the blind spot. As Fuchs pointed out, if a straight line enters and ends within the blind spot, visual completion will not occur. Fuchs explained these findings by invoking gestalt principles. He argued "completion can and does occur only if the 'seen' part implies a *whole* of which it is a part — i.e. whose law it already contains." "The tendency towards wholeness exhibited by an incomplete *part* is a tendency towards simplicity or *Prägnanz*". Only when the missing part enters into a "totalized whole-apprehension" will the stimulus be completed and the blind spot pass unnoticed. A similar argument has been made by Ramachandran (1992) who demonstrated that the filling in of the blind spot is a perceptually 'primitive' process, occurring at an early stage of visual processing.

Gattass, Fiorani, Rosa et al. (1992) provided a neurophysiological mechanism for completion of the blind spot. They did unit recordings on neurons in layer 4C of V1 in the area of the representation of the blind spot. They found a significant potentiation of the response which occurs when a line stimulus exceeding the diameter of the blind spot was swept across it, if both sides of the blind spot were stimulated as compared to unilateral stimulation. They interpreted their findings on the basis that the neurons 'interpolated' the area across the blind spot and completed this region of blindness. Reviewing the recent literature, Walker and Mattingly (1997) conclude that unawareness of the blindspot does not necessarily require a "filling in" process. Instead, they argue that the blindspot may be simply ignored.

With regard to acquired scotomata and hemianopias, most investigators have found that patients are unaware of these conditions more often than not. Critchley (1953) found that anterior lesions, within the eye or optic nerve, were more likely to be noticed by patients than posterior lesions, in visual cortex, and that lack of awareness did not correlate with mental confusion. Bender and Teuber (1946) noted that patients with homonymous visual field defects usually do not appreciate that their vision is split in the middle, though they may notice blurring of vision. Both of these authors maintained that lesions sparing the macular were more likely to be missed by patients than those splitting the macular.

Critchley described two types of experience associated with hemianopia. "Positive hemianopias", in which objects appear bisected with one half obscured, occur rarely in posteriorly situated cerebral lesions. Alternatively, patients may have a "negative hemianopia", in which no obscurity is experienced, though there is the experience of something missing on the impaired side. Critchley terms this the "*hémi-nanopsie nulle* of Defour (1889)". Teuber, Battersby and Bender (1960) found that of 46 cases of visual field defects due to penetrating gun shot wounds of the brain, only two experienced positive scotomata, while 44 experienced negative scotomata, such as a 'blank' or 'void'. If they were aware of the visual problems most patients attributed their difficulties to deficits in the eye contralateral to the occipital lesion. Patients were generally unaware of the ipsilateral (nasal field) defect. Teuber et al. (1960) proposed that greater subjective awareness of the impaired temporal field of the contralateral eye resulted from the functional dominance of the crossed temporal field over the uncrossed nasal field.

Another factor associated with unawareness of visual defects cited by Bender and Teuber (1946) and Critchley (1953) is the development of the 'pseudo-fovea'. Originally described by Fuchs (1955a,b), the pseudo-fovea is an adaptation to hemianopia in which the patient undergoes a shift in 'central' fixation towards the hemianopic side resulting in a new center of maximal acuity. In this manner, the functional significance of the hemianopia is decreased, facilitating unawareness of the visual defect.

The presence of perceptual completion is another factor of significance in unawareness of hemianopias. According to Poppelreuter (1917), if a figure, such as a circle or square, were presented with a portion of it falling into a hemianopic field, the patient would claim to see the whole figure. Furthermore, he reported that even when objectively incomplete figures were presented, such that the gap fell within the hemianopic field, perceptual completion would nonetheless occur.

Fuchs (1955a,b) found that patients who experience visual blackness in the defective region do not complete figures. In those few patients reporting completion, Fuchs found that: (1) 'simple' geometric figures, such as circles and squares, whether objectively partial or whole, could be completed; (2) complex figures including highly familiar percepts, such as a dog, face, or bottle, or symmetric percepts, such as a butterfly, would not be completed; (3) figures presented in defective fields might be *extinguished* (disappear from awareness) if presented simultaneously with an unrelated stimulus in the normal field, but might enter into completion with the normal field if an appropriate 'gestalt' were formed. Bender and Teuber (1946) suggested that completion resulted from residual visual perception occurring in a damaged area of the brain. Completion of a stimulus in an area of perimetric blindness could occur if stimuli were presented briefly enough to prevent the occurrence of extinction. In their view, completion was the 'absence of extinction'; it would only occur with objectively intact objects, and could not result from the 'psychological filling in' of a missing part. Likewise, Torjussen (1978) could only demonstrate completion in hemianopic subjects with objectively complete stimuli. He suggested that completion resulted from an interaction in which the normal field facilitated perception in the abnormal field.

Many investigators have argued over the years that insight into hemianopic defects is inversely related to perceptual completion (Bender and Teuber, 1946; Fuchs, 1955a,b; Gassel and Williams, 1963). Fuchs found that completion did not occur when the patient was encouraged to adopt a 'critical attitude' towards his perceptual experience. Both Fuchs (1955a,b) and Bender and Teuber (1946) found the subjective fields varied with the extent of completion. Gassel and Williams (1963) evaluated 35 hemianopic patients for perceptual completion. Patients fixated either to the examiner's nose or to the eye opposite the lesion and were asked whether the whole face was seen. They were tested with and without a black object covering the portion of the face falling in the defective field. Completion of the face occurred in 28 of the 35 patients. Gassel and Williams (1963) made the following relevant observations: (1) completion would occur even when a black object was slowly interposed to cover the completed side of the face, and no residual perception of that side was possible: (2) when patients were encouraged to adopt an 'analytic attitude' toward their perceptions, the degree of completion tended to decrease; and (3) completion and awareness of defects were inversely related. Another issue emphasized by these authors is that gaps in the visual fields have no direct sensory sensation, but rather are *deduced* when the missing aspects of a stimulus are detected. In their words: "The hemianopic field is an area of absence which is discovered rather than sensed; it is a negative area whose presence is judged from some specific failure in function, rather than directly perceived."

Warrington (1962) studied 20 patients with homonymous hemianopic defects from various etiologies. She observed completion of both whole and half figures and found that all 11 patients who were unaware of their visual defects showed visual completion, while none of those patients who were aware of their defects demonstrated completion. Completion was associated with parietal lobe damage and tended to be associated with unilateral neglect, but not mental deterioration.

In the presence of neglect, therefore, incomplete stimuli may be completed, and this phenomenon cannot be explained by latent perception made explicit via a process of facilitation. Rather, it is more appropriate to describe these patients as having *confabulated* the missing aspects of the stimulus. Significantly, Warrington (1962) found this type of completion to be inversely related to awareness of defect. Zangwill (1963) surmised that "completion, far from being a compensatory reaction to hemianopia (as Poppelreuter supposed) is in fact a variety of visual confabulation constrained by unawareness or denial of defect". Zangwell attributed this "anosognosic misperception" to parietal lobe pathology.

Most recently Celesia, Brigell and Vaphiades (1997) have argued that "filling in" is only one factor contributing to anosognosia for hemianopia and that unawareness of defect may be dissociable from both hemispatial neglect and parietal lobe involvement.

Unawareness of divided visual fields in split-brain patients

The corpus callosum, anterior commissure, and hippocampal commissure provide the only direct pathways connecting the right and left hemispheres of the neocortex. Unilateral neocortical contributions to sensorimotor functions, learning and cognition are unified through these connections (Bogen, 1993; Gazzaniga, 1970; Gazzaniga, Bogen and Sperry, 1962; Gazzaniga and Le Doux, 1978; Myers, 1956; Myers and Sperry, 1953; Sperry, 1961; Sperry, Gazzaniga and Bogen, 1969; Trevarthen, 1991; Trevarthen and Sperry, 1973). Following cerebral commissurotomy, the patient develops what is essentially a foveal splitting 'double hemianopia' (Bogen, 1993) with regard to the two hemispheres. As a result, the patient cannot compare stimuli that require detailed visual discrimination across the vertical meridian (Bogen, 1993; Frendrich and Gazzaniga, 1989; Trevarthen, 1991). Yet, it has repeatedly been reported that split-brain patients are not aware of any changes in vision after the acute post-operative period (Sperry, 1984; Sperry et al., 1969). In fact, with the exception of cases of alien hand syndrome involving inter-manual conflict (Feinberg, Schindler, Flanagan and Haber, 1992), patients appear to be largely unaware of any alteration in themselves.

Many possible mechanisms may explain how these patients compensate for their deficits while remaining subjectively unaware (anosognosic) of any change in brain function. Sperry (1984, 1990) notes that several sensory projection systems, such as audition, tactile representation of the face, and crude representation of pain, temperature, and position sense maintain bilateral cortical projections. Thus, each hemisphere develops a degree of independent sensory representation. Furthermore, a degree of unification of action can be seen in instances of bilateral motor control (Sperry, 1990), i.e. ipsilateral control of eye movements. The emotional response to a stimulus which is presented to one hemisphere may spread to the contralateral hemisphere via an intact anterior commissure (Myers and Sperry, 1953) or remaining brainstem connections (Sperry, 1984, 1990). This can yield unification or double representation of emotional experiences (Levy, Trevarthen and Sperry, 1972; Sperry, Zaidel and Zaidel, 1979). Exploratory head and eye movements and cross-cueing strategies (Gazzaniga and Le Doux, 1978) are functional means of providing the disconnected hemispheres with a shared experience. While the split hemispheres are functionally disconnected for the detailed perception which involves foveal geniculostriate vision, ambient non-geniculostriate vision remains undivided after callosal division (Trevarthen, 1991; Trevarthen and Sperry, 1973). Thus, the speaking left hemisphere can report the presence and, to an extent, the direction, of an ipsilaterally presented flash of light. Additionally, in the case of high contrast, low spatially resolved stimuli (Trevarthen, 1991), a degree of attention to ipsilaterally positioned targets is possible. Transfer via the anterior commissure may also account for the lack of disconnection in some cases (Bogen, 1993; Trevarthen, 1991).

Another set of factors may be important in the lack of divided self-awareness in split-brain patients. Levy et al. (1972) presented callosally sectioned patients with 'chimeric' figures composed of two different halves joined at the midline. Under the condition of central fixation, where each hemisphere would receive a different visual input, it was demonstrated that if a single response was called for, patients typically responded to either the left or right side of the chimeric stimulus. The side they responded to was determined to a large extent by task requirements (Levy, 1977, 1990; Levy et al., 1972; Levy and Trevarthen, 1976; Trevarthen, 1974). Thus, if a verbal response or a match based on semantic knowledge was required, the right half of the chimeric presented to the subject's left hemisphere determined the response. If a visual match based on the objects appearance was required, the left half of the chimeric presented to the subject's right hemisphere determined the response.

From the standpoint of unawareness, a number of points are pertinent here. First, patients are not aware they have seen chimeric figures, though both hemispheres have processed, at least partially, the contralateral aspects of the chimerics. Trevarthen (1974) pointed out that one of his patients (L.B.), though able to respond to *both* sides of the chimeric simultaneously, never became aware that the stimuli were chimerics. Levy noted that when the patient's left hemisphere responded verbally and even *confabulated* a response to a stimulus which only the right hemisphere knew, the right hemisphere never indicated that it knew via a "frown or head shake" whether the response was in error. Likewise, the patient's left hemisphere did not verbally object to a right hemisphere response.

Secondly, 'completion' of the conflicting or absent aspects of the stimulus probably contributes to this unawareness. Trevarthen (1974) noted that, when a verbal response was called for, split-brain patients completed the missing left side of objectively partial figures and reported a whole face when shown chimerics with only the right half of a drawing of a face (Myers and Sperry, 1953). When shown a chimeric with the left side of a tree, the patient's left hand drew a whole tree when instructed to draw what it 'saw'. Thus, each hemisphere was capable of experiencing a 'whole' stimulus though each actually saw only half.

Thirdly, we suggest that this phenomenon occurs as a result of *confabulatory completion*. As noted previously, the conception of completion developed by Bender and Teuber (1946) and Torjussen (1978) was that completion resulted from residual visual function in a damaged area of the brain. According to this view, completion would only occur with objectively intact objects and could not be the result of a 'psychological filling in' of a missing part. In split-brain patients, however, the completed aspects of the stimulus which these patients claim to see in the ipsilateral field do not need to be objectively present. This phenomenon, which does not rely on the presence of the actual stimulus in the impaired field, is thus an example of *confabulatory completion* and should be distinguished from the *veridical completion*, a term suggested by Weizkrantz (1986), of objectively complete figures as described by Bender and Teuber (1946) and Torjussen (1976, 1978). It thus may be concluded that the unawareness of defect in split-brain patients depends in part upon the presence of this form of perceptual confabulation.

Anton's syndrome (unawareness of blindness)

Von Monakow is credited with the first scientific report of unawareness of cortical blindness in patients with bilateral posterior cortical pathology (Bisiach and Geminiani, 1991; Förstl, Owen and David, 1993; Gerstmann, 1942; McGlynn and Schacter, 1989; Redlich and Dorsey, 1945; Von Monakow, 1885). Similar cases were described by Dejerine and Vialet (1983) and Müller (1918). Gabriel Anton, in a series of papers between 1893 and 1899, presented the first systematic discussion of unawareness of neurological signs, including visual loss, cortical deafness, and hemiparesis (McGlynn and Schacter, 1989).

Anton is best known for his description of unawareness of cortical blindness which Albrecht (1918) termed 'Anton's symptom' in 1918. It is now known as 'Anton's syndrome'. Anton's most widely cited case (Anton, 1899) involved a 56-year-old seamstress who was unaware of her visual loss in spite of complete amaurosis of central origin (Förstl et al., 1993; McGlynn and Schacter, 1989; Redlich and Dorsey, 1945). The autopsy revealed bilateral cystic necrosis of the white matter of the occipital lobes. Though Anton did find generalized cognitive impairment in many of his patients with unawareness of deficits, he maintained that their unawareness could not be explained solely on this basis. He proposed they were mentally blind '(seelenblind)' for their neurological defects (Förstl et al., 1993). Anton suggested that unawareness of neurological deficits required the destruction of association tracts between primary sensory areas and the remaining brain.

The causes of Anton's syndrome are diverse. The most common etiology of the blindness is bilateral occipital lobe infarctions (McDaniel and McDaniel, 1991; Redlich and Dorsey, 1945; Swartz and Brust, 1984). For example, Redlich and Dorsey (1945), found that 4 of 6 patients with Anton's had bilateral hemianopias. However, they concluded that the appearance of the Anton's syndrome did not depend on the cause of the blindness. A more recent review of the syndrome (Swartz and Brust, 1984) also included the opinion that the blindness may be caused by lesions at any point along the visual pathways. According to Geschwind (1965), while patients with occipital infarctions may manifest unawareness without clouding of consciousness, blindness caused by peripheral lesions is much less likely to cause unawareness of deficit in the absence of significant dementia.

Previous authors have observed clinical similarities between Anton's and Korsakoff's syndrome (McDaniel and McDaniel, 1991). Stuss and Benson (1986) noted that bilateral infarction in the posterior cerebral artery distribution is a frequent cause of Anton's syndrome and can produce damage to hippocampus and limbic structures which may result in a Korsakoff-like syndrome. In this circumstance, these two syndromes involving both unawareness of defects and confabulation, may share a common limbic neuropathology (Benson, Marsden and Meadows, 1974).

Other evidence points to the importance of frontal pathology. Stengel and Steele (1946) reported the presence of denial of blindness in a patient with bilateral optic atrophy and frontal lobe tumors. Stuss and Benson (1986) described a patient with bilateral traumatic optic neuropathy and frontal damage sustained as a result of a motor vehicle accident. The patient was alert, oriented and without other neurological deficits. While admitting his lack of vision, he stated that with the proper illumination he could see perfectly. McDaniel and McDaniel (1991) described a similar case of a patient with monocular blindness due to optic nerve pathology and bifrontal encephalomalacia. This patient denied both visual loss and illness in general. She exhibited visual as well as generalized confabulation. The anosognosia and confabulation persisted after the resolution of an acute confusional state. The authors suggested that memory impairment coupled with a failure of self monitoring, due to frontal pathology, produced the denial of blindness citing Bychowski as the first to propose this mechanism (Bychowski, 1920).

The presence of generalized cognitive impairment has frequently been associated with Anton's syndrome (Bergman, 1957; Hemphill and Klein, 1948; McGlynn and Schacter, 1989; Redlich and Dorsey, 1945; Swartz and Brust, 1984) particularly, as noted above, when the visual loss is due to peripheral pathology (Geschwind, 1965). However, the presence of total denial of blindness in the absence of significant cognitive impairment, has confirmed Anton's view that cognitive impairment alone does not explain Anton's syndrome (Geschwind, 1965; McDaniel and McDaniel, 1991; Redlich and Bonvicini, 1907; Redlich and Dorsey, 1945).

Anton's syndrome commonly, if not universally, co-occurs with visual and other forms of confabulation. Redlich and Dorsey (1945) who found prominent confabulation in their patients suggested that "Anton's syndrome may be said to consist of a Korsakoff psychosis in a blind person." Brockman and von Hagen (1946) also noted prominent confabulation in Anton's syndrome. McDaniel and McDaniel (1991) suggested that in virtually all cases of Anton's syndrome, whether due to peripheral or central pathology, confabulation is present in relation to the visual defect as well as to other aspects of the patient's condition. They found confabulation and anosognosia to be closely allied conditions and considered confabulation to be necessary for the production of Anton's regardless of the site of damage to the visual system. Finally, Goldenberg, Mullbacher and Nowak (1995) described a case of Anton's syndrome where confabulation of visual experience appeared to be related to intact visual imagery.

Delusional misidentification syndromes

The term delusional misidentification syndrome (DMS) refers to conditions in which a patient incorrectly identifies and/or reduplicates persons, places, objects or events (Christodoulou, 1991; Feinberg and Roane, 1997b; Mendez, Martin, Smyth and Whitehouse, 1992; Spier, 1992). The most commonly reported form of misidentification for persons is known as Capgras syndrome. The syndrome was first reported in 1923 by Capgras and Reboul-Lachaux (1923) who described a 53-year-old woman with a chronic paranoid psychosis who developed the delusion that numerous persons known to her, including members of her family, had been replaced by imposters. She also claimed the existence of several duplicates of herself. Starting with this original case, hundreds of instances of Capgras syndrome have been reported. The essence of the disorder lies in the delusional belief that a person, generally someone close to the patient, has been replaced by a 'double' or imposter (Christodoulou, 1991).

A related form of misidentification is the Frégoli syndrome (Courbon and Fail, 1927). First reported in 1927 this syndrome is named after an Italian actor, Leopoldo Frégoli, who was a renowned impersonator. This condition involves the belief that a person familiar to the patient is impersonating, and hence taking on the appearance of, a stranger in the patient's environment. Several authors have analyzed the relationship between the Capgras and Frégoli syndromes (Christodoulou, 1976, 1977; Vié, 1930). Christodoulou (1977) suggested that Capgras represents a "hypoidentification" in which a person known by the patient is felt to be an imposter, while Frégoli is a manifestation of a "hyperidentification" in which a known person is seen in the guise of others. The syndrome of intermetamorphosis, described by Courbon and Tusques (1932) is another example of DMS in which the patient believes that persons known to them have exchanged identities with each other. In the delusion of subjective doubles (Christodoulou, 1978), the patients believe that they, themselves, have been replaced. Other varieties of DMS exist, and different varieties may co-occur in any given patient.

The existence of a relationship between the delusional misidentification syndromes and the syndrome of reduplicative paramnesia has been suggested by Alexander, Stuss and Benson (1979). They described a case of Capgras syndrome associated with a large right frontal subdural hematoma in which the patient stated that his wife and five children had been replaced by a nearly identical family. He persisted in his conviction even when challenged by his examiners. Alexander et al. (1979) noted a similarity between their case and reduplicative paramnesia, a syndrome originally described by Pick (1903). Pick's patient was a 67-year-old woman who confabulated the existence of two clinics both headed by Professor Pick. While Capgras had traditionally been considered a psychiatric condition, reduplicative paramnesia had been viewed as a neurological disorder generally seen in the setting of brain disorders and often associated with confusion and memory loss. Reduplication, in contrast to Capgras syndrome, typically involves misidentification of places rather than persons. However, there is no clear distinction between the two conditions. Weinstein, Kahn and Sugarman (1952a) reported cases of reduplication, in the setting of brain disease, which involved duplication of persons, events, body parts, and even the self. Furthermore, Weinstein found that reduplication was frequently associated with other psychiatric features, including other delusions, hallucinations, and mood changes. It has, therefore, become customary to include reduplicative paramnesia in the general category of DMS.

The Capgras delusion is commonly associated with psychiatric illness and is often accompanied by derealization and depersonalization (Christodoulou, 1986; Spier, 1992) and by other paranoid symptomatology (Kimura, 1986; Todd, Dewhurst and Wallis, 1981). Literature reviews of patients with the Capgras delusion have demonstrated the diagnostic heterogeneity of this condition (Kimura, 1986; Merrin and Silberfarb, 1970; Signer, 1987). Schizophrenia, mood disorders and organic conditions, including Alzheimer's disease (Mendez et al., 1992) have all been associated with Capgras.

Misidentification and reduplication have been associated with a wide variety of medical and neurological conditions (Förstl, Almeida, Owen et al., 1991a; Signer, 1992). In a large literature review of reduplication, Signer (1992) found cases due to drug intoxication or withdrawal, infectious and inflammatory disease, and endocrine disorders. Neurological conditions, included seizures, cerebral infarction, and head injury. Diffuse brain syndromes including delirium, dementia, and mental retardation accounted for over 40% of patients with diagnosable organic conditions. Misidentification has also been associated with Parkinsonism (Roane, Rogers, Robinson and Feinberg, 1998) and with electroconvulsive therapy (Hay, 1986; Weinstein, Linn and Kahn, 1952b).

Neuroanatomical correlates of DMS

In a report of 29 personally examined patients with misidentification for person, Joseph (1986a) found that 16 patients had bilateral cortical atrophy demonstrated on CAT scans, including 88% with bifrontal atrophy, 73% with bitemporal atrophy, and 60% with biparietal atrophy. Weinstein and Burnham (1991) suggested that the most common neurological findings in DMS were bilateral and diffuse brain involvement with right hemisphere predominance. Feinberg and Shapiro (1989) reviewed the anatomical pathology in a selected series of case reports of patients with misidentification–reduplication. They also found the common occurrence of bilateral cortical involvement with a frequency of 62% in Capgras patients and 41% in reduplication cases. When considering cases with unilateral cerebral dysfunction, they found a highly significant predominance of right hemisphere abnormalities in reduplication (52% right vs. 7% left). There was a statistical trend for more frequent right hemisphere damage in the smaller number of Capgras cases (32% right vs. 7% left). Förstl et al. (1991a), reviewing a wide range of misidentification cases, found that 19 of 20 patients with focal lesions on brain CT scans had right-sided abnormalities. In a separate report, Förstl, Burns, Jacoby and Levy (1991b) found that patients with Alzheimer's dementia and misidentification had significantly greater atrophy in the right frontal lobe than did Alzheimer's patients without DMS. In a study utilizing positron emission tomography, Mentis, Weinstein, Horwitz et al. (1995) found significant hypometabolism in bilateral orbitofrontal and cingulate regions of Alzheimer's patients with DMS compared to Alzheimer's patients without DMS. Based on three cases of head trauma, Benson, Gardner and Meadows (1978) demonstrated an association between reduplicative paramnesia and bifrontal impairment in combination with damage to the posterior portion of the right hemisphere. Hakim, Verma and Greiffenstein (1988), in a prospective study of 50 patients with alcoholism, found acute right hemisphere lesions in three of four reduplicators. They presumed all patients to have chronic bifrontal damage resulting from chronic alcohol use which was confirmed with neuropsychological testing. Finally, Fleminger and Burns (1993) compared right vs. left hemisphere asymmetries in CT scans of patients with misidentification. In one selected group, asymmetry was found, with greater right hemisphere damage in the occipitoparietal area. In the analysis of a second group of patients, they detected greater right hemisphere damage in frontal, temporal, and parietal lobes.

At present, some evidence suggests that a right hemisphere lesion (Feinberg and Shapiro, 1989) (particularly right frontal impairment (Kapur, Turner and King, 1988)) can be necessary and sufficient to produce misidentification (Kapur et al., 1988). However, the bulk of cases support the argument that misidentification is much more likely to be associated with a right hemisphere lesion in the context of bifrontal or diffuse cortical disturbance. This finding is consistent with the tendency in these patients to demonstrate confabulation in general.

Representative theories of DMS

Delusional misidentification has been viewed as a symptom, rather than a distinct syndrome, associated with a large number of psychiatric and neurological diagnoses (Enoch and Trethowan, 1979). Nonetheless, a variety of explanations have sought to account for a broad range of misidentification phenomena. Anatomical disconnection has been considered as a mechanism by several authors. Joseph (1986a) theorized that misidentification could result from hemispheric disconnection of cortical areas responsible for orientation. Thus, if each hemisphere could maintain an independent 'image' of person, place, and time, reduplication of entities in the environment might result. However, Ellis, De Pauw, Christodoulou et al. (1993) showed that patients with Capgras can make judgements regarding faces more rapidly with bilateral than with unilateral presentation, a finding that they suggested was inconsistent with the hemispheric disconnection hypothesis. Mentis et al. (1995) conclude in their PET study that DMS results from impaired connectivity between multimodal cortical association regions and paralimbic areas such that patients perceive accurately, but fail to appreciate the 'emotional significance and relevance' of the perception. Staton, Brumback and Wilson (1982) suggested that reduplication could represent a failure to integrate previously stored memories and new information as a result of disconnection of the right hippocampus. Alexander et al. (1979) proposed that the disconnection of right temporal and limbic areas from the frontal lobes could disturb the patient's experience of familiarity for people and places, preventing them from utilizing available information appropriately.

The mechanisms proposed by Alexander et al. (1979) and Staton et al. (1982) attribute misidentification specifically to the loss of functions subsumed by the right hemisphere. Other investigations of the causes of DMS and reduplication have stressed the importance of non-dominant hemisphere functions including disorders of visual–spatial orientation (Hakim et al., 1988; Kapur et al., 1988), problem solving (Kapur et al., 1988), and the ability to determine the exact identity and uniqueness of stimuli (Cutting, 1991). A study by Ellis et al. (1993) confirmed that three Capgras patients lacked the normal right hemisphere superiority for visual processing of faces.

A final approach entailing disconnection, formulated by Ellis and Young (1990), posits two anatomically independent pathways for facial recognition: a 'ventral route' subserving explicit recognition and a 'dorsal route' responsible for recognition of the emotional significance of faces, but not sufficient to allow for conscious identification (Bauer, 1986). While Capgras syndrome has been linked with prosopagnosia (Bidault, Luaute and Tzavaras, 1986; Shraberg and Weitzel, 1979; Lewis, 1987), Ellis and Young (1990) argue that the two are dissociable as they result from separate lesions. The ventral route disconnection causes prosopagnosia while the dorsal route interruption yields Capgras. In support of this hypothesis, Ellis, Young, Quayle and De Pauw (1997) showed that Capgras patients failed to differentiate familiar from unfamiliar faces on the basis of autonomic response, as measured by skin conductance; yet, they could demonstrate overt recognition of the familiar faces. In a recent review, Edelstyn and Oyebode (1999) point out that the various studies of face processing in Capgras have not consistently demonstrated any specific pattern of impairment.

Relying on a case study and a review of the literature, Sellal, Fontaine, Van Der Linden et al. (1996) attribute misidentification for place to visual–perceptual impairment in the context of a defect in self-awareness. In the case that they report, neuropsychological testing showed that their patient consistently misused visual details in the process of orienting herself. With regard to Fregoli-like misidentifications, Rapcsak, Polster, Glisky and Comer (1996) found that patients with right hemisphere pathology who falsely recognized unfamiliar faces divided into two categories. Patients with both false recognition and prosopagnosia had posterior lesions and impaired face perception or face recognition on neuropsychological testing. False recognition without prosopagnosia was associated with prefrontal damage and confabulation rather than perceptual impairment. Discussing a case of Fregoli which did involve both a right posterior temporoparietal infarct and significant face processing deficits, Ellis and Szulecka (1996) conclude that perceptual impairment alone cannot account for delusional misidentification. They support the view that the delusional nature of this symptom requires "a failure at a higher level where self beliefs are monitored."

The position of Ellis and Szulecka (1996) and of Sellal et al. (1996) is consistent with the notion that the *interaction* of neurological and psychiatric factors is critical in the production of DMS. Early important work emphasizing the link between neurological and psychiatric factors in DMS can be found in the writings of Jacques Vié (1930, 1944a,b, 1944c). Vié noted that the diverse misidentification syndromes (méconnaissance systématique) including Capgras and Frégoli paralleled the neurological syndromes of anosognosia and asomatognosia (denial of ownership of limb). Vié pointed out that these conditions were all characterized by systematic and selective misidentifications which could not be explained simply on the basis of generalized confusion.

Another possible connection between neurological and psychiatric causation of DMS may be derived from the fact that dissociative symptoms occur in DMS associated with both neurological and psychiatric disorders (Weinstein and

TABLE 1

Prior formulations of basic dichotomization of Capgras and Frégoli syndromes

Author	Capgras	Frégoli
Vié (1930)	Illusion of negative doubles	Illusion of positive doubles
Christodoulou (1977)	Delusional hypo-identification	Delusional hyper-identification
Christodoulou (1976)	Physically identical-psychologically different	Physically different — psychologically identical
De Pauw et al. (1987); De Pauw (1989, 1994)	Hypo-identification Denial of familiarity Jamais vu (Capgras)	Hyper-identification Affirmation of familiarity Déjà vu (environmental reduplication)
Feinberg and Shapiro (1989)	Pathological unfamiliarity Jamais vu Substitute familiar for unfamiliar (Capgras)	Pathological familiarity Déjà vu Substitute unfamiliar for familiar (environmental reduplication)

Burnham, 1991). Capgras, in the original report (1923), emphasized the importance of the "sentiment d'étrangeté" in the production of the syndrome in his chronic paranoid patient. Many authors have provided additional support for an association between depersonalization/derealization and DMS (Christodoulou, 1976, 1977, 1986). Christodoulou has suggested that depersonalization/derealization symptoms, under certain circumstances such as paranoia, cerebral dysfunction, or a charged emotional circumstance), may evolve into DMS. Weinstein and coworkers (Weinstein and Burnham, 1991; Weinstein, Marvin and Keller, 1962) have noted that patients with retrograde amnesia after head injury may also display elements of depersonalization and derealization. Feelings of altered familiarity also occur during psychomotor seizures and with temporal lobe stimulation (see Feinberg and Shapiro, 1989 for review).

DMS can be viewed as being especially related to, and perhaps a special instance of, dissociative disorders and we regard the origin of these symptoms as a perturbation, as opposed to a loss, of personal relatedness. DMS cleaves along the dimension of personal relatedness into three basic groups based upon the pattern of relatedness between the object (person, event, or experience) and the self. The various subtypes of DMS and reduplication can thusly be characterized as showing a pattern of decreased (withdrawal) or increased (insertion of) personal relatedness (or both) between the self and the misidentified object or event. The dichotomization into patterns of withdrawal or insertion of personal relatedness corresponds in part to several previously suggested dichotomies (Table 1) and is consistent with the viewpoint that Capgras may be similar to jamais vu phenomenon (De Pauw, 1989, 1994; De Pauw, Szulecka and Poltock, 1987; Feinberg and Shapiro, 1989; Todd et al., 1981), and that Frégoli (De Pauw et al., 1987) and environmental reduplication (De Pauw, 1989, 1994; De Pauw et al., 1987; Feinberg and Shapiro, 1989; Sno, Linszen and De-Jonghe, 1992) are similar to déjà vu phenomena. Our model, however, differs in the basic means of distinguishing Capgras from Frégoli (Table 2). These syndromes have previously been categorized on the basis of physical versus psychological substitution or hypo-identification versus hyper-identification. In contrast, we view the distinguishing feature to be alteration of personal relatedness or significance. Those syndromes exemplified by decreased relatedness may be said to represent a disavowal, estrangement, or alienation from persons object or events, while those with increased relatedness are manifestations of an over-identification with elements in the environment. It is possible that the neurological lesion, and certain neurological lesions in particular, cause a distortion of vision, memory, and awareness. The response to this distortion, particularly when it involves personally significant objects or events, creates the circumstances which, in the susceptible individual, results in DMS.

TABLE 2

Proposed model of common DMS

Examples of misidentified entities	Mechanism supporting misidentification/reduplication and clinical examples		
	Withdrawal of personal relatedness	Insertion of personal relatedness	Combined withdrawal/insertion of personal relatedness
Persons	Misidentifies wife as "impostor" (Capgras — jamais vu)	Misidentifies stranger as son (Frégoli — déjà vu)	Misidentifies personal physician as a friend from home [a] (Capgras/Frégoli — jamais vu/déjà vu)
Hemiplegic arm (asomatognosia) [a]	Denies ownership of arm		Misidentifies own arm as belonging to close friend [a]
Hospital (environmental reduplication) [a,b,c,d]	Calls the hospital a "branch" or "annex" of actual hospital	Mislocates actual hospital closer to patient's own neighborhood	Misidentifies hospital as "annex" of actual hospital and locates it closer to patient's own neighborhood [e]
Traumatic events (temporal reduplication) accident [a,b,c,f]	Denies accident occurred to patient (jamais vécu)	Claims similar accident happened previously to patient (déjà vécu)	Minimizes own accident, but claims reduplicated brother "Martin", i.e. car killed in (fictitious) car accident
Illness [a,b,c]	Denial of illness	Had similar illness previously	Patient denies illness, but claims reduplicated child Bill called "Willie" had same illness as patient [e] Patient with aneurysm minimizes it, claims her relatives have aneurysms

[a] Weinstein, 1969.
[b] Weinstein et al., 1952a.
[c] Weinstein and Burnham, 1991.
[d] Ruff and Volpe, 1981.
[e] Weinstein and Kahn, 1955.
[f] Baddeley and Wilson, 1986.

Acknowledgements

We would like to acknowledge Jean Zarate, B.S. for editorial assistance.

References

Albrecht O: Drei Fälle mit Anton's symptom. Archiv für Psychiatrie: 59; 883–941, 1918.

Alexander MP, Stuss DT, Benson DF: Capgras syndrome: a reduplicative phenomenon. Neurology: 29; 334–339, 1979.

Anton G: Ueber die Selbstwahrnehmung der Herderkrankungen des Gehirns durch den Kranken bein Rindenblindheit und Rindentaubheit. Archiv für Psychiatrie: 32; 86–127, 1899.

Babinski J: Anosognosie. Revue of Neurology (Paris): 31; 365–367, 1918.

Baddeley AD, Wilson B: Amnesia autobiographical memory and confabulation. In Rubin DC (Ed), Autobiographical Memory. Cambridge: Cambridge University Press, 1986.

Barkman A: Del'anosognosie dans l'hemiplegie cerebrale: contribution clinique a l'etude de ce symptome. Acta Medica Scandinavica: 62; 235–254, 1925.

Barre JA, Morin L, Kaiser: Etude clinique d'un nouveau cas d'Anosognosie de Babinski. Revue of Neurology (Paris): 39; 500–503, 1923.

Bauer RM: The cognitive psychophysiology of prosopagnosia. In Ellis H, Felves M, Newcombe F et al. (Eds), Aspects of Face Processing. Dordrecht: Martinus Nijhoff, 1986.

Bender MB: Disorders in visual perception. In Halpern L (Ed), Problems of Dynamic Neurology, Jerusalem: Jerusalem Post Press, pp. 319–375, 1963.

Bender MB, Teuber HL: Phenomena of fluctuation, extinction and completion in visual perception. Archives of Neurology and Psychiatry: 55; 627–658, 1946.

Benson DF, Gardner H, Meadows JC: Reduplicative paramnesia. Neurology: 26; 147–151, 1978.

Benson DF, Marsden DC, Meadows JC: The amnesic syndrome of posterior cerebral artery occlusion. Acta Neurologica Scandinavica: 50; 133–145, 1974.

Bergman PS: Cerebral blindness. Archives of Neurology and Psychiatry: 78; 568–584, 1957.

Berlyne N: Confabulation. British Journal of Psychiatry: 120; 31–39, 1972.

Bidault E, Luaute JP, Tzavaras A: Prosopagnosia and the delusional misidentification syndromes. Biblotheca Psychiatrica: 164; 80–91, 1986.

Bisiach E, Geminiani G: Anosognosia related to hemiplegia and hemianopia. In Prigatano GP, Schacter DL (Eds), Awareness of Deficit After Brain Injury. Clinical and theoretical issues. New York: Oxford University Press, 1991.

Bogen JE: The callosal syndromes. In Heilman KM, Valenstein E (Eds), Clinical Neuropsychology. New York: Oxford University Press, pp. 337–407, 1993.

Brockman NW, von Hagen KO: Denial of own blindness (Anton's syndrome). Bulletin of the Los Angeles Neurological Society: 11; 178–180, 1946.

Bychowski Z: Ueber das fehlen der Wahrnehmung der eigen Blindheit bei zwei Kriegsverletzen. Neurologisches Centralblatt: 106; 354–357, 1920.

Capgras J, Reboul-Lachaux J: L'illusion des 'sosies' dans un délire systématisé. Bulletin de la Société Clinque de Médecine Mentale: 11; 6–16, 1923.

Celesia GG, Brigell MG, Vaphiades MS: Hemianopic anosognosia. Neurology: 49; 88–97, 1997.

Christodoulou GN: Delusional hyper-identifications of the Frégoli type. Acta Psychiatrica Scandinavica: 54; 305–314, 1976.

Christodoulou GN: The syndrome of Capgras. British Journal of Psychiatry: 130; 556–564, 1977.

Christodoulou GN: Syndrome of subjective doubles. American Journal of Psychiatry: 135; 249–251, 1978.

Christodoulou GN: Role of depersonalization-derealization phenomena in the delusional misidentification syndromes. In Christodoulou GN (Ed), The Delusional Misidentification Syndromes. Basle: Karger, 1986.

Christodoulou GN: The delusional misidentification syndromes. British Journal of Psychiatry: 14; 65–69, 1991.

Courbon P, Fail G: Syndrome 'd'illusion de Frégoli' et schizophrenie. Annals of Medical Psychology: 85; 289–290, 1927.

Courbon P, Tusques J: L'illusion d'intermetamorphose et de charme. Annals of Medical Psychology: 90;401–406, 1932.

Critchley M (Ed): The Parietal Lobes. New York: Hafner, 1953.

Cutting J: Delusional misidentification and the role of the right hemisphere in the appreciation of identity. British Journal of Psychiatry: 159; 70–74, 1991.

Defour M: Sur la vision nulle dans i'hémianopsie. Revue Medicale do la Suisse Romande: 9; 445–451, 1889.

Dejerine and Vialet: Sur un casee de cécieté corticate diagnostiquée pendant la vie et confirmée par l'autopsie. Comptes Rendus Hebdomadaires des Séances et Mémoires de la Société de Biologie. Series 9: 5; 9983–9987, 1983.

De Pauw KW: Delusional misidentification syndromes. In Bizon Z, Szyszkowski W (Eds), Proceedings of the 35th Congress of Polish Psychiatrists. Warsaw: Polish Psychiatric Association, 1989.

De Pauw KW: Delusional misidentification: A plea for an agreed terminology and classification. Psychopathology: 27; 123–129, 1994.

De Pauw KW, Szulecka TK, Poltock TL: Frégoli syndrome after cerebral infarction. Journal of Nervous and Mental Disease: 175; 433–438, 1987.

Edelstyn NMJ, Oyebode F: A review of the phenomenology and cognitive neuropsychological origins of the Capgras syndrome. International Journal of Psychiatry: 14; 48–59, 1999.

Ellis HD, De Pauw KW, Christodoulou GN, Papageorgious L, Milne AB, Joseph AB: Responses to facial and non-facial stimuli presented tachistoscopically in either or both visual fields by patients with the Capgras delusion and paranoid schizophrenics. Neurology, Neurosurgery and Psychiatry: 56; 215–219, 1993.

Ellis HD, Szulecka TK: The disguised lover: a case of Fregoli Delusion. In Halligan PW, Marshall JC (Eds), Method in

Madness: Case Studies in Cognitive Neuropsychiatry. East Sussex: Psychology Press, pp. 37–50, 1996.

Ellis HD, Young AW: Accounting for delusional misidentifications. British Journal of Psychiatry: 147; 239–248, 1990.

Ellis HD, Young AW, Quayle AH, De Pauw KW: Reduced autonomic responses to faces in Capgras delusion. Proceedings of the Royal Society of London: 264; 1085–1092, 1997.

Enoch MD, Trethowan WH: Uncommon Psychiatric Syndromes. Bristol: John Wright and Sons, 1979.

Feinberg TE: Anosognosia and confabulation. In Feinberg TE, Farah M (Eds), Behavioral Neurology and Neuropsychology. New York: McGraw-Hill, pp. 369–390, 1997.

Feinberg TE, Roane DM: Anosognosia, completion and confabulation: the neutral-personal dichotomy. Neurocase: 3; 73–85, 1997a.

Feinberg TE, Roane DM: Misidentification syndromes. In Feinberg TE, Farah M (Eds), Behavioral Neurology and Neuropsychology. New York: McGraw-Hill, pp. 391–398, 1997b.

Feinberg TE, Roane DM, Kwan PC, et al: Anosognosia and visuoverbal confabulation. Archives of Neurology: 51; 468–473, 1994.

Feinberg TE, Schindler RJ, Flanagan NG, Haber LD: Two alien hand syndromes. Neurology: 42; 19–24, 1992.

Feinberg TE, Shapiro RM: Misidentification-reduplication and the right hemisphere. Neuropsychiatry and Neuropsychology: Behavioural Neurology: 2; 39–48, 1989.

Finger S: Origins of Neuroscience. A History of Explorations into Brain Function. New York: Oxford University Press, 1994.

Fleminger S, Burns A: The delusional misidentification syndromes in patients with and without evidence of organic cerebral disorder: a structured review of case reports. Biological Psychiatry: 33; 22–32, 1993.

Förstl H, Almeida OP, Owen A, Burns A, Howard R: Psychiatric, neurological and medical aspects of misidentification syndromes: a review of 260 cases. Psychological Medicine: 21; 905–950, 1991a.

Förstl H, Burns A, Jacoby R, Levy R: Neuroanatomical correlates of clinical misidentification and misperception in senile dementia of the Alzheimer type. Journal of Clinical Psychiatry: 52; 268, 1991b.

Förstl H, Owen AM, David AS: Gabriel Anton and 'Anton's symptom': on focal disease of the brain which are not perceived by the patient (1898). Neuropsychiatry Neuropsychology and Behavioral Neurology: 1; 1–8, 1993.

Frendrich R, Gazzaniga MS: Evidence for foveal splitting in a commissurotomy patient. Neuropsychologia: 27; 273–281, 1989.

Fuchs W: Eine Pseudofovea bei hamianopikern. Psychologische Forschung: 1; 157–186, 1922. In Ellis WD (Ed), A Source Book of Gestalt Psychology. London: Routledge and Kegan Paul, 1955a.

Fuchs W: Untersuchungen über das sehen der hemianopiker und hemiamblyopiker: I. Verlagerungserscheinungen, Ztsch. F Psychol: 84; 67–169, 1920. II. Die totalisierende Gestaltauffassung, ibid.: 86; 1–143, 1921. Translated as: Completion phenomena in hemianopic vision. In Ellis WD (Ed), A Source Book of Gestalt Psychology. London: Routledge and Kegan Paul, 1955b.

Gassel MM, Williams D: Visual function in patients with homonymous hemianopia. III. The completion phenomenon; insight and attitude to the defect; and visual functional efficiency. Brain: 86; 229–260, 1963.

Gattass R, Fiorani M Jr, Rosa MGP, Piñon MCGP, De Sousa APB, Soares JGM: Visual responses outside the classical receptive field in primate striate cortex: A possible correlate of perceptual completion. In: Lent R (Ed), The Visual System from Genesis to Maturity. Boston: Birkhauser, 1992.

Gerstmann J: Problem of imperception of disease and of impaired body territories with organic lesions. Archives of Neurology and Psychiatry: 48; 890–913, 1942.

Gazzaniga MS: The Bisected Brain. New York: Appleton-Century-Crofts, 1970.

Gazzaniga MS, Bogen JE, Sperry RW: Some functional effects of sectioning the cerebral commissures in man. Proceedings of the National Academy of Sciences of the United States of America: 48; 1765–1769, 1962.

Gazzaniga MS, Le Doux JE: The Integrated Mind. New York: Plenum, 1978.

Geschwind N: Disconnexion syndromes in animals and man. Brain: 88; 237–294, 1965.

Giacino JT, Cicerone KD: Varieties of deficit unawareness after brain injury. Journal of Head Trauma and Rehabilitation: 13; 1–15, 1998.

Goldenberg G, Mullbacher W, Nowak A: Imagery without perception — a case study of anosognosia for cortical blindness. Neuropsychologia: 33; 1373–1382, 1995.

Hakim H, Verma NP, Greiffenstein MF: Pathogenesis of reduplicative paramnesia. Neurology, Neurosurgery and Psychiatry: 51; 839–841, 1988.

Hay GG: Electroconvulsive therapy as a contributor to the production of delusional misidentification. British Journal of Psychiatry: 148; 667–669, 1986.

Head H, Holmes G: Sensory disturbances from cerebral lesion. Brain: 34; 102–254, 1911.

Heilman KM: Anosognosia: possible neuropsychological mechanisms. In Prigatano GP, Schacter DL (Eds), Awareness of deficits after brain injury: clinical and theoretical issues. New York: Oxford University Press, pp. 53–62, 1991.

Heilman KM, Barrett AM, Adair JC: Possible mechanisms of anosognosia: a defect in self-awareness. Philosophical Transactions of the Royal Society of London. Series B: Biological Sciences: 353; 1903–1909, 1998.

Hemphill RE, Klein R: Contribution to the dressing disability as a focal sign and to the imperception phenomena. Journal of Mental Science: 94; 661–622, 1948.

Joseph AB: Focal central nervous system abnormalities in patients with misidentification syndromes. In Christodoulou GN (Ed), The Delusional Misidentification Syndromes. Basle: Karger, 1986a.

Joseph R: Confabulation and delusional denial: frontal lobe dysfunction. Journal of Clinical Psychology: 42; 845–860, 1986b.

Kapur N, Turner A, King C: Reduplicative paramnesia: possible

anatomical and neuropsychological mechanisms. Neurology, Neurosurgery and Psychiatry: 51; 579–581, 1988.
Kimura S: Review of 106 cases with the syndrome of Capgras. Bibliotheca Psychiatric: 164; 121–130, 1986.
Levine DH, Calvanio R, Rinn WE: The pathogenesis of anosognosia for hemiplegia. Neurology: 41; 1770–1781, 1991.
Levy J: Manifestations and implications of shifting hemi-inattention in commissurotomy patients. In Weinstein EA, Freidland RP (Eds), Advances in Neurology. New York: Raven Press, 1977.
Levy J: Regulation and generation of perception in the asymmetric brain. In Trevarthen C (Ed), Brain Circuits and Functions of the Mind. New York: Cambridge University Press, pp. 231–248, 1990.
Levy J, Trevarthen C: Metacontrol of hemispheric function in human split-brain patients. Journal of Experimental Psychology: Human Perception and Performance: 2; 299–312, 1976.
Levy J, Trevarthen C, Sperry RW: Perception of bilateral chimeric figures following hemispheric disconnection. Brain: 95; 60–78, 1972.
Lewis SW: Brain imaging in a case of Capgras' syndrome. British Journal of Psychiatry: 150; 117–120, 1987.
McDaniel KD, McDaniel LD: Anton's syndrome in a patient with posttraumatic optic neuropathy and bifrontal contusions. Archives of Neurology: 48; 101–105. 1991.
McGlynn SM, Schacter DL: Unawareness of deficits in neuropsychological syndromes. Journal of Clinical and Experimental Neuropsychology: 11; 143–205, 1989.
Mendez MF, Martin RJ, Smyth KA, Whitehouse PJ: Disturbances of person identification in Alzheimer's disease: a retrospective study. Nervous and Mental Disease: 180; 94, 1992.
Mentis MJ, Weinstein EA, Horwitz B, McIntosh AR, Pietrini P, Alexander GE, Furey M, Murphy DGM: Abnormal brain glucose metabolism in the delusional misidentification syndromes: a positron emission tomography study in Alzheimer disease. Biological Psychiatry: 38; 438–449, 1995.
Merrin EL, Silberfarb PM: The Capgras phenomenon. Archives of General Psychiatry: 33; 965, 1970.
Müller F: Ein Beitrag zur Kenntnis der Seelenblindhert. Archiv für Psychiatrie: 24; 857–917, 1918.
Myers RE: Function of corpus callosum in interocular transfer. Brain: 79; 358–363, 1956.
Myers RE, Sperry RW: Interocular transfer of a visual form discrimination habit in cats after section of the optic chiasm and corpus callosum. Anatomical Record: 115; 351, 1953.
Nathanson M, Bergman PS, Gordon GG: Denial of illness: its occurrence in one hundred consecutive cases of hemiplegia. Archives of Neurology and Psychiatry: 68; 380–387, 1952.
Pick A: Clinical studies. Brain: 26; 242–267, 1903.
Poppelreuter W: Die Psychischem Schadigungen durch Kopfschuss im Kriege. Leipzig: Leopold Voss, 1917.
Prigatano GP, Schacter DL (Eds): Awareness of Deficit After Brain Injury: Clinical and Theoretical Issues. New York: Oxford University Press, 1991.
Ramachandran VS: Filling in gaps in perception: Part I. Current Directions in Psychological Science: 1; 199–205, 1992.
Rapcsak SZ, Polster MR, Glisky ML, Comer JF: False recognition of unfamiliar faces following right hemisphere damage: neuropsychological and anatomical observations. Cortex: 32; 593–611, 1996.
Redlich E, Bonvicini G: Über mangelnde Wahrnehmung (Autoanästhesie) der Blindheit bei cerebralen Erkrankugen. Neurologisches Centralblatt: 20; 945–951, 1907.
Redlich FC, Dorsey JF: Denial of blindness by patients with cerebral disease. Archives of Neurology and Psychiatry: 53; 407–417, 1945.
Roane DM, Rogers JD, Robinson JH, Feinberg TE: Delusional misidentification in association with Parkinsonism. Journal of Neuropsychiatry and Clinical Neuroscience: 10; 194–198, 1998.
Ruff RL, Volpe BT: Environmental reduplication associated with right frontal and parietal lobe injury. Neurology Neurosurgery and Psychiatry: 44; 382–386, 1981.
Sellal F, Fontaine SF, Van Der Linden M, Rainville C, Labrecque R: To be or not to be at home? A neuropsychological approach to delusion for place. Journal of Clinical and Experimental Neuropsychology: 18(2); 234–248, 1996.
Shraberg D, Weitzel WD: Prosopagnosia and the Capgras syndrome. Clinical Psychiatry: 40; 313–316, 1979.
Signer SF: Capgras' syndrome: the delusion of substitution. Journal of Clinical Psychiatry: 48; 147–150, 1987.
Signer SF: Psychosis in neurologic disease: Capgras symptom and delusions of reduplication in neurologic disorders. Neuropsychiatry, Neuropsychology and Behavioral Neurology: 5; 138–143, 1992.
Sno HN, Linszen DH, DeJonghe F: Déjà vu experiences and reduplicative paramnesia. British Journal of Psychiatry: 161; 565–568, 1992.
Sperry RW: Cerebral organizations and behavior. Science: 133; 1749–1757, 1961.
Sperry RW: Consciousness, personal identity and the divided brain. Neuropsychologia: 22; 661–673, 1984.
Sperry RW: Forebrain commissurotomy and conscious awareness. In Trevarthen C (Ed), Brain Circuits and Functions of the Mind. New York: Cambridge University Press, pp. 371–388, 1990.
Sperry RW, Gazzaniga MS, Bogen JE: Interhemispheric relationships: the neocortical commissures; syndromes of hemispheric disconnection. In Vinken PJ, Bruyn GW (Eds), Handbook of Clinical Neurology. Amsterdam: North Holland, pp. 273–290, 1969.
Sperry RW, Zaidel E, Zaidel D: Self recognition and social awareness in the disconnected minor hemisphere. Neuropsychologia: 17; 153–166, 1979.
Spier SA: Capgras' syndrome and the delusions of misidentification. Psychiatric Annals: 22; 279–285, 1992.
Staton RD, Brumback RA, Wilson H: Reduplicative paramnesia: a disconnection syndrome of memory. Cortex: 18; 23–36, 1982.
Stengel E, Steele GDF: Unawareness of physical disability (anosognosia). British Journal of Psychiatry: 92; 379–388, 1946.
Stuss DT: Disturbance of self-awareness after frontal system damage. In Prigatano GP, Schacter DL (Eds), Awareness of

Deficits after Brain Injury: Clinical and Theoretical Issues. New York: Oxford University Press, pp. 63–83, 1991.

Stuss DT, Benson DF: The Frontal Lobes. New York: Raven Press, pp. 144, 1986.

Swartz BE, Brust JCM: Anton's syndrome accompanying withdrawal hallucinosis in a blind alcoholic. Neurology (Cleveland): 34; 969–973, 1984.

Teuber HL, Battersby WS, Bender MB: Visual Field Defects after Penetrating Missile Wounds of the Brain. Cambridge: Harvard University Press, p. 87, 1960.

Todd J, Dewhurst K, Wallis G: The syndrome of Capgras. British Journal of Psychiatry: 139; 319–327, 1981.

Torjussen T: Residual function in cortically blind hemifields. Scandanavian Journal of Psychology: 17; 320–322, 1976.

Torjussen T: Visual processing in cortically blind hemifields. Neuropsychologia: 16; 15–21, 1978

Trevarthen C: Functional relations of disconnected hemispheres with the brain stem and with each other: monkey and man. In Kinsbourne M, Smith WL (Eds), Hemispheric Disconnection and Cerebral Function. Springfield: Thomas, pp. 187–207. 1974.

Trevarthen C: Integrative functions of the cerebral commissures. In Nebes RD, Corkin S (Eds), Handbook of Neuropsychology. New York: Elsevier, pp. 49–83, 1991.

Trevarthen C, Sperry RW: Perceptual unity of the ambient visual field in human commissurotomy patients. Brain: 96; 547–570, 1973.

Vié J: Un trouble de l'identification des personnes: l'illusion des sosies. Annals of Medical Psychology: 88; 214–237, 1930.

Vié J: Les méconnaissances systématiques. Annales Medico-Psychologique: 102; 410–455, 1944a.

Vié J: Le substratum morbide et les stades évolutifs des méconnaissances systématiques. Annales Medico-Psychologique: 102; 1–15, 1944b.

Vié, J: Etude psychopathologique des méconnaissances systématiques. Annales Medico-Psychologique: 102; 1–15, 1944c.

Von Monakow C: Experimentelle und patholgisch-anatomische Untersuchungen über die Beziehungen der sogenannten Sehsphäre zu den infracorticalen Opticuscentren und zum N. opticus. Archiv für Psychiatrie: 16; 151–199, 317–352, 1885.

Walker R, Mattingly JB: Ghosts in the machine? Pathological visual completion phenomena in the damaged brain. Neurocase: 3; 313–335, 1997.

Warrington EK: The completion of visual forms across hemianopic field defects. Neurology, Neurosurgery and Psychiatry: 25; 208–217, 1962.

Weinstein EA: Patterns of reduplication in organic brain disease. In Vinken PJ, Bruyn GW (Eds), Handbook of Clinical Neurology. Amsterdam: North Holland, 1969.

Weinstein EA, Burnham DL: Reduplication and the syndrome of Capgras. Psychiatry: 54; 78, 1991.

Weinstein EA, Kahn RL: Denial of Illness. Springfield: Charles C Thomas, 1955.

Weinstein EA, Kahn RL, Sugarman LA: Phenomenon of reduplication. American Medical Association Archives of Neurology and Psychiatry: 67; 808–814, 1952a.

Weinstein EA, Linn L, Kahn RL: Psychosis during electroshock therapy: its relation to the theory of shock therapy. American Journal of Psychiatry: 109; 22–26, 1952b.

Weinstein EA, Marvin SL, Keller NJA: Amnesia as a language pattern. Archives of General Psychiatry: 6; 269–270, 1962.

Weizkrantz L: Blindsight — a Case Study and Implications. New York: Oxford University Press, 1986.

Zangwill OL: The completion effect in hemianopia and its relation to anosognosia. In Halpern L (Ed), Problems of Dynamic Neurology. Jerusalem: Jerusalem Post Press, pp. 274–282, 1963.

Handbook of Neuropsychology, 2nd Edition, Vol. 4
M. Behrmann (Ed)

CHAPTER 8

Neuropsychological disorders of visual object recognition and naming

Glyn W. Humphreys * and M. Jane Riddoch

Behavioural Brain Sciences Research Centre, School of Psychology, University of Birmingham, Birmingham B15 2TT, UK

Introduction

Visual object recognition operates with amazing rapidity in normal observers. For example, we are able to recognize objects drawn from wide sets of classes even when only shown them briefly, for 100 ms or less (Thorpe, Fize and Marlot, 1996). Object recognition is also difficult for normal observers to suppress. Thus the semantic relations between objects can influence performance on tasks which only require judgements to their physical properties (e.g. when matching objects for global size or orientation; see Boucart and Humphreys, 1992). However the ease and automaticity of object recognition belies the complexity of the process. Something of this complexity can be gleaned by studying patients with selective disturbances of object recognition, following brain lesion. For instance, damage can result in selective impairments in the perceiving some of the basic features that make up objects, such as their form (Goodale, Milner, Jakobson and Carey, 1991), colour (Heywood, Cowey and Newcombe, 1991) and motion (Zihl, Von Cramon and Mai, 1983). The dissociations in processing these basic features in different patients suggest that the features are processed in separable neural pathways, despite our impression of an integrated coherent world! (see Heywood and Cowey, 1999; Heywood and Zihl, 1999, for recent reviews). The processes that underlie visual object recognition are not necessarily those that we have conscious access to. In this chapter, we discuss selective impairments of visual form perception (or visual agnosia), attempting to use the clinical evidence to help understand some of the (hidden) component processes involved.

* Corresponding author. E-mail: g.w.humphreys@bham.ac.uk

Disorders of form perception (apperceptive agnosia)

The neurologist Lissauer first distinguished two classes of visual recognition problem that can occur after brain damage, labelling the problems *apperceptive* and *associative* agnosia (Lissauer, 1890). The term apperceptive agnosia has subsequently been used to describe patients whose recognition appears to be contingent on poor perception of object form, and the term associative agnosia patients without a deficit in form perception but who have difficulty in matching form information to memory (an impaired 'association' process) (see Farah, 1990; Humphreys and Riddoch, 1987, 1993; Warrington, 1985, for reviews). We begin by using this simple dichotomy to describe sub-classes of recognition problem, though we will also elaborate differences between patients within each sub-class. We go on to consider whether the distinction, between apperceptive and associative processes, is the best way to conceptualise object recognition.

The apperceptive agnosias

Processing elementary form information

Several cases have now been described where the recognition impairment seems to be caused by impaired perception of elementary aspects of visual form (e.g. see Benson and Greenberg, 1969; Efron, 1968; Milner et al., 1991). One clinical test used to assess form perception is the 'Efron' shape matching task, in which the patient is asked to discriminate between squares and rectangles of the same size area and brightness (see Fig. 1). Patients can be impaired at this task, though perceptual judgements based on 'surface' properties of objects (colour, brightness, texture) may still be made. There is also poor copying of even simple line drawings. In many instances, patients with these deficits have been exposed to carbon monoxide poisoning. Carbon monoxide can produce multiple, disseminated lesions throughout the cortex (Garland and Pearce, 1967). Campion and Latto (1985) argued that these disseminated lesions have the effect of introducing a 'peppery' mask to the patient's visual world. This leads to a loss of detail about the global shape of objects. However, this seems overly simplistic. For example, on this account, we might expect patients to adapt over time, 'filling in' the 'holes' in their visual field. In addition, moving objects should be integrated across the peppery mask, and stationary objects should be integrated when the observer moves. Despite this recognition is severely compromised in free vision in everyday life.

Others have argued that the problem with visual recognition in such patients is due to impaired grouping of visual features, an account we discuss more extensively below (Humphreys, Riddoch, Quinlan et al., 1992). There is physiological evidence that there is grouping of features into larger wholes from early stages of cortical vision (see Von der Heydt and Peterhans, 1989). Damage to early cortical areas may prevent patients from grouping parts into coherent perceptual structures even for simple shape-matching tasks. Vecera and Gilds (1998) attempted to contrast the 'peppery mask' and grouping accounts of apperceptive agnosia in studies with normal subjects. Subjects had to respond to a spatially cued target under two viewing conditions: either a peppery mask was present, or stimuli were degraded to mimic impaired grouping (the stimuli were rectangles that could have corners removed). Targets (small squares) could appear in the same rectangle as the cue or in another object the same distance away from the cued position. Egly, Driver and Rafal (1994) showed that there is normally an 'object' benefit, with RTs being faster to targets in the cued object (relative to when the target appears in the non-cued object). Vecera and Gilds (1998) found that the object-cueing advantage was disrupted when the corners of the cued objects were removed. In contrast, the effects of object-cueing were additive with the slowing of processing due to the peppered mask. They suggest that the object-cueing effect reflects processes involved in coding simple shape representations. These processes are selectively impaired when grouping is disrupted (by removing the corners of the shapes). A peppery mask can slow processing, but it does not selectively disrupt the shape coding that gives rise to the object-cueing effect.

Other evidence contradicting a simple masking account comes from studies of 'implicit' visual processing in patients with apperceptive agnosia. In implicit tasks, patients do not have to make conscious perceptual judgements to objects, but the properties of objects may nevertheless affect other judgements or actions. This was first reported by Milner and his colleagues (Milner et al., 1991). Patient DF had suffered carbon monoxide poisoning from fumes leaking from a faulty gas water heater. Her visual object recognition was subsequently severely impaired; she could recognise few real objects and no line drawings. Her copying was poor, and she was at chance at making perceptual judgements even about the basic dimensions of form such as their size or

Fig. 1. Example of stimuli used in the Efron shape discrimination task.

orientation (see Milner et al., 1991). Yet, strikingly, DF was able to reach appropriately to objects. Her grasp aperture and hand orientation were tuned to the size and orientation of stimuli and the kinematics of her movements were relatively normal. DF could reach appropriately to objects that she could not make perceptual size judgements to.

To account for this marked difference between perceptual judgements and action, Milner and Goodale (1995) stress the contrast between the ventral and dorsal streams of the visual cortex. The ventral stream passes from the occipital lobe to the temporal lobe and is standardly thought to mediate visual pattern recognition; the dorsal stream passes from the occipital lobe to the parietal lobe, and is usually thought to be important for visuo-spatial processing (e.g. localising where objects are; see Ungerleider and Mishkin, 1982). Milner and Goodale propose that DF's lesion affected the ventral visual system, so that perceptual judgements about even the basic dimensions of form were disrupted. In contrast they suggest that the dorsal visual stream remained intact. According to Milner and Goodale (1995), the dorsal stream not only codes stimulus location, but also provides visual information for prehensile actions — such as reaching and grasping. This can take place independently of the processing of the same information in the ventral stream. Consequently, in a patient such as DF, orientation and size information can be coded by the dorsal stream and used for action, even though, concurrently, use of the same information by the ventral stream is impaired. On this account, the ventral stream (for object recognition) and the dorsal system (for location coding and action) are separated even from early stages of cortical coding.

An alternative possibility is that vision for action is not completely independent of vision for perceptual judgements and object recognition (see Jeannerod, 1997), but dissociations can be observed in patients because 'vision for action' can bring into play feedback processes that do not operate in recognition. In particular, when we reach to objects, we gain visual feedback about hand position and hand size and orientation relative to objects. The dorsal system may mediate rapid feedback in visually guided prehensile actions, and so generate improved action relative to 'perception' in some patients (see Edwards and Humphreys, 1999, for some evidence on the use of visual feedback in reaching). In the absence of this feedback (e.g. when asked solely to make perceptual judgements), patients with ventral lesions may perform poorly.

Interestingly, DF's ability to code orientation has been shown not only in action, but also in perceptual judgement tasks where orientation information does not have to be consciously appreciated. The McCollough effect is a long-lasting negative after-effect that is contingent on the relative orientations of 'adapting' and 'test' patterns (McCollough, 1965). For example, when we look for a prolonged period at a vertical pattern with green and black stripes (the 'adaptation stimulus'), and then view a test pattern with white and vertical stripes, we see the test pattern as pink rather than white. However, if the test pattern has horizontal stripes then we do not see the negative colour after-effect. To demonstrate the effect then, one must code orientation along with colour. Evidence of a positive McCullough effect with DF suggests several possibilities. One is that orientation is processed jointly with colour in a colour-sensitive pathway in the brain, which remains intact in DF. Provided her judgements are based on outputs from that pathway, she shows sensitivity to orientation. Her deficits become apparent only when she attempts to use orientation coded within a pathway sensitive to visual form. An alternative is that DF can use orientation information implicitly but not explicitly for perceptual judgements (e.g. she is not conscious of orientation information even when it affects her perceptual judgements, as in the McCullough after-effect). She only has explicit access to orientation information when it is used for action.

Integrating parts to wholes

In contrast to cases such as DF, other patients seem able to extract basic features of visual forms and to perform some elementary grouping of these features, but they are still impaired at binding features more wholistically into shapes. These problems are most clearly demonstrated when there are multiple items present, when there is competition in assigning elements between shapes. This is illustrated by studies conducted with the visual agnosic patient HJA (see Riddoch and Humphreys, 1987a; Riddoch

Fig. 2. Examples of HJA's copies, with the exemplars on the left (guitar and owl).

et al., 1999). HJA suffered bilateral damage to areas of pre-striate cortex, including the lingual and fusiform gyri and posterior regions of the inferior temporal gyri. This left him with a variety of perceptual deficits — a marked visual agnosia, plus also poor word recognition (alexia) and face recognition (prosopagnosia). For example, he was typically only able to identify about one in three line drawings shown to him, and he failed to identify the faces of even close members of his family. Despite this, HJA performed well at the Efron shape matching task (Fig. 1; see Humphreys et al., 1992), and he was generally able to produce identifiable copies of objects that he failed to recognize (see Fig. 2). Due to his reasonable performance on such tests, it might be concluded that his deficit was associative rather than apperceptive in nature (cf. Lissauer, 1890). However, a closer analysis reveals that this is not correct. HJA's copying of objects, for example, was often rather slow and errors could be induced under particular circumstances. When given sets of overlapping figures, and asked to copy each different figure in a different coloured pen, HJA accurately depicted the contours present but mis-segmented the shapes so that parts of different shapes were assigned the same colour and parts of the same shape were assigned different colours (see Fig. 3a). Also, when given occluding shapes, he sometimes made errors by drawing in the occluded contour present in the shape in the background (Fig. 3b). Normal subjects do not make either of these errors. HJA's object recognition was also strongly affected by varying the quality of the perceptual information available. He found it difficult not only to copy, but also to identify overlapping forms, his identification levels decreased in an abnormally rapid way when stimulus presentation times were reduced and he tended to find line drawings more difficult to identify than silhouettes (Riddoch and Humphreys, 1987a; Riddoch et al., 1999). All of these last results are consistent with there being a perceptual origin to his deficits.

Further studies have indicated that the perceptual problems experienced by HJA reflect an impairment in integrating local form elements into more wholistic shapes. This is revealed by two rather different sets of experiments — one set using visual search procedures and the other shape-matching tasks. Visual search typically requires subjects to detect a particular target shown amongst varying numbers of distractors. If targets and distractors differ in some salient local feature (e.g. line orientation), search can be little affected by the number of distractors present; this is consistent with subjects detecting such targets in a spatially parallel manner ('single feature search'). Search is usually more difficult when targets and distractors have the same features, but in different arrangements (e.g. an L and a T, which both contain horizontal and vertical line elements), when subjects appear to have to inspect each item serially to find the target. Even here though search can become efficient if the distractors form a homogeneous set which, by grouping, can be segmented from the target (Duncan and Humphreys, 1989; Humphreys, Quinlan and Riddoch, 1989). In single feature search tasks (e.g. for targets defined by an orientation difference), HJA performed well. He could also conduct a normal serial scan in a difficult search task. However, he was markedly impaired in search tasks where grouping is normally important (e.g. when targets and distractors have the same features, but distractors form a homogeneous set). HJA's deficit in search was revealed under conditions sensitive to what we may term 'parallel binding' of feature elements into shapes. The ability to group and segment targets and distractors differing only in their arrangements of features depends on the prior binding of the elements into each shape. HJA is impaired at doing this in parallel across all the elements present.

The second piece of evidence comes from studies of shape matching. Giersch, Humphreys, Boucart and Kovacs (2000) presented HJA with line drawings of three geometric shapes that could be spatially separated, superimposed, or occluding (see Fig. 4). In addition, sets of occluding silhouettes were also presented. After a brief interval, the target was exposed again along with a distractor in which the positions of the shapes were rearranged. HJA had to discriminate which of the second two stimuli was the same as the first. Giersch et al. found that he performed particularly poorly with occluding shapes. This deficit was most pronounced when the length of the occluded edge was small — the condition when the missing fragment should be easiest to compute based on collinearity between the non-occluded edges. It appears that HJA computed the occluded edge, but this then led to him having difficulties in coding the occluding shapes — which was in front, which behind and so on. This was not a simple problem in depth perception, since other aspects of HJA's depth perception were good (e.g. the ability to see depth from stereo images; see Humphreys and Riddoch, 1987). Rather, it was a problem in integrating line elements into shapes when there were complex two-dimensional depth relations also to be coded.

This last finding, of poor matching of occluded shapes, fits with the evidence from HJA's copying, where he sometimes draws in an occluded contour onto the occluding surface (see Fig. 3b). The result was interesting not only because it reveals something of the underlying disorder for HJA, but also because it has implications for understanding normal vision. The data show that HJA computes the occluded contour even though he is subsequently impaired at coding the correct figure–ground rela-

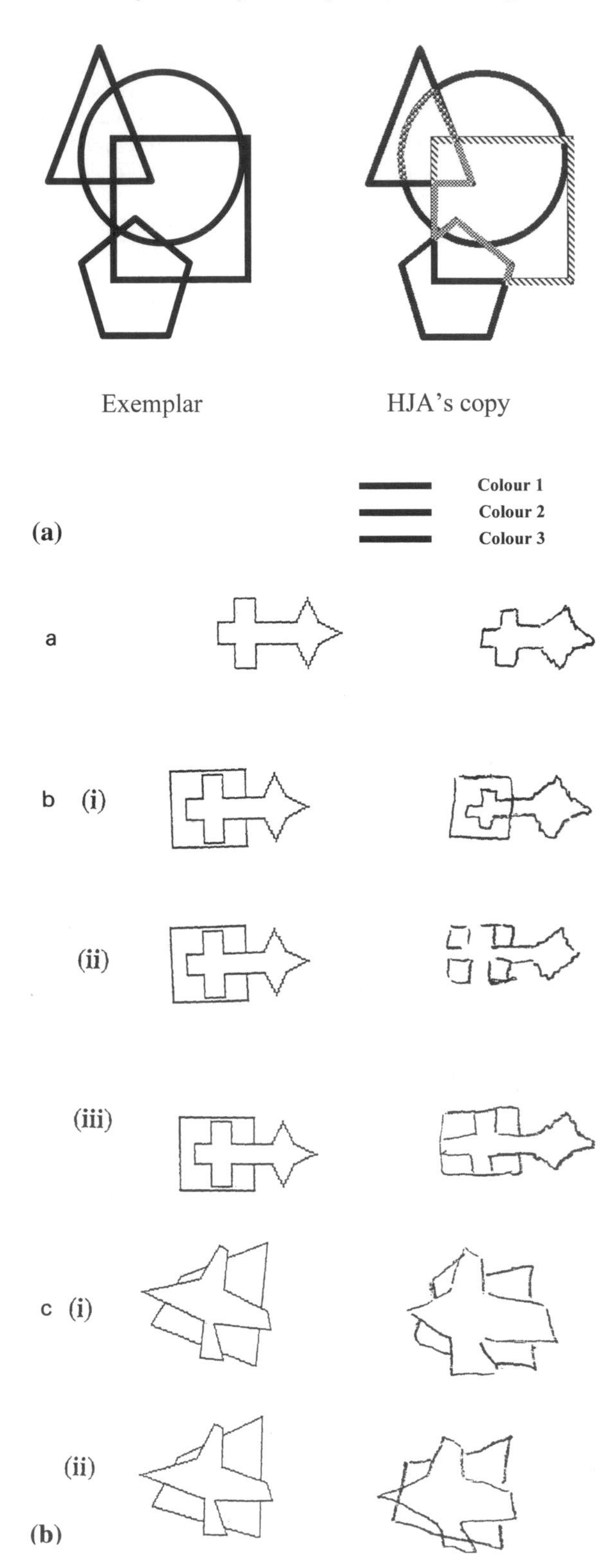

Fig. 3. (a) Example of overlapping figures and HJA's copying response (different textures signify the use of different coloured pens, to indicate when he thought a new shape began). (b) Example of HJA's copies of non-occluding (a) and occluding shapes (b and c). In b(i) and c(i) HJA includes the occluded contour in his drawing.

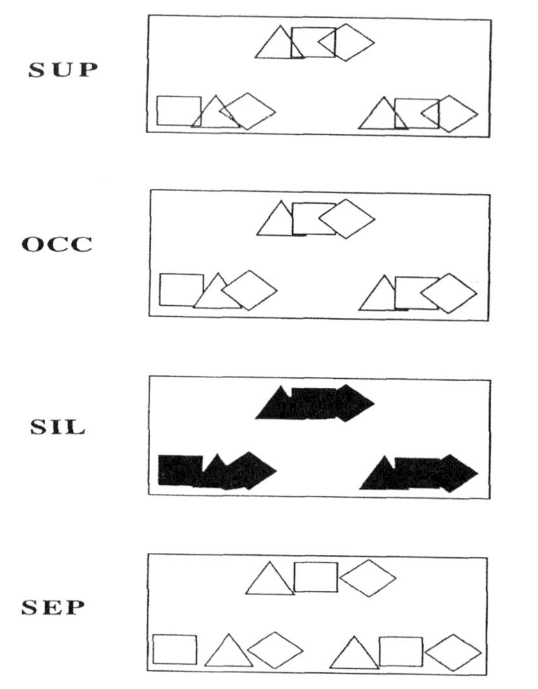

Fig. 4. Example stimuli used by Giersch et al. (2000). SUP, superimposed shapes; OCC, occluding shapes; SIL, silhouettes; and SEP, spatially separated shapes.

tions between the shapes. Thus, it must be that the occluded contour can be computed prior to figure–ground relations being represented between shapes. The occluded contour can be computed locally from the presence of collinearity between edge elements, whereas figure–ground representation depends on more wholistic coding between the shapes present. HJA can code local form features into edges, but he is impaired at integrating the edges into shapes and in coding the figure–ground relations between shapes.

In a further study, Giersch et al. tested HJA's threshold for linking collinear, local features into edges. For this, HJA had to find the circular pattern in displays, such as those shown in Fig. 5, and the number of background 'distractors' were increased until the target became impossible to find. Interestingly, HJA's threshold on this task was entirely normal! This provides direct evidence of a normal ability to group elements into oriented edge features. We conclude that this constitutes a first stage of grouping in form perception, followed by a subsequent stage in which the edge elements are integrated into shapes and assigned their figure–ground relations. HJA's deficit is at this second stage.

Other studies have shown that the difference between HJA's performance with silhouettes and line drawings extends beyond simple shape matching; for example, it can also be found in tasks for which access to memory is required. Riddoch and Humphreys (1987a), for example, first reported this in an object decision task (see also Lawson and Humphreys, 1999), for further recent evidence). They suggested that the internal contours present in line drawings are used by HJA to segment objects inappropriately, so that he then fails to identify them. With silhouettes, HJA may rely on the global shape information, which he remains able to compute. It may also be that silhouettes are useful because they have single-textured surfaces, which may help the parts to 'cohere', aiding identification. Chainay and Humphreys (2001) examined the effects of surface detail. They compared HJA's identification of black and white line drawings, correctly coloured line drawings and drawings filled with incorrect colours. They found an advantage for the coloured drawings over black and white drawings, but this held whether the colours were correct or wrong. This demonstrates that colour per se was relatively uninformative; what mattered was whether the colours divided the object up into appropriate parts. Division into appropriate parts based on surface texture should occur with incorrectly coloured and correctly coloured drawings alike; it follows that HJA's recognition should be facilitated in both conditions.

It is possible that surface information is also important for the 'real object advantage' shown by many agnosics: real objects being identified more easily than drawings. Other factors may also be important, however, such as depth information conveyed by binocular disparity and/or motion. Chainay and Humphreys evaluated this. HJA's ability to identify objects was tested under number of viewing conditions, with real objects seen (i) from within arm's length or at a distance out of arm's reach, (ii) binocularly or monocularly, and (iii) with or without free head movements. Binocular cues are particularly useful for depth when objects fall close to the body, and depth from disparity drops rapidly as distance increases (see Bruce, Green and Georgeson, 1996).

Fig. 5. Example stimuli from Giersch et al. (2000), used to test whether HJA had intact computation of edge elements.

When objects fall at a distance depth information may nevertheless be derived by motion disparity, for example due to head movements relative to an object. Chainay and Humphreys (2001) reported that there were advantages for real objects viewed binocularly from a close distance, and for objects seen at a distance provided that small head movements were allowed. Real objects viewed at a distance without head movements were identified no more accurately than line drawings. This suggests that depth information was important for the real object advantage over line drawings. Furthermore, when depth cues were minimized (objects at a distance, with no head movements), HJA made copying errors in which he segmented and omitted some parts of objects. It appears that depth information, perhaps like surface texture, can provide information about the parts of objects and their inter-relations. Both depth and surface texture can help to 'glue' the parts of objects together when integration by form information alone is impaired.

Although much of the above discussion has concentrated on one case, albeit studied in detail, there are similar patterns present in other patients in the literature. For example, Butter and Trobe (1994) reported detrimental effects of figural overlap on identification in their agnosic subject, who also generated better performance with silhouettes. Like HJA, the patients reported by De Renzi and Lucchelli (1994) and Kartsounis and Warrington (1991) were impaired at the perception overlapping figures despite good discrimination of simple Efron shapes, whilst the 'piecemeal' approach to object identification characteristic of HJA has been noted in several other cases (see Goldstein and Gelb, 1918; Grossman, Galetta and D'Esposito, 1997; Sirigu, Duhamel and Poncet, 1991; Wapner, Judd and Gardner, 1978, for other examples).

Interestingly, although agnosics seem to 'weight' individual parts strongly in object identification, they typically do not report the whole object as if it were just the part (e.g. describing a bicycle as a wheel). It appears that agnosic patients can have some information about 'whole' objects, but do not assign this information a large role in recognition. In an additional test of this idea with HJA, Humphreys, Riddoch and Quinlan (1985) examined responses to compound stimuli in which the whole is composed of separately identifiable local parts (e.g. a large letter made up of smaller letters; cf. Navon, 1977). They reported that HJA responded normally to the global form but, unlike normal subjects, there was no effect of the global form on response latencies to the local parts (see also Lamb, Robertson and Knight,

1990, for a similar result with patients with unilateral lesions to the superior temporal gyrus). The global form of an object may be conveyed by low spatial frequency components in an image, but these components will typically fail to specify local parts in sufficient detail to enable accurate identification of specific objects. Humphreys and Riddoch (1987) proposed that global form information is usually embellished by information about the local parts of objects, to provide a description that serves for accurate object recognition. In patients such as HJA, the integration of local part information with wholistic shape seems to break down.

Recognition across viewpoints

We have interpreted the neuropsychological evidence as indicating that there are at least two separable early stages in object recognition — coding elements into oriented edges and primitive shapes, and integrating parts with more wholistic information to form more complex shape representations. Theories differ on what processes might follow these early stages, and in particular they differ on whether object recognition proceeds directly from the image as coded or whether there is a form of 'normalisation' in which a viewpoint-invariant representation of the object derived. Warrington and colleagues (e.g. Warrington and James, 1986; Warrington and Taylor, 1973, 1978) first described a syndrome in which patients with damage to the right hemisphere were poor at tasks where they had to match prototypical views of objects with 'unusual' views. Warrington and James (1986) suggested that patients had difficulty in extracting critical features that would enable objects to be matched across viewpoints. Humphreys and Riddoch (1984) documented a further double dissociation between patients who were either affected by alteration of critical features across the viewpoints or by changes in the principal axis of the object. They manipulated two factors: whether the 'unusual' view reduced the saliency of the critical features of object (they termed this the minimal feature condition) or whether it maintained these critical features but foreshortened the main axis of the object (the foreshortened condition). Fig. 6 gives an example of a typical trial in the study. Three stimuli were presented, two were different views of the same target, the third was a different, distractor object. The task was to point to the distractor. In Fig. 6, one view of the target (a pepper-pot) is foreshortened. One patient was reported with impaired performance in the minimal feature condition, but not the foreshortened condition, whilst four other patients were reported with poor matching of foreshortened, but not minimal feature images. Humphreys and Riddoch (1984) provided other converging evidence that foreshortening was important, since the difficulty with foreshortened images for some patients was reduced when foreshortened objects were depicted against a background with strong linear perspective cues to depth. Presumably these depth cues enabled the patients to code more easily the main axis of the objects. These results are consistent with the idea that recognition depends on viewpoint invariant representations. For example, Marr (1982) proposed

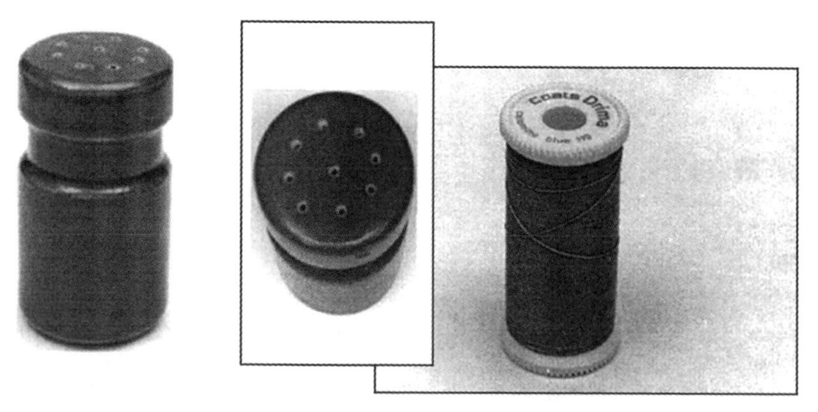

Fig. 6. Example stimuli used in tests of matching across viewpoints.

that recognition depends on a 3D model representation in which the parts of objects are coded in relation to the principal axis. Humphreys and Riddoch's evidence suggests that some patients find it difficult to derive such representations when the principal axis is foreshortened. However, it remains questionable whether this 'normalisation' process is *necessary* for object recognition. For instance, poor matching of objects in 'unusual views' could reflect impaired procedures for dealing with degraded objects, but these procedures may play little part in recognition when objects are not degraded. Consistent with this last view, many of the patients with deficits on 'unusual views' are able to recognize objects in prototypical views (see also Davidoff and De Bleser, 1994; Davidoff and Warrington, 1999). Thus, evidence from such patients does not necessarily tell us how objects are recognized in familiar viewpoints. We return to these issues when we discuss the hemisphere-specialisation approach to object recognition, below.

The associative agnosias

After perceptual processing of objects has taken place to a sufficient degree, objects must be matched to memory, for recognition to occur. Neuropsychological evidence here indicates that this process too can be fractionated. This is illustrated by patterns of sparing and deficits on 'object-decision' tasks. In these tasks patients have to discriminate depictions of real objects from those of non-objects. The non-objects can vary in their similarity to real objects, and, in cases where non-objects are formed by combining parts from real objects, the non-objects can be as 'perceptually good' as real objects (see Fig. 7). With perceptually good non-objects, object decisions likely require access to stored knowledge (is this stimulus familiar?) rather than being based on perceptual information alone. Object-decision tasks may thus be used to assess whether patients can access stored knowledge from objects. Interestingly, there are now several reports of patients who succeed on difficult object decision tasks, but who remain impaired at recognizing objects (Hillis and Caramazza, 1995; Riddoch and Humphreys, 1987b; Sheridan and Humphreys, 1993; Stewart, Parkin and Hunkin, 1992). For instance, patient JB (Riddoch

Fig. 7. Examples of non-objects used for object decision tasks.

and Humphreys, 1987b) performed object decisions at a normal level but was poor at judging from vision which two of three objects would be used together (e.g. hammer, nail, spanner). This problem with matching objects based on their functional associations was modality specific; when given the name of the objects, JB carried out the same task with ease. Thus JB was impaired at accessing functional-associative knowledge from vision, but could access forms of visual knowledge to perform the difficult object-decision task. Riddoch and Humphreys proposed that this reflected a distinction between access to stored structural descriptions for objects and access to stored semantic information (specifying functional and associative knowledge). The former, but not the latter, was intact in JB. Note that access to both forms of knowledge conform to what Lissauer (1890) originally termed the association process. We suggest that this association process is composed of separable hierarchically arranged stages including access to stored structural descriptions followed by access to semantic knowledge. A framework illustrating this hierarchical approach to object identification is given in Fig. 8.

There are other reports of patients who are impaired at object decision, but who remain able to accomplish tests stressing earlier perceptual processes (including unusual view matching) (Forde, Francis, Riddoch et al., 1997; Humphreys and Rumiati, 1998; Rumiati, Humphreys, Riddoch and Bateman,

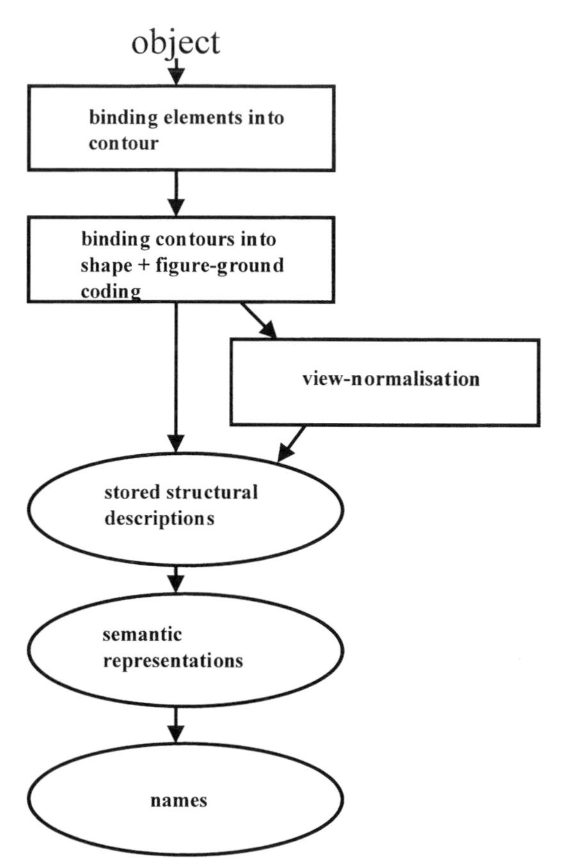

Fig. 8. A framework for object recognition which can account for the different disorders of object recognition.

1994; Sartori and Job, 1988). These patients are typically poor not only at visual recognition, but also at answering questions about the visual properties of objects when asked verbal questions (e.g. does an elephant have a long tail relative to its body?). One interpretation of this is that stored structural descriptions are accessed not only in order to recognise objects visually, but also when we must retrieve visual knowledge when the input is non-visual. The problem for such patients can be attributed to an impaired ability to 'map' structural knowledge about the visual properties of objects onto other forms of stored knowledge (e.g. semantic information about the object's use and prior associations). This process of mapping from structural to semantic knowledge may be particularly difficult when the stimuli belong to categories of object that are both visually and semantically close — for instance, if the stimuli are living things rather than artefacts. Humphreys, Riddoch, and Quinlan (1988) reported that living things tended to share more similar global shapes than stimuli from other categories, and they tend to have more parts in common. Perhaps due to this, normal subjects can be slower to name living things relative to artefacts (see also Lloyd-Jones and Humphreys, 1997, for evidence on an advantage for artefacts over living things with normal observers). With patients, this difference between living things and artefacts can be found on response accuracy. This can occur even in patients who show intact access to stored structural knowledge about objects, evidenced by good object decision performance. Thus, JB (see above; Riddoch and Humphreys, 1987b) was more likely to identify artefacts than he was living things. Humphreys et al. (1988) proposed that the difference between living things and artefacts could be due to the greater overlap between both structural and semantic representations for living things. This should render identification more difficult for a patient who has difficulty in mapping between structural and semantic representations. For example, let us assume that, for recognition to occur, activation from a structural level must be mapped through representations within a 'semantic space'. If activation at a structural level leads to rather imprecise activation of a number of related semantic representations, the problem in discriminating between the semantic representations would be exacerbated when they are close to one another than when they are more distant.

Arguin, Bub and colleagues (Arguin, Bub and Dudek, 1996; Dixon, Bub and Arguin, 1997) have made quite similar arguments. They had an agnosic patient learn relationships between visual shapes and names. The shapes varied along either one or two dimensions (e.g. elongation and bending, to describe a banana-like shape). The patient found it difficult to learn names for the shapes when (1) the stimuli varied along two rather than one dimension, and (2) the names that had to be paired with the shapes came from a semantically close set. Semantic proximity alone had little effect provided the stimuli varied along a single dimension. Likewise, having two rather than one dimension of relevance had little effect when the names came from a set of semantically dissimilar items. From this it appears that the difficulty arose when quite complex visual information (varying along two rather than one dimension) had to be related to semantic representations that were in some sense quite close. Outside the laboratory, these difficulties may occur for visually complex and semantically similar living things. Other accounts of differences between the recognition of living and non-living things have been summarised recently by Humphreys and Forde (Forde and Humphreys, 1999; Humphreys and Forde, 2001).

In patients such as JB (Riddoch and Humphreys, 1987b), there seems to be a selective problem in mapping from visual knowledge to semantic information about object association and function; semantic knowledge, accessed via other modalities, seemed relatively intact (see above). In other patients, though, recognition problems can be caused by a semantic deficit. Such patients may be unable to demonstrate knowledge of functional and associative properties of objects whether tested visually (from object) or verbally (from names). Nevertheless, access to stored structural descriptions, assessed via object decision tasks, can be preserved (see Sheridan and Humphreys, 1993; Stewart et al., 1992). Patients with impaired access to semantic knowledge, and patients with impaired semantic knowledge, appear to constitute two different sub-categories of associative agnosia.

Impaired naming of visually present objects: optic aphasia

The model outlined in Fig. 8 has a final step of name retrieval for objects. For the model, name retrieval operates after access to semantic knowledge has been achieved. Does this mean then that all one's semantic knowledge must be accessed before name retrieval can take place? We think not. For example, it is possible that each stage in the model may be initiated on the basis of partial activation at earlier stages ('in cascade'), even if full access to the earlier knowledge has not occurred (see Humphreys et al., 1988). We discuss this idea in more detail below. Nevertheless, the model does suppose that access to some forms of semantic information is necessary if objects are to be named. Evidence against this could come in the form of patients being able to name objects that they have no semantic knowledge about (e.g. the object's category or what it might be used for). However, for now, that evidence is weak (Hodges and Greene, 1998, though see Brennen, Danielle, Fluchaire and Pellat, 1996).

For models such as the one we have outlined, the syndrome of optic aphasia is somewhat puzzling. In this syndrome, patients may misname visually presented objects, yet they can often gesture how the object could be used (unlike agnosic patients, who fail at gesturing from vision). These gestures may be taken as evidence that semantic access is achieved (see Lhermitte and Beauvois, 1973). It is tempting then to think that the problem is a general one of naming, along with intact comprehension. But, as the name for the syndrome implies, the problem is confined to vision. For example, such patients can name objects when given verbal definitions (e.g. what is used to cut paper?); there is not a general naming impairment. The syndrome is puzzling if it assumed that object naming is achieved via access to a 'core' semantic system that is common across modalities, because, on the one hand, semantic access appears to be achieved from vision (given the good gesturing to objects), whilst, on the other, semantically based naming seems possible given good naming to verbal definition (see Riddoch, 1999). How then can the syndrome be accounted for?

Based on the kind of reasoning we have just outlined, some authors have proposed that our semantic knowledge is divided according to the modality of input (e.g. semantic knowledge for objects, semantic knowledge for words; cf. McCarthy and Warrington, 1994) or according to the type of knowledge stored (e.g. for visual knowledge or verbal knowledge about objects; cf. Beauvois, 1982; Shallice, 1987). On this view, optic aphasia could be due to patients accessing visual semantic knowledge (hence the good gesturing), but not verbal semantic knowledge. Access to verbal semantic knowledge is assumed to be necessary for naming to take place. Another proposal is that optic aphasia occurs because of the way semantic and name information is represented in the brain. In particular, semantic knowledge may be bilaterally represented, whilst name information may be represented unilaterally, in the left hemisphere. Coslett and Saffran (1989, 1992), for example, have argued that optic aphasia is associated with posterior brain damage to the left hemisphere, that disrupts visual coding by this hemisphere and that also prevents transmission of information from the right hemisphere to other (intact) areas of the left hemisphere that control name retrieval. On this view, patients can access intact semantics in their right hemisphere. However, because the lesion disconnects the right hemisphere from the left, visual naming is impaired. In contrast, naming to a verbal definition can proceed because that is based on auditory access to left hemisphere semantic and name retrieval operations.

Though these accounts are interesting, they are not unproblematic either. For example, the 'right hemisphere' account of optic aphasia needs to explain why there can be accurate gestures when there is a left hemisphere dominance not only for naming, but also for gesturing (see De Renzi and Faglioni, 1999 for a recent review). If the patient's access to semantic information takes place solely within the right hemisphere, how may gesturing take place? Also, detailed tests of semantic access from vision have been carried out with some patients with optic aphasia (e.g. having to match between related sets of objects), and, in these cases, deficits in detailed semantic knowledge have been shown (De Renzi and Faglioni, 1999; Hillis and Caramazza, 1995; Riddoch and Humphreys, 1987b). As an example of this, consider again the case of JB (see above). As already noted, JB carried out accurate object decisions but he was impaired at making functional/associative judgements to visually presented objects. He was also able to make gestures to visually presented objects. In some cases, these gestures were not only object-specific, but also hand-specific (e.g. using his left hand to gesture to a fork, and his right hand to gesture to a knife). Because of JB's problems in making functional/associative judgements to objects, we have previously argued that we should be cautious in taking gestures as testimony to access to semantic knowledge. For instance, gestures could be based on direct associations between stored visual knowledge of objects and over-learned actions, and these direct associations may operate independently of access to semantic knowledge. These object–action associations may even extend beyond single object usage to include familiar action routines, where objects are used sequentially. Lauro-Grotto, Piccini and Shallice (1997) reported a dementia patient (RM) who appeared to have lost semantic (functional and associative) knowledge about objects. Despite this, RM was able to perform routine cooking tasks, with objects being used appropriately in the correct order. Similar evidence has recently been reported by Hodges, Spatt and Patterson (1999).

In other instances, patients seem able to make appropriate actions even when they do not recognize objects by basing their actions on the visible parts of objects. Sirigu et al. (1991), for example, described an agnosic patient (FB) with bilateral temporal lobe lesions who was unable to match visually presented objects using functional or contextual information. Nevertheless, FB made reasonably accurate gestures to objects at the same time describing how these actions were inferences from the parts present. We can interpret such a result in terms of the parts of objects 'affording' actions without the objects being recognised — where we use the term recognition to refer to access to stored perceptual as well as functional knowledge (cf. Gibson, 1979).

A similar account of the good gestures made by optic aphasic patients has been proposed by Hillis and Caramazza (1995), though they suggest that partial semantic knowledge may also be used to support gesturing (though this same partial semantic information is insufficient to generate correct naming). The framework offered in Fig. 7 is consistent with these latter views of optic aphasia.

A hemispheric specialisation approach to object recognition and naming

So far we have stressed the functional processes leading to visual object recognition and naming — the grouping of object parts, the normalisation for viewpoint, the access to different types of stored knowledge and so forth. Other approaches, however, have stressed the anatomical localisation of object recognition, with the assumption being that anatomical localisation reflects the functional organisation of the system. Most notably, Warrington and colleagues (Rudge and Warrington, 1991; Warrington and James, 1986; Warrington and Taylor, 1973, 1978) have proposed that there is hemispheric specialisation for the processes of perceptual and semantic classification, which characterize two major stages of recognition. Perceptual classification involves assigning objects with different image structures to a common higher-level perceptual category.

This process is probed by the unusual-views matching task that we discussed in the last section. On this view, the process of view normalisation (see Fig. 8) is achieved by perceptual classification, and Warrington and colleagues have argued that this takes place within the right hemisphere. Consistent with this, patients with posterior right hemisphere damage are often poor at matching objects presented in unusual views (though see Bulla Helwig, Ettlinger, Dommasch et al., 1992; Mulder, Bouma and Ansink, 1995, for counter evidence). The functional processes involved, however, have not been specified in detail. Warrington and James (1986) suggested that classification was based on the extraction of critical features from objects (though see Humphreys and Riddoch, 1984 for evidence for axis-based coding). It is unclear, though, whether feature-extraction and matching may be based purely on image properties or whether access to stored knowledge is also required (in the latter case, we might expect perceptual classification to be better for known relative to unknown — though possible — objects). Warrington and colleagues have further proposed that, following perceptual classification, information is fed forward to a semantic categorisation stage located in the left hemisphere. Consequently patients with left hemisphere damage are impaired at making functional/associative judgements to objects though 'perceptual classification' can be achieved (assessed by means of unusual view matches). On this view, semantic categorisation is a necessary precursor to object naming.

This hemispheric specialisation account has many similarities to the hierarchical model outlined in Fig. 8, though the hemispheric account is unclear on the role of stored structural descriptions in the recognition process. For instance, Rudge and Warrington (1991) found that patients with impaired unusual view matching were not agnosic for prototypical views of objects. From this they argued that prototypical views may be recognised directly by the left hemisphere, by-passing a stage of perceptual classification. One might question, however, whether this is possible without there being some access to stored structural knowledge about objects. Functional imaging studies also suggest that perceptual descriptions for objects are at least as strongly represented within the left as in the right hemisphere. In some studies, there is bilateral activity in posterior areas of the ventral cortex (lateral and middle occipital regions) associated with objects and structurally plausible non-objects, when compared with visual noise or meaningless shape baselines (see Kanwisher, Woods, Iacoboni and Mazziotta, 1997; Martin, Wiggs, Ungeleider and Haxby, 1996; Price, Moore, Humphreys et al., 1996; Schacter et al., 1995). Access to structural representations does not seem confined to the right hemisphere. In a functional imaging study concerned with the processing of objects in unusual views, there was also activation in the inferior parietal cortices of both hemispheres (Kosslyn et al., 1994), along with bilateral activity in dorsolateral frontal cortex. Kosslyn et al. attribute the frontal activity to problem solving processes being used when objects are distorted from their familiar views. Such problem solving strategies are unlikely to be part of a perceptual classification system used in everyday object recognition.

Turnbull and colleagues (Turnbull, 1997; Turnbull, Breschin and Della Sala, 1997; Turnbull, Laws and McCarthy, 1995) have also provided evidence that damage to the right parietal lobe can impair judgements of whether objects are in an upright orientation or not. In some cases, patients believe that objects rotated in the plane are upright; and, in simple copying tasks, rotated versions of the objects can be depicted as upright. This 'orientation agnosia' can be understood if damage to the parietal lobes impairs the ability to encode object orientation, making performance reliant on a ventral visual system that is insensitive to orientation. For example, the ventral object recognition system should be relatively viewpoint invariant, with rotated versions of objects being mapped onto these viewpoint invariant representations by having matching features (see Humphreys and Quinlan, 1987). In the absence of parietal information specifying the retinal and/or environmental orientation of the object, judgements about whether objects are really upright may be difficult.

If the parietal lobes are indeed sensitive to object orientation, then they should be important for identifying objects depicted from unusual viewpoints. For example, the parietal lobe may help in deriving a principle axis for an object (coding its primary orientation), in encoding features across the orientation change, and in mental rotation conducted as an explicit problem-solving strategy. For this account, hemispheric differences in object processing are subservient to differences between ventral and dorsal visual areas in coding different object properties (view-independent and orientation-sensitive information).

Agnosia, long-term visual knowledge and imagery

Although by definition agnosic patients have impaired visual recognition, they may, nevertheless, have quite intact stored knowledge about the visual appearance and functions of objects. For instance, HJA, when initially tested, was able to draw items from memory and to provide detailed descriptions of the same items despite his profound problem in perceptual processing (see above) (Riddoch and Humphreys, 1987a). Apparently impaired perception does not necessarily impact on long-term visual knowledge (though see below for some caveats).

Evidence on whether agnosic patients have visual memories is relevant to the debate about the relationship between long-term visual knowledge, visual perception and visual imagery. Arguments for a shared substrate between perception and imagery come from studies of functional brain activation and from studies of patients with cortical blindness. Thus several papers have documented activation even of primary visual cortex during imagery tasks, measured using SPECT (Goldenberg et al., 1989), PET (Kosslyn et al., 1993), fMRI (Le Bihan, Turner, Zeffiro et al., 1993) and EEG (Farah, Peronnet, Gonon and Giard, 1988). However, other data (e.g. using PET) reveal activation from imagery in occipitoparietal and temporoparietal regions rather than in primary striate cortex (Decety, Kawashima, Gulyàs and Roland, 1992; Roland and Gulyás, 1994). These variations may reflect differences across imagery tasks (see Policardi et al., 1996).

Now, if primary striate cortex is critical for visual imagery, then its loss (e.g. in patients with cortical blindness) should result in a severe impairment in imagery. In line with this, Policardi et al. (1996) described a case (TC) with cortical blindness following a road traffic accident who failed on a myriad of visual imagery tasks (including measures of topographical imagery, symbol imagery, animal and object imagery, and colour imagery). Neuroimaging studies showed bilateral metabolic reduction in calcarine and associative occipital areas, which extended to mesial and temporal cortex. However, in contrast to patient TC, other cases of cortical blindness do not indicate a close relation between imagery and perception. For instance, Chattergee and Southwood (1995) and Goldenberg, Müllbacher and Nowak (1995) have both reported *intact* visual imagery in patients with cortical blindness following damage to striate cortex.

Patients with agnosia along with good visual imagery also suggest some dissociation between imagery and perception (see Behrmann, Winocur and Moscovitch, 1992, 1994; Jankowiak, Kinsbourne, Shalev and Bachman, 1992; Riddoch and Humphreys, 1987a; Servos and Goodale, 1995; Servos, Goodale and Humphrey, 1993; Young, Humphreys, Riddoch et al., 1994 for examples). For example, patients may able to draw from memory objects that they can no longer recognise from vision. Nevertheless, in a long-term follow-up of the agnosic patient HJA, Riddoch et al. (1999) found some deterioration in long-term knowledge and visual imagery over time. This was also most pronounced for objects from categories with visually similar exemplars (natural kinds). For these objects, HJA's drawings became rather general, depicting generic animals and fruits/vegetables rather than individual exemplars. This was also mirrored by his verbal definitions of objects, which increasingly stressed verbal/functional rather than visual attributes. These findings are consistent with visual perception and memory interacting over time. For instance, visual memories of objects may be consistently up-dated by perceptual processing, so that these memories remain tuned to the visual properties of objects in the world. Think of our memories of family members, which are constantly updated as they age. When perceptual inputs are impaired, in agnosia, visual memorial processes may gradually decline because there is less 'fine tuning' of the system to the visual properties of objects.

These results on the relation between perception and memory can be related to recent PET studies on visual perceptual learning. An object in a degraded image can appear meaningless when seen for the first time, but later it can be easily recognised if an undegraded image of the object is presented beforehand (so that the recognition system is 'primed'). Dolan, Frith and colleagues (Dolan et al., 1997; Frith and Dolan, 1997) found that changes between the first (naive) and second (primed) state were associated with enhanced processing of inferior cortical regions bordering the occipital and temporal lobes (particularly the fusiform gyrus). Effects were also differentially lateralised for objects and faces, suggesting that item-specific learning takes place in these regions (see also Gauthier et al., 1999). The data match results on learning-related tuning of temporal lobe activity in the monkey (Sakai and Miyashita, 1994, 1995; Tovee, Rolls and Ramachandran, 1996). In addition, Dolan and Frith reported enhanced activity in medial and lateral parietal cortex that was specific to perceptual learning (the change between the naive and primed state). They suggested that the parietal activity could reflect the involvement of imagery in reconstructing degraded stimuli and in binding the parts of these stimuli together. The critical lesions in forms of apperceptive (perceptual) agnosia involve the inferior occipito-temporal regions, consistent with the site of item-specific learning in PET studies. It is possible that this brain area is intimately involved in the up-dating of visual knowledge about specific objects in everyday life, a process can be impaired after brain lesions (see Riddoch et al., 1999).

Objects, faces and words

Our visual system processes many different perceptual forms — including faces and words as well as objects, such as dogs, cars and desks. Neuropsychological studies of reading and face recognition are dealt with in detail in other chapters in the book. However, it is relevant for us at this juncture to consider whether we have developed specialised neural processes for different types of stimuli, or whether the different stimuli are processed in the same way but perhaps to contrasting degrees (e.g. face recognition requires the identification of a specific exemplar within a visually homogenous category, while objects are generally only categorized at a 'base' level — 'dog' but not dalmation; see Henke, Schweinberger, Grigo et al., 1998). This question is particularly relevant for understanding the nature of visual agnosia, as we elaborate below.

Farah (1990) argued that perceptual aspects of face, object and word recognition could be characterized in terms of two broad types of visual process: wholistic pattern recognition and parts-based recognition (where the whole object is recognized by the parts present and their inter-relations). According to this idea, stimuli differ in terms of whether they stress wholistic or parts-based recognition processes. Faces stress wholistic recognition processes. Words stress parts-based recognition processes (e.g. letter identification as a precursor to word identification). Other objects may stress either wholistic or parts-based processing to varying degrees, depending on their structure. As a consequence of this, a disorder affecting wholistic patterns recognition should disrupt face recognition and perhaps also the recognition of some objects; word recognition should be unaffected. The contrary pattern may be expected after damage to parts-based recognition processes (word recognition should be affected, and perhaps also object recognition in some measure; face recognition should be preserved). In a review of historical cases, Farah noted that there were patients solely with problems in visual word recognition ('pure' alexia) and patients with problems solely in face recognition ('pure' prosopagnosia), but no convincing cases of 'pure' agnosia (i.e. without concomitant deficits with either words or faces). These 'pure' cases would be expected from selective and relatively minor damage to parts-based and wholistic recognition processes respectively (if there damage were not minor, we might also expect some impairments of object recognition). Also, while there were patients with 'mixed' deficits such as (1) agnosia and alexia, (2) agnosia and prosopagnosia, and (3) agnosia, alexia and prosopagnosia, patients had not been documented with a 'mixed' impairment including alexia and prosopagnosia, but not agnosia. Note that this particular mixed deficit should not occur if visual recognition disorders were characterized by just two forms of damage.

In line with the arguments developed by Farah (1990), we would agree that there is considerable behavioural, neurophysiological and also neuropsychological evidence that face recognition can be distinguished from word recognition (e.g. see Allison, McCarthy, Nobre et al., 1994; Biederman and Kaloscai, 1997; Farah, Tanaka and Drain, 1995; Farah, Wilson, Drain and Tanaka, 1998; Nobre, Allison and McCarthy, 1994; Puce, Allison, Asgari et al., 1995; Puce, Allison and McCarthy, 1999). Furthermore, there is evidence for normal word recognition being mediated by parts-based processing (letter identification; e.g. Adams, 1979; McClelland, 1976), whilst face recognition seems to be more wholistic (e.g. Farah et al., 1995). Nevertheless, there is some evidence that wholistic pattern recognition may play a part in word recognition too. For example, the term attentional dyslexia is used to describe patients whose ability to read single words is relatively good, but who are impaired at identifying the individual letters present (Shallice and Warrington, 1977). Such patients can also show very marked effects of CaSe MiXiNg, showing abnormal sensitivity to changes in the familiar form of words. They may also retain an ability to identify abbreviations (BBC, IBM), but only if the letters are shown in their familiar case; the same items are not identified when the opposite case is used (bbc, ibm), though letter identities are then the same (Hall, Humphreys and Cooper, 2001; see also Howard, 1987, for converging evidence). Such patients seem to rely on visually familiar letter groups and have poor access to individual letter identities. Thus an over-strict alignment of face and word recognition with wholistic and parts-based processing alone, may not be justified.

It is also the case that recent cases reports go against a strict two-process account of disorders of object processing. Rumiati, Humphreys and colleagues (Humphreys and Rumiati, 1998; Rumiati et al., 1994), for example, have documented two patients who appeared to have a relatively 'pure' agnosia, where both face and word recognition were relatively preserved (reading words at a normal rate rather than letter-by-letter). Both patients suffered neural degeneration and had problems in retrieving semantic information even from words; nevertheless, the problems were more serious with objects. Both patients were also impaired at object decision tasks, tapping access to structural knowledge about objects (see above), and one primarily made visual errors (Humphreys and Rumiati, 1998). This pattern of impairment suggests that the patients had impaired stored visual memories for objects. It may be that stored memory representations differ for objects, words and faces, so that there can be selective loss of memories for objects, but not for the other classes of stimulus.

A second pattern of deficit against a simple two-process account has been noted by Buxbaum, Grosser and Coslett (1999) and by De Renzi and De Pellegrino (1998), who report patients with alexia and prosopagnosia along with relatively preserved object recognition. Again the associated deficits in these patients may reflect impaired stored knowledge rather than an impairment of perceptual coding, though this remains an issue to explore.

Overall, then, we conclude that not all recognition deficits are perceptual in nature, and that some reflect memorial rather than perceptual impairments — as suggested by both hierarchical and hemispheric specialisation accounts of recognition disorders (see above). The dichotomy between holistic and parts-based descriptions may account for many of the perceptual differences between face, object and word recognition, but memorial deficits provide part of the spectrum of visual agnosia. In addition, further work is needed to distinguish between parts-based descriptions that are coded independently (e.g. the individual letters in words) and those that are grouped to form a larger perceptual unit (e.g. supra-letter codes in words). Any full account of face, object and word processing will need to accommodate how features are grouped in vision and the role of these grouped features in recognition.

Interactive effects in recognition and naming

So far, our discussion has emphasized bottom-up processes in object recognition, with recognition taking place following a succession of discrete processing stages: there is a stage of visual grouping prior to access to stored structural descriptions, and access to structural description precedes access to semantic knowledge. However, it is also likely that processing operates in a top-down as well as a bottom-up manner, so that 'later' forms of information influence 'earlier' processes. This would occur if there is transmission of partial activation between processing stages rather than each stage being discrete. One example of this comes from studies of figure–ground coding. Peterson and colleagues (e.g. Peterson and Gibson, 1994) had normal subjects make figure–ground judgements to stimuli with ambiguous figure–ground relationships. They found that judgements to perceptual figures are biased to familiar forms: people tend to assign the familiar form to the 'figure' rather than the 'ground'. This suggests that information about the familiarity of objects can be activated whilst figure–ground coding takes place — at least when figure–ground coding is not strongly determined by bottom-up factors.

Top-down activation may also be important for the process of assigning names to objects. Price et al. (1996) conducted a functional brain imaging study of object naming in which they examined four conditions: subjects named or said 'yes' to drawings of objects, or they named the colour or said 'yes' to drawings of non-objects. The naming tasks allowed measurement of brain areas involved in the retrieval of learned names associated to visual stimuli, relative to the 'say yes' baselines. The tasks with objects allowed measurement of brain regions associated with object processing, relative to the non-object baseline conditions. The interaction between these effects reflected areas enhanced in name retrieval specific to objects. Price et al. found enhanced activation of regions of the posterior, inferior temporal cortex when object naming in particular was required. These posterior regions are typically thought to be involved in high-level visual processing of stimuli and they are areas often lesioned in agnosic patients (e.g. Riddoch and Humphreys, 1987a). The evidence that these areas show increased activation when naming rather than recognition is stressed [1] suggests that these visual areas are subject to increased interrogation when name retrieval takes place. This is consistent with top-down activation particularly coming into play when activation needs to be sufficiently precise to enable a unique name to be derived (see Humphreys, Riddoch and Price, 1997, for this argument).

Neuropsychological evidence relevant to this issue was reported by Forde et al. (1997) and Humphreys et al. (1997). These authors documented evidence on patients with unilateral (left) medial extra-striate lesions who had difficulties in identifying living things (animals, fruit and vegetables). This problem was much more pronounced in naming than in tasks assessing object recognition — for example, the patients could sort objects into separate categories of fruit and vegetables, but remained impaired at naming the individual items. To account for this, we suggest that the posterior lesion disrupted top-down reactivation of perceptual knowledge, required to name rather than to recognise objects. This top-down recruitment of visual knowledge may be particularly important for identifying living things, since perceptual knowledge may be strongly weighted in the representations of such stimuli (e.g. see Farah and McClelland, 1991; McRae and Cree, 2001; Warrington and Shallice, 1984; see Thompson-Schill, Aguirre, D'Esposito and Farah, 1999, for further evidence from functional imaging).

[1] Activation associated with object recognition is shown by the general contrast between the object and non-object conditions, summed over the naming and 'say yes' conditions.

Summary

We have reviewed evidence that visual object recognition and naming can break down in a variety of ways after brain damage. In particular, it is possible to distinguish between different forms of visual agnosia, according to the nature of the functional deficit suffered by the patient. We can separate disorders of: (1) feature binding; (2) shape segmentation; (3) view-normalisation; (4) access to stored structural descriptions; (5) access to semantic knowledge; and (6) access to names. These different disorders can be conceptualised in several ways and we have discussed the hierarchical and hemispheric specialisation views, contrasting these with the idea that recognition disorders are solely perceptual in nature (due to damage to the coding of perceptual wholes or of the parts of objects). Our view is that impairments of object recognition can reflect impaired memories for objects (in forms of associative agnosia) as well as impaired perceptual encoding (in forms of apperceptive agnosia), and that distinct forms of both memorial and perceptual deficit can be identified. Furthermore, even when perceptual deficits of object recognition exist, visual information may still be used to direct action, consistent with there being separate routes from vision to object recognition and to action. We have also reviewed evidence on the relations between visual perception and imagery, and on the role of top-down as well as bottom-up factors in vision. This evidence indicates two ways in which visual processing seems to be interactive: (1) it is constantly updating our visual memories of the world; and (2) even in on-line naming tasks, top-down processes may be involved in recruiting further visual information in order to differentiate the target object from other objects from the same class. Selective damage to posterior regions of ventral cortex can thus disrupt the updating of visual memories, and the use of top-down knowledge in naming. The neuropsychological evidence suggests that, in normality, there are multiple, interactive processes underlying the façade of efficient object recognition and naming.

Acknowledgements

This work was supported by grants from the Medical Research Council (UK) and the Wellcome Trust.

References

Adams MJ: Models of word recognition. Cognitive Psychology: 11; 133–176, 1979.

Allison T, McCarthy G, Nobre A, Puce A, Belger A: Human extrastriate visual cortex and the perception of faces, words, numbers and colours. Cerebral Cortex: 5; 544–554, 1994.

Arguin M, Bub DN, Dudek G: Shape integration for visual object recognition and its implication in category-specific visual agnosia. Visual Cognition: 3; 221–275, 1996.

Beauvois M-F: Optic aphasia: a process of interaction between vision and language. Philosophical Transactions of the Royal Society B: 289; 35–47, 1982.

Behrmann M, Moscovitch M, Winocur G: Intact visual imagery and impaired visual perception in a patient with visual agnosia. Journal of Experimental Psychology: Human Perception and Performance: 20; 1068–1087, 1994.

Behrmann M, Winocur G, Moscovitch M: Dissociation between mental imagery and object recognition in a brain damaged patient. Nature: 359; 636–637, 1992.

Benson DF, Greenberg JP: Visual form agnosia. A specific deficit in visual discrimination. Archives of Neurology: 20; 82–89, 1969.

Biederman I, Kaloscai P: Neurocomputational bases of object and face recognition. Philosophical Transactions of the Royal Society B: 352; 1203–1220, 1997.

Boucart M, Humphreys GW: The computation of perceptual structure from collinearity and closure: Normality and pathology. Neuropsychologia: 30; 527–546, 1992.

Brennen T, Danielle D, Fluchaire I, Pellat J: Naming faces and objects without comprehension. Cognitive Neuropsychology: 15; 93–110, 1996.

Bruce V, Green P, Georgeson MA: Visual Perception. London: Psychology Press, 1996.

Bulla Helwig M, Ettlinger G, Dommasch D, Ebel E, Skreczeck W: Impaired visual perceptual categorisation in right brain-damaged patients. Failure to replicate. Cortex: 28; 261–272, 1992.

Butter CM, Trobe JD: Integrative agnosia following progressive multifocal leukoencephalopathy. Cortex: 30; 145–158, 1994.

Buxbaum LJ, Grosser G, Coslett HB: Impaired face and word recognition with object agnosia. Neuropsychologia: 37; 41–50, 1999.

Campion J, Latto R: Apperceptive agnosia due to carbon monoxide poisoning: an interpretation based on critical band masking from disseminated lesions. Behavioural Brain Research: 15; 227–240, 1985.

Chainay H, Humphreys GW: The effects of surface and depth information on object recognition: the real object advantage in agnosia. Cognitive Neuropsychology, in press.

Chattergee A, Southwood MH: Cortical blindness and visual imagery. Neurology: 45; 2189–2195, 1995.

Coslett HB, Saffran EM: Evidence for preserved reading in 'pure alexia'. Brain: 112; 327–359, 1989.

Coslett HM, Saffran EM: Optic aphasia and the right hemisphere: a replication and extension. Brain and Language: 43; 148–161, 1992.

Davidoff J, De Bleser R: A case study of photographic anomia: impaired picture naming with preserved object naming and reading. Brain and Cognition: 24; 1–23, 1994.

Davidoff J, Warrington EK: The bare bones of object recognition: implications from a case of object recognition impairment. Neuropsychologia: 37; 279–292, 1999.

De Renzi E, De Pellegrino D: Prosopagnosia and alexia without object agnosia. Cortex: 34; 41–50, 1998.

De Renzi E, Faglioni P: Apraxia. In Denes G, Pizzamiglio L (Eds), Handbook of Clinical and Experimental Neuropsychology. Hove: Psychology Press, pp. 421–440, 1999.

De Renzi E, Lucchelli F: Are semantic systems separately represented in the brain? The case of living category impairment. Cortex: 30; 3–25, 1994.

Decety J, Kawashima R, Gulyàs B, Roland PE: Preparation for reaching: a PET study of the participating structures in the human brain. NeuroReport: 3; 761–764, 1992.

Dixon M, Bub DN, Arguin M: The interaction of object form and object meaning in the identification performance of a patient with a category-specific visual agnosia. Cognitive Neuropsychology: 14; 1085–1130, 1997.

Dolan RJ, Fink GR, Rolls E, Booth M, Holmes A, Frackowiak RSJ, Friston KJ: How the brain learns to see faces and objects in an impoverished context. Nature: 389; 596–599, 1997.

Duncan J, Humphreys GW: Visual search and visual similarity. Psychological Review: 96; 433–458, 1989.

Edwards MG, Humphreys GW: Pointing and grasping in unilateral neglect: effect of on-line visual feedback in grasping. Neuropsychologia: 37; 959–973, 1999.

Efron R: What is perception? Boston Studies in Philosophy of Science: 4; 137–173, 1968.

Egly R, Driver J, Rafal RD: Shifting visual attention between objects and locations: evidence from normal and parietal lesion subjects. Journal of Experimental Psychology: General: 123; 161–171, 1994.

Farah MJ: Visual Agnosia. Cambridge, MA: MIT Press, 1990.

Farah MJ, McClelland JL: A computational model of semantic memory impairment: modality specificity and emergent category specificity. Journal of Experimental Psychology: General: 120; 339–357, 1991.

Farah MJ, Peronnet F, Gonon MA, Giard MH: Electrophysiological evidence for a shared representational medium for visual images and percepts. Journal of Experimental Psychology: General: 117; 248–257, 1988.

Farah MJ, Tanaka JN, Drain M: What causes the face inversion effect? Journal of Experimental Psychology: Human Perception and Performance: 21; 628–634, 1995.

Farah MJ, Wilson KD, Drain M, Tanaka JN: What is 'special' about face perception? Psychological Review: 105; 482–498, 1998.

Forde EME, Francis D, Riddoch MJ, Rumiati RI, Humphreys GW: On the links between visual knowledge and naming: a single case study of a patient with a category-specific impairment for living things. Cognitive Neuropsychology: 14; 403–458, 1997.

Forde E, Humphreys GW: Category-specific recognition impairments: a review of important case studies and influential theories. Aphasiology: 13; 169–193, 1999.

Frith C, Dolan RJ: Brain mechanisms associated with top-down processes in perception. Philosophical Transactions of the Royal Society: 352; 1221–1230, 1997.

Garland H, Pearce J: Neurological complications of carbon monoxide poisoning. Quarterly Journal of Medicine: 144; 445–455, 1967.

Gauthier I, Tarr MJ, Anderson AW, Skudlarski P, Gore JC: Activation of the middle fusiform 'face area' increases with expertise in recognizing novel objects. Nature Neuroscience: 2; 568–573, 1999.

Gibson JJ: The ecological approach to visual perception. Boston: Houghton Mifflin, 1979.

Giersch A, Humphreys GW, Boucart M, Kovacs I: The computation of occluded contours in visual agnosia: evidence of early computation prior to shape binding and figure-ground coding. Cognitive Neuropsychology: 17; 131–159, 2000.

Goldenberg G, Müllbacher W, Nowak A: Imagery without perception — a case study of anosagnosia for cortical blindness. Neuropsychologia: 33; 1373–1382, 1995.

Goldenberg G, Podreka I, Steiner M, Willmes K, Suess E, Deecke L: Regional blood flow patterns in visual imagery. Neuropsychologia: 27; 641–664, 1989.

Goldstein K, Gelb A: Psychologische Analysen hirnpathologischer Falle auf Grund von Untersuchungen Hirnverletzer. Zeitschrift fuer die gesamte Neurologie und Psychiatrie: 41; 1–142, 1918.

Goodale MA, Milner AD, Jakobson LS, Carey DP: A neurological dissociation between perceiving objects and grasping them. Nature: 349; 154–156, 1991.

Grossman M, Galetta S, D'Esposito M: Object recognition difficulty in visual apperceptive agnosia. Brain and Cognition: 33; 306–342, 1997.

Hall D, Humphreys GW, Cooper A: Multi-letter units in reading: evidence from attentional dyslexia. Quarterly Journal of Experimental Psychology, in press.

Henke K, Schweinberger SR, Grigo A, Klos T, Sommer W: Specificity of face recognition: recognition of exemplars of non-face objects in prosopagnosia. Cortex: 34; 289–296, 1998.

Heywood CA, Cowey A, Newcombe F: Chromatic discrimination in a cortically blind observer. European Journal of Neuroscience: 3; 802–812, 1991.

Heywood CA, Cowey A: Cerebral achromatopsia. In Humphreys GW (Ed), Case Studies in the Neuropsychology of Vision. Hove: Psychology Press, pp. 17–40, 1999.

Heywood CA, Zihl J: Motion blindness. In Humphreys GW (Ed), Case Studies in the Neuropsychology of Vision. Hove: Psychology Press, pp. 1–16, 1999.

Hillis AE, Caramazza A: Cognitive and neural mechanisms underlying visual and semantic processing: implications from 'Optic Aphasia'. Journal of Cognitive Neuroscience: 7; 457–478, 1995.

Hodges JR, Greene JDW: Knowing about people and naming them: can Alzheimer's disease patients do one without the other? Quarterly Journal of Experimental Psychology: 51A; 121–134, 1998.

Hodges JR, Spatt J, Patterson KE: 'What' and 'how': evidence for the dissociation of object knowledge and mechanical problem-solving skills in the human brain. Proceedings of the National Academy of Science: 96; 9444–9448, 1999.

Howard D: Reading without letters? In Coltheart M, Sartori G, Job R (Eds), The Cognitive Neuropsychology of Language. London: Lawrence Erlbaum, pp. 27–58, 1987.

Humphreys GW, Forde EME: Hierarchies, similarity and interactivity in object recognition: on the multiplicity of 'category-specific' deficits in neuropsychological populations. Behavioural and Brain Sciences, in press.

Humphreys GW, Quinlan PT: Normal and pathological processes in visual object constancy. In Humphreys GW, Riddoch MJ (Eds), Visual Object Processing: A Cognitive Neuropsychological Approach. London: Lawrence Erlbaum, pp. 43–106, 1987.

Humphreys GW, Quinlan PT, Riddoch MJ: Grouping effects in visual search: Effects with single- and combined-feature targets. Journal of Experimental Psychology: General: 118; 258–279, 1989.

Humphreys GW, Riddoch MJ: Routes to object constancy: implications from neurological impairments of object constancy. Quarterly Journal of Experimental Psychology: 36A; 385–415, 1984.

Humphreys GW, Riddoch MJ: To see but not to see: a case of visual agnosia. London: Lawrence Erlbaum, 1987.

Humphreys GW, Riddoch MJ: Object agnosia. In Kennard (Ed), Ballière's Clinical Neurology. London: Ballière Tindall, pp. 339–359, 1993.

Humphreys GW, Riddoch MJ, Price CJ: Top-down processes in object identification: evidence from experimental psychol-

ogy, neuropsychology and functional anatomy. Philosophical Transactions of the Royal Society B: 352; 1275–1282, 1997.
Humphreys GW, Riddoch MJ, Quinlan PT: Interactive processes in perceptual organisation: evidence from visual agnosia. In Posner MIMI, Marin OSM (Eds), Attention and Performance XI. Hillsdale, NJ: Erlbaum, pp. 301–318, 1985.
Humphreys GW, Riddoch MJ, Quinlan PT: Cascade processes in picture identification. Cognitive Neuropsychology: 5; 67–103, 1988.
Humphreys GW, Riddoch MJ, Quinlan PT, Donnelly N, Price CA: Parallel pattern processing and visual agnosia. Canadian Journal of Psychology: 46(3); 377–416, 1992.
Humphreys GW, Rumiati RI: When joys come not in single spies but in battalions: Within-category and within-modality identification increases the accessibility of degraded store knowledge. Neurocase: 4; 111–126, 1998.
Jankowiak J, Kinsbourne M, Shalev RS, Bachman DL: Preserved visual imagery and categorisation in a case of associative visual agnosia. Journal of Cognitive Neuroscience: 4; 119–131, 1992.
Jeannerod M: The Cognitive Neuroscience of Action. Oxford: Blackwells, 1997.
Kanwisher N, Woods RP, Iacoboni M, Mazziotta JC: A locus in human extrastriate cortex for visual shape analysis. Journal of Cognitive Neuroscience: 9; 133–142, 1997.
Kartsounis LD, Warrington EK: Failure of object recognition due to a breakdown of figure–ground discrimination in a patient with normal acuity. Neuropsychologia: 29; 969–980, 1991.
Kosslyn SM, Alpert NM, Thompson WL, Chabris CF, Rauch SL, Anderson AK: Identifying objects seen from different viewpoints: a PET investigation. Brain: 117; 1055–1071, 1994.
Kosslyn SM, Alpert NM, Thompson WL, Maljkovic V, Weise SB, Chabris CF, Hamilton SE, Rauch SL, Buonanno FS: Visual mental imagery activates topographically organised visual cortex: PET investigations. Journal of Cognitive Neuroscience: 5; 263–287, 1993.
Lamb MR, Robertson LC, Knight RT: Component mechanisms underlying the processing of hierarchically organised patterns — inferences from patients with unilateral cortical lesions. Journal of Experimental Psychology: Learning, Memory and Cognition: 16; 471–483, 1990.
Lauro-Grotto R, Piccini C, Shallice T: Modality-specific operations in semantic dementia. Cortex: 33; 593–622, 1997.
Lawson R, Humphreys GW: The effects of view in depth on the identification of line drawings and silhouettes of familiar objects: normality and pathology. Visual Cognition, 1999.
Le Bihan O, Turner R, Zeffiro TA, Cuenod CA, Bonnerot V: Activation of human primary visual cortex during visual recall: a magnetic resonance imaging study. Proceedings of the National Academy of Sciences: 90; 11802–11805, 1993.
Lhermitte F, Beauvois MF: A visual-speech disconnection syndrome. Report of a case with optic aphasia. Brain: 96; 695–714, 1973.
Lissauer H: Ein fall von seelenblindheit nebst einem beitrage zur theorie derselben. Archiv für Psychiatrie und Nervenkrankheiten: 21; 222–270, 1890.
Lloyd-Jones TJ, Humphreys GW: Perceptual differentiation as a source of category effects in object processing: evidence for naming and objects decision. Memory and Cognition: 25; 18–35, 1997.
Marr D: Vision. San Fransisco: W.H. Freeman, 1982.
Martin A, Wiggs CL, Ungeleider LG, Haxby JV: Neural correlates of category-specific knowledge. Nature: 379; 649–652, 1996.
McCarthy R, Warrington EK: Disorders of semantic memory. Philosophical Transactions of the Royal Society of London: 346; 89–96, 1994.
McRae K, Cree GS: Factors underlying category-specific semantic deficits. In Forde EME, Humphreys GW (Eds), Category-Specificity in Mind and Brain. London: Psychology Press, in press.
McClelland JL: Preliminary letter recognition in the perception of words and nonwords. Journal of Experimental Psychology: Human Perception and Performance: 2; 80–91, 1976.
McCollough C: Colour adaptation of edge-detectors in the human visual system. Science: 149; 1115–1116, 1965.
Milner AD, Goodale MA: The Visual Brain in Action. Oxford: Oxford University Press, 1995.
Milner AD, Perrett DI, Johnston RS, Benson PJ, Jordan TR, Heeley DW, Bettucci D, Mortara F, Mutani R, Terazzi E, Davidson DLW: Perception and action in 'visual form agnosia'. Brain: 114; 405–428, 1991.
Mulder JL, Bouma A, Ansink BIJ: The role of visual discrimination disorders and neglect in perceptual categorisation deficits in right and left hemisphere damaged patients. Cortex: 31; 487–501, 1995.
Navon D: Forest before trees: The precedence of global features in visual perception. Cognitive Psychology: 9; 353–383, 1977.
Nobre AC, Allison T, McCarthy G: Word recognition in the human inferior temporal lobe. Nature: 372; 260–263, 1994.
Peterson MA, Gibson BS: Must figure–ground organisation precede object recognition? Psychological Science: 5; 253–259, 1994.
Policardi E, Perani D, Zago S, Grassi F, Fazio F, Làdavas E: Failure to evoke visual images in a case of long-standing cortical blindness. Neurocase: 2; 381–394, 1996.
Price CJ, Moore CJ, Humphreys GW, Frackowiak RSJ, Friston KJ: The neural regions sustaining object recognition and naming. Proceedings of the Royal Society B: 263; 1501–1507, 1996.
Puce A, Allison T, Asgari M, Gore JC, McCarthy G: Differential sensitivity of human visual cortex to faces, letter strings and textures: a functional magnetic imaging study. Journal of Neuroscience: 16; 5205–5215, 1995.
Puce A, Allison T, McCarthy G: Electrophysiological studies of human face perception. III: Effects of top-down processing on face-specific potentials. Cerebral Cortex: 9; 445–458, 1999.
Riddoch MJ: Optic aphasia: a review of some classic cases. In Humphreys GW (Ed), Case Studies in the Neuropsychology of Vision. Hove: Psychology Press, pp. 133–160, 1999.
Riddoch MJ, Humphreys GW: A case of integrative agnosia. Brain: 110; 1431–1462, 1987a.
Riddoch MJ, Humphreys GW: Visual object processing in optic

aphasia: a case of semantic access agnosia. Cognitive Neuropsychology: 4; 131–185, 1987b.

Riddoch MJ, Humphreys GW, Gannon T, Blott W, Jones V: Memories are made of this: the effects of time on stored visual knowledge in a case of visual agnosia. Brain: 122; 537–559, 1999.

Roland PE, Gulyás B: Visual imagery and visual representation. Trends in the Neurosciences: 17; 281–287, 1994.

Rudge P, Warrington EK: Selective impairment of memory and visual perception in splenial tumours. Brain: 114; 349–360, 1991.

Rumiati RI, Humphreys GW, Riddoch MJ, Bateman A: Visual object agnosia without prosopagnosia or alexia: evidence for hierarchical theories of object recognition. Visual Cognition: 1; 181–225, 1994.

Sakai K, Miyashita Y: Neuronal tuning to learned complex forms in vision. Neuroreport: 5; 829–832, 1994.

Sakai K, Miyashita Y: Neural organisation for long-term memory of paired associates. Nature: 354; 152–155, 1995.

Sartori B, Job R: The oyster with four legs: a neuropsychological study on the interaction of visual and semantic information. Cognitive Neuropsychology: 5; 677–709, 1988.

Schacter DL, Reiman E, Uecker A, Polster MR, Yun LS, Cooper LA: Brain regions associated with retrieval of structurally coherent visual information. Nature: 376; 587–590, 1995.

Servos P, Goodale MA: Preserved visual imagery in visual form agnosia. Neuropsychologia: 33; 1383–1394, 1995.

Servos P, Goodale MA, Humphrey GK: The drawing of objects by a visual form agnosic: Contribution of surface properties and memorial representations. Neuropsychologia: 31; 251–259, 1993.

Shallice T: Impairments of semantic processing: Multiple dissociations. In Coltheart M, Sartori G, Job R (Eds), The Cognitive Neuropsychology of Language. London: Lawrence Erlbaum Associates, pp. 111–128, 1987.

Shallice T, Warrington EK: The possible role of selective attention in acquired dyslexia. Neuropsychologia: 15; 31–41, 1977.

Sheridan J, Humphreys GW: A verbal-semantic category-specific recognition impairment. Cognitive Neuropsychology: 10(2); 143–184, 1993.

Sirigu A, Duhamel J-R, Poncet M: The role of sensorimotor experience in object recognition. Brain: 114; 2555–2573, 1991.

Stewart F, Parkin AJ, Hunkin HN: Naming impairments following recovery from herpes simplex encephalitis. Quarterly Journal of Experimental Psychology: 44A(2); 261–284, 1992.

Thompson-Schill SL, Aguirre GK, D'Esposito M, Farah MJ: A neural basis for category and modality specificity of semantic knowledge. Neuropsychologia: 37; 671–676, 1999.

Thorpe S, Fize D, Marlot C: Speed of processing in the human visual system. Nature: 381; 520–521, 1996.

Tovee MJ, Rolls ET, Ramachandran VS: Visual learning in neurons of the primate temporal visual cortex. Neuroreport: 7; 2757–2760, 1996.

Turnbull OH: A double dissociation between knowledge of object identity and object orientation. Neuropsychologia: 35; 567–570, 1997.

Turnbull OH, Breschin N, Della Sala S: Agnosia for object orientation: Implication for theories of object recognition. Neuropsychologia: 35(2); 153–163, 1997.

Turnbull OH, Laws KR, McCarthy RA: Object recognition without knowledge of object orientation. Cortex: 31; 387–395, 1995.

Ungerleider LG, Mishkin M: Two cortical visual systems. In Ingle J, Goodale MA, Mansfield RJW (Eds), Analysis of Visual Behavior. Cambridge, MA: MIT Press, pp. 549–586, 1982.

Vecera SP, Gilds KS: What processing is impaired in apperceptive agnosia? Evidence from normal subjects. Journal of Cognitive Neuroscience: 10; 568–580, 1998.

Von der Heydt R, Peterhans E: Mechanisms of contour perception in monkey visual cortex 1. Lines of pattern discontinuities. Journal of Neuroscience: 9; 1731–1748, 1989.

Wapner W, Judd T, Gardner H: Visual agnosia in an artist. Cortex: 14; 343–364, 1978.

Warrington EK: Agnosia: The impairment of object recognition. In Vinken PJ, Bruyn GW, Klawans HL (Eds), Handbook of Clinical Neurology, Vol. 45. Amsterdam: Elsevier Science, pp. 222–349, 1985.

Warrington EK, James M: Visual object recognition in patients with right hemisphere lesions: Axes or features? Perception: 15; 355–356, 1986.

Warrington EK, Shallice T: Category-specific semantic impairment. Brain: 107; 829–854, 1984.

Warrington EK, Taylor A: The contribution of the right parietal lobe to object recognition. Cortex: 9; 152–164, 1973.

Warrington EK, Taylor A: Two categorical stages of object recognition. Perception: 9; 7695–7705, 1978.

Young AW, Humphreys GW, Riddoch MJ, Hellawell DJ, de Haan EHF: Recognition impairments and face imagery. Neuropsychologia: 32; 693–702, 1994.

Zihl J, Von Cramon D, Mai N: Selective disturbance of movement vision after bilateral brain damage. Brain: 106; 313–340, 1983.

Handbook of Neuropsychology, 2nd Edition, Vol. 4
M. Behrmann (Ed)

CHAPTER 9

Face recognition: evidence from intact and impaired performance

Marlene Behrmann [a,*] and Morris Moscovitch [b]

[a] *Department of Psychology, Carnegie Mellon University, Pittsburgh, PA 15213-3890, USA*
[b] *Rotman Research Institute, Baycrest Centre for Geriatric Care, 3560 Bathurst Street, North York ON, M6A 2E1, Canada*

Introduction

There are strong indications from the neurological literature that face recognition is distinct from many aspects of recognition of other complex visual stimuli. This point is brought home dramatically by CK, a person we have been studying for a number of years. CK sustained a closed head injury in 1988. He recovered well, but not fully, from the trauma. Although he exhibits the preserved ability to recognize faces without hesitation, whether in person or from photographs, such as a faded black-and-white photograph of Albert Einstein, he has great difficulty recognizing objects and reading. Shown a line drawing of a common object like a tennis racquet, he responds ‘a fencer’s mask’. Likewise, shown a picture of an abacus, he responds ‘kebabs on skewers’. He also fails to recognize a colored photograph of a tortoise, reporting it as a ‘German army helmet’, and then elaborates on the camouflage coloring and the phalange-like shape in support of his interpretation. His failure to recognize objects and animals is not attributable to the fact that these were shown to him as photographs or line drawings; the same impairment is observed when he is presented with real, three-dimensional objects although he is able to gain some benefit from the surface cues, as is true of other patients like him (Farah, 1990; Humphrey, Goodale, Jakobson and Servos, 1994).

CK’s failure to name the objects cannot be accounted for by a semantic deficit nor by an anomia; given the same real objects to palpate and recognize while blindfolded, he names all of them correctly. He also provides detailed descriptions of the objects he fails to name and can draw objects well when given their names auditorily (see Fig. 1). He is also able to write, although he cannot recognize his own written

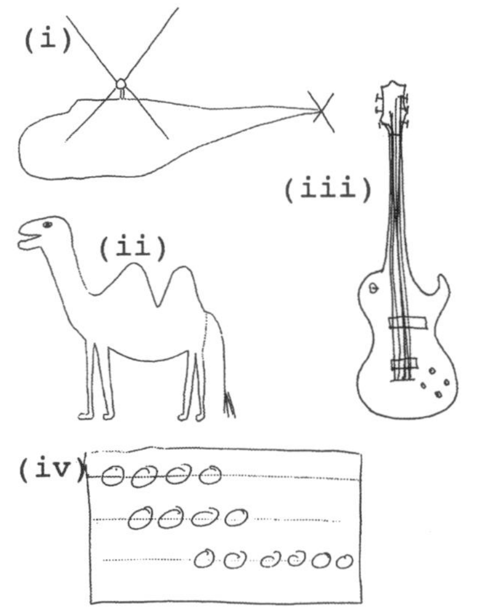

Fig. 1. CK’s copy of objects he cannot recognize when presented as black-and-white line drawings. (i) Helicopter, (ii) camel, (iii) guitar, (iv) abacus.

* Corresponding author. E-mail: behrmann+@cmu.edu

output when it is shown to him a short while later. Based on these findings (Behrmann, Moscovitch and Winocur, 1994; Behrmann, Winocur and Moscovitch, 1992; Moscovitch, Winocur and Behrmann, 1997), CK's impairment is interpreted as a failure to access the meaning of information presented to him through the visual modality, a disorder known as visual agnosia (see related chapter by Humphreys and Riddoch, 2001, this volume).

Despite his dramatic object recognition impairment, CK is able to recognize faces of a range of individuals, shown to him as photographs or as line drawings, in color or in black and white, in profile or disguised with head coverings, glasses, or mustaches (as in Fig. 2). Importantly, not only can CK recognize individuals whom he knew prior to the accident, but also individuals who attained fame after he had sustained his brain damage in 1988 (for example, Boris Yeltsin the President of Russia; Jean Chretien, the Prime Minister of Canada; and Bill Clinton, the President of the United States). That he recognizes individuals who attained fame recently attests to the fact that he is not merely recognizing faces based on a pre-existing memory trace, but that he is also able to learn to recognize new faces (see also Moscovitch et al., 1997). The extent of CK's face recognition abilities is indeed remarkable: he is able to point out from a huge array those faces that share a family resemblance and he can match faces that are transformed by age, i.e. young faces and their mature and old counterparts. Furthermore, he correctly identifies caricatures, cartoons, disguised faces, and even face parts if they are presented in association with other features of a familiar face. He also is able to perceive a face as a face when the parts of the face are made of objects (for example, fruit face) but, unlike controls, he rarely is aware that the face is composed of objects, unless his attention is drawn specifically to those features. What seems to be critical to CK's ability to recognize faces is that faces be upright and that they retain the configurational integrity among the internal facial features, the eyes, nose and mouth. When the faces, or just the internal features, are inverted or when the configurational gestalt is broken by fracturing the face or by misaligning the top and bottom halves, CK's performance suffers far more than that of control subjects (Moscovitch et al., 1997).

How is it that CK is able to recognize faces, but not other objects, even though many of the objects are apparently perceptually simpler than faces? Why is it that the configuration and orientation of the face, and particularly the internal features, are critical de-

Fig. 2. (a) Black-and-white photograph of Queen and Queen Mother in profile and with head coverings and (b) picture of Ronald Reagan in disguise (from Moscovitch et al., 1997) recognized by CK.

terminants of his success? In this chapter, we will explore the relationship between the brain–behavior mechanisms mediating face recognition and those mediating the recognition of other non-face objects. In addition to the data from CK, we will present data from patients with brain-damage who are the complement of CK, namely, patients whose face recognition is poor, a deficit referred to as prosopagnosia. We will review the evidence in these prosopagnosic patients concerning the spared recognition of other classes of nonface objects and compare their performance on these other classes with their performance on faces. In addition, we will examine, in these same patients the extent to which there might be covert or implicit processing of faces in the absence of their overt ability to recognize faces. We will also draw on evidence from functional neuroimaging, neurophysiology, and developmental studies of normal and brain-damaged infants to examine how 'special' face processing might be. Finally, we will review and evaluate some of the theoretical claims made regarding the processing of faces and nonface objects.

Are faces 'special'?

Faces are perhaps the most compelling visual stimuli in our world, providing important information for interpersonal interactions. Faces convey not only the age and gender of the person, but also the identity and mood of the individual. A particularly interesting claim that arises from the human behavioral literature, supported by evidence from many other disciplines, is that faces are 'special' or that they require a domain-specific (perhaps even exclusively dedicated) system for their recognition. A strong version of this argument is that there is a region of the brain which constitutes a special purpose, possibly innate, mechanism specialized for the detection (and/or recognition) of faces. In this first section, we examine the data from several methodological approaches supporting the distinction between mechanisms for recognition of faces and mechanisms for recognition of other types of objects. As will be evident, the picture that emerges is consistent with such a specialized mechanism. There are, however, challenges to this perspective and, in the second section, we review evidence and arguments that favor an alternative interpretation of the findings.

Evidence favoring a specialized mechanism

Monkey neurophysiology

Evidence consistent with the existence of a distinct, face-recognition mechanism comes from neurophysiological studies of face-selective cells in nonhuman primates (Gross, Rocha-Miranda and Bender, 1972; Perrett, Rolls and Caan, 1982). The criterion adopted for determining selectivity in these neurophysiological studies is one of magnitude of neuronal response; if the magnitude of the cell's response to a face is more than twice that to any other object, then the cell is considered to be face-selective (Rolls and Baylis, 1986). Face-sensitive neurons have been located throughout inferotemporal cortex, but they cluster in certain regions, such as in the inferotemporal cortex or in the superior temporal sulcus (STS) where they constitute between 10 and 20% of all visually responsive cells (Rolls and Baylis, 1986). Although each cell does not uniquely represent a single face, a particular face will evoke a specific pattern of activation over a subset of the face cell population. These face-selective cells display invariance over position and size, and in some cases, orientation (Ashbridge, Perrett, Oram and Jellema, 2000), and respond vigorously to faces, but only minimally to nonface objects or scrambled arrays of face parts (for example, Desimone and Gross, 1979). These cells are also responsive to facial identity (Baylis, Rolls and Leonard, 1985; Yamane, Kaji and Kawano, 1988), emotional expression (Hasselmo, Rolls and Baylis, 1989), direction of gaze (Perrett, Oram, Harries et al., 1991) and parts of a face (Perrett et al., 1982), but it appears that the configurational relations between multiple facial features might be especially critical (Yamane et al., 1988).

Activity in single cells in the temporal cortex of alert infant monkeys (as young as 5 weeks of age) also show some selectivity to stimulus domain although only a small number of cells specifically responsive to faces have been found (Rodman, Scalaidhe and Gross, 1993). It is not clear, however, that these cells show exactly the same properties as those identified in adults; the magnitude of the response is lower and the latencies more variable and longer in these young monkeys. The detailed characteristics of these cells have not been extensively studied thus far, but the existing findings are consistent with the idea that face-selectivity is in place very early (even if it is not innate) in development.

Developmental studies

Consistent with the findings that young monkeys show some selectivity for faces, data obtained from human newborns has been used to argue that face preference is innate. During the first few hours of life, newborns show preferential orienting to faces compared with other objects. These infants will move their eyes more and sometimes their head as well to follow a schematic moving face compared with other patterns, including faces made of scrambled features (Johnson, Dziurawiec, Ellis and Morton, 1991; Maurer and Young, 1983). Moreover, newborns will even direct their attention to a face-like pattern when simultaneously presented with a nonface stimulus that has the optimal spatial frequency for the newborn visual system (Valenza, Simion, Cassia and Umilta, 1996). Infants also appear able to discriminate identity and, in the first few days of life, show preferential recognition of the mother's face, relative to other female faces (Pascalis, de Schonen, Morton et al., 1995).

Whether or not the infant system is merely a developmentally earlier version of the adult system is a matter of debate. There appears to be consensus, at least among some research groups, that the face preference in infants, unlike that in adults, appears to be mediated by a subcortical mechanism initially, with increasing cortical influence taking place later (Mondloch, Lewis, Budreau et al., 1999). Data to support this claim come from the finding that newborns, but not slightly older infants, show particular behavioral effects. For example, when presented with schematic faces, newborns, but not infants of 6 or 12 weeks of age, show an inversion effect (greater response to upright than inverted faces) which is taken to be a critical reflection of face selectivity. This inversion effect is then seen in older individuals again. Although there does not seem to be a simple explanation for why newborns, but not older infants, show this effect, the important point is that there is a change in behavior as the infant matures. This change over time is also seen in another context in which newborns prefer stimuli reflecting the amplitude, rather than the phase, of a studied face, whereas this preference is not observed in slightly older infants (see also Johnson and de Haan, 2001). What is particularly impressive about the findings from the newborn studies, even if the system is not identical to the adult version, is the apparent early selectivity for faces and for familiar over unfamiliar faces.

Functional imaging and human electrophysiology

Perhaps as compelling, and rapidly accumulating, is the recent evidence in support of a specialized face system obtained from studies using functional neuroimaging (PET and functional MRI) and evoked response potentials (ERPs) in which activation or waveform differences to faces and nonface objects have been compared in normal people. The major finding from many of these studies is that faces and objects differ in both the pattern and location of electrophysiological and blood flow responses they elicit (Allison, Ginter, McCarthy et al., 1994a; Allison, McCarthy, Nobre et al., 1994b; Bentin, Allison, Puce et al., 1996; Bobes, Valdes-Sosa and Olivares, 1994). For example, the amplitude of some ERP waveforms, particularly the N170, is greater and the latency is shorter to faces than to objects (Bentin and Deouell, 2000; Jeffreys, 1996). The waveform may also be specifically modulated by attention to faces such that one obtains an enhanced negativity for faces versus chairs at lateral temporal electrodes and an early enhanced positivity at midline sites (Eimer, 2000). Data from a new study using magneto-encephalography, which provides very good temporal and spatial resolution, is also consistent with this: face stimuli evoked a larger response than 12 other nonface stimulus types early in processing, at 160 ms after stimulus onset, at bilateral occipitotemporal sensors in the region of the fusiform gyrus (Liu, Higuchi, Marantz and Kanwisher, 2000).

Differences in site of activation is also observed as faces and objects appear to activate distinct loci in the same general location, usually in the right fusiform gyrus (for example, Allison et al., 1994a; Grady, McIntosh, Horwitz et al., 1995; Haxby, Grady, Horowitz et al., 1991; Haxby, Horowitz, Ungerleider et al., 1994; Kanwisher, Chun, McDermott and Ledden, 1996; Puce, Allison, Gore and McCarthy, 1995; Sergent, Ohta and MacDonald, 1992) though bilateral activation is observed in many individuals. Typically, the site of activation for faces is medial to that of objects. Even when the low-level visual features of the stimuli are controlled for, regions of the fusiform gyrus (usually middle fusiform) show increased activation for faces over other nonface objects (Haxby, Ungerleider, Clark et al., 1999; Haxby et al., 1996; Kanwisher, Woods, Iacoboni and Mazziotta, 1997). Additionally, these same 'face' areas appear to be optimally tuned for faces; in a functional MRI (fMRI) study, activations were equally strong for entire human faces, faces with eyes occluded, cat faces, and cartoon faces (Tong, Nakayama, Moscovitch et al., 2000). Taken together, the highly replicable functional imaging and ERP results endorse the strong claim that there are different neural mechanisms mediating face and nonface processing.

Human behavioral studies

Without making reference to the neural substrate per se, behavioral data from normal subjects also suggest differences in processes subserving face and nonface recognition. A particularly well-known behavioral marker is the inversion effect (already alluded to in the discussion of newborns) in which inversion from the upright affects recognition of faces more adversely than that of any other objects (Bruce, 1988; Bruce and Humphreys, 1994; Tanaka and Farah, 1993; Yin, 1969, 1970). This exaggerated orientation or inversion effect for faces suggests that once faces are inverted, the distinctiveness of face-recognition at a perceptual and neural level is lost, supporting the idea that face-recognition mechanisms, unlike those for other objects, are selectively tuned to the upright. Thus, the latency of the N170, which is selectively tuned to faces and some face parts, is delayed for inverted faces (Allison et al., 1994a; Bentin et al., 1996; Jeffreys, 1993). Indeed, Moscovitch et al. (1997) found that although CK recognizes upright faces normally, he is severely impaired at recognizing inverted faces, supporting the claim that recognition of inverted faces, unlike upright faces, depends on contributions from object-recognition mechanisms (Yin, 1970) which are impaired in CK. Consistent with this finding of Haxby et al. (1996) that in addition to the fusiform gyrus, inverted, faces activate larger regions associated with object recognition than do upright faces.

A second behavioral marker is that of the differential effect of context for face versus object recognition. By this, we mean that recognition of face parts as belonging to a particular individual is poor if the parts are viewed separately rather than embedded in a face context. Recognition of object parts does not suffer as much when taken out of the object context. A particularly good demonstration of this difference has been provided by Tanaka and Farah (1993) who first taught their subjects to associate a name with eight different houses or with eight different faces. They later tested each subject's recognition of the whole house or face or of a part of the face or house (for example, the door or the nose). Subjects were significantly better at recognizing the whole stimulus than simply the part, but an additional critical finding was that subjects were better able to identify the doors than the noses. These results suggest that the discrimination of parts as belonging to a particular stimulus is better for nonface objects than for faces (but see Donnelly and Davidoff, 1999). Further evidence for the role of contextual effects in face recognition comes from a recent study of a brain-damaged patient, LH, who is particularly poor at face recognition. Interestingly, LH appeared unable to attend to the parts of a face unless the face was inverted or the parts were scrambled (De Gelder and Rouw, 2000). This restriction suggests that he had some residual face processing ability and it was only when the faces were fragmented or inverted and thus truly lost the distinctiveness of a face, that he was able to represent, and recognize, the parts. The issue of part and whole relations and their processing is also discussed in more detail later in the chapter.

Brain-damaged patients

A final and longstanding source of both neural and behavioral evidence that bears on the face–nonface distinction is that obtained from neuropsychological studies of brain-damaged patients. Of primary importance is the finding of a double-dissociation between the recognition of faces and objects. This double dissociation has been taken as support for the claim that there are independent and segregated systems for the recognition of these two different stimulus types. Patients with prosopagnosia (Bodamer, 1947; Hècaen and Angelergues, 1962), a severe deficit in face recognition, know when they are looking at a face and can identify and describe the features, but the face appears to have lost its value and familiarity (De Haan, 1999). At a neuroanatomical level, prosopagnosia is usually associated with bilateral damage to the inferior aspect of the temporal cortex, in the region of the fusiform gyrus (Benton, 1980; Damasio, Damasio and Hoesen, 1982; Damasio, Tranel and Damasio, 1990; Farah, 1990; Meadows, 1974; Sergent and Signoret, 1992a; Whiteley and Warrington, 1977) though unilateral damage to the same region on the right is sufficient to produce the deficit (Clarke, Lindemann, Maeder et al., 1997; De Renzi, 1986, De Renzi, Perani, Carlesimo and Silveri, 1994; Landis, Cummings, Christen et al., 1986; Michel, Poncet and Signoret, 1989). The opposite pattern of deficits, impaired object recognition but with relatively spared face recognition, can be obtained with damage to the inferotemporal cortex on the left (Farah, 1991; Feinberg, Schindler, Ochoa et al., 1994), though, as with prosopagnosia, visual object agnosia is commonly associated with bilateral damage (Farah, 1990; Hècaen, Goldblum, Masure and Ramier, 1974; McCarthy and Warrington, 1990).

Brain damage that affects the recognition of faces, but not the recognition of objects, appears to be resistant to plasticity or compensation. For example, Farah, Rabinowitz, Quinn and Liu (2000) report on a patient who sustained bilateral occipito-temporal lesions following streptococcal meningitis at day 1 of age. When tested at age 16, this patient was somewhat impaired at object recognition, scoring 87% on photographs of common objects, but he was severely impaired at face recognition. Notably, he matched only 11 out of 21 faces on the Benton test of facial recognition (Benton, des Hamsker, Varney and Spreen, 1978) and his overall score of 36 falls within the severely impaired range. He also failed to recognize even one out of 30 photographs of characters from the popular TV show, Baywatch, despite that fact that he watched the program regularly (and the photographs were specially selected as he knew the characters in the show). Bentin, Deouell and Soroker (1999) also report evidence of a developmental prosopagnosic person with intact object recognition, with no known lesions, but with an abnormal N170 response. These findings suggest that there is an innate mechanism for face recognition which, when disrupted, is not easily compensated for by other mechanisms whereas a deficit in object recognition can be accommodated to a greater extent.

Extensive behavioral data from studies in prosopagnosic individuals help to pinpoint the nature of the deficit in more detail. The general result is that prosopagnosic individuals are remarkably impaired at face recognition although their ability to detect faces, recognize a face as a face, and identify objects is relatively preserved. The data also suggest that prosopagnosia is not a failure to recognize all faces, but is restricted to human faces. For example, WJ (McNeil and Warrington, 1993), who was prosopagnosic, and went on to become a sheep farmer after his brain damage, was unable to recognize human faces, but was able to recognize sheep faces. A dissociation between recognizing human and cow faces was also reported by Assal (1984) in a Swiss farmer. A distinction between human and animal faces is also present in CK who rapidly and accurately not only detects human faces, but identifies the individual. His detection and recognition of animal faces is less good; when presented with a picture of an animal's face, he usually knows that it is an animal (from gathering coarse information about the structure) although he is not always able to say what kind of animal it is. His recognition of individual animals within a category, such as a particular German Shepherd dog from other German Shepherds is severely impaired (Moscovitch et al., 1997, Experiments 18 and 19). Although the distinction between animal and human faces may appear at odds with the imaging results that suggest that both are mediated by the face area in the fusiform gyrus (Tong et al., 2000), the data, in fact, are consistent in that activation of the fusiform gyrus is sensitive only to detection of faces, and not to identity of particular faces.

The deficit in face recognition also does not appear to be a failure of within-class exemplar recognition (Damasio et al., 1990). De Renzi (1986) has described prosopagnosic patients who were able to perform visual recognition tasks which resemble face recognition in terms of the within-category task demands. For example, one such patient was able to recognize his own car in the parking lot, his own wallet from a similar array of wallets, and his own handwriting amidst that of others. One might argue, for example, that the findings from De Renzi are not that compelling given that the patient may have singled out his own possessions or handwriting based on some single idiosyncratic feature or features and that the foils might not have been particularly well controlled in these more naturalistic experiments. In a more controlled study along similar lines, Farah, Levinson and Klein (1995a) showed that their patient, LH, was able to differentiate studied objects (such as forks, chairs and eyeglasses) from new objects drawn from the same categories, whereas he was significantly impaired, relative to control subjects, in differentiating between studied and new faces. CK showed the opposite pattern. Based on these results, it has been suggested that prosopagnosia is not a problem that affects the recognition of within-category exemplars that may be hard to discriminate. Rather, the claim is that it is faces per se that are affected in prosopagnosia.

Studies of the inversion effect in prosopagnosia have also provided insight into the nature of processing in these patients. Interestingly, unlike normal subjects who are relatively worse at identifying inverted than upright faces (but not other objects), there are some prosopagnosic patients who show an inversion superiority effect, i.e. they are better at matching inverted than upright faces (De Gelder, Bachoud-Levi and Degos, 1998; De Gelder and Rouw, 2000; Farah, Wilson, Drain and Tanaka, 1995b; Marotta, McKeeff and Behrmann, 2001). The explanation offered for this rather paradoxical result is that in face processing, the face is stored as a whole and that individual parts are not stored separately. This is particularly so for upright faces. When the specialized face system is damaged, the patient resorts to using an alternative, less-than-ideal part-processing mechanism. Because this part-based system is no longer inhibited by the competing holistic system, especially in the inverted case, it operates without restraint and can, therefore, yield better performance on parts than does the usual face mechanism. CK's severe impairment in recognizing inverted faces, which we noted above when considered in light of his normal ability to recognize upright faces, is consistent with this interpretation. The issue of holistic versus part-based processing is taken up for further discussion later.

The neuropsychological support for a special face processing system comes predominantly from patients with prosopagnosia, as described above, but patients, such as CK, who show the converse pattern, also support this claim. Although CK is the only patient to date who shows a clear cut dissociation between faces and objects, with relative preservation of faces, there are other, similar cases who are relatively better at recognizing faces than other kinds of objects (Feinberg et al., 1994; McCarthy and Warrington, 1986).

In sum, there appears to be overwhelming evidence from a variety of disciplines that faces and nonface objects are mediated by different neural and behavioral systems. Data from neurophysiological recordings in monkeys, behavioral findings from normal infants and adults, functional imaging data and results from patients with neuropsychological deficits are remarkably consistent in their support for a distinct mechanism for face recognition. Despite this, the evidence is open to other interpretations, to which we now turn.

Evidence against a specialized mechanism

Although the data presented above suggest a coherent and rather straightforward picture regarding the distinctiveness of faces, there appears to be another side to the story. Findings from approaches using the very same methods as those described above challenge not only the data themselves but, in those cases where the data are replicated, challenge the interpretation of the findings. In this section, we present these alternative results and perspectives.

Monkey neurophysiology

One of the challenges that has to be addressed concerns the extent to which face-selective neurons are really involved in face recognition. Although face-selective neurons have been identified in monkeys and have been taken as evidence for a special form of processing for faces, Heywood and Cowey (1992) showed that after ablation of STS, the region in which the face selective cells are most concentrated, monkeys were still able to recognize faces. The monkeys did, however, exhibit an impairment, but this was in the ability to discriminate gaze direction. Interestingly, this same deficit has been observed in humans with prosopagnosia (Campbell et al., 1990). Recent human neuroimaging data supports the finding that the STS is activated by the perception of eye gaze, whereas regions in the fusiform gyrus are activated by face identity (Hoffman and Haxby, 2000). Consistent with this, it has been argued that other regions in monkey inferotemporal cortex, homologous to the fusiform gyrus in humans, likely is the more crucial region for face-recognition (Sergent, 1994) or, alternatively, that the system is distributed and there is no single region solely responsible for face recognition per se.

A further complication of the single-unit recording data is that, although there are cells which appear to respond selectively to faces, there is no obvious segregation of these cells from cells that respond to nonface objects. Furthermore, the subsets of cells that purport to mediate faces and objects show other commonalities: both show spatial invariance and both are modifiable by experience (Gross and Sergent, 1992), suggesting perhaps more overlap rather than uniqueness.

Developmental studies

The data from the newborn studies also lend themselves to further scrutiny. Despite the strong evidence suggesting that newborns can orient to faces and track them during the first hours of life, suggesting an innate cortical module for face processing, an alternative ontogenetic view has been suggested in which there is emergent specialization of face processing within cortex. Johnson and de Haan (2001) review the evidence both for the localization and specialization of face processing in infants and argue that the evidence for each of these is not as strong as initially suggested. To address these issues, they performed an ERP study that compared the response to upright and inverted faces by adults and by 6-month-old infants. Whereas adults showed an N170 waveform that was both larger in amplitude and shorter in peak latency for upright over inverted faces (one of the signatures of face-specific processing, see above), especially over the right hemisphere sensors, consistent with previous ERP studies (Bentin et al., 1996; George, Evans, Fiori et al., 1996), the infants showed a quite different pattern. Although infants did show an amplitude and latency difference between upright and inverted faces, the peak was much later (370 ms). Additionally, there was equivalent difference in both left and right hemisphere sensors. Thus, infants appear to be less localized in their processing of upright faces than adults.

Further investigation analyzed the specificity of the waveform; whereas adults showed no inversion effect for monkey faces as reflected in the ERP responses at posterior temporal sensors (see above discussion on human versus nonhuman faces), infants did. Furthermore, the infants showed the same inversion effect for monkey faces as for human faces at P400, leading to the conclusion that the infant system is not yet fully specialized for human faces. The earlier upright-specific face potentials seen in adults compared to infants cannot be attributed to general slowing of the infant visual system; when a checkerboard was presented foveally to these two groups of subjects, the first positive P1 peak was recorded at about the same latency. Instead, the difference appears to be attributable to the fact that adults show face selectivity that is consistent with activation of the anterior end of the ventral pathway but infants only show the face-specific effect around P400 when there is re-activation of earlier cortical areas in a top-down fashion, notably the P1 reprise.

The developmental time course (rather than innate specification) of a system associated with face detection is also seen in a task in which infants have to recognize faces. De Haan et al. showed that 3-month-old infants were able to extract the invariance from a set of four faces such that they treated a composite or prototype of these four faces as less novel than any of the individual training faces (De Haan and Johnson, in press). The same was not true for 1-month-old infants even though they showed a novelty preference when a trained face was shown alongside a novel face.

Where does this leave the argument based on the developmental data? The findings from these studies call into question the claim that there is extensive prespecification or innate infrastructure for face recognition. However, there does not appear to be any single datum that argues definitively against the existence of some preference for faces over other objects, or over faces that lose their configurational properties through scrambling the components or inversion. This face preference may not be as developed as in adults nor as localized or specialized, and may even be subcortically mediated initially, but the presence of a face preference does not appear to be totally undermined. The conclusion that one reaches based on these studies is that there may be a mechanism predisposed to processing faces, just as there may be one predisposed for processing speech and language, but whose workings are modified by maturation and experience as well as by the underlying anatomical architecture and patterns of connectivity (Jacobs, 1997). The data suggest that even early in infancy there is something about face-recognition that is special, though it may simply be that it is based on a rudimentary template whose properties may be refined with time, that allows for easy detection and recognition of face-like stimuli.

Functional imaging and human electrophysiology

An alternative to the claim that there is a system dedicated to face recognition is the hypothesis that face recognition relies on a more general-purpose, visual object recognition system. The question then is why one sees such selectivity for faces, as reviewed in the first section. This selectivity may be explained by recourse to several different factors that differentially affect the recognition of faces. Three major factors which have been proposed thus far are object-form topology, task demands, and experience. We deal with each in turn.

Object form topology

One suggestion that emerges from some recent imaging work is that the functional architecture of the ventral visual pathway is not arranged by category. Rather the claim is that the ventral pathway is organized by a continuous representation of information about object form that has a highly consistent and orderly topographical arrangement. The data from recent fMRI studies reveal three distinct regions of activation in ventral cortex, each responding preferentially and maximally to houses, chairs or faces (Ishai, Ungerleider, Martin and Haxby, 2000; Ishai, Ungerleider, Martin et al., 1999). Although this result lends itself to being interpreted as three distinct and domain-specific modules, each area also responded significantly to stimuli from the nonpreferred categories albeit to a lesser degree. These results challenge a view of punctate localization and specialization. Rather, these findings are interpreted as favoring the view that the representations of visual stimuli are not restricted to anatomically discrete regions, but appear to be distributed across ventral cortex (but see arguments against this interpretation in Gauthier (2000) Tarr and Gauthier (2000) and Kanwisher (2000)). This expanse of cortex has a consistent topological organization and suggests that characteristics of an object cluster together. What the nature of these characteristics are remains unclear, but one proposal is that the representations may instantiate features similar to the object shape primitives outlined by Tanaka's studies of single cell responses to complex objects in monkey inferior temporal cortex (Tanaka, 1993).

Few people, even those supporting domain-specific modules for face-recognition, would dispute the claim that faces activate wide regions of cortex, or that non-face stimuli are capable of activating the face-specific region to some extent. The face-recognition region may act as a convergence zone (Damasio, 1989) in which information from all the other regions activated by faces is collated to yield a neural representation of faces in general or of a particular face. Similar regions may exist for other objects, though the particular properties and location of the other systems differ from faces, and may differ from each other.

Task demands

Topology, however, does not seem to account for all the data. When the geometry of objects is held constant, one can still see differential activation of a specific region of the fusiform gyrus. For example, the area of the fusiform gyrus typically associated with faces is differentially activated when subjects are shown the same stimulus, but when the task demands differ. For example, greater activation is observed when subjects label a picture of a car with an individual label (e.g. TR3) compared with when they simply label it 'car' (Gauthier, Anderson, Tarr et al., 1997). Thus, this region is more active for judgements requiring classification at a subordinate level compared to more categorical judgements and this applies across a large variety of objects, living or artifactual. The claim from these studies is that this ventral region, typically associated with mediating faces rather than other objects, can also be activated for other objects when subordinate level discrimination is required, as is usually the case for faces (Gauthier et al., 1997; Gauthier, Tarr, Moylan et al., 2000b).

Expertise
Subordinate level categorization is generally associated with more detailed knowledge of the domain and, in fact, expertise appears to be a powerful determinant of activation of this so-called face area. Recent data reveal that the 'face' area as well as a similarly selective occipital area in the right hemisphere are both recruited and become activated when observers become experts at discriminating between objects from visually homogeneous categories. In one relevant study, activation associated with attending to the location or identity of various familiar objects was compared for novice versus expert observers (Gauthier, Skudlarski, Gore and Anderson, 2000a). In novices, the homogeneous classes of birds and cars elicited more activity in the face area than a set of various familiar objects and this was more pronounced when the subjects attended to the identity than the location of the objects. In contrast, experts showed more activity in the right fusiform face area for their category of expertise, birds or cars, regardless of whether they attended to the identity or the location. A similar result was obtained in an ERP study with an enhanced N170 in the experts for the domain of expertise (Tanaka and Curran, 2001).

A related experiment further endorses the claim that the face area is activated by visual stimuli for which one has expertise. Subjects trained to discriminate novel objects called Greebles come to be expert observers for this class of objects in about 10 h of training and show activation of the face area once expertise is attained (Gauthier, Tarr, Skudlarski and Gore, 1999b; for examples of Greebles, see Fig. 3). When these subjects become expert at identifying Greebles, they show activation of the face area even under passive viewing conditions (Gauthier et al., 1999b). Furthermore, this increased activation is correlated with a behavioral measure which suggests

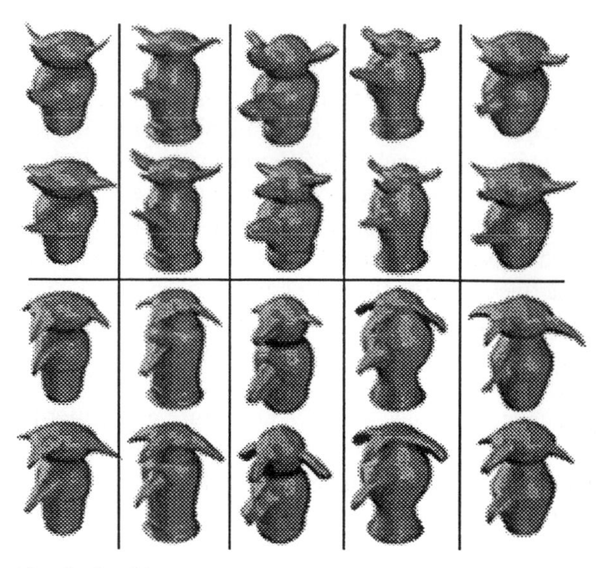

Fig. 3. Greebles are organized into five 'families' (columns) according to their body shape, and two 'genders' defined by the orientation of the parts (up/down) in the top two versus lower two rows.

that experts engage a more holistic form of processing the visual image than do novices. While novices can focus selectively on the top half of a composite Greeble (made of the top of one Greeble and the bottom of another), Greeble experts cannot help but process the bottom part. This 'composite effect' is correlated with the neural activity across subjects and suggests that the increased activation in the fusiform area may arise as a function of a more configural or holistic means of processing. The relationship between expertise and face processing is also supported by the observation that normal subjects show an 'other race effect' with faces from another race being more difficult to process than faces from one's own race (Byatt and Rhodes, 1998; Levin, 1996).

The data from these imaging studies, taken together, suggest that factors, such as topology, level of categorization and expertise possibly in some interacting fashion, may explain most of the face-selectivity in the functional imaging studies thus far and therefore one need not appeal to an explanation of domain-specific processing. In rebuttal, those who favor the distinct processing/mechanism view of face-recognition argue that the discrepancy lies in the way that the face-sensitive region in the fusiform gyrus is specified or defined (Kanwisher, 2000; Kanwisher and Moscovitch, 2000). The region is more circumscribed in studies that support the distinct mechanism view than in those that do not. Because the region is larger in the latter studies, it allows for the possibility of having non-face objects activate what is 'mistakenly' taken to be a face-recognition area. Moreover, it should be noted, that the amount of activation in the fusiform face area, though greater for objects in the expert, than non-expert, category, was still much smaller than for faces.

Human behavioral studies

The claim that faces are uniquely subject to the inversion effect has also been challenged recently. For example, a decrement in the recognition of other objects, such as shoes (De Gelder et al., 1998; Koriat and Norman, 1989), has been reported in a patient with visual agnosia and a decrement in performance on inverted handwriting has been seen in normal subjects (for example, Bruyer and Crispeels, 1992). The interpretation offered for these results was not that faces are special, but that the increased sensitivity to inversion arises because faces are mono-oriented and when stimuli, such as shoes or handwriting, which have particular orientations, are used, the inversion effect is also obtained. This more generalized inversion effect fits in with explanations of expertise — if an object is seen in a particular orientation repeatedly, irrespective of category, inversion will be observed. The idea that the inversion effect might only be observed in normal individuals who have much experience with faces is is supported by the developmental prosopagnosic patient studied by De Gelder, Rouw and Rossion (2000). This patient was insensitive to face orientation and showed no inversion effect. This patient's performance can be contrasted with that of individuals who became prosopagnosic in adulthood, i.e. had significant experience with faces, and who are very sensitive to inversion, as mentioned above (see also Marotta et al., 2001). Others, too, have suggested an alternative explanation for the inversion effect based on the frequency with which objects are seen in a typical, upright orientation rather than on the existence of a specialized face-processing device (Bentin et al., 1996; Wright and Roberts, 1996).

Brain-damaged patients

The critical claim that following brain damage patients may have a selective impairment for face recognition has been taken as strong support for a face-specific system. To evaluate the claim, we need to consider the data both from patients like CK who have spared face recognition as well as from prosopagnosic patients who are impaired at face recognition. The alternative to the face-specific preservation or impairment is that these patients have a similar pattern of preservation or impairment that extends beyond faces. Specifically, the question in the case of CK, is whether he has the ability to recognize any other class of objects as well as he can recognize faces. We sought support for this by examining his recognition of two other classes of objects, airplanes and toy soldiers. CK had grown up near an air field and was very knowledgeable about different airplanes. He also had a hobby of collecting toy soldiers and had an enormous collection. We failed to find any preserved recognition of either planes or soldiers and, in fact, CK no longer sets out his toy soldier collection as he does not derive any enjoyment from it. We also examined whether CK was able to recognize Greebles, dogs or cars at an individual level. On a variety of tasks, his performance was severely impaired.

On the surface, the lack of preserved recognition in these other domains is evidence for a face-specific mechanism but his experience with these other classes of objects is so minimal compared with faces that this comparison is not perfect. The absence of another spared class of stimuli, therefore, need not argue in favor of a face-specific system, but might be interpreted as suggesting that the face area is an area that is tuned to process stimuli from any class holistically and that expertise optimizes its function. If we could find a class of stimuli with which CK has similar experience, i.e. if we could solve the stimulus equivalence problem, the claim of face-specificity might be put to a better test.

An important question is whether CK might be taught to recognize a class of stimuli. It seems unlikely that his residual face system can be harnessed through training as he has lost the ability to recognize objects (and faces?) in a non-holistic fashion and, in particular, the ability to move from being a novice to being an expert in another class of objects. Arguments of this sort, however, are weighted unfairly against the face-specific processing hypothesis since negative evidence is always qualified, whereas positive evidence of preserved subordinate level processing is taken at face value. That CK lost all ability to recognize very familiar objects at a subordinate level, whereas his ability to recognize faces survived virtually intact, should give pause to advocates of the subordinate-level or individuation hypothesis (Moscovitch et al., 1997).

A careful analysis of the literature indicates that patients with prosopagnosia do appear to have impairments that extend beyond faces. The argument favoring face-selectivity from such patients is often obtained from studies that report accuracy differences for faces and other objects. Most often these studies do not report the potential response biases of the patients, although these may be quite dramatic. For example, the developmental prosopagnosic patient, Adam, refused to guess the identity of any of the faces shown to him, producing 0% accuracy in face recognition. As acknowledged by the authors (Farah et al., 2000), this pattern might reflect an extremely conservative response bias rather than an impairment in face recognition per se. Additionally, if a patient believes that she/he is more impaired (perhaps incorrectly) at faces than other objects, she/he might spend less time and allocate fewer attentional resources to encoding and recalling faces, resulting in poorer performance. To address the issue of response bias, data were collected from two prosopagnosic patients who performed individual-level recognition of faces, Greebles and visually similar non-face objects (Gauthier, Behrmann and Tarr, 1999a). Although the patients did about as well as control subjects in recognizing objects and Greebles, they showed a speed–accuracy trade-off to achieve this. That is, even though recognition was good (and hence one might conclude that they had no impairment on non-face objects), they spent far more time than the control subjects to achieve this level of accuracy. Moreover, when patients were forced to spend the same amount of time as the controls, accuracy as measured by d' (a statistic capturing the subject's ability to discriminate or remember items independent of response bias) revealed that prosopagnosic patients are impaired at recognizing visually similar objects, regardless of category. These data suggest that prosopagnosia may extend beyond faces and are consistent with reports of a prosopagnosic farmer who was no longer able to recognize his cows (Bornstein, Sroka and Munitz, 1969) or a bird watcher who could no longer discriminate birds (Bornstein, 1963). Alternatively, these data may indicate that the area of damage extended beyond the region specialized for recognition of faces. Indeed, the subjects in Gauthier et al. (1999a), like many prosopagnosic patients, are also object agnosic as determined by standard tests and sometimes serve as subjects in studies designed to illuminate the nature of object recognition (Suzuki, Peterson, Moscovitch and Behrmann, 2001; Behrmann and Kimchi, 2001). There are also findings in the literature that reflect the more widespread impairment in prosopagnosia and, indeed, there may not be any single case of prosopagnosia for whom it can be shown without reasonable doubt that the recognition of nonface objects is unaffected. Patient LH, for example, considered to be one of the best cases of prosopagnosia (Farah et al., 1995a; Farah et al., 1995b) and showing a strong dissociation between the recognition of faces and spectacles appears not to be normal in his recognition of nonface objects. He has been reported as having some problems in object and animal recognition (Etcoff, Freeman and Cave, 1991) and, in a recent study, was equally at chance when required to match a target face with one of two face choices or a target shoe with one of two shoe choices (De Gelder and Rouw, 2000). The poor performance with nonface objects may have been observed because this task required fine discrimination and, because he has only a mild object agnosia, this might have gone undetected previously. Also, in this task he was required to make a subordinate level or individual differentiation of the stimulus (matching a target face or shoe with one of two faces or shoes) and, as mentioned previously, this task demand is often not equated in the testing of faces and other nonface objects. He also showed an inversion superiority effect for shoes as he does for faces.

It is also the case that, like many other patients with prosopagnosia, the recognition of living objects is more affected than nonliving objects in LH. He named only 52% of living things correctly with better accuracy on nonliving things. Adam, the developmental prosopagnosic patient, correctly named

75% of nonliving objects, but only 40% of living things. This may reflect the greater within-category visual homogeneity of living versus non-living things (Warrington and McCarthy, 1987). Dixon, Bub and Arguin (1998) argued for a semantic contribution to face and object recognition. They showed that within-class discrimination of faces or other similar-looking objects depends, as well, on their separation in semantic space making them semantically distinct. For example, they found that prosopagnosic patients who also had difficulty making some within-class discrimination of objects, could learn to distinguish between faces if they belonged to different semantic categories (e.g. politicians and hockey players) than if they were of the same category. The same was true of the objects they had difficulty distinguishing (Arguin, Bub, and Dudek, 1996). They proposed an interactive-activation model of face and object recognition in which semantic representations help in making structural representations distinct.

However, these neuropsychological data simply present an association between faces and other classes of objects and, as is well known, arguing from association is not as powerful as an argument based on a dissociation. Moreover, a large proportion of prosopagnosic patients are also achromatopsic and have topographic agnosia, yet no one would claim that the same mechanisms serve all these domains. The question, then, is whether there exists a prosopagnosic patient who, like CK with regard to object agnosia, shows a strong and clear-cut dissociation between faces and other objects. Farah (1991, 1994a, 1999) has pointed out that there are many cases of profound face recognition impairment with little or no evidence of object agnosia. Whether or not this is indeed the case is difficult to tell. As stated above, these patients may be taking more time over nonface objects than over faces and many of these studies provide only accuracy data (and, in some, the data are rather more anecdotal than experimental). Additionally, response bias might be a factor as outlined above.

A review of some cases whose data are often used to argue for the selective impairment of faces suggests that the impairment might indeed encompass more than faces. As mentioned above, patient LH who is well known to be a good case of prosopagnosia is impaired at a range of other objects. The three cases of Whiteley and Warrington (1977) whose data are often cited to support the face-selectivity argument might also not hold up. Cases 1 and 2, for example, fall below the range of the control subjects in naming or identifying objects from unusual views, whereas case 3 was impaired at identifying incomplete letters. In the discussion, the authors concede that the patients were markedly impaired on tests of face matching and that there was a variable impairment on tests of perception of objects and letters. A final case whose data are often cited is the patient described by McNeil and Warrington (1993). This patient is especially interesting as he was able to recognize sheep faces better than human faces even though normal subjects find human faces easier. His knowledge of sheep faces extended beyond his own flock of 36 sheep as he could learn names to associate with unknown sheep faces better than he could do with unknown human faces. Interestingly, this man acquired the flock of sheep after his injury and learned the sheep faces through multiple exposure to the animals. What was astonishing was that he was unable to overcome his prosopagnosia. At first glance, this seems to be very powerful evidence in favor of a face-specific mechanism. Some recent data from another patient, however, call these findings into question.

In one recent study, a prosopagnosic patient, SM, was trained to identify Greebles at an individual level (as well as identify the gender and family of the Greeble; see Fig. 3), using a modified procedure of the Gauthier et al. (1999b) expertise training procedure. The transfer of this learning to faces was then assessed. The first result was that SM's ability to identify individual Greebles improved with training (beyond 80% accuracy and significant reaction time improvement). Some generalization occurred as he was also able to perform individual match tasks with Greebles he had not seen in the training set. Of striking interest was the finding that as his individual level recognition of Greebles improved, so his face recognition appeared to be somewhat poorer than it was initially (and it was not very good to begin with) (Berhmann et al., unpublished data).

These data suggest that, as in the case of the sheep farmer, prosopagnosic patients may be able to learn a new stimulus class but because of the limited number of neurons remaining following their brain-damage, the recognition of faces may remain unchanged, at best, and may even suffer in the process. These data may then not speak directly to the selective impairment of faces, but may reflect the residual capabilities of the ventral temporal brain regions. On the other hand, this result can be taken as a strong argument that subordinate-level recognition of nonface stimuli, even those designed to have formal properties similar to faces, is fundamentally different from recognition of faces, and may even interfere with it. Additionally, SM as well as the sheep farmer, WJ, were also impaired on other perceptual tasks and so this improvement in a domain other than human faces may not be pertinent for discussions of prosopagnosia per se. Whether it is indeed possible to find prosopagnosia in the absence of any other perceptual deficit is still open to question, as is evident from this chapter, but the argument in favor or against a face-specific account of prosopagnosia should not hinge on this demonstration. The crucial issue in this debate, as in all others concerning double dissociation, is not whether one system is completely preserved when the other is damaged, but whether it is possible to obtain a greater deficit in face-recognition than object recognition in some patients, and the reverse effect in others. What remains to be resolved is whether a face-specific interpretation of prosopagnosia provides the best account of this dissociation.

Summary

We have reviewed in detail the data from studies on faces versus nonface objects in a host of different populations and using different methodologies. The data favoring a distinct system hypothesis are compelling and transparently support a category-specific and modular organization of the brain with different subsystems mediating different stimulus types. The challenging data are, in their own right, also compelling and favor a view in which general purposes processors can come to be altered with experience and are also subject to task demands (for example, requiring subordinate level categorization versus basic level categorization). We should note, however, that explanations relying on general purpose mechanisms, as all single mechanism or processes, fail to explain both sides of the double dissociations that are observed. Thus, if face-recognition is relatively preserved in object agnosia because one has more experience with faces than with other objects, it cannot also selectively impaired in prosopagnosia for the same reason. What is perhaps most clear from all the above findings is that it is possible to obtain distinctions between faces and nonface objects. This relative dissociation between the object types might indicate differential processing of faces and nonface objects or increased reliance of processing for objects on a more parts-based mechanism and for faces on a more holistic mechanism. This view is explored in the next section.

Whole and part-based face processing

It has been suggested that what distinguishes the recognition of faces and non-face objects is their differential reliance on two different processing systems, a part-based system for faces and a holistic, or gestalt system for objects. The claim is that one form of processing is more holistic and relies on or exploits configural processing, whereas the other form is more feature-based. What precisely is meant by holistic and by part-based processes and representations, however, is currently under discussion in the literature and vigorous investigation in the laboratory. The various proposals bear a family resemblance to one another. We, therefore, summarize them here, and refer the reader to our own work (Moscovitch et al., 1997) and to excellent reviews on face-recognition for detailed expositions and critiques (Bruce, 1988; Bruce and Humphreys, 1994; Bruyer, 1986; Carey and Diamond, 1994; Ellis, Jeeves, Newcombe and Young, 1986; Farah, 1990; Nachson, 1995; Young, 1994).

All proposals which claim that face perception is holistic have in common the idea that the whole of the face, its global structure or gestalt as determined by the spatial relations among its components, is greater than the sum of its parts, the individual features which comprise the face. As applied to faces, this idea is linked to the neurologically based notion that the right hemisphere is holistic and, among other things, specializes in processing faces, and the left hemisphere is analytic, and specializes in processing words and nameable objects (for an early version of this idea see Jackson, 1874, 1915; which later was revived by Levy-Agresti and Sperry, 1968; see Bradshaw and Nettleton, 1981, and Moscovitch, 1979 for a review and critique of some of these ideas and Rhodes, 1993 and Corballis, 1991, for some recent reviews, refinements, and developments). For example, although faces are processed more quickly when presented to the right hemisphere (left visual field in a tachistoscopic presentation), this advantage is reduced or even eliminated when the faces are inverted, suggesting that it is the right hemisphere that engages in holistic or gestalt processing. When subjects are required to adopt a feature-by-feature strategy by a task manipulation, a left hemisphere superiority is obtained. This differential hemispheric involvement was supported by a recent PET study in which more activation in the right fusiform gyrus was observed when subjects matched whole faces than when they matched parts of faces, either the eyes or the mouth. The reverse effect was obtained in the homologous left middle fusiform areas (Rossion, Dricot, Devolder et al., 2000).

The difficulty, however, always has been to determine exactly what is considered a gestalt, which relations are crucial, and what constitutes a part. Some early views were that facial features which formed a gestalt would be processed in parallel whereas those which did not would be processed serially (Bradshaw and Wallace, 1971; Bradshaw and Nettleton, 1981). Another was that face-recognition was dependent primarily on low, but not high, spatial frequencies (Harmon, 1973; Sergent and Hellige, 1986). Both views have been repudiated on empirical and theoretical grounds (see Bruce, 1988; Moscovitch and Radzins, 1987) and have been replaced by more computational theories.

Holistic theories and hypotheses

In reviewing the various holistic theories, Moscovitch et al. (1997) identified four different hypotheses.

(1) The *configural hypothesis* states that what is crucial in face-recognition are the relations among first order features, such as the eyes and nose, and this includes their spatial relations and their location with respect to the contours of the face (Rhodes, 1988; Rhodes, Brake and Atkinson, 1993). Configural relations are also interactive in the sense that there is informational dependency and mutual influence among the parts of the face (Sergent, 1984; Takane and Sergent, 1983).

(2) The *second-order relational hypothesis* distinguishes between two types of relational features. First-order relational features are the spatial relations among parts or isolated features and are sufficient for identifying most objects, or at least specifying their category membership. Second-order relational features are "distinctive variations of a shared configuration" (Carey and Diamond, 1994, p. 255; Murray, Yong and Rhodes, 2000), the spatial arrangements of the parts relative to some prototypical arrangement which exists for a class of items. Because the parts of a face always bear the same relation to each other, faces can be individuated only on the basis of their second-order relational features.

(3) According to the *norm-based coding hypothesis*, the computations that are crucial are those which code relations between a face and a norm which is derived by averaging or superimposing a large number of faces (Rhodes, Brennan and Carey, 1987).

In contrast to the norm-based hypothesis, *the density alone (or noise) hypothesis* states that individual faces are identified by their overall point-by-point representations in multidimensional space or by a principal component analysis (Valentine, 1991). In recent experiments, Rhodes, Carey and Brennan (1998) showed that recognition of caricatures of famous people depends more on their proximity to a target defined in terms of its location within multidimensional space rather than its deviation from a norm, thereby supporting the density alone hypothesis.

(4) The *gestalt or template hypothesis* assumes that holistic representations are unparsed (Corballis, 1991; Farah, 1990; Tanaka and Farah, 1993; see Bradshaw and Nettleton, 1981; Garner, 1974 and Moscovitch, 1979, for review of some of the earlier ideas). The component parts, though separable in principle, are not processed or coded independently. Their identity depends on the gestalt or template of which they are a part. Insofar as faces are special, they are holistic in this sense. Part-based representations, which are assumed to underlie recognition of objects and inverted faces, depend on decomposing items into their component parts and then integrating those parts in relation to each other and to the shape which binds them (Biederman, 1987).

As we understand it, the gestalt hypothesis says nothing about the algorithm relating the parts to each other; and configural theories are neutral as to the ability of the parts to have an identity independent of the whole. If we are to have a full understanding of face-recognition, a theory that incorporates elements of both types of hypotheses will be needed.

Each of these proposals captures some of the crucial differences between faces and other objects, and each has been useful in explaining different aspects of face perception. Nonetheless, many problems remain, which suggests either that the proposals are deficient or the way they are tested are not adequate. For example, in a number of studies, inversion either does not affect what is construed, on principled grounds, to be relational or norm-based processing or it paradoxically affects recognition of face parts, rather than relations among them. (Rhodes, Brake and Atkinson, 1993). As well, markers of what is taken to be a common underlying relational process seem to have different developmental time courses. Thus, the full effects of inversion are not observed until 10 years of age whereas interference effects caused by combining seamlessly the upper and lower parts of two different faces (Young, Hellawell and Hay, 1987) emerges as early as age 3 (Diamond and Carey, 1994). These results suggest one of the following: that there are different types of relational processes each of which contribute to face-recognition and make it special (Rhodes et al., 1993); that there is an inherent ambiguity in classifying aspects of the face as parts or relations (Rhodes et al., 1993); or that the theories themselves are inadequate.

Internal vs. external features

Some of the problems facing the various hypotheses are brought into relief when considering the relative contributions that internal (mouth, nose, and eyes) and external features make to face recognition. In general, recognition of unfamiliar faces depends more on external features, whereas recognition of familiar or famous people depends as much, if not more, on internal features (see Ellis, Shepherd and Davies, 1979; Moscovitch and Moscovitch, 2000, and references therein). These findings indicate that internal features carry more of the burden of recognition as experience grows. The problem arises as to which aspect of internal features is important: the individual features themselves, the spatial relations among them and those to external features, or a combination of all factors. The holistic theories, as well as the subordinate level discrimination theories, would argue in favor of the latter two possibilities. Our own data on CK bear this out. We found that CK's recognition of famous people is impaired when internal, but not external, features are inverted (Moscovitch et al., 1997) within the context of the whole face, but his recognition is normal if he is presented with a unified set of internal features in isolation. When presented with just the external features, his recognition suffers in comparison to that of a control group (see Table 1).

Although the holistic theories focus on the relational information, it is also apparent that spatial relations between the features matter even for part-based theories. It is not sufficient merely to identify the parts but to have an appreciation of how they are related to each other. Inversion is believed to alter the holistic aspect of face recognition, forcing the individual to rely more on part-based information. Even when faces are inverted, recognition accuracy is about 70% in normal people but only about 20% in CK who has a damaged part-based system which presumably is needed for identification of inverted faces.

The question, however, remains: do we identify inverted faces only on the basis of individual features or do we also need information about the spatial relations among them? To address this question, Moscovitch and Moscovitch (2000) had normal subjects identify inverted faces that were intact or fractured. We chose to use fractured faces because our data on CK indicated that fracturing an upright face, like inverting it, destroyed the facial gestalt and led to comparably poor levels of identification. If recognition of inverted faces depends only on the piecemeal identification of individual features, then recognition of inverted fractured faces should be no worse than inverted faces alone. In fact, we found that performance was much worse in the combined condition. Moreover, the effects of inversion and fracturing were additive, as evident in Table 2. We concluded that if recognition of inverted faces depends on a part-based system, then the following assumptions must be made: (1) the representation of individual features is orientation-specific and nor-

TABLE 1

The average number of correctly recognized faces in each whole upright condition and the percentage (SD) of them recognized in each of the other conditions[a]

	Whole upright			Whole inverted		Int.[b] upright		Int. inverted		Ext. upright		Ext. inverted	
	No.	SD	%	%	SD	%	SD	%	SD	%	SD	%	SD
Controls ($n = 12$)	19.9	2.95	86.5	72.5	15.2	75.2	17.1	21.9	13.3	63.8	10.1	22.0	9.7
CK	21.8		94.7		22.7		86.4		4.5		33.3		9.5

[a] From Moscovitch and Moscovitch, 2000, p. 205.
[b] Int. = internal, Ext. = external.

TABLE 2

The number (SD) of correctly recognized faces in the whole upright condition and the percentage (SD) of them recognized in each of the other conditions

	Whole upright[c]		Fractured inverted		Fractured upright		Whole inverted	
	No.	SD	%	SD	%	SD	%	SD
Controls ($n = 6$)	32.7	6.1	50.8	12.3	84.0	7.0		
Controls ($n = 6$)	37.0	2.8					6.95	11.5
CK[b]	34				38			

[a] Version 1, from Moscovitch and Moscovitch, 2000, p. 212.
[b] From Moscovitch et al. (1997), Experiment 15.
[c] Maximum = 40.

malization processes are needed to deal with inversion; and (2) the synthesis of parts into a whole depends on having access to information about the spatial relations of the parts (see also Murray et al., 2000). Though relational, this information need not be configurational in the sense that it forms a gestalt or specifies a template. Instead it may be categorical in that it specifies the coordinate (left–right, up–down), qualitative relations among parts, or the local relations needed for the piecemeal integration of individual features, much in the way that local relational information is needed for alignment or grouping of pieces in a jigsaw puzzle.

According to this view, there are two types or representations for faces: a holistic representation in which individual features derive their metric value from the relationship within a template; and a part-based representation which is a *counterpart* to the holistic representation (see Biederman and Kalocsai (1997) for a computational model that is compatible with this suggestion). To recognize faces when the gestalt is altered, such as when faces are inverted or fractured, the two systems must interact with each other. Exactly how this is accomplished remains to be determined. We presume that information about individual parts and their relations in the *facial counterpart* is transferred to the face system where this information can be used to activate candidate holistic representations of different faces, which in turn leads to identification. What is important to keep in mind is that normal identification of faces, even when they are inverted or fractured, depends ultimately on gaining access to the holistic face system. The part-based representations cannot support normal face recognition on their own.

If part-based and holistic representations can exist for faces, there is no reason why they should not also exist for objects. According to this proposal, identification of objects at a basic level depends on a part-based system, whereas subordinate-level discrimination (identification) or individuation, depends on a holistic system. It remains to be determined whether this proposal is valid, and if it is, whether the holistic system needed for subordinate level identification of objects is similar or different from the holistic system needed to identify faces.

Farah (1991) also suggested that object recognition was dependent on both the part-based and holistic systems, so that if both were damaged, object recognition would be impaired. She postulated that deficits in face-recognition (prosopagnosia) were indicative of damage to the holistic system and that deficits in reading (acquired dyslexia) were indicative of damage to the part-based system, since face-recognition and reading were the prototypical functions of the holistic and part-based systems, respectively. Because she believed that object recognition relies on both systems, she predicted that if a patient was both prosopagnosic and dyslexic, then the patient would also have an object agnosia. Recent evidence did not support her prediction. There now have been a number of reports of patients with acquired dyslexia and prosopagnosia whose object recognition is normal (Buxbaum, Glosser and Coslett, 1999; Rumiati and Humphreys, 1997; Rumiati, Humphreys, Riddoch and Bateman, 1994). These more recent findings suggest that if there is a holistic system which supports face-recognition, it is not unitary; it does not also support the recognition of objects. These findings, and the conclusion that follows, also cast doubt on the subordinate-level hypothesis of Gauthier and her colleagues. If face-recognition is impaired, then subordinate level recognition of objects should also be impaired to the extent that they rely on common, holistic processes (see data from CK).

Evidence for implicit processing of faces

Research has indicated that some, but not all (Newcombe, Young, and De Haan, 1989), patients with prosopagnosia have available to them some information about the identity of faces, even though they may be unable to report this information explicitly. Evidence to support this claim comes both from psychophysiological measures as well as behavioral measures. For example, Renault, Signoret, De Bruille et al. (1989) reported that their prosopagnosic patient generated higher P300 amplitudes at shorter latencies to familiar than unfamiliar faces. Differences in the scan paths for familiar versus unfamiliar faces has also been observed in the eye movements of prosopagnosic patients (Rizzo, Hurtig and Damasio, 1987).

Consistent with this, familiar faces elicited more frequent and larger skin conductance responses in four prosopagnosic patients described by Tranel and colleagues (Tranel and Damasio, 1987; Tranel and Damasio, 1988). Some patients are better able to match previously familiar than unfamiliar faces (Bruyer, Laterre, Seon et al., 1983; Sergent and Poncet, 1990) or show priming from previously seen faces (De Haan, Young and Newcombe, 1987a,b; Greve and Bauer, 1990). Implicit knowledge for the individual identity of a face has also been observed in a number of studies. For example, when patients were required to match a name with a presented face, performance was at chance. The skin conductance response, however, was larger when the name corresponded to the face than when it did not (Bauer, 1984; Bauer and Verfaellie, 1988). A similar result was observed in a behavioral paradigm in which prosopagnosic patients were less able to learn incongruent (non-matching) names and faces than a name and face that corresponded despite the inability to overtly recognize faces (Bruyer et al., 1983; De Haan et al., 1987b; see also De Haan, Bauer and Greve, 1992, for related results). The preservation of covert face identity is not the only implicit form of face processing observed; De Gelder, Pourtois, Vroomen and Bachoud-Levi (2001) used a cross-modal paradigm in which a face was presented along with a voice to a patient with severe prosopagnosia and with no apparent covert recognition of face identity. Notwithstanding the impairment in identifying the face stimuli, the concurrent appearance of a face altered the patient's ratings of the expression of the voice.

Finally, some patients still appear to have access to semantic knowledge about faces even though they cannot overtly report this. Some patients show interference when learning to associate names with untrue occupations (De Haan et al., 1987b; Sergent and Poncet, 1990) or names with untrue countries of residence (Sergent and Signoret, 1992b). Interference from a noncongruent distractor was also observed when a patient was required to classify names according to whether they belonged to politicians or not, leading to longer classification response times. Because the patient was at chance when asked to classify the faces per se, the data suggest that the knowledge of faces was only available implicitly (De Haan et al., 1987b; see also, De Haan et al., 1992;

Sergent and Signoret, 1992b). Cross-domain semantic priming has also been reported in prosopagnosia. Patient PH judged printed names as familiar or unfamiliar and the names were preceded by primes that were familiar faces, but were either related or unrelated to the target name (Young, Hellawell and de Haan, 1988). Like normal controls, PH showed speeded judgements when the names were preceded by related faces compared with unrelated faces. Although his responses were facilitated by primes in the same way as normal subjects, he was unable to identify the faces used as primes. Such degraded representations may combine with other sources of information to allow for covert recognition of face identity but also of facial expression (De Gelder et al., 2001).

Not all prosopagnosic patients, however, reveal evidence of preserved face processing. A possible distinction between those patients who appear to process faces covertly, and those who do not, concerns the nature of the deficit. Two different forms of prosopagnosia have been identified, one affecting the more perceptual components of face processing and the other, the more memorial or mnestic aspects. According to Newcombe et al. (1989) and Sergent and Signoret (1992b), only those patients with mnestic deficits appear to be able to perform implicit processing. It is in these cases that the ability to retrieve the face information from memory is affected and that this knowledge can be recovered implicitly.

Various explanations have been offered for the residual covert processing in prosopagnosia (see Köhler and Moscovitch, 1997). For example, one line of explanation concerns the fact that familiarity of faces affects the autonomic responses, but not the overt or explicit identification of faces. On the basis of the psychophysiological data (enhanced skin conductance responses to correct names than to foils) and the possible anatomy and lesion sites of his patients, Bauer (1984, 1986) suggested that two routes exist in face recognition. Specifically, the claim is that a more dorsal visual route, connected to the limbic system, is preserved and could account for the automatic or autonomic aspects of face processing where ventral occipito-temporal routes, which mediate overt recognition and verbal report, and disrupted.

The claim that there are two separate routes, one devoted to autonomic responses and the other to more cognitive aspects of faces, has been challenged by de Haan and colleagues. In their studies with patient PH (De Haan et al., 1987a,b), using paradigms that involve matching faces with words or paired associate learning, they have obtained evidence of preserved implicit knowledge of faces. What is particularly relevant is that this evidence is not autonomic in nature. The explanation they offer then is that it is not that there are two separate systems mediating face recognition with one being preserved for autonomic readout. Rather, they claim that face recognition is subserved by a single route, but that the output from an otherwise adequately functioning system is disconnected from those processes that are needed to support awareness of recognition. This view is compatible with the claim that implicit processing reflects a failure to access consciousness (Schacter et al., 1988). Thus, the fact that some prosopagnosic patients show effects of repetition priming suggests that the representation of faces is intact, but is somehow disconnected from consciousness (Moscovitch, 1992). A related proposal is that the absence of integration between implicit and explicit processing results in failure to access consciousness (Tranel and Damasio, 1988). After reviewing the evidence, Breen, Caine and Coltheart (2000) offer a different interpretation. They propose a model that involves two pathways subsequent to the system responsible for face recognition: one pathway to a system containing semantic and biographical information about the seen face, and a second pathway responsible for the generation of affective responses to faces that are familiar. What is crucial here is that the systems are not distinguished primarily by their access to consciousness (though that may be the outcome) but by the type of information they represent or access.

Finally, implicit face processing has also been interpreted (as is also the case with several other neuropsychological deficits) as arising from degraded representations which are not sufficiently activated for explicit report but which may suffice for covert recognition (Farah, 1994b). This argument is substantiated by evidence from computational simulations and from a study with normal subjects. In the modeling work, Farah, O'Reilly and Vecera (1993) 'lesioned' those parts of a connectionist network of face recognition that were involved in the perceptual analysis of the face. The performance of the lesioned network paralleled that of the prosopagnosic patients, exhibiting residual implicit knowledge without accurate covert performance. The explanation offered by this work is that a more coarse representation may suffice for the implicit task, whereas a more precise representation is required to generate a specific and overt response. To further support this claim, Wallace and Farah (1992) trained a group of normal subjects to learn a set of face–name associations and then re-tested them 6 months later. Although the subjects could not recall the associations explicitly, they showed savings in relearning the true rather than recombined associations. The claim is that the preserved knowledge of the normal subjects in memory mirrors that of the prosopagnosic patients in perception and that the residual implicit knowledge emerges from the functioning of degraded representations.

Köhler and Moscovitch (1997) note, however, there is no basis for this assumption other than the comparable effects obtained by Farah and Wallace in the learning task with only two normal subjects. For their claims to be convincing, they would have to show that the nature of impaired recognition memory of forgotten faces in normal people is similar to impaired identification in prosopagnosic people.

The claim that degraded representations suffice for implicit, but not explicit, recognition has not gone without challenges either. One prediction that might be made on the basis of these degraded models is that the magnitude of the priming effect might be reduced, based on the degradation. However, data from a patient like PH has shown that he not only covertly recognized the faces, but also that his priming from the unrecognized faces was not significantly reduced compared with priming from names (Hezewijk and De Haan, 1994; see also Köhler and Moscovitch, 1997).

In reviewing the evidence on unconscious visual processing, Köhler and Moscovitch (1997) identified four different models which are exemplified by the different interpretations offered for the dissociation between conscious and unconscious face-recognition. The *disconnection model* postulates that unconscious recognition when explicit recognition is impaired, arises from the disconnection of structural representational systems or perceptual modules for faces from a conscious awareness system. The proposal by De Haan et al. would be consistent with this model. The *degraded representational model* assumes that implicit knowledge is a degraded form of explicit knowledge. Implicit knowledge is lower in quality, but of the same type, as explicit knowledge. This is the view advanced by Farah and her colleagues. The third model is the *distinct knowledge model* which states that distinct mechanisms and representations support implicit and explicit knowledge. Breen et al. (2000) come closest to endorsing this kind of model. The crucial question that this model raises is whether the representation of faces that underlies implicit knowledge is of one type and that which mediates explicit knowledge is of another. For example, it would be interesting to know whether implicit and explicit face-recognition depend equally on holistic or part-based processes. The fourth model is an *interactionist model* which posits that consciousness arises as a results of interactions across various components or processes within a domain (see also Tranel and Damasio, 1988, for similar view). No clear winner has emerged just yet and considerable work remains.

Concluding comments

It is evident from this review that many issues remain to be resolved. Whether or not faces are special and what the ramifications of this are for part- and whole-based processing, and for the neural representation of faces and objects, remains at the center of much debate. Because the two authors hold opposing views, the chapter presents both without attempting to argue forcefully in favor of one or the other. Given the intelligence and ingenuity of investigators of these issues, their tenacity and stubbornness, and the shifting terms of the debate as more evidence is gathered, it is not clear whether the debate will ever be resolved. One hopes, however, that in the course of these investigations other important questions will be answered. Whether or not faces are distinct from objects, what are the processes that permit the rapid identification of both types of stimuli, and the neural mechanisms that mediate them? What are the properties of the inferior temporal lobes that make them ideally substrates to support rapid recognition of complex visual stimuli be they faces, objects, or words?

References

Allison T, Ginter H, McCarthy G, Nobre AC, Puce A, Luby M, Spencer DD: Face recognition in human extrastriate cortex. Journal of Neurophysiology: 71(2); 821–825, 1994a.

Allison T, McCarthy G, Nobre AC, Puce A, Belger A: Human extrastriate visual cortex and the perception of faces, words, numbers and colors. Cerebral Cortex: 5; 544–554, 1994b.

Arguin M, Bub DN, Dudek G: Shape integration for visual object recognition and its implication in category specific visual agnosia. Visual Cognition: 3(3); 221–275, 1996.

Ashbridge E, Perrett DI, Oram MW, Jellema T: Effect of image orientation and size on object recognition: responses of single units in the macaque temporal cortex. Cognitive Neuropsychology: 17(1–3); 13–34, 2000.

Assal G: Nonrecognition of familiar animals by a farmer. Rev Neurol (Paris): 140; 580–584, 1984.

Bauer R: Autonomic recognition of names and faces in prosopagnosia: a neuropsychological application of the knowledge test. Neuropsychologia: 22; 457–469, 1984.

Bauer RM: The cognitive psychophysiology of face recognition. In Ellis HD, Jeeves MA, Newcombe F, Young A (Eds), Aspects of Face Processing. Dordrecht: Martinus Nijhoff, pp. 253–267, 1986.

Bauer RM, Verfaellie M: Electrodermal recognition of familiar but not unfamiliar faces in prosopagnosia. Brain and Cognition: 8; 240–252, 1988.

Baylis GC, Rolls ET, Leonard CM: Selectivity between faces in the responses of a population of neurons in the cortex of the superior temporal sulcus of the monkey. Brain Research: 342; 91–102, 1985.

Behrmann M, Kimchi R: Perceptual organization in visual agnosia. In Kimchi R, Behrmann M, Olson C (Eds), Perceptual Organization in Vision: Behavioral and Neural Perspectives. Hillsdale, NJ: Lawrence Erlbaum Associates, 2001, in press.

Behrmann M, Moscovitch M, Winocur G: Intact visual imagery and impaired visual perception in a patient with visual agnosia. Journal of Experimental Psychology: Human Perception and Performance: 20(5); 1068–1087, 1994.

Behrmann M, Winocur G, Moscovitch M: Dissociations between mental imagery and object recognition in a brain-damaged patient. Nature: 359; 636–637, 1992.

Bentin S, Allison T, Puce A, Perez E, McCarthy G: Electrophysiological studies of face perception in humans. Journal of Cognitive Neuroscience: 8(6); 551–565, 1996.

Bentin S, Deouell L: Structural encoding and identification in face processing: ERP evidence for separate mechanisms. Cognitive Neuropsychology: 17(1–3); 35–54, 2000.

Bentin S, Deouell LY, Soroeer N: Selective visual streaming in face recognition: evidence from developmental prosopagnosia. NeuroReport: 10; 823–827, 1999.

Benton AL: The neuropsychology of face recognition. American Psychologist: 35; 176–186, 1980.

Benton AL, des Hamsker K, Varney, NR, Spreen O: Facial Recognition: Stimulus and Multiple Choice Pictures. New York: Oxford University Press, 1978.

Biederman I: Recognition-by-components: a theory of human image understanding. Psychological Review: 94; 115–147, 1987.

Biederman I, Kalocsai P: Neurocomputational basis of object and face recognition. Philosophical Transactions of the Royal Society of London, Series B: Biological Sciences: 352; 1203–1219, 1997.

Bobes MA, Valdes-Sosa M, Olivares E: An ERP study of expectancy violation in face perception. Brain and Cognition: 26; 1–22, 1994.

Bodamer J: Die Prosop-agnosie. Archiv für Psychiatrie und Nervkrankheiten: 179; 6–53, 1947.

Bornstein B: Prosopagnosia. In Halpern L (Ed), Problems of Dynamic Neurology. Jerusalem: Hadassha Medical School, 1963.

Bornstein B, Sroka M, Munitz H: Prosopagnosia with animal face agnosia. Cortex: 5; 164–169, 1969.

Bradshaw JL, Nettleton NC: The nature of hemispheric specialization in man. The Behavioural and Brain Sciences: 4; 51–92, 1981.

Bradshaw JL, Wallace G: Models for the processing and identification of faces. Perception and Psychophysics: 9; 443–448, 1971.

Breen N, Caine D, Coltheart M: Models of face recognition and delusional misidentification: A critical review. Cognitive Neuropsychology: 17; 55–71, 2000.

Bruce V: Recognizing Faces. Hillsdale, NJ: Lawrence Erlbaum Associates, 1988.

Bruce V, Humphreys GW: Recognizing objects and faces. Visual Cognition: 1(2/3); 141–180, 1994.

Bruyer R (Ed): The Neuropsychology of Face Perception and Facial Expression. Hillsdale, NJ: Erlbaum, 1986.

Bruyer R, Crispeels G: Expertise in person recognition. Bulletin of the Psychonomic Society: 30; 501–504, 1992.

Bruyer R, Laterre C, Seron X, Feyereisen P, Strypstein E, Pierrard E, Rectem D: A case of prosopagnosia with some preserved covert remembrance of familiar faces. Brain and Cognition: 2; 257–284, 1983.

Buxbaum LJ, Glosser G, Coslett HB: Impaired face and word recognition without objects agnosia. Neuropsychologia: 37; 41–50, 1999.

Byatt G, Rhodes G: Recognition of own-race and other-race caricatures: implications for models of face recognition. Vision Research: 38(15–16); 2455–2468, 1998.

Campbell R, Heywood C, Cowey A, Regard M, Landis T: Sensitivity to eye gaze in prosopagnosia patients and monkeys with superior temporal sulcus ablation. Neuropsychologia: 28; 1123–1142, 1990.

Carey S, Diamond R: Are faces perceived as configurations more by adults than by children? Visual Cognition: 1(2/3); 253–274, 1994.

Clarke S, Lindemann A, Maeder P, Borruat FX, Assal G: Face recognition and postero-inferior hemispheric lesions. Neuropsychologia: 35(12); 1555–1564, 1997.

Corballis MC: The Lopsided Ape: The Evolution of the Generative Mind. New York: Oxford University Press, 1991.

Damasio AR: Time-locked multiregional retroactivation: A systems-level proposal for the neural substrates of recall and recognition. Cognition: 33; 25–62, 1989.

Damasio AR, Damasio H, Hoesen GWV: Prosopagnosia: Anatomic basis and behavioral mechanisms. Neurology: 32; 331–341, 1982.

Damasio AR, Tranel D, Damasio H: Face agnosia and the neural substrates of memory. Annual review of Neuroscience: 13; 89–109, 1990.

De Gelder B, Bachoud-Levi AC, Degos JD: Inversion superiority in visual agnosia may be common to a variety of orientation polarised objects besides faces. Vision Research: 38(18); 2855–2861, 1998.

De Gelder B, Pourtois G, Vroomen J, Bachoud-Levi A-C: Covert processing of faces in prosopagnosia is restricted to facial expressions: Evidence from cross-modal bias. Brain and Cognition: 44: 425–444, 2000.

De Gelder B, Rouw R: Paradoxical inversion effect for faces and objects in prosopagnosia. Neuropsychologia: 38; 1271–1279, 2000.

De Gelder B, Rouw R, Rossion B: Early stages of face processing: contrasting acquired and developmental prosopagnosia, in press.

De Haan EHF: Covert recognition and anosognosia in prosopagnosic patients. In Humphreys GW (Ed), Case Studies in the Neuropsychology of Vision. Hove, East Sussex: Psychology Press, pp. 161–180, 1999.

De Haan EHF, Bauer RM, Greve KW: Behavioral and physiological evidence for covert face recognition in a prosopagnosic patient. Cortex: 28(1); 77–95, 1992.

De Haan M, Maurer D, Johnson MH: Recognition of individual faces and average face prototype by 1- and 3-month-old infants. Cognitive Development, in press.

De Haan EHF, Young AW, Newcombe F: Face recognition without awareness. Cognitive Neuropsychology: 4; 385–415, 1987a.

De Haan EHF, Young AW, Newcombe F: Faces interfere with name classification in a prosopagnosic patient. Cortex: 4; 385–415, 1987b.

De Renzi E: Current issues in prosopagnosia. In Ellis H, Jeeves MA, Newcombe F, Young AW (Eds), Aspects of Face Processing. Dordrecht: Martinus Nijhoff, 1986.

De Renzi E, Perani D, Cartesimo GA, Silveri MC: Prosopagnosia can be confined to damage to the right hemisphere – an MRI and PET study and review of the literature. Neuropsychologia: 32; 893–902, 1994.

Desimone R, Gross CG: Visual areas in the temporal cortex of the macaque. Brain Research: 178; 363–380, 1979.

Diamond R, Carey S: Why faces are not special: An effect of expertise. Journal of Experimental Psychology: General: 115; 107–117, 1986.

Dixon M, Bub D, Arguin M: Semantic and visual determinants of face recognition in a prosopagnosia patient. Journal of Cognitive Neuroscience: 10(3); 362–376, 1998.

Donnelly N, Davidoff J: The mental representation of faces and houses: issues concerning parts and wholes. Visual Cognition: 6; 320–343, 1999.

Eimer M: Attention modulation of event-related brain potentials sensitive to faces. Cognitive Neuropsychology: 17(1–3); 103–116, 2000.

Ellis HD, Jeeves MA, Newcombe F, Young AW (Eds): Aspects of Face Processing. Dordrecht: Martinus Nijhoff, 1986.

Ellis HD, Shepherd JW, Davies GM: Identification of familiar and unfamiliar faces from internal and external features: source implication for theories of face recognition. Perception: 8; 431–439, 1979.

Etcoff N, Freeman R, Cave KR: Can we lose memories of faces? Content specificity and awareness in a prosopagnosic. Journal of Cognitive Neuroscience: 3(1); 25–41, 1991.

Farah MJ: Visual Agnosia: Disorders of Object Recognition and What They Tell Us About Normal Vision. Cambridge, MA: MIT Press, 1990.

Farah MJ: Patterns of co-occurrence among the associative agnosias: implications for visual object recognition. Cognitive Neuropsychology: 8(1); 1–19, 1991.

Farah MJ: Dissociable systems for visual recognition: a cognitive neuropsychology approach. In Kosslyn SM, Osherson D (Eds), Invitation to Cognitive Science. Cambridge, MA: MIT Press, pp. 101–120, 1994a.

Farah MJ: Perception and awareness after brain damage. Current Opinion in Neurobiology: 4; 177–182, 1994b.

Farah MJ: relations among the agnosias. In Humphreys GW (Ed), Case studies in the Neuropsychology of Vision Hove, East Sussex: Psychology Press, pp. 181–200, 1999.

Farah MJ, Levinson KL, Klein KL: Face perception and within-category discrimination in prosopagnosia. Neuropsychologia: 33; 661–674, 1995a.

Farah MJ, O'Reilly RC, Vecera SP: Dissociated overt and covert recognition as an emergent property of a lesioned neural network. Psychological Review: 100; 571–588, 1993.

Farah MJ, Rabinowitz C, Quinn GE, Liu GT: Early commitment of neural substrates for face recognition. Cognitive Neuropsychology: 17(1–3); 117–123, 2000.

Farah MJ, Wilson KD, Drain HM, Tanaka JR: The inverted face inversion effect in prosopagnosia: evidence for mandatory, face-specific perceptual mechanisms. Vision Research: 35; 2089–2093, 1995b.

Feinberg TE, Schindler RJ, Ochoa E, Kwan PC, Farah MJ: Associative visual agnosia and alexia without prosopagnosia. Cortex: 30; 395–412, 1994.

Garner WR: The processing of information and structure. Hillsdale, NJ: Erlbaum, 1974.

Gauthier I: What constrains the organization of the ventral temporal cortex? Trends in Cognitive Sciences: 4; 1–2, 2000.

Gauthier I, Anderson AW, Tarr M, Skudlarski P, Gore JC: Levels of categorization in visual object studied with functional MRI. Current Biology: 7; 645–651, 1997.

Gauthier I, Behrmann M, Tarr MJ: Can face recognition really be dissociated from object recognition? Journal of Cognitive Neuroscience: 11, 4; 349–370, 1999a.

Gauthier I, Skudlarski P, Gore JC, Anderson AW: Expertise for cars and birds recruits brain areas involved in face recognition. Nature Neuroscience: 3(2); 191–197, 2000a.

Gauthier I, Tarr MJ, Moylan J, Anderson AW, Gore JC: Does visual subordinate-level categorization engage the functionally defined fusiform face area? Cognitive Neuropsychology: 17(1–3); 143–164, 2000b.

Gauthier I, Tarr MJ, Skudlarski P, Gore JC: Activation of the middle fusiform 'face area' increases with expertise in recognizing novel objects. Nature Neuroscience: 2(6); 568–573, 1999b.

George N, Evans J, Fiori N, Davidoff J, Renault B: Brain events related to normal and moderately scrambled faces. Cognitive Brain Research: 4; 65–76, 1996.

Grady CL, McIntosh AR, Horwitz B, Maisog JM, Ungerleider LG, Mentis MJ, Pietrini P, Schapiro MB, Haxby JV: Age-related reductions in human recognition memory due to impaired encoding. Science: 269; 218–222, 1995.

Greve KW, Bauer RN: Implicit learning of new faces in prosopagnosia: an application of the mere-exposure paradigm. Neuropsychologia: 28; 1035–1041, 1990.

Gross CG, Rocha-Miranda CE, Bender DB: Visual properties of neurons in inferotemporal cortex of the macaque. Journal of Neurophysiology: 35; 96–111, 1972.

Gross C, Sergent J: Face recognition. Current Opinion in Neurobiology: 2; 156–161, 1992.

Harmon LD: The recognition of faces. Scientific American: 227; 71–82, 1973.

Hasselmo ME, Rolls ET, Baylis GC: The role of expression and identity in the face-selective responses of neurons in the temporal visual cortex. Behavioral Brain Research: 32; 203–218, 1989.

Haxby JV, Grady CL, Horwitz B, Ungerleider LG, Mishkin M, Carson RE, Herscovitch P, Schapiro MB, Rapoport SI: Dissociation of object and spatial visual processing pathways in human extrastriate cortex. Proceedings of the National Academy of Sciences of the United States of America: 88; 1621–1625, 1991.

Haxby JV, Horwitz B, Ungerleider LG, Maisog JM, Pietrini P, Grady CL: The functional organization of human extrastriate cortex; a PET rCBF study of selective attention to faces and locations. Journal of Neuroscience: 14; 6336–6353, 1994.

Haxby JV, Ungerleider LG, Clark V, Schouten JL, Hoffman EA, Martin A: The effect on face inversion on activity in human neural systems for face and object perception. Neuron: 22; 189–199, 1999.

Haxby JV, Ungerleider LG, Horwitz B, Maisog JM, Rapoport SI, Grady CL: Face encoding and recognition in the human brain. Neurobiology: 93; 922–927, 1996.

Hècaen H, Angelergues R: Agnosia for faces (prosopagnosia). Archives of Neurology: 7; 92–100, 1962.

Hècaen H, Goldblum MC, Masure M, Ramier AM: Une novelle observation d'agnmosie d'object: deficit l'association ou de la categorisation, specifique de la modalité visuelle. Neuropsychologia: 12; 447–464, 1974.

Heywood CA, Cowey A: The role of face-cell area in the discrimination and recognition of faces by monkeys. Philosophical Transactions of the Royal Society of London, Series B: Biological Sciences: 335; 31–38, 1992.

Hezewijk R, De Haan EHF: The symbolic brain or invisible hand. Behavioral and Brain Sciences: 17; 85–86, 1994.

Hoffman EA, Haxby JV: Distinct representations of eye gaze and identity in the distributed human neural system for face perception. Nature Neuroscience: 3(1); 80–84, 2000.

Humphrey GK, Goodale MA, Jakobson LS, Servos P: The role of surface information in object recognition: studies of a visual form agnosic and normal subjects. Perception: 23; 1457–1481, 1994.

Humphreys GW, Riddoch MJ: Neuropsychological disorders of visual object recognition and naming. In Behrmann M (Ed), Disorders of Visual Behavior, Handbook of Neuropsychology, 2nd ed, vol 4. Amsterdam, Elsevier, pp. 000–000, 2001.

Ishai A, Ungerleider LG, Martin A, Haxby JV: The representation of objects in the human occipital and temporal cortex. Journal of Cognitive Neuroscience: 12; 35–51, 2000.

Ishai A, Ungerleider LG, Martin A, Schouten JL, Haxby JV: Distributed representations of objects in the human ventral visual pathway. Proceedings of the National Academy of Sciences of the United States of America: 96(16); 9379–9384, 1999.

Jacobs RA: Nature, nurture and the development of functional specializations: a computational approach. Psychonomic Bulletin and Review: 4(3); 299–309, 1997.

Jackson JH: On the Nature of the Duality of the Brain. Circular 1. Medical Press, p. 19, 1874.

Jackson JH: On the nature of the duality of the brain. Brain: 38; 80–103, 1915.

Jeffreys DA: The influence of stimulus orientation on the vertex positive scalp potential evoked by faces. Experimental Brain Research: 96; 163–172, 1993.

Jeffreys DA: Evoked potential studies of face and object processing. Visual Cognition: 3; 1–47, 1996.

Johnson MH, de Haan M: Developing cortical specialization for visual–cognitve function: The case of face recognition. In: McClelland JL, Siegler RS (Eds), Mechanisms of Cognitive Development: Behavioral and Neural Perspectives. Mahwah, NJ: Erlbaum, 2001.

Johnson MH, Dziurawiec S, Ellis H, Morton J: Newborns' preferential tracking of face-like stimuli and subsequent decline. Cognition: 40; 1–19, 1991.

Kanwisher N: Domain specificity in face perception. Nature Neuroscience: 3(8); 759–763, 2000.

Kanwisher N, Chun MM, McDermott J, Ledden PJ: Functional imaging of human visual recognition. Cognitive Brain Research: 5; 55–67, 1996.

Kanwisher N, Moscovitch M: The cognitive neuroscience of face processing: an introduction. Cognitive Neuropsychology: 17(1–3); 112, 2000.

Kanwisher N, Woods RP, Iacoboni M, Mazziotta JC: A locus in human extrastriate cortex for visual shape analysis. Journal of Cognitive Neuroscience: 9(1); 133–142, 1997.

Köhler S, Moscovitch M: Unconscious visual processing in neuropsychological syndromes: a survey of the literature and evaluation of models of consciousness. In Rugg M (Ed), Cognitive Neuroscience. Cambridge, MA: MIT Press, pp. 305–373, 1997.

Koriat A, Norman J: Why is word recognition impaired by disorientation while the identification of single letters is not? Journal of Experimental Psychology: Human Perception and Performance: 15(1); 153–163, 1988.

Landis T, Cummings JL, Christen L, Bogen JI, Imhof H: Are unilateral right posterior cerebral lesions sufficient to cause prosopagnosia? Clinical and radiological findings in six additional patients. Cortex: 22; 243–252, 1986.

Levin DT: Classifying faces by race: The structure of face categories. Journal of Experimental Psychology: Learning, Memory and Cognition: 22; 1364–1382, 1996.

Levy-Agresti J, Sperry RW: Differential perceptual capacities in major and minor hemispheres. Proceedings of the National Academy of Sciences of the United States of America: 61; 1151, 1968.

Liu J, Higuchi M, Marantz A, Kanwisher N: The selectivity of the occipitotemporal M170 for faces. NeuroReport: 2; 337–341, 2000.

Marotta JJ, McKeeff T, Behrmann M: The effects of inversion and rotation on face processing in prosopagnosia. Submitted for publication, 2001.

Maurer D, Young R: Newborns' following of natural and distorted arrangements of facial features. Infant Behavior and Development: 6; 127–131, 1983.

McCarthy R, Warrington EK: Visual associative agnosia: a clinico-anatomical study of a single case. Journal of Neurology, Neurosurgery and Psychiatry: 49; 1233–1240, 1986.

McCarthy R, Warrington EK: Cognitive Neuropsychology. London: Academic Press, 1990.

McNeil M, Warrington EK: Prosopagnosia: a face-specific disorder. Quarterly Journal of Experimental Psychology: 46A; 1–10, 1993.

Meadows JC: The anatomical basis of prosopagnosia. Journal of Neurology, Neurosurgery, and Psychiatry: 37; 489–501, 1974.

Michel F, Poncet M, Signoret J-L: Les lesions responsables de la prosopagnosie sont-elles toujours bilatèrales. Revue Neurologique: 146; 764–770, 1989.

Mondloch CJ, Lewis TL, Budreau DR, Maurer D, Dannemiller JL, Stephens BR, Kleiner-Gathercoal KA: Face perception during early infancy. Psychological Science: 10(5); 419–422, 1999.

Moscovitch M: Information processing and cerebral hemispheres. In Gazzaniga MS (Ed), Handbook of Behavioral Neurobiology, vol 2. New York: Plenum Press, pp. 379–446, 1979.

Moscovitch M: Memory and working-with-memory: a component process model based on modules and central systems. Journal of Cognitive Neuroscience: 4; 257–267, 1992.

Moscovitch M, Moscovitch D: Super face-inversion effects for isolated internal or external features, and for fractured faces. Cognitive Neuropsychology: 17(1–3); 201–220, 2000.

Moscovitch M, Radzins M: Backward masking of lateralized faces by noise, pattern, and spatial frequency. Brain and Cognition: 6; 72–90, 1987.

Moscovitch M, Winocur G, Behrmann M: What is special about face recognition? Nineteen experiments on a person with visual object agnosia and dyslexia but normal face recognition. Journal of Cognitive Neuroscience: 9(5); 555–604, 1997.

Murray JE, Yong E, Rhodes G: Revisiting the perception of upside-down faces. Psychological Science: 11; 492–496, 2000.

Nachson I: On the modularity of face recognition: the riddle of domain specificity. Journal of Clinical and Experimental Neuropsychology: 17; 256–275, 1995.

Newcombe F, Young AW, De Haan EHF: Prosopagnosia and object agnosia without covert recognition. Neuropsychologia: 27; 179–191, 1989.

Pascalis O, de Schonen S, Morton J, Deruelle C, Frabre-Grent M: Mother's face recognition by neonates: a replication and an extension. Infant Behavior and Development: 18; 79–95, 1995.

Perrett DI, Oram MW, Harries MH, Bevan R, Hietanen JK, Benson PJ, Thomas S: Viewer-centered and object-centred coding of heads in the macaque temporal cortex. Experimental Brain Research: 86; 159–173, 1991.

Perrett DI, Rolls ET, Caan W: Visual neurons responsive to faces in the monkey temporal cortex. Experimental Brain Research: 47; 329–342, 1982.

Puce A, Allison T, Gore JC, McCarthy G: Face-sensitive regions in human extrastriate cortex studied by functional MRI. Journal of Neurophysiology: 74(3); 1192–1199, 1995.

Renault B, Signoret JL, De Bruille B, Breton F, Bolgert F: Brain potentials reveal covert facial recognition in prosopagnosia. Neuropsychologia: 27; 905–912, 1989.

Rhodes G: Configural coding, expertise and the right hemisphere advantage for face recognition. Brain and Cognition: 22; 19–41, 1993.

Rhodes G: Looking at faces: First-order and second-order features as determinates of facial appearance. Perception: 17; 43–63, 1988.

Rhodes G, Brake S, Atkinson AP: What's lost in inverted faces? Cognition: 47; 25–57, 1993.

Rhodes G, Brennan S, Carey S: Identification and ratings of caricatures: implications for mental representation of faces. Cognitive Psychology: 19; 473–497, 1987.

Rhodes G, Carey S, Byatt G, Proffitt F: Coding spatial variation in faces and simple shapes: A test of two models. Vision Research: 15–16; 2307–2321, 1998.

Rizzo M, Hurtig R, Damasio AR: The role of scanpaths in facial recognition and learning. Annals of Neurology: 22; 41–45, 1987.

Rodman HR, Scaliadhe SP, Gross CG: Response properties of neurons in temporal cortical areas of infant monkeys. Journal of Neurophysiology: 70; 1115–1136, 1993.

Rolls ET, Baylis GC: Size and contrast have only small effects on the responses to faces of neurons in the cortex of the superior temporal sulcus of the monkey. Experimental Brain Research: 65; 38–48, 1986.

Rossion B, Dricot L, Devolder A, Bodart J-M, Crommelinck M, de Gelder B, Zoontjes R: Hemispheric asymmetries for whole-based and part-based face processing in the human brain. Journal of Cognitive Neuroscience: 12; 793–802, 2000.

Rumiati RI, Humphreys GW: Visual object agnosia without alexia or prosopagnosia: Arguments for separate knowledge stores. Visual Cognition: 4(12); 207–218, 1997.

Rumiati RI, Humphreys GW, Riddoch MJ, Bateman A: Visual object agnosia without prosopagnosia or alexia: evidence for hierarchical theories of visual recognition. Visual Cognition: 1(2/3); 181–225, 1994.

Schacter DL, McAndrews MP, Moscovitch M: Dissociations between implicit and explicit knowledge in neuropsychological syndromes. In Weiskrantz L (Ed), Thought Without Language. Oxford: Oxford University Press, pp. 242–278, 1988.

Sergent J: An investigation into component and configurational processes underlying face perception. British Journal of Psychology: 75; 221–242, 1984.

Sergent J: Brain-imaging studies of cognitive functions. Trends in Neurosciences: 17(6); 221–227, 1994.

Sergent J, Hellige JB: Role of input factors in visual-field asymmetries. Brain and Cognition: 5; 174–179, 1986.

Sergent J, Ohta S, MacDonald B: Functional neuroanatomy of face and object processing. Brain: 115; 15–36, 1992.

Sergent J, Poncet M: From covert to overt recognition of faces in a prosopagnosia patient. Brain: 113; 989–1094, 1990.

Sergent J, Signoret J-L: Functional and anatomical decomposition of face processing; evidence from prosopagnosia and PET study of normal subjects. Philosophical Transactions of the Royal Society of London, Series B: Biological Sciences: 335; 55–62, 1992a.

Sergent J, Signoret JL: Implicit access to knowledge derived from unrecognized faces in prosopagnosia. Cerebral Cortex: 2; 389–400, 1992b.

Suzuki S, Peterson MA, Moscovitch M, Behrmann M: Identification of one-part and two-part volumetric objects: selective deficits in encoding spatial arrangements of parts in visual object agnosia. Submitted for publication, 2001.

Takane Y, Sergent J: Multidimensional scaling models for reaction times and same–different judgements. Psychometrika: 48; 393–423, 1983.

Tanaka K: Neuronal mechanisms of object recognition. Science: 262; 685–688, 1993.

Tanaka J, Curran T: A neural basis for expert object recognition. Psychological Science, in press, 2001.

Tanaka JW, Farah MJ: Parts and wholes in face recognition. Quarterly Journal of Experimental Psychology: 46A; 225–245, 1993.

Tarr ML, Gauthier I: FFA: A flexible fusiform area for subordinate-level processing automatized by experience. Nature Neuroscience: 3(8); 764–769, 2000.

Tong F, Nakayama K, Moscovitch M, Weinrib O, Kanwisher N: Response properties of human fusiform face area. Cognitive Neuropsychology: 17(1–3); 257–279, 2000.

Tranel D, Damasio A: Evidence for covert recognition of faces in global amnesia. Journal of Clinical and Experimental Neuropsychology: 9; 15, 1987.

Tranel D, Damasio AR: Non-conscious face recognition in patients with face agnosia. Behavioral Brain Research: 30; 235–249, 1988.

Valentine T: A unified account of the effects of distinctiveness, inversion, and race in face recognition. The Quarterly Journal of Experimental Psychology: 43A; 161–204, 1991.

Valenza E, Simion F, Cassia VM, Umilta C: Face preference at birth. Journal of Experimental Psychology: Human Perception and Performance: 22; 892–903, 1996.

Wallace M, Farah MJ: Savings in relearning as evidence for covert recognition in prosopagnosia. Journal of Cognitive Neuroscience: 4; 150–154, 1992.

Warrington EK, McCarthy R: Categories of knowledge: Further fractionations and an attempted integration. Brain: 110; 1273–1296, 1987.

Whiteley AM, Warrington EK: Prosopagnosia: a clinical, psychological, and anatomical study of three patients. Journal of Neurology, Neurosurgery and Psychiatry: 40; 395–403, 1977.

Wright AA, Roberts WA: Monkey and human face perception: inversion effect for human faces but not for monkey faces or scenes. Journal of Cognitive Neuroscience: 8(3); 278–290, 1996.

Yamane S, Kaji S, Kawano K: What facial features activate face neurons in the inferotemporal cortex of the monkey? Experimental Brain Research: 73; 209–214, 1988.

Yin RK: Looking at upside-down faces. Journal of Experimental Psychology: 81; 141–145, 1969.

Yin RK: Face recognition by brain-injured patients: A dissociable ability? Neuropsychologia: 8; 395–402, 1970.

Young AW: Conscious and nonconscious recognition of familiar faces. In Umiltà C, Moscovitch M (Eds), Attention and Performance XV: Conscious and Unconscious Information Processing. Cambridge, MA: MIT Press/Bradford Books, pp. 153–178, 1994.

Young AW, Hellawell D, de Haan EHF: Cross-domain semantic priming in normal subjects and a prosopagnosic patient. Quarterly Journal of Experimental Psychology: 40A; 561–580, 1988.

Young AW, Hellawell D, Hay DC: Configurational information in face perception. Perception: 16; 747–759, 1987.

Handbook of Neuropsychology, 2nd Edition, Vol. 4
M. Behrmann (Ed)

CHAPTER 10

Peripheral dyslexias

H. Branch Coslett [a,c,*] and Eleanor M. Saffran [a,b,c]

[a] *Department of Neurology, Temple University School of Medicine, Temple University Hospital, 3401 N. Broad St., Philadelphia, PA 19140, USA*
[b] *Department of Communication Sciences, Temple University, Temple University Hospital, 3401 N. Broad St., Philadelphia, PA 19140, USA*
[c] *Moss Research Institute, Moss Rehabilitation Hospital, 12th St. and Tabor Rd., Philadephia, PA 19141, USA*

Introduction

Children acquire spoken language in the natural course of events, but learning to read and write usually requires explicit instruction. For this reason, it has been suggested that there are no neural mechanisms that are specifically or exclusively dedicated to written language, and that people may differ in the manner in which they acquire these abilities (Farah, 1990). Nevertheless, like spoken language, these mechanisms also usually depend on left hemisphere structures, and are disrupted by damage to this region of the brain. As these impairments involve the breakdown of skills that had previously been mastered, they are termed acquired (as opposed to developmental) dyslexias and dysgraphias. The disturbances take a variety of forms that reflect the breakdown of specific aspects of the reading and/or writing process. In this chapter, we are concerned with 'peripheral' as opposed to 'central' dyslexias — that is, disorders that affect reading prior to contact with stored lexical information or mechanisms of grapheme-to-phoneme translation.

* Corresponding author. Present address: University of Pennsylvania School of Medicine, 3400 Spruce St., Philadelphia, PA 19140, USA. E-mail: hbc@mail.med.upenn.edu

Reading mechanisms and the classification of reading disorders

Under normal circumstances, written word recognition occurs so rapidly that one might conclude that the word is identified as a unit, much as we identify an object from its visual form. But the evidence does not support such a model. It appears that the letters must first be identified as alphabetic symbols. It has been shown that presenting words in a format that is not familiar to the reader — for example, by alternating the case of the letters (e.g. wOrD) — has minimal effects on reading speed (e.g. McClelland and Rumelhart, 1981). This finding suggests that the processing of written words includes a stage of letter identification, in which the graphic form (whether printed or written) is transformed into a string of alphabetic characters (W-O-R-D), sometimes referred to as 'abstract letter identities'. In addition, the positions of the letters must be maintained. How this is accomplished has yet to be determined. Possibilities include associating the letter in position one to the letter in position two, and so on; binding each letter to a frame that specifies letter position; or labeling each letter with its position in the word. Next, the letter string is identified as a word by matching it to a stored entry in an orthographic lexicon, which ultimately yields access to the word's meaning along with its syntactic properties and its phonological form. This operation is similar to looking up a word in a dictionary. Alternatively, according to some models, the letter string can be converted directly into phonological form through a set of learned correspondences between orthography and phonology; the meaning of the word can then be accessed via its phonological form.

To recognize a word, then, the ordered sequence of abstract letter units must either access entries in the internal orthographic lexicon, or be converted directly into phonological form. There is evidence that both processes involve parallel processing of the letter string; that is, the letters are not processed sequentially, but rather the string (or a significant portion of it, if it is lengthy) is referred to the set of stored lexical entries and/or the mechanisms for phonological conversion. This mode of operation requires rapid parallel processing of the letters, as well as maintenance of the letters in the sequence in which they are presented. These operations can be disrupted by brain damage, in several different ways, a number of which are discussed below.

Neglect dyslexia

Parietal lobe lesions can result in a deficit that involves neglect of stimuli on the side of space contralateral to the lesion, a disorder referred to as hemispatial neglect (see Chapter 4). In most cases, this disturbance arises with damage to the right parietal lobe; therefore, attention to the left side of space is most often affected. The severity of neglect is generally greater when there are stimuli on the right as well as on the left; attention is drawn to the right-sided stimuli, at the expense of those on the left, a phenomenon known as 'extinction'. Typical clinical manifestations include bumping into objects on the left, failure to dress the left side of the body, drawing objects that are incomplete on the left, and reading problems that involve neglect of the left portions of words, i.e. 'neglect dyslexia'.

With respect to neglect dyslexia, it has been found that such patients are more likely to ignore letters in non-words (e.g. the first two letters in bruggle) than letters in real words (compare with snuggle). This suggests that the problem does not reflect a total failure to process letter information but rather an attentional impairment that affects conscious recognition of the letters (e.g. Behrmann, Moscovitch, Black and Mozer, 1990; Sieroff, Pollatsek and Posner, 1988). Performance often improves when words are presented vertically or spelled aloud. In addition, there is evidence that semantic information can be processed in neglect dyslexia, and that the ability to read words aloud improves when oral reading follows a semantic task (Làdavas, Shallice and Zanella, 1997).

Cases of neglect dyslexia have also been reported in patients with left hemisphere lesions (Caramazza and Hills, 1990; Greenwald and Berndt, 1999). In these patients, the deficiency involves the right sides of words. Here, visual neglect is usually confined to words, and is not ameliorated by presenting words vertically or spelling them aloud. This disorder has therefore been termed a 'positional dyslexia', whereas the right hemisphere deficit has been termed a 'spatial neglect dyslexia' (Ellis, Young and Flude, 1993). Greenwald and Berndt (1999) have proposed that positional dyslexia arises in encoding the order of abstract letter identities prior to lexical access, that is, in an 'ordinal graphemic code'. Neglect dyslexia is discussed in substantially greater detail in Chapter 4.

Attentional dyslexia

Attentional dyslexia is a disorder characterized by at least relatively preserved reading of single words but impaired reading of words in the context of other words or letters. This infrequently described disorder was first reported by Shallice and Warrington (1977) who reported two patients with brain tumors involving (at least) the left parietal lobe. Both patients exhibited relatively good performance with single letters or words but were significantly impaired in the recognition of the same stimuli when presented as part of an array. For example, both patients read single letters accurately but made significantly more errors naming letters when presented as part of 3×3 or 5×5 arrays. Similarly, both patients correctly read greater than 90% of single words, but read only approximately 80% of words when presented in the context of three additional words. Although not fully investigated, it is worth noting that the patients were also impaired in recognizing line drawings and silhouettes when presented in an array.

Two additional observations from these patients warrant attention. First, Shallice and Warrington (1977) demonstrated that for both patients naming of single black letters was adversely affected by the simultaneous presentation of red flanking stimuli and that flanking letters were more disruptive than numbers. For example, both subjects were more likely to correctly name the black (middle) letter when presented '37L82' as compared to 'ajGyr'. Second, the investigators examined the errors produced in the tasks in which patients were asked to report letters and words in rows of two to four items. They found different error patterns with letters and words. Whereas both patients tended to err in the letter report task by naming letters that appeared in a different location in the array, patients often named words that were not present in the array. Interestingly, many of these errors were interpretable as letter transpositions between words. This phenomenon was extensively investigated by Saffran and Coslett, 1996 (see also Shallice and McGill, 1977) and will be discussed in more detail below.

Citing the differential effects of letter versus number flankers as well as the absence of findings suggesting a deficit in response selection, these investigators attributed the disorder to a "failure of transmission of information from a non-semantic perceptual stage to a semantic processing stage" (p. 39; but see Shallice, 1988). We will return to alternative accounts of these data below.

A second report of attentional dyslexia was provided by Warrington, Cipolotti and McNeil (1993). These investigators reported a patient, BAL, who suffered a left fronto-parietal intracerebral hemorrhage. BAL was able to read single words, but exhibited a substantial impairment in the reading of letters and words in an array. Like the patients reported by Shallice and Warrington (1977), BAL exhibited no evidence of visual disorientation and was able to identify a target letter in an array of 'X's or 'O's. He was impaired, however, in the naming of letters or words when these stimuli were flanked by other members of the same stimulus category. He differed from Shallice and Warrington's patients, however, in that naming of line drawings was not adversely affected by flanking line drawings.

Warrington et al. (1993) explored the effect of a number of additional manipulations. They found, for example, that the naming of individual letters was not significantly influenced by flanking words, nor was the naming of words impacted by flanking letters. Finally, the investigators demonstrated that the naming of individual letters was not significantly influenced by the case of the flanking letters (e.g. ULH vs. uLh).

In light of the stimulus class effects of flanking stimuli, Warrington et al. (1993) attributed the performance of BAL as well as Shallice and Warrington's patients to an impairment in the 'filter' mechanism controlling the transition from a parallel to a serial stage of lexical processing. These investigators differ from Shallice (1988) in that they consider the deficit to be post lexical, arising "after letters and words are processed as units" (p. 883).

Price and Humphreys (1993) reported a patient with alexia without agraphia and anomia, PR, who also exhibited an impairment in the naming of stimuli in an array. PR named 94% of single letters and 93% of three letter words but was able to name only 48% of letters within 3-letter arrays. Similarly, she was able to name 75% of pictures presented individually, but only 25% of the same pictures when the pictures were presented in an array of three. Interestingly, she performed relatively well on tests requiring access to semantics from three item picture arrays; for example, she scored 45/52 correct on the Pyramids and Palm Trees test (Howard and Patterson, 1992). The investigators attributed her impairment in naming items in an array to a combination of a deficit in access from semantics to phonology and an impairment in the selective allocation of attention to elements in the array (see also Buxbaum and Coslett, 1998).

More recently, Saffran and Coslett (1996) reported a patient, NY, with biopsy-proven Alzheimer's disease which appeared to selectively involve posterior cortical regions (cf. Coslett, Stark, Rajaram et al. 1995; Saffran, Fitzpatrick-DeSalme and Coslett, 1990) who exhibited attentional dyslexia. NY scored within the normal range on verbal subtests of the WAIS-R, but was unable to perform any of the Performance subtests. He performed normally on the Boston Naming Test. NY performed quite poorly on a variety of experimental tasks assessing visuo-spatial processing and visual attention. Despite his visuo-perceptual deficits, however, NY's reading of single words was essentially normal. He read 96% of 200 words presented for 100 ms (unmasked). Like previously reported patients with this disorder, NY exhibited a substantial decline in performance when asked to read two words presented simultaneously. He read both words correctly on only 50% of 385 trials with a 250-ms stimulus exposure. Most errors were omissions of one word. Of greatest interest, however, was the fact that NY produced a substantial number of 'blend' errors in which letters from the two words were combined to generate a response that was not present in the display. For example, when shown *flip shot*, NY responded 'ship'. Like the blend errors produced by normal subjects with brief stimulus presentation (Shallice and McGill, 1977), NY's blend errors were characterized by the preservation of letter position information; thus, in the preceding example, the letters in the blend response ('ship') retained the same serial position in the incorrect response. NY produced significantly more blend errors than five controls whose overall level of performance had been matched to NY's by virtue of brief stimulus exposure (range 83–17 ms). A subsequent experiment demonstrated that for NY, but not controls, blend errors were encountered significantly less often when the target words differed in case (*desk FEAR*).

Like Shallice, 1988 (see also McClellend and Mozer, 1986; Mozer, 1991), we consider the central deficit in attentional dyslexia to be an impairment in the control of a filtering mechanism that normally serves to suppress input from unattended words or letters in the display. More specifically, we suggest that as a consequence of the patient's inability to effectively deploy the 'spotlight' of attention to a particular region of interest (e.g. a single word or a single letter), multiple stimuli fall within the attentional spotlight. As on many accounts, visual attention serves to integrate visual feature information, impaired modulation of the spotlight of attention would be expected to generate word blends and other errors reflecting the incorrect concatenation of letters. We note that the frequency effects exhibited by NY and other subjects with attentional dyslexia are also consistent with this account; partial letter information (e.g. 'ta-') is more likely to activate a high (e.g. 'table') as compared to a low frequency word (e.g. 'talon').

We have previously argued that, at least for NY, loss of location information also contributes to NY's reading deficit. Several lines of evidence support such a conclusion. First, NY was impaired relative to controls both with respect to accuracy and RT on a task in which he was required to indicate if a line was inside or outside a circle. Second, NY exhibited a clear tendency to omit one member of a double letter pair (e.g. *reed* → 'red'). This phenomenon, which has been demonstrated in normals (Mozer, 1991), has been attributed to the loss of location information that normally helps to differentiate two tokens of the same object (Mozer, 1989; cf. Kanwisher, 1991). Finally, we note in this context that the well-documented observation that the blend errors of normals as well as attentional dyslexics preserve letter position is not inconsistent with the claim that impaired location information contributes to attentional dyslexia. We suggest that migration or blend errors reflect a failure to link words or letters to a location in space, whereas the letter position constraint reflects the properties of the word processing system. The latter, which is assumed to be at least relatively intact in patients with attentional dyslexia, specifies letter location with respect to the word form rather than space.

This account of attentional dyslexia is consistent with data from NY as well as the patients reported by Shallice and Warrington (1977) and Price and Humphreys (1993). It does not, however, provide a complete account of the impairment demonstrated by BAL (Warrington et al., 1993), whose deficit was restricted to verbal materials and was not influenced by physical properties of the stimuli (e.g. color, case). Whether the difference in performance exhibited by these patients reflects different loci of impairment, as suggested by Warrington et al. (1993), or is attributable to differences between the patients with respect to severity or site of brain dysfunction is not clear.

Pure alexia (alexia without agraphia; letter-by-letter reading)

This disorder is among the most common of the peripheral reading disturbances. It is associated with a left hemisphere lesion affecting left occipital cortex (responsible for the analysis of visual stimuli

TABLE 1

Speed of oral reading as a function of word length (in s)

Patient	No. of letters				
	3	4	5	6	7
JG	9	13	17	27	28
TL	2	3	3	5	4
JC	2	6	17	16	30
AF	31	83	...	...	...
JWC	16	21	26	26	60

on the right side of space) and/or the structures (left lateral geniculate nucleus of the thalamus; white matter, including callosal fibers from the intact right visual cortex) that provide input to this region of the brain. It is likely that the lesion blocks direct visual input to the mechanisms that process printed words in the left hemisphere. Some of these patients seem to be unable to read at all, while others do so slowly and laboriously by means of a process that involves serial letter identification (termed 'letter-by-letter' reading). At first, letter-by-letter readers often pronounce the letter names aloud; in some cases, they misidentify letters, usually on the basis of visual similarity, as in the case of N → M; see Patterson and Kay, 1982, for relevant data). Later on, the serial reading process is apparent in the monotonic relationship between word length and reading time. Although normal readers typically take no longer to read six-letter than three-letter words, these patients show an increase in reading time as word length increases (see Table 1 for an example). Their reading is also abnormally slow.

It was long thought that patients with pure alexia were unable to read, except letter-by-letter. There is now evidence that some of them do retain the ability to recognize letter strings, although this does not guarantee that they will be able to read aloud. Several different paradigms have demonstrated the preservation of word recognition. Some of the patients demonstrate a word superiority effect (e.g. Bowers, Bub and Arguin, 1996; Bub, Black and Howell, 1989; Friedman and Hadley, 1992; Reuter-Lorenz and Brunn, 1990); this effect reflects superior letter recognition when the letter is part of a word (e.g. the R in WORD than when it occurs in a string of unrelated letters (e.g. WKRD). Second, some of them have been able to perform lexical decision tasks (determining whether a letter string constitutes a real word or not) and semantic categorization tasks (indicating whether or not a word belongs to a category, such as foods or animals) at above chance levels, when words are presented too rapidly to support letter-by-letter reading (e.g. Coslett and Saffran, 1989a; Shallice and Saffran, 1986). Brevity of presentation is critical, in that longer exposure to the letter string seems to engage the letter-by-letter strategy, which appears to interfere with the ability to perform the covert reading task (Coslett and Saffran, 1989a; Coslett, Saffran, Greenbaum and Schwartz, 1993). In fact, the patient may show better performance on lexical decision at shorter (e.g. 250 ms) than at longer presentations (e.g. 2 s) that engage the letter-by-letter strategy, but do not allow it to proceed to completion (Coslett and Saffran, 1989a). A compelling example comes from the patient reported by Shallice and Saffran (1986), who was given two seconds to scan the card containing the stimulus. The patient did not take advantage of the full inspection time when he was performing lexical decision and categorization tasks; instead, he glanced at the card briefly and looked away, perhaps to avoid letter-by-letter reading. The capacity for covert reading has also been demonstrated in two pure alexics who were completely unable to employ the letter-by-letter reading strategy (Coslett and Saffran, 1989b, 1992). These patients appeared to recognize words, but were rarely able to report them, although they sometimes generated descriptions that were related to the word's meaning (for example, cookies → 'candy, a cake' (Coslett and Saffran, 1992)). In some cases, patients have shown some recovery of oral reading over time, although this capacity appears to be limited to concrete words (Buxbaum and Coslett, 1996; Coslett and Saffran, 1989a).

The mechanisms that underlie 'implicit' or 'covert' reading remain controversial. Dejerine (1892), who provided the first description of pure alexia, suggested that the analysis of visual input in these patients is performed by the right hemisphere, as a result of the damage to the visual cortex on the left. (It should be noted, however, that not all lesions to the left visual cortex give rise to alexia. A critical feature that supports continued left hemisphere processing is the preservation of callosal input from the visual processing on the right.) One possible account is that covert reading reflects printed word recognition on the part of the right hemisphere, which is unable either to articulate the word or (in most cases) to adequately communicate its identity to the language area of the left hemisphere (e.g. Coslett and Saffran, 1989a, 1994; Saffran and Coslett, 1998). On this account, letter-by-letter reading is carried out by the left hemisphere using letter information transferred serially and inefficiently from the right. Furthermore, the account assumes that when the letter-by-letter strategy is implemented, it may be difficult for the patient to attend to the products of word processing in the right hemisphere. Consequently, performance on lexical decision and categorization tasks declines (Coslett and Saffran, 1989a; Coslett, Schwartz, Goldberg et al., 1993).

One finding that supports the right hemisphere account is the effect of word type in patients who show partial recovery; there is evidence that the right hemisphere lexicon may be biased towards concrete words. Such a bias has been observed in a left hemispherectomy patient (Patterson, Vargha-Khadem and Polkey, 1989), in a patient whose entire left hemisphere had been damaged by stroke (Rapscak, Beeson and Rubens, 1991), and in words flashed to the left visual field (hence right hemisphere) of a patient with damage to the posterior fibers of the corpus callosum (Michel, Henaff and Intrilligator, 1996). An important additional finding is that magnetic stimulation applied to the skull, which disrupts electrical activity in the brain below, interfered with the reading performance of a partially recovered pure alexic when it affected the parieto-occipital area of the right hemisphere (Coslett and Monsul, 1994). The same stimulation had no effect when it was applied to the homologous area on the left. And a recent case report demonstrated that right occipital damage disrupted the residual reading capacity of a patient who had earlier suffered a left occipito-temporal lesion (Bartolomeo, Bachoud-Levi, Degos and Boller, 1998). Finally, Bone, Maher, Mao and Haist (2000) reported data from an investigation involving fMRI in two subjects with pure alexia. They found that reading letter-by-letter resulted in activation in the posterior portion of the left hemisphere, whereas processing of briefly presented letter strings activated the right parieto-temporal region (see also Leff et al., 2001).

Alternative accounts of pure alexia have also been proposed. Behrmann and colleagues (Behrmann, Plaut and Nelson, 1998; Behrmann and Shallice, 1995), for example, have proposed that the disorder is attributable to impaired activation of orthographic representations. On this account, the deficit in activating orthographic representations is not absolute, however. Degraded orthographic information is assumed to be processed to some degree by the normal reading system; the lexical and semantic effects exhibited by patients with this disorder (e.g. frequency and imageability effects) are assumed to reflect the "residual functioning of the same interactive system that supported normal reading premorbidly" (p. 7, Behrmann et al., 1998).

Other investigators have attributed pure dyslexia to a visual impairment which precludes activation of orthographic representations (Farah and Wallace, 1991). Chialant and Caramazza (1998), for example, reported a patient, MJ, who processed single, visually presented letters normally and performed well on a variety of tasks assessing the orthographic lexicon with auditorily presented stimuli. In contrast, MJ exhibited significant impairments in the processing of letter strings. The investigators suggest that MJ was unable to transfer information from the intact visual processing system in the right hemisphere to the intact language processing mechanisms of the left hemisphere.

For additional information regarding these and additional accounts of pure alexia the interested reader is referred to Cognitive Neuropsychology: 15(1–2); 1998.

Other disorders

Peripheral dyslexias may be observed in a variety of conditions involving visuo-perceptual or attentional deficits. Patients with simultanagnosia, a disorder characterized by an inability to 'see' more than one object in an array, are often able to read single words but are incapable of reading text (Baylis, Driver, Baylis and Rafal, 1994; Coslett and Saffran, 1991). Other patients with simultanagnosia exhibit substantial problems in reading even single words (Wolpert, 1924).

Patients with degenerative conditions involving the posterior cortical regions may also exhibit profound deficits in reading as part of their more general impairment in visuo-spatial processing. Several patterns of impairment may be observed in these patients. Patients such as NY (Saffran and Coslett, 1996) may exhibit attentional dyslexia with letter migration and blend errors, whereas other patients exhibiting deficits which are, in certain respects, rather similar, do not produce migration or blend errors in reading or illusory conjunctions in visual search tasks (Treisman and Souther, 1985). We have suggested that at least some patients with these disorders suffer from a progressive restriction in the domain to which they can allocate visual attention. As a consequence of this impairment, these patients may exhibit an effect of stimulus size such that they are able to read words in small print, but when shown the same word in large print, see only a single letter (Coslett et al., 1995; Saffran et al., 1990).

Concluding remarks

There is thus evidence that reading can be disrupted by disorders that arise prior to lexical access or contact with phonological translation mechanisms. In none of these instances have we arrived at a well-accepted account of the problem. In neglect and attentional dyslexia, the explanation clearly involves attentional mechanisms which are not yet well elaborated. In the case of pure alexia, the deficit involves interhemispheric transfer of information, as well as putative capacities of the right hemisphere, both of which are poorly understood. It is reasonable to expect, however, that these challenges will be taken up, and that a more complete understanding of these deficits will ultimately be provided.

References

Bartolomeo P, Bachoud-Levi AC, Degos JD, Boller F: Disruption of residual reading capacity in a pure alexic patient after a mirror-image right-hemispheric lesion. Neurology: 50; 286–288, 1998.

Baylis GC, Driver J, Baylis LL, Rafal RD: Reading of letters and words in a patient with Bálint's syndrome. Neuropsychologia: 32; 1273–1286, 1994.

Behrmann M, Moscovitch M, Black SE, Mozer M: Perceptual and conceptual mechanisms in neglect dyslexia. Brain: 113; 1163–1183, 1990.

Behrmann M, Plaut DC, Nelson J: A literature review and new data supporting an interactive account of letter-by-letter reading. Cognitive Neuropsychology: 15; 7–52, 1998.

Behrmann M, Shallice T: An orthographic not spatial disorder. Cognitive Neuropsychology: 12; 409–454, 1995.

Bone RB, Maher L, Mao W, Haist F: Functional neuroimaging of implicit and explicit reading in patients with pure alexia (abstract). Journal of the International Neuropsychological Society: 6(2); 157, 2000.

Bowers JS, Bub DN, Arguin M: A characterization of the word superiority effect in a case of letter-by-letter surface alexia. Cognitive Neuropsychology: 13; 415–442, 1996.

Bub DN, Black S, Howell J: Word recognition and orthographic context effects in a letter-by-letter reader. Brain and Language: 36; 357–376, 1989.

Buxbaum LJ, Coslett HB: Deep dsylexic phenomenon in pure alexia. Brain and Language: 54; 136–167, 1996.

Buxbaum LJ, Coslett HB: Spatio-motor representations in reaching: evidence for subtypes of optic ataxia. Cognitive Neuropsychology: 15; 279–312, 1998.

Caramazza A, Hills A: Levels of representation, coordinate frames and unilateral neglect. Cognitive Neuropsychology: 7; 391–455, 1990.

Chialant D, Caramazza A: Perceptual and lexical factors in a case of letter-by-letter reading. Cognitive Neuropsychology: 15; 167–202, 1998.

Coslett HB, Monsul N: Reading with the right hemisphere: evidence from transcranial magnetic stimulation. Brain and Language: 46; 198–211, 1994.

Coslett HB, Saffran EM: Evidence for preserved reading in 'pure alexia'. Brain: 112; 327–359, 1989a.

Coslett HB, Saffran EM: Preserved object identification and reading comprehension in optic aphasia. Brain: 112; 1091–1110, 1989b.

Coslett HB, Saffran E: Simultanagnosia: to see but not two see. Brain: 114; 1523–1545, 1991.

Coslett HB, Saffran EM: Optic aphasia and the right hemisphere: a replication and extension. Brain and Language: 43; 148–161, 1992.

Coslett HB, Saffran EM: Mechanisms of implicit reading in alexia. In Farah M, Ratcliff G (Eds), The Neuropsychology of High-Level Vision: Collected Tutorial Essays. Hillsdale, NJ: Lawrence Erlbaum, 1994.

Coslett HB, Saffran EM, Greenbaum S, Schwartz H: Preserved reading in pure alexia: the effect of strategy. Brain: 116; 21–37, 1993.

Coslett HB, Schwartz MF, Goldberg G, Haas D, Perkins J: Multi-modal hemispatial deficits after left hemisphere stroke: a deficit in attention? Brain: 116; 527–554, 1993.

Coslett HB, Stark M, Rajaram S, Saffran EM: Narrowing the spotlight: a visual attentional disorder in Alzheimer's disease. Neurocase: 1; 305–318, 1995.

Dejerine J: Contribution a l'etude anatomo-pathologique et clinique des differentes varietes de cecite verbale. Comptes Rendus des Seances de la Societé de Biologie: 4; 61–90, 1892.

Ellis AW, Young AW, Flude BM: Neglect and visual language. In Robertson IH, Marshall JC (Eds), Unilateral neglect: clinical and experimental studies. Hove: Lawrence Erlbaum, 1993.

Farah MJ: Visual Agnosia: Disorders of Object Vision and What They Tell Us About the Brain. Cambridge, MA: MIT Press/Bradford, 1990.

Farah MJ, Wallace MA: Pure alexia as a visual impairment: a reconsideration. Cognitive Neuropsychology: 8; 313–334, 1991.

Friedman RB, Hadley JA: Letter-by-letter surface alexia. Cognitive Neuropsychology: 9; 185–208, 1992.

Greenwald ML, Berndt RS: Impaired encoding of abstract letter code order: severe alexia in a mildly aphasic patient. Cognitive Neuropsychology: 16; 513–556, 1999.

Howard D, Patterson K: The Pyramid and Palm Trees Test. Suffolk, England: Thames Valley Test Company, 1992.

Kanwisher N: Repetition blindness and illusory conjunctions: errors in binding visual types with visual tokens. Journal of Experimental Psychology: Human Perception and Performance: 17; 404–421, 1991.

Làdavas E, Shallice T, Zanella MT: Preserved semantic access in neglect dyslexia. Neuropsychologia: 35; 257–270, 1997.

Leff AP, Crewes H, Plant GT, Scott SK, Kennard C, Wise RJ: The functional anatomy of single-word reading in patients with hemianopic and pure alexia. Brain: 124; 510–521, 2001.

McClelland JL, Mozer MC: Perceptual interactions in two-word displays: familiarity and similarity effects. Journal of Experimental Psychology: Human Perception and Performance: 12; 18–35, 1986.

McClelland JL, Rumelhart DE: An interactive activation model of context effects in letter perception: Part I. An account of basic findings. Psychological Review: 88; 375–407, 1981.

Michel F, Henaff MA, Intrilligator J: Two different readers in the same brain after a posterior callosal lesion. NeuroReport: 7; 786–788, 1996.

Mozer MC: Types and tokens in visual letter perception. Journal of Experimental Psychology: Human Perception and Performance: 15; 287–303, 1989.

Mozer MC: The Perception of Multiple Objects. Cambridge, MA 1991: MIT Press, 1991.

Patterson K, Kay J: Letter-by-letter reading: psychological descriptions of a neurological syndrome. Quarterly Journal of Experimental Psychology: 34A; 411–441, 1982.

Patterson KE, Vargha-Khadem F, Polkey CF: Reading with one hemisphere. Brain: 112; 39–63, 1989.

Price CJ, Humphreys GW: Attentional dyslexia: the effects of co-occurring deficits. Cognitive Neuropsychology: 6; 569–592, 1993.

Rapscak SZ, Beeson PM, Rubens AB: Writing with the right hemisphere. Brain and Language: 41; 510–530, 1991.

Reuter-Lorenz PA, Brunn JL: A prelexical basis for letter-by-letter reading: a case study. Cognitive Neuropsychology: 7; 1–20, 1990.

Saffran EM, Coslett HB: 'Attentional dyslexia' in Alzheimer's disease: a case study. Cognitive Neuropsychology: 13; 205–228, 1996.

Saffran EM, Coslett HB: Implicit vs. letter-by-letter reading in pure alexia: a tale of two systems. Cognitive Neuropsychology: 15; 141–166, 1998.

Saffran EM, Fitzpatrick-DeSalme EJ, Coslett HB: In Schwartz MF (Ed), Modular Deficits in Alzheimer-type Dementia. Cambridge, MA: MIT Press, pp. 297–327, 1990.

Shallice T: From Neuropsychology to Mental Structure. Cambridge: Cambridge University Press, 1988.

Shallice T, McGill J: The origins of mixed errors. In Reguin J (Ed), Attention and Performance VII. Hillsdale, NJ: Lawrence Erlbaum, pp. 193–208, 1977.

Shallice T, Saffran EM: Lexical processing in the absence of explicit word identification: evidence from a letter-by-letter reader. Cognitive Neuropsychology: 3; 429–458, 1986.

Shallice T, Warrington EK: The possible role of selective attention in acquired dyslexia. Neuropsychologia: 15; 31–41, 1977.

Sieroff E, Pollatsek A, Posner MI: Recognition of visual letter strings following injury to the posterior visual spatial attention system. Cognitive Neuropsychology: 5; 427–449, 1988.

Treisman A, Souther J: Search asymmetry: a diagnostic for preattentive processing of separable features. Journal of Experimental Psychology: General: 114; 285–310, 1985.

Warrington EK, Cipolotti L, McNeil J: Attentional dyslexia: a single case study. Neuropsychologia: 31; 871–886, 1993.

Wolpert I: Die Simultanagnosie: storung der gesamtauffassung. Zeitschrift fur die Gesamte Neurologie und Psychiatrie: 93; 397–413, 1924.

Handbook of Neuropsychology, 2nd Edition, Vol. 4
M. Behrmann (Ed)

CHAPTER 11

Blindsight

L. Weiskrantz *

Department of Experimental Psychology, University of Oxford, South Parks Road, Oxford OX1 3UD, UK

Introduction

In non-human primates, there are nine visual pathways originating in the retina in addition to the major route to dorsal lateral geniculate nucleus (LGN) and thence to striate cortex. These extra-striate pathways allow retinal information to reach the superior colliculus, the ventral LGN, the accessory optic tract nuclei, the suprachiasmatic region of the hypothalamus, the pulvinar, and of course their subsequent projections in turn. The major projection of the dorsal LGN is, of course, to the striate cortex, but there is also a pathway from the dorsal LGN to prestriate cortex, and even after total striate cortex removal some LGN cells of origin of the prestriate pathway remain undegenerated (Benevento and Yoshida, 1981; Cowey and Stoerig, 1989, 1991; Fries, 1981; Hernandez-Gonzalez and Reinoso-Suarez, 1994; Yukie and Iwai, 1981). All of these extra-striate pathways remain open when the geniculo-striate pathway is blocked or completely damaged (cf. Weiskrantz, 1972). More broadly, it is likely that no region of the brain normally in receipt of visual information can be completely deprived of it by virtue of a lesion of striate cortex.

It is not surprising, therefore, that, with complete removal of the striate cortex bilaterally, monkeys can still make visual discriminations, albeit not as skilfully as normal animals. They can detect and reach with reasonable accuracy for brief and small targets whose positions are randomly shifted from trial to trial (Humphrey, 1974; Weiskrantz, Cowey and Passingham, 1977), and can discriminate lines differing in orientation in the frontal plane by as little as 8° from each other (Pasik and Pasik, 1980). Their visual acuity is reduced by about 2 octaves (Miller, Pasik and Pasik, 1980), but the resulting capacity — approximately 11 cycles/deg — is still better than that of the normal cat. The spectral sensitivity of hemianopic monkeys with unilateral striate cortex removal is qualitatively normal, although reduced in sensitivity (Cowey and Stoerig, 1999). With subtotal lesions of striate cortex, subtotal field defects arise with the shape and approximate size to be expected from the cortical projection map of the retina, but these scotomata still allow good detection and localization of stimuli within them. Indeed, with appropriate training, the field defects show some recovery of function and shrinkage (see below, Cowey, 1963; Cowey and Weiskrantz, 1963; Mohler and Wurtz, 1977; cf. also Weiskrantz and Cowey, 1970). On the other hand, animals appear to be agnosic with respect to the meaning of the stimuli that they can readily detect (Cowey, 1963; Humphrey, 1974; Luciani, 1884), except in the sense that detection per se can serve as a cue for reward or for trained discriminations.

Given the close similarity in anatomical organization of the human visual system to that of the infra-human primate, parsimoniously it would be expected that a comparable pattern of residual capacities would be found in humans after damage to the striate cortex. But the typical clinical outcome of damage to the occipital lobes in humans is a densely blind scotoma of a size and shape to be expected

* Tel. +44 (1865) 271362; Fax: +44 (1865) 310447;
E-mail: larry.weiskrantz@psy.ox.ac.uk

from the classical retino-cortical maps (Holmes, 1918). And so the question that arises is whether these disparate patterns of results can be reconciled, or are humans and monkeys qualitatively different despite the similarity of their visual anatomy?

As simple as the question appears, there are some serious difficulties that stand in the way of an answer. The first is geometrical and straightforward: the striate cortex of the human is mainly buried in the medial surface in the calcarine fissure, whereas in the monkey the macular projection is on the lateral surface and readily accessible. It is rare, in the human brain, for any lesion of the striate cortex to occur without damage to overlying tissue, including visual association cortex, whereas it is relatively easy for lesions restricted to striate cortex to be studied in experimental animals. The difference is important for two reasons. First, it has been reported that the effects of enlarging a striate cortex lesion in the monkey so as to include posterior association cortex leads to a significant reduction in residual visual capacity (Pasik and Pasik, 1971). Secondly, it is becoming clear that the outputs from striate cortex to more anterior cortical regions are functionally segregated and that their cortical targets — closely packed within a small distance of each other — may have partially specialized capacities of a modular type, e.g. colour, movement, spatial features, form, etc. (cf. Cowey, 1985; Zeki, 1978, 1993). As at least some of these regions are likely to be damaged in the human whenever striate cortex is also damaged, the pattern of deficits can differ considerably from patient to patient with relatively slight differences in the disposition of the lesions. Therefore, the comparisons with experimental striate lesions in monkey and clinically occurring lesions in the human are not typically comparisons of like with like, and moreover there are inherent, but structurally sound, sources of variance in the clinical material. There is a further difference that often occurs — lesions to striate cortex in a clinical population will have variable histories of onset and of subsequent course, or may even have been present prenatally. The classical animal studies were based largely on adolescent or mature animals with lesions that had an abrupt onset rather than a developmental history.

A second difficulty in answering the question of human/animal comparability is methodological. Residual vision in the animal is perforce studied behaviourally, typically by making reward contingent upon a particular choice between alternative responses which are arbitrarily linked to one of two stimuli chosen by the experimenter for comparison. For systematic studies of particular dimensions or discrimination, or even of detection per se, a long history of training and large series of trials are entailed. Human visual assessment is rarely carried out in such a fashion clinically. Instead, patients in clinical examination are asked to respond to a verbal instruction to report whether or not they 'see' a presented stimulus, and perhaps to describe it.

But when patients with field defects caused by occipital lesions are studied psychophysically with 'animal-type' forced-choice methodology, unsuspected visual capacities may be uncovered that do not necessarily correlate with their reported experiences, and often are radically and surprisingly different. Some years ago, good capacity was demonstrated in some well-studied patients despite their claiming no visual experience whatever of the stimuli to which they respond and discriminate (Pöppel, Held and Frost, 1973; Weiskrantz, Warrington, Sanders and Marshall, 1974; cf. an early report by Bard, 1905). That extreme situation gave rise to the term 'blindsight' — visual discrimination in the absence of acknowledged awareness (Sanders, Warrington, Marshall and Weiskrantz, 1974; Weiskrantz, 1986; Weiskrantz et al., 1974) — but generically subsumed under the larger topic of the residual capacity mediated by extra-striate pathways in humans following damage to the striate cortex, when subjects are tested by forced-choice or non-verbal methodologies. That is the subject of this review. The subject and the related background issues surrounding it are also discussed more fully elsewhere (Cowey and Stoerig, 1991, 1992; Stoerig and Cowey, 1997; Weiskrantz, 1972, 1980, 1986, 1998).

Residual visual capacities and attributes within scotomata

Because of the lengthy testing required, and because selected cases may be especially relevant, much of the literature concerns single cases or small group studies. As in other areas of neuropsychology, single cases are especially illuminating when they reveal what dissociations may be *possible*. The first case to be extensively studied over several years was D.B., who was considered to have a relatively restricted lesion of the right calcarine fissure (resulting from surgical removal of a benign angioma). He is the subject of a detailed monograph and review (Weiskrantz, 1986, updated 1998). More recently, other subjects have been studied, especially subject G.Y., who suffered left occipital damage in an car accident and who has been the focus of a large number of illuminating investigations and brain scans by a large number of different research groups in several countries over the past 25 years. No single review exists of G.Y. as yet, especially as the studies are still ongoing, but references will appear as appropriate in the sections below.

Localizing

Several subjects investigated by a large number of investigators have demonstrated a capacity to localize stimuli within their 'blind' fields. Sometimes the response has been a saccade to the supposed locus of the stimulus, typically a briefly flashed spot, after it has been terminated. Indeed, it was this response that first produced evidence for Pöppel et al. (1973) of residual visual function in the field defects, in war veterans with gunshot wounds of the occipital lobes. Sometimes, the response has been of pointing or touching the locus of a target on a perimeter screen. In one study, G.Y. was trained to give a numerical score on a ruled scale to successfully describe the locus (Barbur, Ruddock and Waterfield, 1980). In all studies, the accuracy is typically not as high as in the intact visual field, but nevertheless can be very impressive. Of course, success in this task necessarily entails successful detection of the stimulus per se, but detection has also been studied independently of localizing (Azzopardi and Cowey, 1997; Barbur et al., 1980; Stoerig, 1987; Stoerig, Hubner and Pöppel, 1985; Stoerig and Pöppel, 1986; Weiskrantz, 1986).

Acuity

Relatively few systematic studies have been carried out, but D.B.'s acuity has been measured both with moirè fringe interference gratings (approximating to sine-wave gratings) and with photographic sine-wave gratings. Interestingly, his acuity was poorer very near (within 5–10°) to the vertical meridian than a bit farther eccentrically, but beyond that point his acuity declines with increasing eccentricity, as expected, and his acuity in the scotoma is always poorer than in a corresponding point of the intact half-field. The reduction in acuity for the region 16–20° eccentric is about 2 octaves as compared to the mirror-symmetric region of the intact field (2.5 cycles/deg compared with 10 cycles/deg) (Weiskrantz, 1986). G.Y.'s acuity has not been measured directly, but the contrast sensitivity function in his scotoma (using a grating of 12°× 12°, with its centre 9° from the fixation point) falls to zero at approximately 7 cycles/deg, which also is consistent with a drop of about 2 octaves compared to his intact field with this stimulus situation (Barbur, Harlow, Weiskrantz and 1994a; Barbur, Harlow, Sahrie et al., 1994b; Weiskrantz, Cowey and Le Mare, 1998).

Orientation

D.B. is unusual in repeatedly demonstrating a good discriminative capacity for orientation in the frontal plane. Although impaired relative to his good field, he could nevertheless discriminate a difference in orientation of 10° between two gratings presented successively and briefly, even at an eccentricity of 45° in the impaired field, with no acknowledged experience of the gratings or even of a flash. Most other subjects who have been tested have shown much less residual capacity for orientation (e.g. Barbur et al., 1980). G.Y. does not show orientation discrimination using gratings, but positive evidence has been obtained using single lines (Morland, Ogilvie, Ruddock and Wright, 1996).

Colour

Evidence for wavelength discrimination in D.B. was at best marginal and slim, although he was not studied extensively (Weiskrantz et al., 1974). The situation has been advanced markedly in more recent studies. Stoerig and Cowey (1989, 1991, 1992) have shown that the spectral sensitivity function can be qualitatively normal in the blind fields in a number of hemianopes, although with quantitatively reduced sensitivity. The spectral sensitivity profile includes the humps and troughs thought to reflect colour opponency; it also shows the characteristic loss of long wavelength sensitivity following dark adaptation, the 'Purkinje shift'. Moreover, wavelength *discrimination*, e.g. red vs. green, but even of more closely spaced wavelengths, is possible in some subjects (Stoerig and Cowey, 1992), using forced-choice guessing. In a related study, Barbur et al. (1994b) demonstrated good discrimination between 'coloured' patches and achromatic patches matched in luminance, using a two-alternative forced-choice paradigm in G.Y. Ruddock and his colleagues (Brent, Kennard and Ruddock, 1994) have also found good discrimination between red and achromatic stimuli in G.Y. In this connection, it would appear that the discriminative sensitivity of the blind field is biased towards the red end of the spectrum. A strong inference that *successive colour contrast* is intact in G.Y. and another hemianopic blindsight subject is derived from pupillometric responses to coloured stimuli (Barbur, Weiskrantz and Harlow, 1999). Colour *simultaneous contrast* in the blind field has not been tested for psychophysically, as far as I am aware.

In all of these studies, the subjects *never* reported any experience of colour per se. For example, Stoerig and Cowey (1991, p. 1496) comment in their spectral sensitivity study which involved repeated measures of thresholds of chosen wavelengths:

> "the patients were often asked whether they could perceive anything when the blind field was tested. Throughout the experiments, which involved from 2 to 4 three-hour sessions per month for approximately six months, they consistently claimed that this was not the case and that they never saw or felt anything that was related to stimulus presentation".

Movement and transient stimuli

A number of reports have been made of detection of moving stimuli by subjects in their impaired fields (Barbur et al., 1980; Brindley, Gautier-Smith and Lewin, 1969; Perenin, 1978), and of course classically Riddoch (1917) and Poppelreuter (1917) described gunshot-wound cases who reported seeing moving, but not stationary, stimuli. D.B. showed a good ability to detect moving targets, although with a reduced sensitivity depending on the location in the blind field (Weiskrantz, 1986). More recently, a number of parametric psychophysical studies of *directional* discrimination of moving spots or bars have been carried out by Barbur and his colleagues on G.Y. (Barbur, Watson, Frackowiak and Zeki, 1993; Sahraie, Weiskrantz and Barbur, 1998; Sahraie, Weiskrantz, Barbur et al., 1997; Weiskrantz, Barbur and Sahraie, 1995), examining the limits of velocity and contrast for successful directional discrimination in the blind field. A clear capacity remains, but with reduced sensitivity. Some of these studies have been linked to the distinction between 'awareness' and 'unawareness' modes, and also to brain imaging (see below).

While there is no question that blindsight subjects can detect moving bars or spots and discriminate their direction of movement, the discrimination of direction of movement of random dot kineograms and plaids has been found lacking, at least in G.Y. (Azzopardi, Fallah, Gross and Rodman, 1998).

Movement is, of course, one form of a *visual transient*. But it has been clear for some time that the transients exemplified by sharp temporal onset/offset of stationary stimuli were also of particular significance in the blind field. This was studied systematically by Weiskrantz, Harlow and Barbur (1991) in G.Y., by varying the temporal slope of the Gaussian envelope of the onset and offset of stimuli in a two-alternative forced-choice paradigm for gratings vs. homogeneous patches (of equal luminance). Performance improved as the temporal slope increased. In a related study, the manipulation of spatial as well as temporal transients also allowed a specification to be made of both the spatial and the temporal parameters required for good detection. From this it was revealed that in G.Y. there is a narrowly tuned spatiotemporal visual 'channel' that is patent in the blind field, with a peak of about 1 cycle/deg and an cut-off ('acuity') of about 7 cycles/deg (Barbur et al., 1994a). Subsequently, this has been linked to a closely similar channel in monkeys revealed by pupillometry (see below).

A related study in which temporal rate of onset was varied systematically was carried out with D.B. in a forced-choice discrimination between a circular, homogeneous luminous disc vs. no stimulus. Although the sharper the rate of onset the better the performance, D.B. still performed reliably well above chance even with very extremely slow rates of onset, e.g. a course from zero to a supra-threshold level occupying 10 s (Weiskrantz, 1986, Chapter 9). Hence, a rapid temporal transient is not a necessary feature for good detection. A similar point emerges from a pupillometric analysis (see below).

Awareness vs. unawareness

There is another attribute of the transient stimuli that more recently has emerged as crucial and potentially valuable; it was already at the heart of the original investigation of blindsight, which by its strict definition is 'visual capacity in the *absence* of acknowledged awareness'. Transient stimuli, whether of movement, or looming and recession, or of abrupt onset and offset, in the blind fields of hemianopes sometimes give rise to a report of '*awareness*', a '*feeling*', a '*knowing*' that an event has occurred. This was perfectly evident in D.B., and has been found in various situations with G.Y. (cf. Weiskrantz, 1997) and so was not strictly 'blindsight' according to the definition. But in D.B. this 'awareness' was something of a nuisance, for two reasons. First, it naturally was compelling to D.B. himself. Any reasonable subject would prefer to discriminate stimuli of which he is aware rather than having to be forced to guess tediously about events of which he has absolutely no awareness, especially if this is required over thousands of trials. And so D.B. would seize upon that attribute, 'awareness', or 'knowing', on which to base his discriminative choices. But, secondly, the attribute could mislead him, because it did not obviously co-vary with the physical attributes of the stimuli. For example, he sometimes described 'feelings' of 'waves' which varied in 'thickness' or 'curvature' or 'quickness', which he was tempted to assign to the discriminative alternatives under study, such as movement or curvature of lines. But these could be generated equally by both of the alternative stimuli he was meant to be discriminating. And so with D.B., special pains were taken to eliminate the 'waves' or the 'knowing' or the 'feeling', and to force D.B. back into the genuine blindsight mode, i.e. discrimination in the complete absence of awareness. This was done successfully primarily by varying the contrast, field location, and size of the stimuli (see Weiskrantz, 1986, Chapter 13).

G.Y. has turned out to be different from D.B. When G.Y. is 'aware of', or 'knows' that there is a stimulus event, although he does not 'see' it, his experience is mainly veridical. It helps him, because it covaries with the relevant stimulus parameter under investigation, such as velocity of movement, or spatial frequency of a grating. With D.B., it was not veridical. The result was that with G.Y. until quite recently virtually all of the studies have used stimulus parameters generating 'awareness' in the absence of 'seeing'. Both he and the various groups of experimenters were happy with this situation because it yielded results of some interest, e.g. those resulting in the spatiotemporal channels described just above.

But it was not 'blindsight' according to the original definition, studied to such good and surprising effect with D.B. Recently the 'awareness' mode — acknowledged experience of events in the blind field, in the absence of acknowledged 'seeing' as such — has been called Blindsight Type 2, to distinguish it from the original definition, Blindsight Type 1, Weiskrantz, 1998, 1999. What brought the focus back to the original definition and back to the earlier phenomenon grew out of an informal observation by Barbur and Weiskrantz (cf. Weiskrantz, 1995) in which it was discovered that G.Y. could mimic with a movement of his arm, and with excellent verisimilitude, the path of a projected laser spot moving rapidly (about 15°/s) in his blind field. The mimicry reflected Blindsight Type 2 — he was 'aware' of the movement. In a recorded interview, he said that he 'knew' that something had moved although he said he did not 'see' anything as such. But when the movement was relatively slow (about 1 or 2°/s), he did not respond at all — his arm remained at rest. The question that arose was whether there would be nevertheless be Blindsight Type 1 — good discrimination without any awareness — for the *slowly moving stimuli*, which yielded no mimicking arm movements (for the background of how the question emerged from a discussion of the matter by Daniel Dennett (1991), see Weiskrantz, 1997, pp. 62–63).

In addition to obtaining evidence about the directional discrimination per se, it was also necessary to obtain evidence about reported awareness or unawareness. In addition to the usual response keys signalling his guesses about direction of motion, two 'commentary keys' were introduced with which he

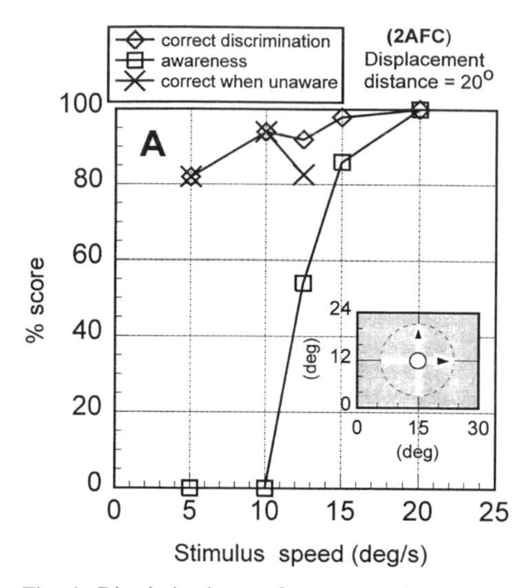

Fig. 1. Discrimination performance and awareness for a directional movement discrimination, as a function of stimulus speed presented in G.Y.'s 'blind' hemifield. On each trial, the subject had to indicate (by guessing, if necessary) whether a spot moved horizontally or vertically, and also to indicate whether he had any experience whatever of the event (pressing the 'yes' key) or none whatever ('no' key). Awareness (squares) refers to the percentage of trials on which he pressed the 'yes' key. 'Correct when unaware' (crosses) refers to performance during those trials when the subject pressed the 'no' key. (From Weiskrantz et al., 1995, with permission. Copyright National Academy of Sciences, USA.).

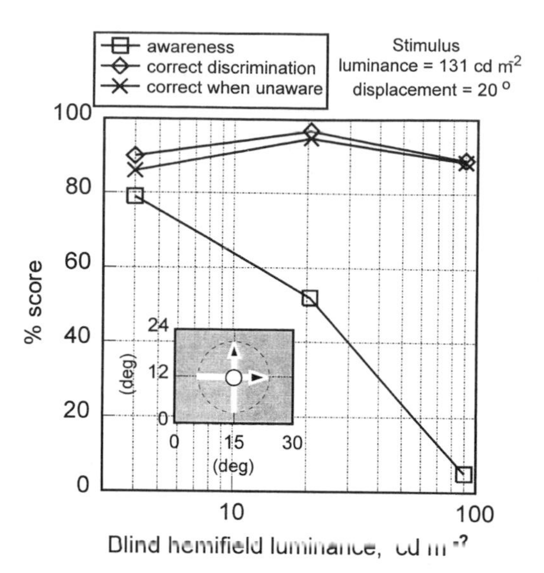

Fig. 2. Conditions as in Fig. 1, except that stimulus contrast was varied instead of velocity. The luminance of the test stimulus was held constant at 131 cd/m^2 and background luminance changed systematically. Speed was 15°/s and displacement was 20°. Note that performance remains relatively stable independently of contrast, but with a steep decline in aware responses as background luminance level increases. (From Weiskrantz et al., 1995, with permission. Copyright National Academy of Sciences, USA.)

could signal awareness (of any variety, such as a 'feeling') or no awareness after each trial. There was clear evidence of Type 1. G.Y. could discriminate at a high levels of success in the absence of any awareness (Weiskrantz et al., 1995), as shown in Fig. 1. It turned out to be practical to use variations in contrast as well as speed to demonstrate the same point (Fig. 2), drawing on experience from earlier work with D.B. (Weiskrantz, 1986, Chapter 13). The matter is discussed in more detail in Sahraie et al., 1997 and Weiskrantz (1997).

And so commentary keys have brought one back to the original exploration of performance in relation to experience — to blindsight in the original sense. The commentary key paradigm has been used in further extensions, for example in the experiments by Kentridge, Heywood and Weiskrantz (1999a,b) on attention and those of Weiskrantz, Cowey and Barbur (1999) on awareness in relation to pupillometry (see below).

The explicit requirement to signal 'awareness' also led us to a consideration of more subtle aspects of commentaries. Traditionally, in psychophysical studies, especially those carried out in the context of signal detection theory, experimenters have asked subjects to indicate their 'confidence level' after each trial or group of trials. This is clearly related to 'awareness level', but is not exactly the same. We found with G.Y. that when he was aware he was also confident, but he could also be confident when not aware of the event. He himself linked confidence to his actual key press response after he had made it, and awareness to an experience of the stimulus event itself, typically prior to the response. The difference is explored in Sahraie et al. (1998). That study also examined the possibility that a binary 'aware' vs. 'unaware' measure used in an earlier study (Weiskrantz et al., 1995) might have been too insensitive to reflect finer values of the experience, but no difference was found for G.Y. using a multi-value scale and a binary scale. For him, 'zero' means 'zero'. The difference between 'awareness' and 'confidence', at least in this context, may have some relevance to the distinction drawn persuasively recently by Milner and Goodale (1995) between 'visual action', and 'visual perception', and their suggestion that the former is mediated via the dorsal anatomical efferent route out of striate cortex, and the latter mediated by the ventral route. G.Y. commented that his confidence judgements arose after he had made his discriminative response, whereas the awareness judgements were made at the time of stimulus presentation and prior to his response.

'Form'

Most reports of evidence for form discrimination have been negative, or weak. An exception was the evidence, replicated several times, for D.B.'s ability to discriminate **X** from **0** (Weiskrantz, 1986; Weiskrantz et al., 1974). Warrington and Weiskrantz re-examined the issue by asking whether the subject's 'form' vision was actually derived from orientation differences between the major components of the discriminative stimuli, given that D.B. has good orientation discrimination. They concluded that this was the case, and that forms which are equated in orientational components are only poorly discriminated by him (cf. Weiskrantz, 1986, 1987). Weiskrantz and Warrington also succeeded in demonstrating 'same–different' matches for simultaneous pairs of 2-D stimulus (**X** and **0**) between the impaired and contralateral intact fields of D.B., but interestingly when the pairs of stimuli were confined to *within* the field defect such matches appeared to be much more difficult (Weiskrantz, 1986).

But the situation may be different if the subject is asked to reach for and grasp solid objects in their blind fields. Both Marcel (1998) and Perenin and Rossetti (1996) have reported that the hand adopts the appropriate arrangement for a shape in advance of grasping it. Such a result would be nicely in accordance with the thesis forwarded by Milner and Goodale (1995) that the shape and orientation of objects can be involved in directed visual actions towards the objects, even when subjects are unable to perceive the objects correctly. Perhaps only crude form discriminations are possible in the absence of visual action, but that finer features of shape can be processed in reaching and grasping into the blind field.

On the other hand, this distinction (between the 'action' mode and the 'perception' mode — linked by Milner and Goodale to separate mediation by the dorsal and ventral visual streams) does not readily account for the striking claim by Marcel (1998) that words flashed into the blind field can influence the interpretation of meanings of words subsequently shown in the intact field. He reports, for example, that 'money' flashed into the blind field will bias the reported meaning of the ambiguous word 'bank' in the intact field — i.e. bank can either related to 'money' or to 'river'. This intriguing report is isolated and deserves to be followed up. It would force a considerable expansion of the known capacity for residual processing of stationary shapes in the blind field. It is hard to reconcile the result with the relatively crude form capacity described above for stationary stimuli, at least as suggested, for D.B. Perhaps there is enough orientation differentiation contained in letters of words for some verbal processing to be undertaken. On the other hand, neuropsychology is full of surprises.

Emotional content

The meaning of the content of the blind field stimulus raises a question about which there is hardly any information whatever: namely, its emotional content. There are claims, for example, that conditioned aversive properties of stimuli in normal human subjects can give rise to autonomic responses even when the subjects have no awareness of them (Esteves, Parra, Dimberg and Øhman, 1994; Øhman and Soares, 1998). Moreover, functional imaging experiments have demonstrated that fear stimuli rendered invisible by backward masking can nevertheless activate the amygdala via a colliculo-pulvinar pathway (Breiter, Etcoff, Whalen et al., 1996; Morris, Øhman and Doland, 1999).

When a fear-evoking stimulus, such as a strange doll, is presented to the blind hemifield of a monkey with unilateral V1 removal, the animal appears to ignore it completely although it emits loud shrieks of fear and outrage when it is confronted in the normal visual field. Nor does it react, for example, to a highly prized banana in the blind field (Cowey, 1967; Cowey and Weiskrantz, 1963). On the other hand, no concurrent measures of autonomic activity have been made, and it is possible that emotion-provoking stimuli would produce responses in the absence of overt behavioural responses, just as, for example, galvanic skin responses can be recorded to familiar faces in prosopagnosic patients who in perceptual tests cannot distinguish familiar from unfamiliar faces (Tranel and Damasio, 1985). A recent study of faces with emotional expression projected to G.Y.'s blind field has some direct bearing on this surmise (De Gelder, Vrooman, Pourtois and Weiskrantz, 1999). He has been shown to be able to discriminate between different facial expressions in moving video images projected into his blind field, e.g. happy vs. sad and angry vs. fearful, and he could also identify which of four different expressions were presented on any single exposure. He failed to 'see' the faces as such, and he was also at chance with inverted faces. It remains unknown so far whether his autonomic system would also be sensitive to those emotional stimuli that he can discriminate in the absence of 'seeing'. The study of these and other aspects of facial expression and other meaningful stimuli with emotional value promises to be of considerable interest for future work.

Attention in the blind field

In testing D.B., there was a suggestion that his performance was helped if he was not required continuously to change his focus of attention in the blind field (Weiskrantz, 1986, p. 49). The role of attention has been studied more systematically in G.Y. It has been shown that attention can confer an advantage in processing stimuli in the blind field either within an attended time interval or at an attended spatial location. A visual cue that provides temporal information about the time window within which the targets will appear in the blind field improves G.Y.'s discrimination of their location (Kentridge et al., 1999a). Cues in the blind field that provide information about the likely spatial location of a target confer an advantage, strikingly in the complete absence of reported awareness of either the cue or the target. Cues in his blind field were effective even in directing his attention to a second location remote from that at which the cue was presented, again under conditions when there was no reported awareness of the cue or the target (Kentridge et al., 1999b).

Indirect, 'implicit' methods of revealing residual visual function

Neither the subject nor the experimenter is fond of the 'heroic' method of testing for blindsight, e.g. by forced-choice guessing or reaching. Parametric studies require multiple and lengthy sessions, often totalling thousands of trials. To suggest to a subject that there is some special scientific value in being cajoled into making repeated guesses about unseen stimuli requires some suspension of credibility. In other areas of cognitive neuropsychology, residual function can be tested quite readily by methods that do not directly assault credibility. For example, the amnesic patient can be asked to try to identify a word when presented with its first three letters, to enable the experimenter to infer that an earlier 'prime' by the word has facilitated its identification.

There are two general approaches to indirect methods of testing for residual visual function that allow an inference without requiring the subject to guess without seeing: (a) the first exploits reflexes to visual stimuli in the blind hemifield; and (b) the second takes advantage of interactions between the intact and impaired hemifields. The field has been surveyed by Weiskrantz (1990) and by Stoerig and Cowey (1997).

Reflexes

Electrodermal responses to visual stimuli in the blind field (as compared with control 'blanks') were already used some time ago by Zihl, Tretter and Singer (1980) to demonstrate a positive response to light. They are useful for revealing the existence of residual capacity, but are difficult to relate in a directly quantitative way to the visual events. Pupillometry, in contrast, provides a direct and incisive quantitative measure, given that the pupil constricts differentially to visual stimuli depending on their spatial frequency, wavelength, movement, when there is no change in the total luminance of the stimuli (Barbur and Forsyth, 1986; Barbur and Thomson, 1987). Thus, the pupil can be used to measure the profile of sensitivity to gratings in the blind field as a function of spatial frequency, and also to obtain the visual acuity. Sensitivity to colour and movement can also be measured. Given that pupillometry does not de-

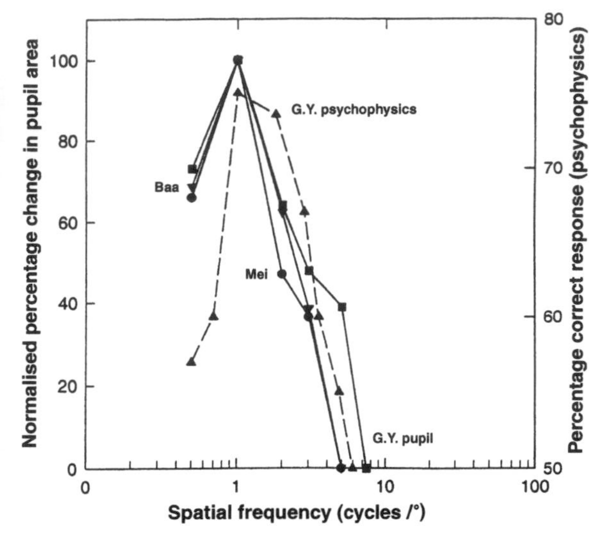

Fig. 3. Relative size of pupillary constriction (solid lines) as a function of spatial frequency of an equiluminant grating presented to the 'blind' hemifields of two monkeys ('Baa' and 'Mei') and human subject (G.Y.). Sizes of pupillary responses were normalized with peak at 100. Dotted line displays psychophysical performance for G.Y. from earlier study (Barbur et al., 1994a), using 2AFC methodology for gratings versus structureless equiluminant stimuli. (From Weiskrantz et al., 1998, with permission. Copyright Oxford University Press.)

pend on the subject's verbal report, it can be used to assess the blind fields of human patients using 'unseen' stimuli, and also those of animals, and also of human infants (cf. Cocker, Moseley, Bissenden and Fielder, 1994).

Recently, Weiskrantz et al. (1998) examined the spatial frequency profiles of the affected hemifields of G.Y. and also of two monkeys with unilateral removal of striate cortex (V1), using the P_Scan apparatus (Barbur, Thomson and Forsyth, 1987). The results are very clear (Fig. 3). In both the human and the monkey, there is a narrowly tuned response of the pupil to different spatial frequencies of an achromatic grating, showing a peak at 1 cycle/deg. The high spatial frequency cut-off (acuity) is at about 7 cycles/deg, which is a reduction of about 2 octaves compared with the intact hemifields under these conditions. G.Y.'s pupillary response could be validated by psychophysical methods, as a spatial temporal tuning curve was obtained in an earlier study (Barbur et al., 1994a). The psychophysical function maps onto the pupillary profile quite closely (see Fig. 3), and confirms the usefulness of the pupillary response.

The relation between the pupil's response in the blind field and awareness is of some interest. When pupillometric responses were being made, which were with gratings which had abrupt onsets and offsets, G.Y. often responded that he was 'aware' of an event, although he did not see any features of the grating as such, i.e. any of the bars or their orientation. (Similarly, with a sharp onset of a red stimulus, he may be aware that an event has occurred, but has no experience whatever its colour, see above). And so it might be speculated that the pupil will constrict only to the transient character of the stimulus. But this turns out not to be the case. Weiskrantz et al. (1999) have recently found that the pupil still constricts to a 1 cycle/deg isoluminant grating even when the onset and offset of the grating are smoothed so as to eliminate G.Y.'s reported awareness of the event, although its size is reduced. (In a recent unpublished study of D.B., not even the size of the pupillary response is reduced for grating stimuli of which he is unaware.) The fact that pupillometric acuity changes with V1 removal means that there must be a direct downstream influence of cortex reaching the midbrain mechanism that provides the final efferent to the pupillary musculature. The strikingly close similarity of the monkey and human results is another piece of evidence that we are dealing with similar mechanisms involved in V1 removal in both species, and also speaks against the view that in residual function, the human must depend upon fragments of intact visual cortex (see below), given that there are demonstrably no such fragments in the monkey.

Interactions between intact and blind hemifields

A good example of this approach is the seminal work of Torjussen (1976, 1978) demonstrating 'completion' of shapes shown to both the blind and intact hemifields simultaneously. The subject reports seeing nothing when a stimulus is presented to the blind field, but sees a normally completed stimulus which bridges both the intact and the impaired field. Since then, the method has been used by Marcel in two hemianopes, one of whom was G.Y. (Marcel, 1998), and also by Perenin, Girard-Madoux and

Jeannerod (1985). This method was also used in tests with hemispherectomized subjects, reviewed in the section on sub-cortical mediation (see below). Interestingly, the present position regarding completion phenomena is paradoxical in the sense that what is demonstrated by the contribution of the hemianopic field is not 'blindsight' but *full sight* embracing the impaired and intact hemifields acting in unison.

A promising method was published by Rafal, Smith, Krantz et al. (1990) in which it was found that the latency of a saccade to a stimulus in the *intact* hemifield was increased if an 'unseen' stimulus was presented just earlier to the blind hemifield of hemianopes. Thus, the subject only responds directly to 'seen' stimuli, but an inference can clearly be drawn about the processing of events in the impaired hemifield because of the modulation of the response to the events in the intact field. This is a method that would allow one to examine specific parameters of visual stimuli, e.g. wavelength, spatial frequency, for their inhibitory control of events in the intact hemifield. Cochrane (1995), unfortunately, had difficulty in replicating Rafal et al.'s results for the types of hemianopes used by them, although the method did work with G.Y.

This method bears a family resemblance to the methods used by Marzi and his colleagues (Corbetta, Marzi, Tassinari and Aglioti, 1990), in which the reaction time of a key-press response to a light in the intact field could be lengthened by a light presented just earlier in the impaired field of human subjects. A similar finding has been reported for the monkey — an unseen target slows the reaction time to the seen target, especially at delays of the order of 400–500 ms (Stoerig and Cowey, 1997). A related approach by Marzi, Tassinari, Lutzemberger and Aglioti (1986) exploited the fact that the reaction time to two flashes presented simultaneously is consistently faster than the reaction time to a single flash, whether or not the two flashes appear in the same hemifield or whether they appear in opposite fields. The reaction time of hemianopes can be speeded up when the two flashes are presented across the vertical meridian, even though the subject only reports seeing a single stimulus, i.e. the one in the intact hemifield. Recently, the same approach has been used by Tomaiuolo, Ptito, Marzi et al. (1997) to demonstrate visual spatial summation in hemispherectomised subjects (see below).

Another striking example of cross-hemifield interaction in G.Y. has recently been reported by Ruddock and his coworkers (Finlay, Jones, Morland et al., 1997). They have found that particular values of moving visual stimuli in the *intact* hemifield actually produce an experience of phenomenal 'seeing' of motion in G.Y.'s *blind* hemifield. This obviously opens up fresh possibilities of exploration in other hemianopes. The phenomenon may be related to cross-field activations found in brain imaging of G.Y. (see above).

Morland, Jones, Finlay et al. (1999) have studied G.Y.'s ability to match the values of stimuli between the intact and blind hemifields, with variations in luminance, movement, or colour. They found that between-field matches could be made for movement or colour, but not for luminance, and interpret the findings in terms of the distinction between Blindsight Type 1 and Type 2 (see above), although commentaries were not recorded as such. This was not a study of between-field interactive effects as such, which might well have been present, but is the interesting use of the good field as an 'assay' of the impaired field.

Sub-cortical mediation

Given that, by definition, any residual visual function in the absence of V1 must be mediated by extra-striate pathways, a priori the superior colliculus would be most likely candidate to explain how retinal information can find the appropriate targets in the brain. It is the second largest sub-component of the optic nerve, comprising about 150,000 fibres. It has been directly implicated in the recovery of monkeys with practice from V1 lesions (Mohler and Wurtz, 1977), and in allowing the continued activity of V5 neurons with V1 blockade (Gross, 1991; Rodman, Gross and Albright, 1989). Also, G.Y.'s fMRI specifically shows increased activity in the superior colliculus in the absence of awareness (see below).

But even if it seems likely to be the favoured route in the absence of V1, of course that is not the end of the story, and the end remains a tabula rasa. The superior colliculus projects widely to ipsilateral extra-striate and non-striate cortical sites, and residual function might depend critically on their integrity. That is, the superior colliculus might simply be a relay to other cortical targets in the same hemisphere, or even in the opposite hemisphere, and it might be such targets that do the work. A condition directly relevant to this question is *hemispherectomy*, in which all of the cortex in one hemisphere is completely removed or functionally disconnected surgically for the relief of severe epilepsy. It is a drastic but effective, life-saving procedure; some patients can possess remarkably intact cognitive capacities, especially if the original brain damage occurred congenitally or at an early age (e.g. see Damasio, Lima and Damasio, 1975). Such patients are hemianopic, but typically retain intact midbrain structures. Do these allow for any residual function?

The matter is controversial. There were early positive reports of intact reaching (reviewed in Weiskrantz, 1986, pp. 120–122; 157–158), and more recently of form and movement discrimination (Ptito, Lassonde, Lepore and Ptito, 1987, 1991). However, doubts have been raised about these reports by recent control experiments suggesting that there may have been stray light entering the intact hemifield (King, Azzopardi, Cowey et al., 1996; reinforced by the results of Stoerig, Faubert, Ptito et al., 1996); when this was precluded, no residual function was found. In the course of these careful control studies using conditions to ensure that there was no stray light, the possibility of using stimuli sufficiently salient to be genuinely effective in the blind field might have been precluded. But a more recent study (Tomaiuolo et al., 1997) using an indirect procedure (see above) demonstrates visual spatial summation across the vertical meridian, despite the subjects' lack of awareness of the stimuli in the blind hemifield. That is, the reaction time to stimuli presented simultaneously to the intact and the blind fields of the hemispherectomized patients was shorter than to the intact field alone. No response was made to stimuli in the blind hemifield. This finding cannot be explained in terms of light diffusion; quite dim LEDs were used, and there was an optic disc control for diffusion of light. It also cannot be explained by the recent report of a possible slight contraction (about 2.5°) of the hemianopic field near the midline (Wessenger, Fendrich, Ptito et al., 1996) in some hemispherectomized patients (which is most likely due to mediation by an overlapping nasal–temporal projection to the intact hemisphere in these early brain damage cases). Tomaiuolo et al., took pains to be well clear of any such expanded vertical strip of recovered vision in the positioning of the stimulus in the blind hemifield. Thus, visual processing *can* take place in the absence of V1 and remaining cortex in at least some hemispherectomized patients.

Sahraie, Vargha-Khadem and Weiskrantz have examined more complex cross-field interactions in hemispherectomized patients, in still unpublished work. They found a clear completion effect for form, as first demonstrated by Torjussen (1976, 1978) and later by Marcel and by Perenin et al. (see above), for patients with occipital damage. This was done by briefly flashing an outline figure to one or other hemifield, or to both. The duration was very brief, a duration of the order of 0.1 ms — the flash was generated by a photo-flash gun positioned behind the cut-out outline figure, in a darkened room. Stimulus presentation was monocular. The subjects were instructed to describe the perceived figure, and were often able to draw it. As shown in Fig. 4, a subject (H.) with complete surgical decortication drew nothing at all when a half circle was projected to the blind field — confirming that it was phenomenally blind. A half circle to the intact field yielded a half circle drawn and located correctly. But a full circle projected simultaneously to *both* the blind and intact half-fields generated a *full* circle, again drawn correctly. This was repeated four times in this subject. Completion was also found in another subject with a functional hemispherectomy. Other variations on this theme were also studied. The results are unlikely to be due to adventitious eye movements, given the brevity of the exposure. Fixation was controlled in a manner to be described in due course in a full paper; it also was designed to rule out a dependence on the narrow nasal–temporal strip of intact vision that might be present in the subjects. Prima facie, the results lead to the inference that the blind hemifield must make its contribution via subcortical pathways on the hemispherectomized side. But before accepting the result, one must carefully consider various possibilities. For example, with subjects with fields defects presumed to occur early in life, a pseudo fovea might develop. Also, careful control experi-

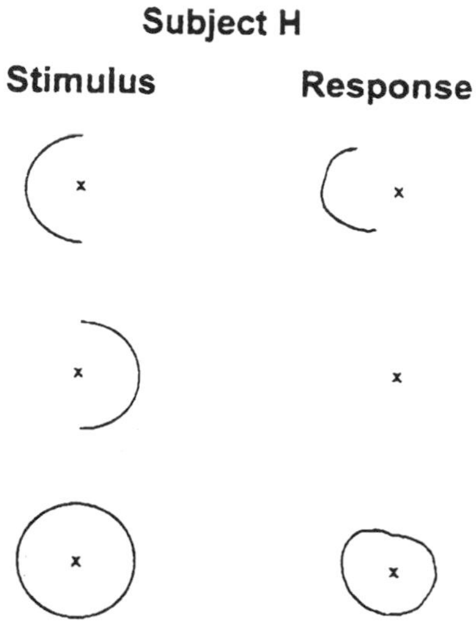

Subject H

Stimulus Response

Fig. 4. Drawings made by a subject (H.) with anatomical decortication of the left hemisphere. The outline stimuli were briefly flashed monocularly to the intact left visual hemifield, the blind right hemifield, or both hemifields simultaneously. Results can be compared with those for subjects with visual cortical lesions by Torjussen (1976), Marcel (1998), and Perenin et al. (1985 abstract, results shown in Weiskrantz, 1990). (Reproduced from Weiskrantz, 1998 edition of 1986, p. xxxvii).

ments must be conducted to ensure that subtle cues due to stray light can be ruled out absolutely, even though the integrity of the drawn figure could not be based on stray light alone. For example, the flash might 'prime' the subject in the intact field and lead to an assumption that there is a symmetrical figure extending in the blind field that completes the one shown in the intact field. It is evident that a rich set of psychophysical questions are opened by the completion phenomena and related 'figural' interaction effects.

These and related matters in hemispherectomized subjects are currently under investigation. Assuming the results are genuine and robust, they raise interesting questions: Is there an interaction between the contralateral and ipsilateral superior colliculi, with the ipsilateral colliculus being relieved of downstream inhibition, as suggested by Sprague (1966) in animal experiments and also by Singer, Zihl and Pöppel (1977) with human subjects? Might the final processing of completion phenomena be carried out in the intact hemisphere (via a midbrain commissure from the lesioned side) leading to veridical *seen* perception? Is the contribution of the 'unseen' stimuli in the blind field to the summation effect for reaction times found by Tomaiuolo et al. (1997) mediated entirely at the subcortical level, or does the cortex of the intact hemisphere play a role. Might it be that in hemispherectomized patients the final processing of the complete figure is carried out by the contralateral (intact) hemisphere, leading to veridical *seen* perception, via an input from the lesioned side over the midbrain commissure? These are matters that could be profitably pursued by functional brain imaging in these patients.

Functional brain imaging

G.Y. has been the subject both of PET and functional MRI investigations. With PET (Barbur et al., 1993), the difference between moving and stationary bars was studied. The results focused on the activation found in area V5 in association with moving stimuli. It had previously been established psychophysically that G.Y. was well able to discriminate movement of bars from non-movement with the parameters used in the PET study. In this situation, G.Y. was typically aware of the movement, i.e. it was Blindsight Type 2; indeed, the authors drew the conclusion that there can be conscious awareness of movement in the absence of V1. Blindsight Type 1 was not investigated.

The distinction between directional movement discrimination *with and without awareness* was the explicit focus of a subsequent fMRI study (Sahraie et al., 1997). The parameters that had previously been used to establish this difference psychophysically (Weiskrantz et al., 1995, see above) served as the basis of the stimuli in the imaging study, using stimulus contrast and velocity as the variables. There was an association between the 'awareness' mode and activity in dorsolateral prefrontal activity (areas 46 and 47), both when the subject was 'aware without seeing' in the blind hemifield, as well as when he was 'aware with seeing' in the intact hemifield. In the 'unaware' mode, but associated with good discrimination, and only in this mode, there was activation in the superior colliculus. But while activation of particular structures were found that were uniquely associated with 'awareness' and 'unawareness' modes, respectively, the conclusion of the paper stressed the general change in general pattern between the two modes — from dorsolateral structures in the former, to medial and subcortical structures in the latter. The results are provocative, but must be considered provisional given the limited number of observations possible in this single subject.

Blakemore and Spekreise in Amsterdam (personal communication) earlier carried out a single photon emission computed tomography (SPECT) brain imaging of G.Y., using the same 'aware' and 'unaware' parameters employed in the Weiskrantz et al. (1995) study. They, too, found a prefrontal focus associated with the 'aware' mode. They also found evidence of activity in an occipital area contralateral to the damaged V1 with visual stimulation of the blind hemifield (also found by Sahraie et al., 1997 (above) with fMRI. The SPECT analysis permitted only a single subtraction, but it is reassuring to find some measure of overlap with fMRI.

Another fMRI study explored the difference between red and green stimuli in G.Y.'s blind hemifield. It had previously been established that there was a response both psychophysically as well as by pupillometry in G.Y. to red but not to green colours, with variable background luminance as a control, demonstrating that the response to red was genuinely chromatic (although it must be stressed, again, that the subject did not report any experience of colour, as such). Here, too, there was an activation of the superior colliculus when the red stimulus was presented to the blind hemifield, but not when the green was. No such midbrain activation was found in the sighted hemifield (Barbur, Sahraie, Simmons et al., 1998).

Animal research and plasticity

The origin of blindsight, as reviewed in the 1986 book, stemmed from the long-standing evidence that infra-human primates could still make visual discriminations in the absence of striate cortex, and that such a capacity perforce must be mediated by extra-striate pathways. It was the fact that humans with such damage describe themselves as being blind to experience in the relevant parts of the visual fields that led to visual tests in humans that did not depend upon acknowledged experience, as recounted in Weiskrantz, 1986.

While the effects of visual cortex damage in monkeys and human 'blindsight' subjects are in many respects similar quantitatively, an important and much deeper qualitative question remains: does the monkey without striate cortex, who can localize and discriminate visual stimuli so impressively, actually *experience* the visual stimuli as 'visual' in its affected hemifield? The seminal experiments addressing this question were carried out by Cowey and Stoerig (1995). They confirmed, first, as had long been known, that monkeys could accurately localize and reach for a briefly presented visual stimulus in their 'blind' hemifields. After this, they proceeded to a second experiment with the same animals: the monkeys were trained to discriminate between randomly presented 'lights' and 'no lights' (i.e. blanks) in their intact hemifields, and rewarded for correct responses (reaching for a light, or pressing a blank panel for a non-light). The crucial question, after this training was completed, was: how would the animals respond to a visual stimulus in their 'blind' field? The answer was clear and robust: the monkeys pressed the 'non-light' panel. Even though the animals had just demonstrated that they could detect the lights at virtually perfect performance, they nevertheless did not treat them as lights. This is just what a human blindsight subject would do, of course. Some further experimental extensions of this paradigm are discussed in Cowey and Stoerig (1997), which is also an excellent review of comparative blindsight research on humans and monkeys. At a more general level, the matter is also discussed in Weiskrantz, 1997, Chapter 4).

Two important recent experiments by Charles Gross and his colleagues are also relevant to the animal–human parallel. Monkeys were trained to make a rapid ('saccadic') eye movement from the point of fixation to a visual target in their blind hemifields (Moore, Rodman, Repp and Gross, 1995). The monkeys could do this very well when they had a warning signal (the turning off of the fixation point). But without this warning, they failed to initiate the eye movement to the target. The authors draw the parallel with clinical testing of human patients with field defects caused by visual cortex damage: typically in clinical perimetric testing, subjects are not given warning signals and are 'blind' to visual events in their field defects. In blindsight experiments carried out in the laboratory, however, warning signals are routinely used.

But, finally, even the need for a warning signal disappears if the unilateral V1 damage is imposed in infancy (Moore, Rodman, Repp and Gross, 1996) — saccades are generated to the visual stimuli even in the absence of a warning signal. We do not know whether comparable findings would emerge in humans with brain damage caused early in infancy, but it would not be surprising if they did, notwithstanding the probability that transneuronal retrograde degeneration of ganglion cells would be more dense in such cases. Other animal work strongly supports the conclusion that greater recovery is possible after early than late damage to the visual system (Payne, 1994), accompanied by anatomical reorganization. It is of interest that the two most thoroughly studied human patients, D.B. and G.Y. both had visual defects in childhood, G.Y. because of head injury at the age of 8, and D.B. because of a putative incipient occipital tumour which first gave rise to a clinical problem at the age of 14, but the defect might well have been present much earlier, perhaps even prenatally (see Weiskrantz, 1986).

The question of plasticity raises the question of the role of practice in recovery of residual function. It was demonstrated some time ago (Cowey, 1967; Mohler and Wurtz, 1977) that if monkeys with visual cortex lesions are given sustained practice with visual discriminations in their blind fields, their sensitivity increases. It can be substantial — as much as 3 log units. And the size of the field defect shrinks. But it only occurs if the animal is actually *required* to practice with stimuli directed within the field defect; indeed, Mohler and Wurtz showed that recovery was specific even to practice *within a subpart* of the field defect. The beneficial effect of practice in human patients, using a procedure based on the method of Mohler and Wurtz, was demonstrated by Zihl and colleagues (Zihl, 1980, 1981; Zihl and von Cramon (1979, 1985) reviewed in Weiskrantz, 1986. More recently, other investigators (Kasten and Sabel, 1995; Kerkhoff, Munsinger and Meier, 1994) have also reported encouraging results with human patients, using similar techniques. The results of Zihl and coworkers, however, were challenged by Balliett, Blood and Bach-y-Rita (1985), who suggested that shrinkage of the field defect with practice was only found when it was measured in a dynamic perimeter, in which moving stimuli are used to plot the field defect, but not with a perimeter using static stimuli. Kasten and Sabel (1995), however, used both types of perimeters, dynamic and static, and have reported positive findings with both. There is a suggestion that G.Y.'s sensitivity, especially for movement, has increased recently. If so, it is not surprising, given that his blind hemifield has been tested repeatedly and intensively within the past few of years by numerous groups in Britain, as well as other groups in America, Belgium, Canada, Holland, Germany, and Slovakia.

Plasticity is often raised in discussion in comparing the results of the early monkey experiments with bilateral striate cortex lesions, e.g. Humphrey (1974), with research on human hemianopes. But the typical hemianope, whether human or animal, has no particular reason to exercise the affected hemifield: there is a perfectly good hemifield with which to negotiate the world, using intact eye and head movements. Greater pressure on subcortical pathways would exist when there are bilateral defects, but such patients often have other neuropsychological deficits. Nevertheless, the study of selected patients with bilateral defects would be of special interest because of the pressures necessarily placed upon extra-striate pathways (cf. Perenin, Ruel and Hécaen, 1980).

Validation and related issues

Issues of validation of blindsight arise with respect to: (a) restricting the delivery of stimuli to the blind part of the field; (b) to the incidence of blindsight in clinical populations; and (c) this, in turn, to the completeness of the visual cortex lesion and extensions to non-striate cortex; (d) to the assessment of the subject's responses and criteria; and (e) whether blindsight differs qualitatively or just quantitatively from normal vision.

Stray light, intraocular diffusion, and other similar possible artifacts

Given that the principal subjects of investigation are hemianopic and thus have an intact, normal visual hemifield ipsilateral to the lesion, it is important to rule out the possibility that supposed processing by the blind field is not, in fact, being carried out by stray light or intraocular diffused light reaching the intact hemifield (Campion, Latto and Smith, 1983). Controls include the use of comparison cases with scotomas caused by retinal pathology (who show no residual capacity), and the use of stimuli which would be severely degraded by diffusion, such as high spatial frequency gratings for measuring acuity in the impaired field. Stray light has been controlled in a variety of ways, for example, by flooding the intact visual hemifield with high levels of illumination so that if there were any stray light it could not be detected. Also, the stray light function has been determined experimentally (Barbur et al., 1994a). Perhaps the most demanding method to ensure that there can be no effective stray light into intact parts of the field is to use the *genuinely* blind part of the eye as a control, the optic disc, in which there are no receptors. As the size of this natural absolutely blind area is fixed and known (5° × 7°), one can be certain that if a small target light projected onto it that cannot be detected by the subject, there can be no diffusion of light beyond the edge of the disc, and hence maximum diffusion would be no more than half of the size of the disc. The critical test comes in requiring the subject to 'guess' whether or not a light has been projected into his 'blind' hemifield. Sometimes the light is shone onto the disc, and in random order, sometimes in neighbouring 'blind' regions. As far as the subject is concerned, all of them are unseen. But when it is on the receptorless disc, the subject's detection performance is at chance, and when it is on the neighbouring region it is significantly above chance. Weiskrantz and Warrington (cf. Weiskrantz, 1986, Chapter 10), Stoerig et al. (1985) and Tomaiuolo et al. (1997) have used this control effectively. It can be said with assurance that residual visual capacity in the blind field of hemianopes cannot be explained away as a matter of stray light or intraocular diffusion.

Continuous eye movement recordings and monitoring is a standard feature of many studies, which have ruled out inadvertent fixation shifts, as well as the use of stimuli too brief to survive a saccade. An eye tracking device has also been used with G.Y., which ensured that even if the eye moves the stimulus would remain fixed on the same retinal location (Kentridge, Heywood and Weiskrantz, 1997). Residual function cannot be explained away in terms of inadvertent fixation shifts.

Incidence

Across a random sample of patients with hemianopias resulting from cortical damage, it would seem that blindsight is found only in a minority. Thus, Blythe, Bromley, Kennard and Ruddock (1985) found five patients (one of whom was G.Y.) with evidence of residual function (responses to movement, and localization by reaching or eye movements) out of a studied population of 25. Similarly, Weiskrantz (1980) found in a study of acute hospital cases that 14 hemianopic patients out of 69 showed some evidence of residual function. In the remainder, either no such evidence was found or remained inconclusive. Why should this be? Briefly, there are at least four reasons (cf. Weiskrantz, 1995, 1996). Probably the most important is the variable extent of the occipital lesions in human subjects, and the unlikelihood of any such lesion being restricted to V1, which itself is buried deep in the medial aspect of the brain. As noted above, animal work has demonstrated that extensions of lesions beyond V1 degrades the degree of residual function, and many lesions seen clinically probably lead to the same diminution, especially as the visual association areas are tightly compressed in the proximity of V1. Secondly, the age at which the lesion occurs could be important, as has already been demonstrated in animal work (Moore et al., 1996; Payne, 1994) (see above). A third reason is that the stimulus parameters used in testing for residual function can critical, and parameters that may be suitable or even optimal for normal function may not apply to that of the blind field. For example, even a slight change in the slope of the temporal onset or offset of the stimulus can transform chance performance into virtually perfect performance. Thus, Hess and Pointer (1989), using particular fixed parameters of temporal and spatial Gaussian envelopes of unstructured stimuli, concluded that there was no residual function in G.Y. (and other subjects). This negative result was confirmed (Weiskrantz et al., 1991) using the same parameters, but a relatively small change in the parameters led to excellent performance by G.Y.

in his blind hemifield. This, and another example of an apparently unfortunate choice of parameters is discussed in Weiskrantz, 1997 (pp. 154–155; 247–248). Finally, another possible reason for variable incidence is the strangeness of the question that the researcher is bound to ask when testing Blindsight Type 1. Some subjects find it awkward or tiresome to be asked to guess about stimuli of which they have no awareness, and some refuse to do so. No doubt some experimenters communicate their scepticism in asking the question. This is compounded by the need to test subjects extensively over tens of hundreds of trials to obtain parametric families of functions. Together with their relatively delimited lesions, this no doubt is why research has been carried out on a relatively few number of long-suffering subjects willing or able to be available. It is also for this reason that indirect methods have been evolved (see above).

The general position, therefore, is that we really do not know what the true incidence of blindsight is. It is hoped that indirect methods of screening, as with pupillometry, combined with higher resolution brain scans, will provide fuller evidence.

Completeness of the visual cortex lesion and extensions to non-striate cortex

The complicating fact that damage in human clinical patients is rarely confined to just striate cortex has already been discussed above. But, as regards completeness of the striate cortical lesion itself, others have argued — continuing a view popular from the late 19th century that assigns special higher properties to cerebral cortex (cf. Weiskrantz, 1961, for a critique) — that intact striate cortex is itself necessary for the capacity for visual discriminations. The view has been advanced by Fendrich, Wessinger and Gazzaniga, 1992; Gazzaniga, Fendrich and Wessinger, 1994, and Wessenger, Fendrich and Gazzaniga, 1997 that blindsight, when demonstrated, may depend critically not on extra-striate pathways, but on small islands of intact striate cortex. Briefly, Gazzaniga and his colleagues found small islands of intact visual functioning (65%, chance being 50%) in an otherwise dead visual hemifield of occipital patients; it was blindsight because the subject reported no awareness of the stimuli within the island. Brain imaging also revealed a small region of intact striate cortex at the occipital pole. It cannot be said, of course, that this tissue corresponded to the island of visual function, especially as the subject had macular sparing of the visual field. Their evidence was found using an eye tracker, which allows the visual image to be fixed on the retina (within limited eccentricities), and which thus eliminates detection due to inadvertent or uncontrolled fixation shifts (although these have been controlled by other methods in earlier studies, see above).

It may well be that some cases are amenable to an explanation in terms of intact, tiny islands of striate cortex, but it does not follow that this is the only explanation even in cases like that described by Gazzaniga and coworkers, nor can it be a general explanation of all examples of residual visual function with V1 lesions. First, while G.Y.'s visual fixation control is excellent, and has been monitored and measured as a matter of routine in several experiments, he too has been tested with an 'eye tracker' device as described by Fendrich et al. (1992) to control for inadvertent eye movements that might allow brief fixation of an 'island'. The result was that *no* islands were found in G.Y., using the same eye-tracking apparatus and the same parameters as in the Fendrich study (Kentridge et al., 1997). The set-up has also been used in an further extension in which commentary keys were incorporated.

Secondly, this explanation cannot apply to the evidence with monkeys, where the completeness of the lesion and the absence of islands can be confirmed with certainty. Gazzaniga et al. (1994) would no doubt acknowledge this, but are unwilling to accept its relevance, even for this early stage of visual processing and despite the close similarity of the monkey's and the human's visual pathways. But, as seen (above), the monkey without V1 classifies those visual events which it can detect in the blind field with almost perfect accuracy as 'non-visual blanks' just as the human blindsight subject does. Also, there is a remarkably close fit between the narrowly tuned visual channel in the blind fields of monkeys and of G.Y., as revealed by pupillometry and by G.Y.'s psychophysics (see above).

Thirdly, even if the visual capacity in the affected hemifield were found to be spatially 'patchy', there is another possible explanation of this at the level of the retina itself. Following V1 damage there is, of course, retrograde degeneration of the large majority of cells in the lateral geniculate nucleus. However, the matter does not stop there — there can be patchy transneuronal degeneration of ganglion cells in the retina (Van Buren, 1963; Cowey, Stoerig and Perry, 1989; Cowey, Stoerig and Williams, 1999), and especially the pβ class of cells. This class of cells, depleted after V1 lesions, is distributed heavily in the macular region of the retina (the region to which the eye-tracker is limited for technical reasons); they are small, have colour opponency properties, and project only to the lateral geniculate nucleus. And so the retina itself can be patchy.

Fourthly, as we have seen (above) G.Y. can mimic with a hand movement the paths of motion of a small spot moved through a variety of trajectories over his affected hemifield. For such a capacity to be explained on the basis of tags of intact tissue would require a virtual archipelago, not just the odd isolated island (Weiskrantz, 1995). High resolution MRI scans do not reveal such intact islands of tissue (aside from at the pole, corresponding to his region of macular sparing), nor do PET or fMRI scans reveal any functioning visual cortex when he is stimulated in his 'blind field'. (Barbur et al., 1993, 1998; Sahraie et al., 1997; and A. Morland, personal communication).

Finally, recent fMRI evidence (Barbur et al., 1998; Sahraie et al., 1997) directly differentially implicates the superior colliculus in relation to capacities of G.Y.'s blind hemifield (see above), and this occurs in conjunction with the failure in these scans and also in structural MRI scans (e.g. Barbur et al., 1993) to find any islands of intact cortex in relation to the blind hemifield.

The assessment of blindsight in relation to response assessment and response criteria

The demonstration of high levels of discrimination performance in blindsight can be assessed in standard statistical terms without any reference to signal detection theory, nor does that theory elucidate the matter. Thus, excellent levels of performance can be matched in the 'blind' and sighted hemifields and yet the blindsight subject says he is aware of the latter but not of the former. Also, Stoerig et al. (1985) deliberately varied response criteria without this affecting detection thresholds with blindsight subjects, although performance levels were admittedly relatively weak.

The region of concern lies more with the much lower levels of performance, usually at chance or near chance levels. The procedures typically involve a 'yes, I see' or 'no, I do not see' response to stimuli in the blind field, and in many situations — as in clinical perimetry — this is the evidence upon which a claim of 'blindness' is based. In signal detection terms, however, a subject may have a high sensitivity (d′) even though the measured performance level is at 50% because of response criterion bias (e.g. if the subject is very cautious and responds 'no' on every trial). Experimental studies of the capacity of the 'blind' field, on the other hand, are often carried out with a more rigorous procedure, such as a two-alternative forced-choice paradigm (2AFC), which tends to be free of response bias. Therefore, the question is whether the dissociation between the reported 'blindness' of the affected field versus its positive residual 'blindsight' function merely reflects different response criteria in the 'yes/no' vs. the 2AFC discriminating modes. It is true to say that signal detection analyses of blindsight have rarely addressed this point; performance measures have generally been cast in percentage correct values and not in terms of sensitivity.

Recently Azzopardi and Cowey (1997) have filled this void in a thorough-going signal detection comparison of two modes of responding, using a grating stimulus vs. an equiluminant uniform patch, and with a range of contrasts. Azzopardi and Cowey compared 2AFC and yes/no paradigms in G.Y. For both paradigms ('was the grating in the first or the second temporal interval?') and ('was there a stimulus or not?') they obtained ROC curves, and hence could derive measures of sensitivity (d′) that were independent of response criteria. The two sets of values could be directly compared when the appropriate mathematical transform was applied for converting 2AFC to yes/no measures. The results were clear: in normal subjects the two measures of sensitivity are identical — saying 'yes' or 'no' yields the same outcome as judging in which of two intervals the stimulus occurred in the 2AFC. But for G.Y. the result was quite different: he was much more sensitive in the 2AFC paradigm than in the 'yes'/'no' paradigm. This is exactly the difference implied in the meaning of blindsight itself: good performance when forced to assign a discriminate as opposed to making a 'see'/'not see' judgment, as in perimetry. Therefore, the difference for the blindsight subject between the 'seeing or not seeing' mode and the 'forced choice discriminating' mode cannot be due to a difference in response criteria because d″ for each was derived with a criterion-free procedure.

Does blindsight differ qualitatively or just quantitatively from normal vision?

Azzopardi and Cowey (1997) take their results to imply "that blindsight is not just normal, near-threshold vision and that information about the stimulus is processed in blindsighted patients in an unusual way" (p. 14190), which is the view originally advanced for blindsight (cf. Weiskrantz, 1986). However, it would not follow, even if criterion-free measures of d″ for 'yes/no' and 2AFC procedures yielded identical values for the blind field, that the existence of qualitative differences would thereby be disproved. The reason is that the subjects can be encouraged to give 'yes/no' responses in a 'guessing' mode, even though they continue to say that they do not '*see*', as such. This was readily found with D.B. throughout all of the investigations with him and was how, in fact, the blindsight evidence was derived. The crux of the matter is not response topography as such but what the subjects take as their task — whether it is to report their experience (or its absence) *in relation to* the ongoing discrimination. It might be questioned whether a signal detection analysis could ever capture this difference, which is between 'off-line' and 'on-line' processes. It might be more meaningful simply to continue to scale each separately, and to plot their correlations or dissociations.

Kentridge et al. (1999a) examined correlations in G.Y. between commentary-key responses ('aware' or 'not aware') and 2AFC spatial localization discriminations in the good and bad fields, selecting approximately similar levels of discrimination for both fields. In fact, a double dissociation emerged: even though G.Y.'s 2AFC performance happened to be poorer in his good field than his blind field, he had a higher level of awareness responses in the good field than in the blind. Warrington and Weiskrantz also reported a double dissociation between the intact and impaired fields of D.B. The conditions were arranged so that the impaired field was poorer than the intact for form discrimination, but better for forced-choice detection of a sine wave grating, leading to the suggestion of a qualitative dissociation between form and detection between the intact and impaired fields (Weiskrantz, 1986, Chapter 16).

There are a number of other considerations that speak against the properties of the blind field being simply a weaker version of normal vision. Briefly, there is a retrograde transneuronal degeneration in the human (Van Buren, 1963), which in the monkey leads to a shift from a predominance of pβ ganglion cells of the affected retina towards pα and pγ cells, which have different structures, different projections in the brain and different functional properties from pβ: the hemiretina corresponding to the field defect is qualitatively different from the normal hemiretina (Cowey et al., 1989). Also, the levels of performance in the blind field can be very high, approaching 100%, even when the subject reports complete absence of awareness (Weiskrantz, 1986, 1995). The performance is not 'degraded', like that found in the shadowy region of near-threshold levels of normal vision.

Also, colour discrimination and detection measured psychophysically or by pupillometry in the blind field appear to favour the red end of the spectrum, unlike that of a normal field. Again, the 'tuning curve' for the blind field, based both on psychophysics and pupillometry alike, is considerably narrower than that for normal vision (see above), but apparently can be no less sensitive at its peak than is the normal hemifield. Finally, there is the recent evidence that there is a different pattern of activation in the fMRI brain images when G.Y. reports awareness and when he does not, despite comparable levels of performance psychophysically under these contrasting conditions.

Concluding comment

The ten anatomical pathways originating in the retina end in a variety of separate targets in the brain. It is hard to consider that such an arrangement is merely a useless remnant of earlier evolution, or that their separation does not support different processing demands, especially given that the different classes of ganglion cell project unequally among them. The two largest pathways — to the tectum, on the one hand, and to the dorsal lateral geniculate, on the other, or their phylogenetic homologue — are a constant feature throughout the whole of the vertebrate kingdom (Karten and Shimizu, 1991), suggesting that they underlie a segregation of functions that it is especially important to maintain. We still do not know fully what these are.

Enough evidence has been mustered, however, to demonstrate that extra-striate pathways in humans, as in other primates, are capable of mediating visual function. Nevertheless, only the early chapters have been written, and clinical material will always be encumbered with variance due to the vagaries of lesions and individual histories. It is gratifying that animal research was instrumental in leading to the uncovering of hitherto unsuspected residual capacities in clinical patients, as well as to the possibility of some rehabilitation. The story has come full circle with the demonstration that hemianopic monkeys appear to have blindsight — they, like human hemianopes, can detect visual stimuli in their affected half-fields with exquisite sensitivity, but classify them as non-visual 'blanks'.

The most intriguing and surprising aspect to emerge from the investigation of residual vision has been the finding of a disconnection, or at least a mismatch, between the subjects' objectively determined capacity and their reported experience as communicated in commentaries, either verbally or on 'commentary keys', including the complete absence of any acknowledged experience in a number of situations and found also in the tactile mode (Paillard, Michel and Stelmach, 1983; Rossetti, Rode, Perenin, and M. Boisson, 1996). Again, how common this will turn out to be is a question for future research, which is now better equipped to find the answer. But by now, there should not be any surprise or mystery in the possibility of such a disconnection. It is seen across a wide spectrum in neuropsychological research, e.g. commissurotomized, amnesia, aphasia, prosopagnosia — indeed, there is no cognitive category in which patients cannot be found who demonstrated residual performance of which they are unaware (e.g. Schacter, McAndrews and Moscovitch, 1988; Weiskrantz, 1991, 1997 for reviews). Much, perhaps even most, neural processing proceeds without any associated awareness or available commentary whatsoever, verbal or otherwise. Indeed, it might be said that awareness is a special privilege necessarily reserved for a limited class of processes. If research on residual visual capacity helps to define that class more precisely, and to point to the critical neural systems involved, it will be a welcome major bonus that was not anticipated.

References

Azzopardi P, Cowey A: Is blindsight like normal, near-threshold vision? Proceedings of National Academy of Sciences of the United States of America: 94; 14190–14194, 1997.

Azzopardi P, Fallah M, Gross CG, Rodman HT: Responses of neurons in visual areas MT and MTS after lesions of striate cortex in macaque monkeys. Society for Neuroscience Abstracts: 24; 648, 1998.

Balliett R, Blood KM, Bach-y-Rita P: Visual field rehabilitation in the cortically blind? Journal of Neurology, Neurosurgery, and Psychiatry: 48; 1113–1124, 1985.

Barbur JL, Forsyth PM: Can the pupil response be used as a measure of the visual input associated with the geniculo-striate pathway? Clinical Visual Science: 1; 107–111, 1986.

Barbur JL, Harlow JA, Weiskrantz L, 1994a: Spatial and temporal response properties of residual vision in a case of hemianopia. Philosophical Transactions of the Royal Society of London, Series B: 343; 157–166, 1994a.

Barbur JL, Harlow JA, Sahraie A, Stoerig P, Weiskrantz L, 1994b: Responses to chromatic stimuli in the absence of V1: pupillometric and psychophysical studies. In: Vision Science and its Applications. Optical Society of America Technical Digest; 2, 312–315, 1994b.

Barbur JL, Ruddock KH, Waterfield VA: Human visual responses in the absence of the geniculo-striate projection. Brain: 102; 905–927, 1980.

Barbur JL, Sahraie A, Simmons A, Weiskrantz L, Williams SCR: Processing of chromatic signals in the absence of a geniculostriate projection. Vision Research: 38; 3447–3453, 1998.

Barbur JL, Thomson WD: Pupil response as an objective measure of visual acuity. Ophthalmic Physiological Optics: 7; 425–429, 1987.

Barbur JL, Thomson WD, Forsyth PM: A new system for the simultaneous measurement of pupil size and two-dimensional eye movements. Clinical Visual Science: 2; 131–142. 1987.

Barbur JL, Watson JAG, Frackowiak RAJ, Zeki S: Conscious visual perception without V1. Brain: 116; 1293–1302, 1993.

Barbur JL, Weiskrantz L, Harlow JA: The unseen color after-effect of an unseen stimulus: insight from blindsight into mechanisms of colour afterimages. Proceedings of National Academy of Sciences of the United States of America: 96; 11637–11641, 1999.

Bard L: De la persistence des sensations luminesces dans le champ avenge des hemianopsiques. La Semaine Medicale: 22; 3–25, 1905.

Benevento LA, Yoshida K: The afferent and efferent organization of the lateral geniculo-striate pathways in the macaque monkey. Journal of Comparative Neurology: 203; 455–474, 1981.

Blythe IM, Bromley JM, Kennard C, Ruddock KH: Visual discrimination of target displacement remains after damage to the striate cortex in humans. Nature London: 320; 619–621, 1985.

Breiter HC, Etcoff NL, Whalen PJ, Kennedy WA, Rauch SL, Buckner RL, Strauss MM, Hyman SE, Rosen BR: Response and habituation of the human amygdala during visual processing of facial expression. Neuron: 17; 875–887, 1996.

Brent PJ, Kennard C, Ruddock KH: Residual colour vision in a human hemianope: spectral responses and colour discrimination. Proceedings of the Royal Society London, Series B: 256; 219–225, 1994.

Brindley OS, Gautier-Smith PC, Lewin W: Cortical blindness and the functions of the non-geniculate fibres of the optic tracts. Journal of Neurology, Neurosurgery, and Psychiatry: 32; 259–264, 1969,

Campion J, Latto R, Smith YM: Is blindsight an effect of scattered light, spared cortex, and near-threshold vision? Behavioral Brain Sciences: 6; 423–448, 1983.

Cochrane KA: Some tests of residual visual functioning in humans with damage to the striate cortex. D. Phil thesis, Radcliffe Science Library, University of Oxford, 1995.

Cocker D, Moseley MJ, Bissenden JG, Fielder AR: Visual acuity and pupillary responses to spatial structure in infants. Investigative Ophthalmology and Visual Science: 35; 2620–2625, 1994.

Corbetta M, Marzi CA, Tassinari G, Aglioti S: Effectiveness of different task paradigms in revealing blindsight. Brain: 113; 603–616, 1990.

Cowey A: The basis of a method of perimetry with monkeys: Quarterly Journal of Experimental Psychology: 15; 81–90, 1963.

Cowey A: Perimetric study of field defects in monkeys after cortical and retinal ablations. Quarterly Journal of Experimental Psychology: 19; 232–245, 1967.

Cowey A: Aspects of cortical organization related to selective attention and selective impairments of visual perception. In Posner MI, Marin OSM (Eds), Attention and Performance, Volume 11. Hillsdale, NJ: Lawrence Erlbaum, pp. 41–62, 1985.

Cowey A, Stoerig P: Projection patterns of surviving neurons in the dorsal lateral geniculate nucleus following discrete lesions of striate cortex: implications for residual vision. Experimental Brain Research: 75; 631–638, 1989.

Cowey A, Stoerig P: The neurobiology of blindsight. Trends in Neuroscience: 29; 65–80, 1991.

Cowey A, Stoerig P: Reflections on blindsight. In Milner D, Rugg MD (Eds), The Neuropsychology of Consciousness. London: Academic Press, pp. 11–37, 1992.

Cowey, A, Stoerig P: Blindsight in monkeys. Nature London: 373; 247–249, 1995.

Cowey A, Stoerig P: Visual detection in monkeys with blindsight. Neuropsychologia: 35; 929–937, 1997.

Cowey A, Stoerig P: Spectral sensitivity of hemianopic macaque monkeys. European Journal of Neuroscience: 11; 2114–2120, 1999.

Cowey A, Stoerig P, Perry VH: Transneuronal retrograde degeneration of retinal ganglion cells after damage to striate cortex in macaque monkeys: Selective loss of P-beta cells. Neuroscience: 29; 65–80, 1989.

Cowey A, Stoerig P, Williams C: Variance in transneuronal retrograde ganglion cell degeneration in monkeys after removal of striate cortex: effects of size of the cortical lesion. Vision Research: 39; 3642–3652, 1999.

Cowey A, Weiskrantz L: A perimetric study of visual field defects in monkeys. Quarterly Journal of Experimental Psychology: 15; 91–115, 1963.

Damasio A, Lima A, Damasio H: Nervous function after right hemispherectomy. Neurology: 25; 89–93, 1975.

De Gelder B, Vrooman J, Pourtois G, Weiskrantz L: Non-conscious recognition of affect in the absence of striate cortex. NeuroReport: 10; 3759–3763, 1999.

Dennett DC: Consciousness Explained. London: Penguin Press, 1991.

Esteves F, Parra C, Dimberg U, Øhman A: Nonconscious associative learning: Pavlovian conditioning of skin conductance responses to masked fear-relevant facial stimuli. Psychophysiology: 31; 375–385, 1994.

Fendrich R, Wessinger CM, Gazzaniga MS: Residual vision in a scotoma; implications for blindsight. Science: 258; 1489–1491, 1992.

Finlay AR, Jones SR, Morland AB, Ogilvie JA, Ruddock KH: Movement elicits ipsilateral activity in the damaged hemisphere of a human hemianope. Proceedings of the Royal Society London, Series B, 1997: 264; 267–297, 1997.

Fries W: The projection from the lateral geniculate nucleus to the prestriate cortex of the macaque monkey. Proceedings of the National Academy of Sciences of the United States of America: 213; 73–80, 1981.

Gazzaniga MS, Fendrich R, Wessinger CM: Blindsight reconsidered. Current Directions in Psychological Science: 3; 93–96, 1994.

Gross CG: Contribution of striate cortex and the superior colliculus to visual function in area MT, the superior temporal polysensory area, and inferior temporal cortex. Neuropsychologia: 29; 497–515, 1991.

Hernandez-Gonzalez CC, Reinoso-Suarez F: The lateral geniculate nucleus projects to the inferior temporal cortex in the macaque monkey. NeuroReport: 5; 2692–2696, 1994.

Hess RF, Pointer JS: Spatial and temporal contrast sensitivity in hemianopia. A comparative study of the sighted and blind hemifields. Brain: 112; 871–894, 1989.

Holmes G: Disturbances of vision by cerebral lesions. British Journal of Ophthalmology: 2; 353–384, 1918.

Humphrey NK: Vision in a monkey without striate cortex: a case study. Perception: 3; 241–255, 1974.

Karten HJ, Shimizu T: Are visual hierarchies in the brains of the beholders? Constancy and variability in the visual system of birds and mammals. In Agnoli A, Hodos W (Eds), The Changing Visual System. New York: Plenum, pp. 51–59, 1991.

Kasten E, Sabel BA: Visual field enlargement after computer training in brain-damaged patients with homonymous deficits: an open pilot trial. Restorative Neurological Neuroscience: 8; 113–127, 1995.

Kentridge RW, Heywood CA, Weiskrantz L: Residual vision in multiple retinal locations within a scotoma: implications for blindsight. Journal of Cognitive Neuroscience: 9; 191–202, 1997.

Kentridge RW, Heywood CA, Weiskrantz L, 1999a: Effects of temporal cueing on residual discrimination in blindsight. Neuropsychologia: 37; 479–483, 1999a.

Kentridge RW, Heywood CA, Weiskrantz L, 1999b: Attention without awareness in blindsight. Proceedings of Royal Society of London, Series B, 266; 1805–1811, 1999b.

Kerkhoff G, Munsinger U, Meier E: Neurovisual rehabilitation in cerebral blindness. Archives of Neurology: 51; 474–481, 1994.

King SM, Azzopardi P, Cowey A, Oxbury J, Oxbury S: The role of light scatter in the residual sensitivity of patients with cerebral hemispherectomy. Visual Neuroscience: 13; 1–13, 1996.

Luciani L: On the sensorial localisations in the cortex cerebri. Brain: 7, 145–160, 1884.

Marcel AJ: Blindsight and shape perception: deficit of visual consciousness or of visual function? Brain: 121; 1565–1588, 1998.

Marzi CA, Tassinari G, Lutzemberger L, Aglioti A: Spatial summation across the vertical meridian in hemianopics. Neuropsychologia: 24; 749–758, 1986.

Miller M, Pasik P, Pasik T: Extrageniculate vision in the monkey. VII. Contrast sensitivity functions. Journal of Neurophysiology: 43; 1510–1526, 1980.

Milner AD, Goodale MA: The Visual Brain in Action. Oxford: Oxford University Press, 1995.

Mohler CW, Wurtz RH: Role of striate cortex and superior colliculus in visual guidance of saccadic eye movements in monkeys. Journal of Neurophysiology: 40; 74–94, 1977.

Moore T, Rodman HR, Repp AB, Gross CG: Localization of visual stimuli after striate cortex damage in monkeys: parallels with human blindsight. Proceedings National Academy Sciences of the United States of America: 92; 8215–8218, 1995.

Moore T, Rodman HR, Repp AB, Gross CG: Greater residual vision in monkeys after striate cortex damage in infancy. Journal of Neurophysiology: 76; 3928–3933, 1996.

Morland AJ, Jones SR, Finlay AL, Deyzac E, Lê S, Kemp S: Visual perception of motion, luminance, and colour in a human hemianope. Brain: 122; 1183–1198, 1999.

Morland AJ, Ogilvie JA, Ruddock KH, Wright JR: Orientation discrimination is impaired in the absence of the striate cortical contribution to human vision. Proceedings of the Royal Society of London, Series B: 263; 633–640, 1996.

Morris JS, Øhman A, Doland RJ: A subcortical pathway to the right amygdala mediating 'unseen' fear. Proceedings of the National Academy of Sciences of the United States of America: 96; 1680–1685, 1999.

Øhman A, Soares JJF: Emotional conditioning to masked stimuli: expectancies for aversive outcomes following non-recognized fear-relevant stimuli. Journal of Experimental Psychology, General: 127; 69–82, 1998.

Paillard J, Michel F, Stelmach G: Localization without content: a tactile analogue of 'blind sight'. Archives of Neurology: 40; 548–551, 1983.

Pasik T, Pasik P: The visual world of monkeys deprived of striate cortex: effective stimulus parameters and the importance of the accessory optic system. In Shipley T, Dowling JE (Eds), Visual Processes in Vertebrates, Vision Research Supplement No. 3. Oxford: Pergamon Press, pp. 419–435, 1971.

Pasik T, Pasik P: Extrageniculate vision in primates. In Lessell S, van Dalen JTW (Eds), Neuroophthalmology, Vol. 1. Amsterdam: Elsevier, pp. 95–119, 1980.

Payne BR: System-wide repercussions of damage to the immature visual cortex. Trends in Neuroscience: 17; 126–130, 1994.

Perenin MT: Discrimination of motion direction in perimetrically blind fields. NeuroReport: 2; 397–400, 1978.

Perenin MT, Rossetti Y: Grasping without form discrimination in a hemianopic field. NeuroReport: 7; 793–797, 1996.

Perenin MT, Ruel J, Hécaen H: Residual visual capacities in a case of cortical blindness. Cortex: 16; 605–612, 1980.

Perenin MT, Girard-Madoux P, Jeannerod M. From completion to residual vision in hemianopic patients. Paper delivered at meeting of European Brain and Behaviour Society, Oxford, 1985.

Ptito A, Lassonde M, Lepore F, Ptito M: Visual discrimination in hemispherectomized patients. Neuropsychologia: 25; 869–879, 1987.

Ptito A, Lepore F, Ptito M, Lassonde M: Target detection and movement discrimination the blind field of hemispherectomized patients. Brain: 114; 497–512, 1991.

Pöppel F, Held R, Frost D: Residual visual function after brain wounds involving the central visual pathways in man. Nature London: 243; 295–296, 1973.

Poppelreuter W: Die psychischen Schadigungen durch Kopfschuss in Knege 1914–16; die Storungen der niederen und hoheren Sehleistungen durch Verletzungen des Okzipitalhirns, Vol. L. Leipzig: Voss, 1917.

Rafal R, Smith W, Krantz J, Cohen A, Brennan C: Extrageniculate vision in hemianopic humans: Saccade inhibition by signals in the blind field. Science: 250; 118–121, 1990.

Riddoch G: Dissociation of visual perceptions due to occipital injuries, with especial reference to appreciation of movement. Brain: 40; 15–17, 1917.

Rodman HT, Gross CG, Albright TD: Afferent basis of visual response properties in area MT of the macaque. I. Effects of striate cortex removal. Journal of Neuroscience: 9; 2033–2050, 1989.

Rossetti Y, Rode G, Perenin, M, Boisson D: No memory for implicit perception in blindsight and numbsense. Abstract of paper delivered at conference, Towards a science of consciousness 'Tucson II', Tucson, AZ, 1996.

Sahraie A, Weiskrantz L, Barbur JL: Awareness and confidence ratings in motion perception without geniculo-striate projection. Behavioural Brain Research: 96; 71–77, 1998.

Sahraie A, Weiskrantz L, Barbur JL, Simmons A, Williams SCR, Brammer ML: Pattern of neuronal activity associated with conscious and unconscious processing of visual signals. Proceedings National Academy of Sciences of the United States of America: 94; 9406–9411, 1997.

Sanders MD, Warrington EK, Marshall J, Weiskrantz L: 'Blindsight': vision in a field defect. Lancet: April 20; 707–708, 1974.

Schacter DL, McAndrews MP, Moscovitch M: Access to consciousness: dissociations between implicit and explicit knowledge in neuropsychological syndromes. In Weiskrantz L (Ed), Thought Without Language. Oxford: Oxford University Press, pp. 242–278, 1988.

Singer W, Zihl J, Pöppel, F: Subcortical control of visual thresholds in humans: evidence for modality specific and retinotopically organized mechanisms of selective attention. Experimental Brain Research: 29; 173–190, 1977.

Sprague JM: Interaction of cortex and superior colliculus in mediation of visually guided behavior in the cat. Science: 153; 1544–1547, 1966.

Stoerig P: Chromaticity and achromaticity: Evidence for a functional differentiation in visual field defects. Brain: 110; 869–886, 1987.

Stoerig P, Cowey A: Wavelength sensitivity in blindsight. Nature London: 342; 916–918, 1989.

Stoerig P, Cowey A: Increment threshold spectral sensitivity in blindsight: evidence for colour opponency. Brain: 114; 1487–1512, 1991.

Stoerig P, Cowey A: Wavelength sensitivity in blindsight. Brain: 115; 425–444, 1992.

Stoerig P, Cowey A: Blindsight in man and monkey. Brain: 120; 535–559, 1997.

Stoerig P, Faubert J, Ptito M, Diaconu V, Ptito A: No blindsight following hemidecortication in human subjects? NeuroReport: 7; 1990–1994, 1996.

Stoerig P, Hubner M, Pöppel E: Signal detection analysis of residual vision in a field defect due to a post-geniculate lesion. Neuropsychologia: 23; 589–599, 1985.

Stoerig P, Pöppel F: Eccentricity-dependent residual target detection in visual defects. Experimental Brain Research: 64; 469–475, 1986.

Tranel D, Damasio AR: Knowledge without awareness: an autonomic index of facial recognition by prosopagnosics. Science: 228; 1453–1455, 1985.

Tomaiuolo F, Ptito M, Marzi CA, Paus T, Ptito A: Blindsight in hemispherectomized patients as revealed by spatial summation across the vertical meridian. Brain: 120; 795–803, 1997.

Torjussen T: Residual function in cortically blind hemifields. Scandinavian Journal of Psychology; 17; 320–322, 1976.

Torjussen T: Visual processing in cortically blind hemifields. Neuropsychologia: 16; 15–21, 1978.

Van Buren KM: The Retinal Ganglion Cell Layer. Illinois: Charles Thomas, 1963.

Weiskrantz L: Encephalisation and the scotoma. In Thorpe WH, Zangwill OL (Eds), Current Problems in Animal Behaviour. Cambridge: Cambridge University Press, pp. 30–85, 1961.

Weiskrantz L: Behavioural analysis of the monkey's visual nervous system (Review Lecture). Proceedings of the Royal Society of London, Series B, 1972: 182; 427–455, 1972.

Weiskrantz L: Varieties of residual experience. Quarterly Journal of Experimental Psychology: 32; 365–386, 1980.

Weiskrantz L: Blindsight. A Case Study and Implications. Oxford: Oxford University Press, 1986. New paperback edition, 1998.

Weiskrantz L: Residual vision in a scotoma: a follow-up study of 'form' discrimination. Brain: 110; 77–92, 1987.

Weiskrantz L: Outlooks for blindsight: explicit methodologies for implicit processes. The Ferrier Lecture. Proceedings of the Royal Society of London, Series B, 1990: 239; 247, 1990.

Weiskrantz L: Disconnected awareness in detecting, processing, and remembering in neurological patients. The Hughlings Jackson Lecture. Journal of the Royal Society of Medicine: 84; 466–470, 1991.

Weiskrantz L: Blindsight: Not an island unto itself. Current Directions in Psychological Science: 4; 146–151, 1995.

Weiskrantz L: Blindsight revisited. Current Opinion in Neurobiology: 6; 215–220, 1996.

Weiskrantz L: Consciousness Lost and Found. A Neuropsychological Exploration. Oxford: Oxford University Press, 1997.

Weiskrantz L: Consciousness and commentaries. In Hameroff SR, Kaszniak AW, Scott AC (Eds), Towards a Science of Consciousness II — The Second Tucson Discussions and Debates. Cambridge, MA: MIT Press, pp. 371–377, 1998.

Weiskrantz L: Blindsight — implications for the conscious experience of emotion. In Lane R, Ahern G, Allen J, Nadel L, Kaszniak A, Rapcsak S, Schwartz G (Eds), Emotion and Cognitive Neuroscience. New York: Oxford University Press, pp. 277–295, 1999.

Weiskrantz L, Barbur JL, Sahraie A: Parameters affecting conscious versus unconscious visual discrimination without V1. Proceedings of National Academy of Sciences of the United States of America: 92; 6122–6126, 1995.

Weiskrantz L, Cowey A: Filling in the scotoma: a study of residual vision after striate cortex lesions in monkeys. In Stellar F, Sprague JM (Eds), Progress in Physiological Psychology, Vol. 3. New York: Academic Press, pp. 237–260, 1970.

Weiskrantz L, Cowey A, Barbur JL: Differential pupillary constriction and awareness in the absence of striate cortex. Brain: 122; 1533–1538, 1999.

Weiskrantz L, Cowey A, Le Mare C: Learning from the pupil: a spatial visual channel in the absence of V1 in monkey and human. Brain: 121; 1065–1072, 1998.

Weiskrantz L, Cowey A, Passingham C: Spatial responses to brief stimuli by monkeys with striate cortex ablations. Brain: 100; 655–670, 1977.

Weiskrantz L, Harlow A, Barbur JL: Factors affecting visual sensitivity in a hemianopic subject. Brain: 114; 2269–2282, 1991.

Weiskrantz L, Warrington EK, Sanders MD, Marshall J: Visual capacity in the hemianopic field following a restricted occipital ablation. Brain: 97; 709–728. 1974.

Wessenger CM, Fendrich R, Gazzaniga MS: Islands of residual vision in hemianopic patients. Journal of Cognitive Neuroscience: 9; 203–221, 1997.

Wessenger CM, Fendrich R, Ptito A, Villemure JG, Gazzaniga MS: Residual vision with awareness in the field contralateral to a partial or complete functional hemispherectomy. Neuropsychologia: 34; 1129–1137, 1996.

Yukie M, Iwai E: Direct projection from dorsal lateral geniculate nucleus to the prestriate cortex in macaque monkeys. Journal of Comparative Neurology: 201; 81–97, 1981.

Zeki S: Functional specialization in the visual cortex of the rhesus monkey. Nature London: 274; 423–428, 1978.

Zeki S: A Vision of the Brain. Oxford: Blackwell Scientific Publications, 1993.

Zihl J: 'Blindsight': improvement of visually guided eye movements by systematic practice in patients with cerebral blindness. Neuropsychologia: 18; 71–77, 1980.

Zihl J: Recovery of visual functions in patients with cerebral blindness. Experimental Brain Research: 44; 159–169, 1981.

Zihl J, Tretter F, Singer W: Phasic electrodermal responses after visual stimulation in the cortically blind hemifield. Behavioural Brain Research: 1; 197–203, 1980.

Zihl J, von Cramon D: Restitution of visual function in patients with cerebral blindness. Journal of Neurology, Neurosurgery, and Psychiatry: 42; 312–322, 1979.

Zihl J, von Cramon D: Visual field recovery from scotoma in patients with postgeniculate damage: a review of 55 cases. Brain: 108; 313–340, 1985.

Handbook of Neuropsychology, 2nd Edition, Vol. 4
M. Behrmann (Ed)

CHAPTER 12

The neuropsychology of mental imagery

Martha J. Farah *

Center for Cognitive Neuroscience, University of Pennsylvania, 3815 Walnut Street, Philadelphia, PA 19104, USA

Introduction

As the other chapters in this volume attest, the field of neuropsychology has made tremendous progress in understanding the neural bases of visual perception. We have mapped out the stages of processing through which visual information passes, from the retina through a series of specialized brain areas that culminate in stimulus recognition and localization. In recent years, neuropsychology has turned its attention to a related ability, involving the processing of visual information in the absence of a retinal signal. Mental imagery, or 'seeing with the mind's eye,' bears an intuitive similarity to veridical perception, but until recently we knew little about its neural bases. Current research focuses on two main questions: What is the relation between mental imagery and visual perceptual representations at different levels of cortical processing? And, by what mechanisms are visual representations activated in the absence of a stimulus?

Relation between imagery and perception

The question of whether imagery shares representations with perception, and if so which ones, came to the fore in neuropsychology after a long period of study in cognitive psychology. Although the question was central to cognitive psychologists' understanding of imagery, it proved impossible to answer definitively with the purely behavioral methods of that field. No matter what behavioral data were marshaled in support of shared representations, various alternative explanations also seemed to fit (see Farah, 1988 for a review of these alternative explanations). In contrast, because neuropsychological data bear a more direct relation to visual representation, providing information about internal stages of processing within the visual system, it offered a resolution to this long standing question (Farah, 1988).

Imagery in patients with lesions of the cortical visual system

One way of determining whether imagery and perception share representations is to study the imagery abilities of brain-damaged patients with selective impairments of visual perception. Damage to perceptual representations that are shared with imagery should result in analogous impairments in mental imagery. This is often the case. For example, DeRenzi and Spinnler (1967) investigated various color-related abilities in a large group of unilaterally brain-damaged patients and found an association between impairment on color vision tasks, such as the Ishihara test of color blindness, and on color imagery tasks, such as verbally reporting the colors of common objects from memory. Beauvois and Saillant (1985) studied the imagery abilities of a patient with a visual–verbal disconnection syndrome. The patient could perform purely visual color tasks (e.g. matching color samples) and purely verbal color tasks (e.g. answering questions such as "What color is associated with envy?") but could not perform tasks in

* Tel.: +1 (215) 573-3531; Fax: +1 (215) 898-7301;
E-mail: mfarah@psych.upenn.edu

which a visual representation of color had to be associated with a verbal label (e.g. color naming). When the patient's color imagery was tested purely visually, by selecting the color sample that represents the color of an object depicted in black-and-white, she did well. However, when the equivalent problems were posed verbally (e.g. "What color is a peach?") she did poorly. In other words, mental images interacted with other visual and verbal task components as if they were visual representations. De Vreese (1991) reported two cases of color imagery impairment, one of whom had left occipital damage and displayed the same type of visual–verbal disconnection as the patient just described, and the other of whom had bilateral occipital damage and parallel color perception and color imagery impairments.

In another early study documenting the relations between imagery and perception, Bisiach and Luzzatti (1978) found that patients with hemispatial neglect for visual stimuli also neglected the contralesional sides of their mental images. Their two right parietal-damaged patients were asked to imagine a well-known square in Milan, shown in Fig. 1. When they were asked to describe the scene from vantage point A in the figure, they tended to name more landmarks on the east side of the square (marked with lower case a's in the figure), that is, they named the landmarks on the right side of the imagined scene. When they were then asked to imagine the square from the opposite vantage point, marked B on the map, they reported many of the landmarks previously omitted (because these were now on the right side of the image) and omitted some of those previously reported.

Levine, Warach and Farah (1985) studied the roles of the "two cortical visual systems" (Ungerleider and Mishkin, 1982) in mental imagery, with a pair of patients. Case 1 had visual disorientation following bilateral parieto-occipital damage, and case 2 had visual agnosia following bilateral inferior temporal damage. We found that the preserved and impaired aspects of visual imagery paralleled the patients' visual abilities: Case 1 could neither localize visual stimuli in space nor accurately describe the locations of familiar objects or landmarks from memory. However, he was good at both perceiving object identity from appearance and describing object appearance from memory. Case 2 was impaired at perceiving object identity

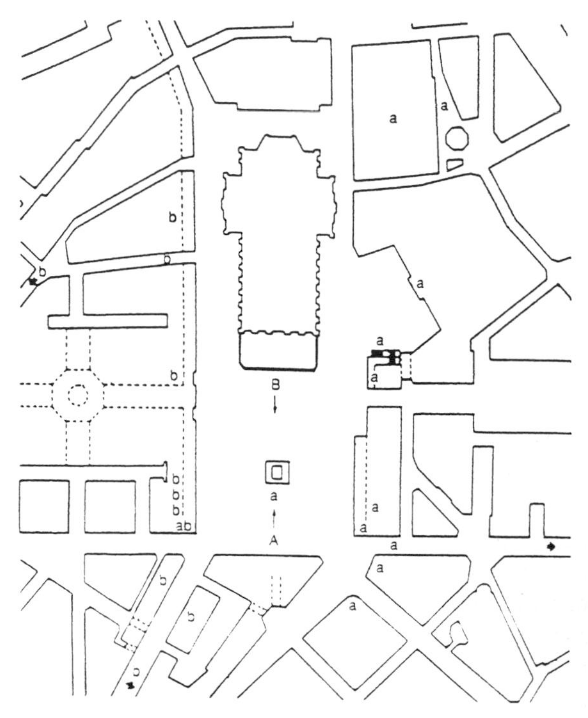

Fig. 1. Map of the Piazza del Duomo in Milan, showing the two positions, 'A' and 'B' from which patients were asked to imagine viewing the piazza, and the landmarks they recalled from each imagined position, labeled 'a' and 'b', respectively.

from appearance and describing object appearance from memory, but was good at localizing visual stimuli and at describing their locations from memory.

Farah, Hammond, Levine and Calvanio (1988a) carried out more detailed testing on the second patient. We adapted a large set of experimental paradigms from the cognitive psychology literature that had been used originally to argue for either the visual nature of imagery (i.e. the 'picture in the head' imagery mentioned in the first paragraph) or for its more abstract spatial nature. Our contention was that both forms of mental imagery exist, contrary to much of the research in cognitive psychology aimed at deciding which of the two characterizations of imagery was correct. On the basis of the previous study, we conjectured that cognitive psychology's so-called visual imagery tasks would be failed by the patient with the damaged ventral temporo-occipital system, whereas cognitive psychology's so-called spatial imagery tasks would pose no problem for him because of his intact dorsal parieto-occipital system.

The visual imagery tasks included imagining animals and reporting whether they had long or short tails, imagining common objects and reporting their colors, and imagining triads of states within the USA and reporting which two are most similar in outline shape. The spatial imagery tasks included such mental image transformations as mental rotation, scanning and size scaling, and imagining triads of shapes and reporting which two are closest to one another. The patient was impaired relative to control subjects at the visual-pattern-color imagery tasks, but entirely normal at the spatial imagery tasks.

The foregoing studies implicate modality-specific visual representations in imagery. However, they do not answer the question of whether the relatively early visual representations of the occipital cortex are involved. My colleagues and I addressed this question by comparing perceptual and imaginal visual fields (Farah, Soso and Dasheiff, 1992). We reasoned that if mental imagery consists of activating relatively early representations in the visual system, at the level of the occipital lobe, then it should be impossible to form images in regions of the visual field that are blind due to occipital lobe destruction. This predicts that patients with homonymous hemianopia should have a smaller maximum image size, or visual angle of the mind's eye. The maximum image size can be estimated using a method developed by Kosslyn (1978), in which subjects imagine walking towards objects of different sizes and report the distance at which the image just fills their mind's eye's visual field and is about to 'overflow'. The trigonometric relation between the distance, object size and visual angle can then be used to solve for the visual angle.

We carried out such a study with an epileptic patient who was undergoing right occipital lobectomy. By testing her before and after her surgery, she could serve as her own control. We found that the size of her biggest possible image was reduced after surgery, as represented in Fig. 2. Furthermore, by measuring maximal image size in the vertical and horizontal dimensions separately, we found that only the horizontal dimension of her imagery field was significantly reduced. These results provide strong evidence for the use of occipital visual representations during imagery.

Although the results from brain-damaged patients are generally consistent with the hypothesis that mental imagery involves representations within the visual system proper, including relatively early representations in the occipital lobe known to be spatial in format, there are discrepant findings as well. For example, Bartolomeo, D'Erme and Gainotti (1994) have described preserved attention to the left sides of mental images in the presence of left visual neglect. Behrmann, Winocur and Moscovitch (1994) and Servos and Goodale (1995) describe severely agnosic patients who demonstrate good visual mental imagery abilities. On the face of things, these observations conflict with the hypothesis that imagery and visual perception share representations. Of course, earlier levels of representation in the central visual system may be less engaged by, and needed for, imagery than later levels, and it is possible that these cases of preserved imagery suffered damage to relatively stages of processing. Even in the patient with the seemingly highest-level impairment, Behrmann et al.'s agnosic, there is evidence that the locus of damage is relatively early, in visual segmentation and grouping processes.

To conclude, in most (but not all) cases of selective visual impairments following damage to the cortical visual system, patients manifest qualitatively similar impairments in mental imagery and perception. Central impairments of color perception tend to co-occur with impairments of color imagery. Spatial attention impairments for the left side of the visual scene also affect the left side of mental images. Higher order impairments of visual spatial orientation, sparing visual object recognition, and the converse, are associated with impairments of spatial imagery sparing imagery for object appearance, and the converse. Finally, hemianopia resulting from surgical removal of one occipital lobe is associated with a corresponding loss of half the mind's eye's visual field.

Two conclusions follow from these findings. First, at least some modality-specific cortical representations perform 'double duty', supporting both imagery and perception. Second, those representations are functioning in analogous ways, specialized for the same kinds of visual or spatial information in both perception and imagery. Let us now turn to a different source of evidence on the relation between imagery and perception.

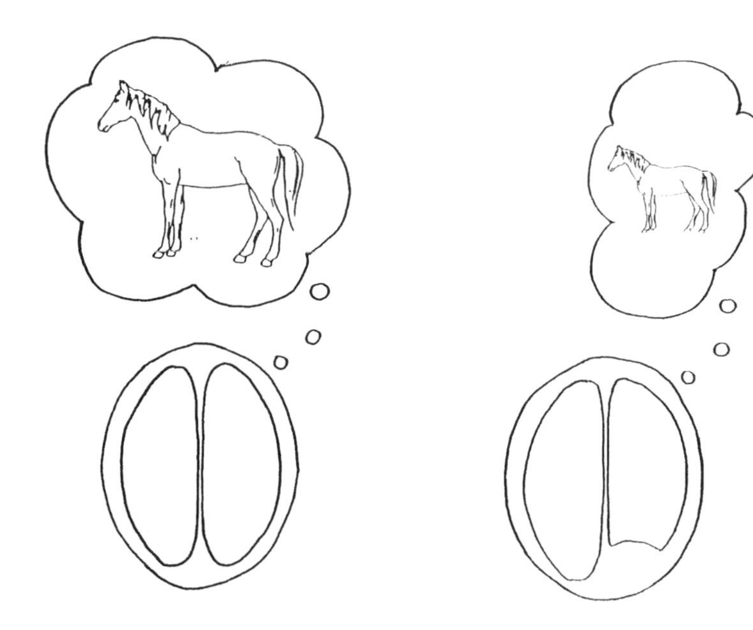

Fig. 2. Representation of the effects of occipital lobectomy on the maximal mental image size of case MGS.

Imaging imagery

Functional neuroimaging in normal subjects provides another approach to identifying which parts of the visual system, if any, are involved in mental imagery. The earliest work in this vein was done with single photon emisson computed tomography (SPECT). Roland and Friberg (1985) examined patterns of regional blood flow while subjects performed three different cognitive tasks, one of which was to visualize a walk through a familiar neighborhood, making alternate left and right turns. In this task, unlike the other tasks, blood flow indicated activation of the posterior regions of the brain, including visual cortices of the parietal and temporal lobes. These results are therefore consistent with the general hypothesis that mental imagery is a function of visual cortical areas, but failed to support the more specific hypothesis of early, occipital involvement.

SPECT was used by Goldenberg and his colleagues in a series of well-designed experiments, in which the imagery task was closely matched with control tasks involving many of the same processing demands except for the mental imagery per se (e.g. Goldenberg, Podreka, Steiner and Willmes, 1987; Goldenberg, Podreka, Steiner, Willmes, Suess and Deecke, 1989; Goldenberg, Podreka, Uhl, Steiner, Willmes and Deecke, 1989; Goldenberg, Podreka, Steiner et al., 1991; Goldenberg, Steiner, Podreka and Deecke, 1992). For example, one imagery task was the memorization of word lists using an imagery mnemonic, and its control task was memorization without imagery (Goldenberg et al., 1987). Another task involved answering questions of equal difficulty, which either required mental imagery (e.g. "What is darker green, grass or a pine tree?") or did not (e.g. "Is the Categorical Imperative an ancient grammatical form?"; Goldenberg et al., 1989a). In all of these studies, visual imagery was found to be associated with occipital and temporal activation. It is possible that the greater parietal involvement observed by Roland and colleagues (Roland and Friberg, 1985; Roland, Eriksson, Stone-Elander and Widen, 1987) is related to the need to represent spatial aspects of the environment in their mental walk task (cf. the findings of Farah et al.,

1988, on dissociable visual and spatial mental imagery).

Charlot, Tzourio, Zilbovicius et al. (1992) used SPECT while subjects generated and scanned images in the classic cognitive psychology image scanning paradigm developed by Kosslyn et al. (1978). These authors also found activation of visual association cortex, including occipital cortex.

In general, the findings with SPECT are consistent with the previous patient work, in showing visual cortical activity associated with mental imagery. Perhaps of greatest interest, pronounced and consistent activation of occipital cortex was observed in these studies. Thus suggests that imagery involves spatially mapped visual representations.

Another early approach to the relation between perception and imagery involved event-related potentials (ERPs). In one study, Farah, Peronnet, Gonon and Giard (1988c) used ERPs to map out, in space and in time, the interaction between mental imagery and concurrent visual perception. We found that imagery affected the ERP to a visual stimulus early in stimulus processing, within the first 200 ms. This implies that imagery involves visual cortical regions that are normally activated in early visual perception. The visual ERP component that is synchronized with the effect of imagery, the N1, is believed to originate in areas 18 and 19, implying a relatively early extrastriate locus for imagery in the visual system. Interpolated maps of the scalp-recorded ERPs were also consistent with this conclusion.

My colleagues and I also used ERPs to study the process of image generation from memory. Farah, Peronnet, Weisberg and Monheit (1989) asked subjects to generate a mental image in response to a visually presented word. By subtracting the ERP to the same words when no imagery instructions were given from the ERP when subjects were imaging, we obtained a relatively pure measure of the brain electrical activity that is synchronized with the generation of a mental image. Again, we constructed maps of the scalp distribution of the ERP imagery effect, in order to determine whether the maxima lay over modality-specific visual perceptual areas. Despite the very different experimental paradigm, we found a highly similar scalp distribution to the previous experiment, clearly implicating visual areas. Fig. 3 shows the evolving scalp distribution of subjects' brain electrical activity as they generate images from memory. When the experiment was repeated using auditory word presentation, the same visual scalp topography was obtained. Control experiments showed that the imagery effects in these

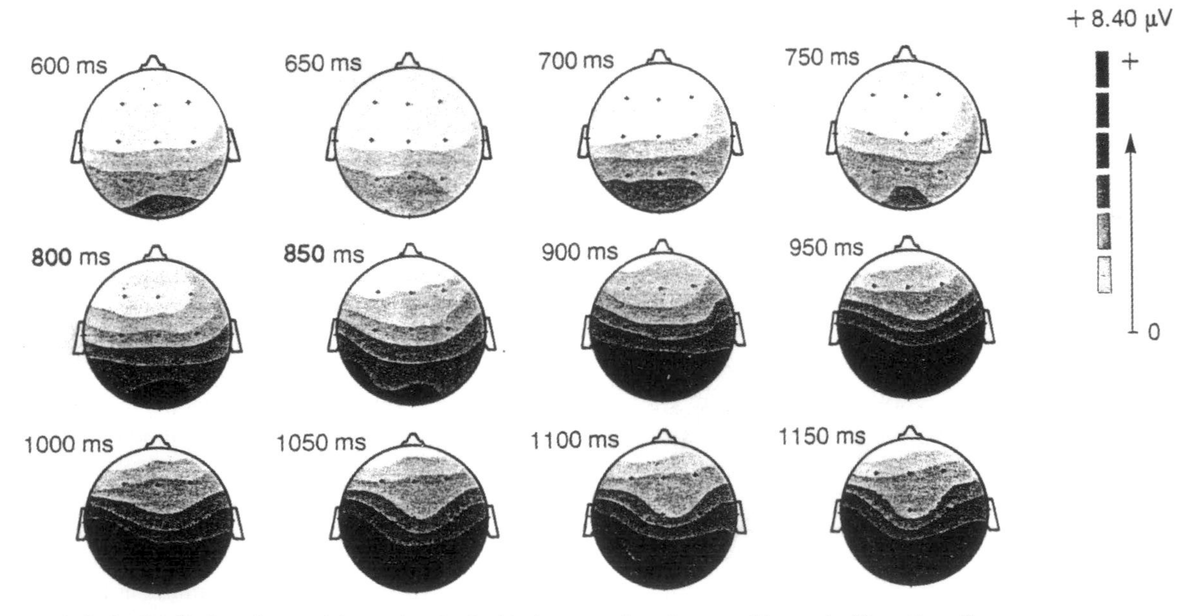

Fig. 3. Scalp distribution of potentials synchronized with the generation of a mental image, in 50-ms time slices.

experiments were not due to the cognitive effort expended by subjects when imaging (as opposed to imagery per se), or to eye movements.

Farah and Peronnet (1989) reported two studies in which subjects who rated their imagery as relatively vivid showed a larger occipital ERP imagery effect when generating images than subjects who claimed to be relatively poor imagers. This result, which we then replicated under slightly different conditions, suggests that some people are more able to efferently activate their visual systems than others, and that such people experience especially vivid imagery.

Uhl, Goldenberg, Lang et al. (1990) used scalp-recorded DC shifts to localize brain activity during imagery for colors, faces, and maps. Following transient positive deflections of the kind observed by Farah et al. (1989), a sustained negative shift was observed over occipital, parietal and temporal regions of the scalp. Consistent with the different roles of the two cortical visual systems, the effect was maximum over parietal regions during map imagery, and maximum over occipital and temporal regions during face and color imagery.

With the advent of positron emission tomography (PET), the spatial localization of cognitive neuroimaging improved greatly, and researchers soon applied this technique to experiments on imagery. An early study by Roland et al. (1987) repeated their mental walk task with PET and again found only higher order visual association cortices activated. In subsequent years Roland and colleagues conducted a number of simple experiments intended to map the neural substrates of imagery, without observing reliable occipital activation (Roland and Gulyas, 1994).

Kosslyn, Alpert, Thompson et al. (1993) also used PET to localize imagery, and obtained results more consistent with the data from focally lesioned patients (e.g. Farah et al., 1992) and the preponderance of neuroimaging studies so far reviewed. In the first two of their experiments, subjects viewed grids in which block letters were either present or to be imagined, and judged whether an 'x' occupying one cell of the grid fell on or off the letter. Comparisons between imagery and relevant baseline conditions showed activation of many brain areas, including occipital visual cortex. In a third experiment, subjects generated either large or small images of letters of the alphabet with eyes closed, and Kosslyn et al. directly compared the two imagery conditions. They found that the large images activated relatively more anterior parts of visual cortex than the small ones, consistent with the known mapping of the visual field onto primary visual cortex. A later study by the same group also found that occipital patterns of activation varied according to image size in a way that is consistent with the anatomy of primary visual cortex (Kosslyn, Thompson, Kim and Alpert, 1995). Other PET studies of imagery have agreed with these studies insofar as occipital cortex was activated, but have disagreed as to whether primary visual cortex is involved (e.g. Mellet, Tzourio, Denis and Mazoyer, 1995; Mellet, Tzourio, Crivello et al., 1996).

Recently, functional magnetic resonance imaging (fMRI) has allowed researchers to obtain blood flow-based images of function with good temporal as well as spatial resolution. The earliest study to exploit these qualities for the study of mental imagery was reported by Le Bihan, Turner, Zeffiro et al. (1993) who measured brain activity in primary visual cortex as subjects alternately viewed flashing patterns and imagined them. The results shown for one subject in Fig. 4 provide a striking demonstration of the involvement of primary visual cortex in mental imagery as well as in perception.

D'Esposito, Detre, Aguirre et al. (1997) measured regional activity throughout the brain with fMRI while subjects performed the image generation task of Farah et al. (1989): either passively listening to words or generating mental images of the words' referents. We found temporo-occipital activation, extending further into occipital cortex for some subjects than for others, but in no case reaching primary visual cortex.

Perhaps not surprisingly, there are differences in the conclusions that can be drawn from the studies reviewed here, which varied in their imaging techniques and cognitive tasks. Nevertheless, some generalizations can be made. In almost every study, mental imagery activates modality-specific visual cortical areas, including spatially mapped regions of occipital association cortex.

The imagery debate revisited

Anderson (1978) reviewed the imagery debate in cognitive psychology, and concluded that the stale-

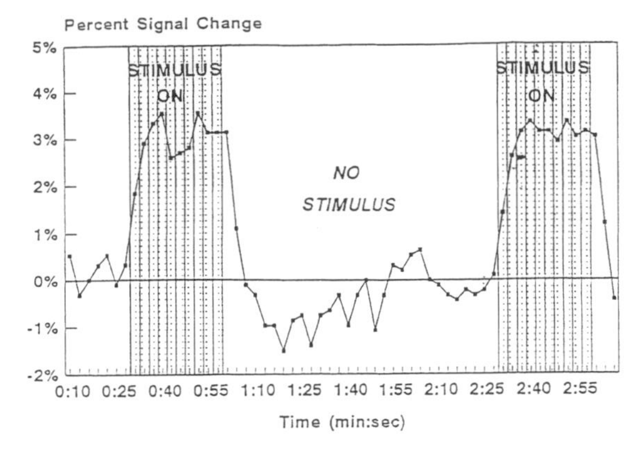

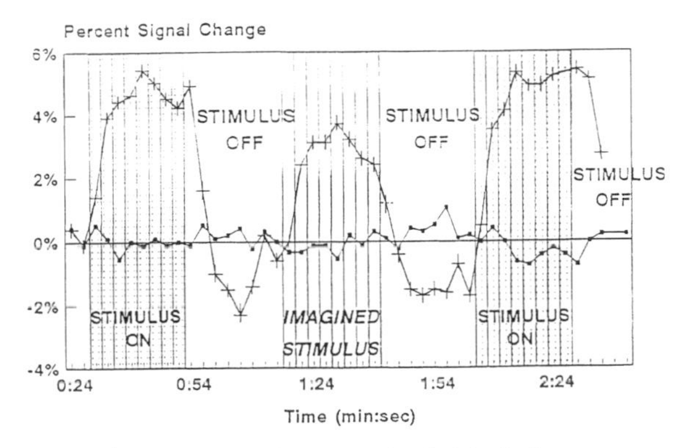

Fig. 4. Plot of activity over time in primary visual cortex measured by MRI, as a function of the subject's activity. In the upper panel, the subject was resting between two real visual stimuli. In the lower panel, the subject imagined the stimuli between actual stimulus presentations.

mate could be broken by physiological data. The cognitive neuroscience research of the 1980s and 1990s amassed a considerable amount of such data, and did indeed resolve the issue in the direction of shared mechanisms for imagery and perception. Although there is much more to find out, and some of our current conclusions will doubtless need to be revised, we can point to a body of converging evidence that supports the modality-specific visual nature of mental images, and suggests that at least some of their neural substrates have a spatial representational format: damage to visual areas representing such specialized stimulus properties as color, location, and form result in the loss of these properties in mental imagery. Spatially delimited impairments of visual attention and of visual representation are accompanied by corresponding impairments in imagery. Psychophysiological studies using blood flow imaging methods and ERPs have operationalized imagery in a wide variety of ways, including instructions to take a mental walk, imagery mnemonics, general knowledge questions about the appearances of familiar objects, the effect of imagery on concurrent perception, instructions to image common objects, self-reported individual differences in vividness of imagery, and judgements about imagined letters of the alphabet. Across all of these superficially different tasks, indices of regional brain activity implicate modality-specific visual cortex in mental imagery.

Image generation

Imagery and perception share representations, but these representations are activated in different ways. During visual perception, the stimulus initiates a cascade of processing beginning at the retina, passing through various intermediate representations in the LGN and occipital cortex that roughly preserve the spatial mapping of the retina, and culminating with relatively abstract representations of object appearance and location in temporal and parietal cortices. The evidence reviewed in the previous sections suggests that, during imagery, the direction of information flow is reversed, and some of the intermediate, spatially mapped, representations are re-activated by higher level mechanisms rather than by a stimulus. The process of activating visual representations 'top-down' rather than 'bottom-up' is known as image generation.

The direction of information flow is not the only difference between imagery and perception. Another important difference concerns the automaticity of the processes involved. One cannot see a familiar object and fail to recognize it. But one can think about familiar objects without inexorably calling to mind a visual mental image. This suggests that the activation of spatially mapped visual cortical regions from memory requires the intervention of a separate, attention-demanding process, needed for image generation, but not for visual perception and object recognition.

Farah (1984) reviewed the neurological literature on imagery impairments and identified a set of cases in which perception was grossly intact. In subsequent years, a small number of additional cases of selectively impaired imagery have been reported (e.g. Farah, Levine and Calvanio, 1988b; Goldenberg, 1992; Grossi, Orsini and Modafferi, 1986; Riddoch, 1991), as well as similar, but weaker, dissociations in subgroups of patients in group studies (Bowers, Blonder, Feinberg and Heilman, 1991; Goldenberg and Artner, 1991; Goldenberg et al., 1989b; Stangalino, Semenza and Mondini, 1995). On the face of things, the preservation of perceptual abilities in the context of impaired imagery is consistent with the existence of a distinct image generation process.

Goldenberg and Artner (1991) propose an alternative possibility, that image generation requires higher quality visual representations than normal perception, and show that patients with an apparent image generation deficit perform poorly on subtle visual discriminations, for example between a bear with pointy ears and a bear with rounded ears. At a very general level, one can view these alternatives as mutually compatible. Image generation may be just the additional visual processing that is needed for difficult perceptual tasks, for example when one forms a search image or, in the case of the study at hand, visualizes a bear from memory to check its ears.

What parts of the brain carry out the generation process itself? This question has evoked controversy. Although mental imagery was for many years assumed to be a function of the right hemisphere, Ehrlichman and Barrett (1983) pointed out that there was no direct evidence for this assumption. Farah (1984) noted a trend in the cases she reviewed for left posterior damage. Farah (1988) suggested that the left temporo-occipital area may be critical. The recent focally-damaged cases mentioned above (Farah et al., 1988a,b; Goldenberg, 1992; Grossi et al., 1986; Riddoch, 1991) have supported this suggestion, as have the group studies to varying degrees (most clearly Goldenberg and Artner, 1991; Stangalino et al., 1995). The rarity of cases of image generation deficit suggests that this function may not be strongly lateralized in most people; however, when impairments are observed after focal unilateral damage, the left or dominant hemisphere is implicated.

This conclusion is supported by the majority of neuroimaging studies, although exceptions exist. Interested readers may consult my (Farah, 2000) review article the neuroimaging evidence as of the mid-nineties concerning the role of left temporo-occipital cortex in image generation (see also D'Esposito et al., 1997).

Conclusions

In the past two decades, we have made enormous progress in our understanding of mental imagery and its neural underpinnings. We have gone from questioning whether imagery bears any relation at all to veridical perceptual processing, to refining hypotheses about the specific levels of processing shared, and the mechanisms by which the intention to imagine engages the substrates of visual perception.

Specifically, there is good consensus that mental imagery is the efferent or 'top-down' activation of some subset of the brain's visual areas. Those areas subserve the same types of representational functions in both cases, for example carrying information specifically about color, shape, spatial location, and so on. Some of the visual areas implicated in imagery, by both lesion and imaging studies, are known to be spatially mapped. This finding provides evidence for the spatial nature of image representation, in contrast to the view that imagery is a propositional, or language-like, mode of representation. Finally, the existence of a distinct mechanism for image generation, separate from the processes needed for normal 'bottom-up' perception, is supported by dissociations between imagery and perception in brain-damaged patients. The evidence from patients strongly implicates a left temporo-occipital localization for this process; neuroimaging data are mixed, but generally support this conclusion.

References

Anderson JR: Arguments concerning representation for mental imagery. Psychological Review: 85; 249–277, 1978.

Bartolomeo P, D'Erme P, Gainotti G: The relationship between visuospatial and representational neglect. Neurology: 44; 1710–1714, 1994.

Beauvois MF, Saillant B: Optic aphasia for colours and colour agnosia: a distinction between visual and visuo-verbal impairments in the processing of colours. Cognitive Neuropsychology: 2; 1–48, 1985.

Behrmann M, Moscovitch M, Winocur G: Intact visual imagery

and impaired visual perception in a patient with visual agnosia. Journal of Experimental Psychology: Human Perception and Performance: 20; 1068–1087, 1994.

Bisiach E, Luzzatti C: Unilateral neglect of representational space. Cortex: 14; 129–133, 1978.

Bowers D, Blonder LX, Feinberg T, Heilman KM: Differential impact of right and left hemiphsre lesions on facial emotion and object imagery. Brain: 114; 2593–2609, 1991.

Charlot V, Tzourio N, Zilbovicius M, Mazoyer B, Denis M: Different mental imagery abilities result in different regional cerebral blood flow activation patterns during cognitive tasks. Neuropsychologia: 30; 565–580, 1992.

D'Esposito M, Detre JA, Aguirre GK, Stallcup M, Alsop DC, Tippett LJ, Farah MJ: Functional MRI study of mental image generation. Neuropsychologia: 35; 725–730, 1997.

De Vreese LP: Two systems for colour-naming defects: verbal disconnection vs colour imagery disorder. Neuropsychologia: 29; 1–18, 1991.

DeRenzi E, Spinnler H: Impaired performance on color tasks in patients with hemispheric lesions. Cortex: 3; 194–217, 1967.

Ehrlichman H, Barrett J: Right hemisphere specialization for mental imagery: a review of the evidence. Brain and Cognition: 2; 39–52, 1983.

Farah MJ: The neurological basis of mental imagery: a componential analysis. Cognition: 18; 245–272, 1984.

Farah MJ: Is visual imagery really visual? Overlooked evidence from neuropsychology. Psychological Review: 95; 307–317, 1988.

Farah MJ: The neural bases of mental imagery. Trends in Neurosciences: 12; 395–399, 1989.

Farah MJ: Mental Imagery. In Gazzaniga M (Ed), The Cognitive Neurosciences, 2nd ed. Cambridge, MA: MIT Press, pp. 965–1061, 2000.

Farah MJ, Hammond KL, Levine DN, Calvanio R: Visual and spatial mental imagery: dissociable systems of representation. Cognitive Psychology: 20; 439–462, 1988a.

Farah MJ, Levine DN, Calvanio R: A case study of mental imagery deficit. Brain and Cognition: 8; 147–164, 1988b.

Farah MJ, Peronnet F: Event-related potentials in the study of mental imagery. Journal of Psychophysiology: 3; 99–109, 1989.

Farah MJ, Peronnet F, Gonon MA, Giard MH: Electrophysiological evidence for a shared representational medium for visual images and percepts. Journal of Experimental Psychology: General: 117; 248–257, 1988c.

Farah MJ, Peronnet F, Weisberg LL, Monheit MA: Brain activity underlying mental imagery: Event-related potentials during image generation. Journal of Cognitive Neuroscience: 1; 302–316, 1989.

Farah MJ, Soso MJ, Dasheiff RM: The visual angle of the mind's eye before and after unilateral occipital lobectomy. Journal of Experimental Psychology: Human Perception and Performance: 18; 241–246, 1992.

Finke RA: Levels of equivalence in imagery and perception. Psychological Review: 87; 113–132, 1980.

Goldenberg G: Loss of visual imagery and loss of visual knowledge — a case study. Neuropsychologia: 30; 1081–1099, 1992.

Goldenberg G, Artner C: Visual imagery and knowledge about the visual appearance of objects in patients with posterior cerebral artery lesions. Brain and Cognition: 15; 160–186, 1991.

Goldenberg G, Podreka I, Steiner M, Franzen P, Deecke L: Contributions of occipital and temporal brain regions to visual and acoustic imagery — a spect study. Neuropsychologia: 29; 695–702, 1991.

Goldenberg G, Podreka I, Steiner M, Willmes K: Patterns of regional cerebral blood flow related to memorizing of high and low imagery words: an emission computer tomography study. Neuropsychologia: 25; 473–486, 1987.

Goldenberg G, Podreka I, Steiner M, Willmes K, Suess E, Deecke L, 1989a: Regional cerebral blood flow patterns in visual imagery. Neuropsychologia: 27; 641–664, 1989a.

Goldenberg G, Podreka I, Uhl F, Steiner M, Willmes K, Deecke L, 1989b: Cerebral correlates of imagining colours, faces and a map — I. Spect of regional cerebral blood flow. Neuropsychologia: 27; 1315–1328, 1989b.

Goldenberg G, Steiner M, Podreka I, Deecke L: Regional cerebral blood flow patterns related to verification of low- and high-imagery sentences. Neuropsychologia: 30; 581–586, 1992.

Grossi D, Orsini A, Modafferi A: Visuoimaginal constructional apraxia: on a case of selective deficit of imagery. Brain and Cognition: 5; 255–267, 1986.

Intons-Peterson MJ: Imagery paradigms: how vulnerable are they to experimenters' expectations? Journal of Experimental Psychology: Human Perception and Performance: 9; 394–412, 1983.

Kosslyn SM: Measuring the visual angle of the mind's eye. Cognitive Psychology: 10; 356–389, 1978.

Kosslyn SM: Image and Mind. Cambridge, MA: Harvard University Press, 1980.

Kosslyn SM: Aspects of a cognitive neuroscience of mental imagery. Science: 240; 1621–1626, 1988.

Kosslyn SM, Alpert NM, Thompson WL, Maljkovic V, Weise S, Chabris CF, Hamilton SE, Rauch SL, FSB: Visual mental imagery activates topographically organized visual cortex: PET investigations. Journal of Cognitive Neuroscience: 5; 263–287, 1993.

Kosslyn SM, Ball TM, Reiser BJ: Visual images preserve metric spatial information: evidence from studies of image scanning. Journal of Experimental Psychology: Human Perception and Performance: 4; 47–60, 1978.

Kosslyn SM, Thompson WL, Kim IJ, Alpert NM: Topographical representations of mental images in primary visual cortex. Nature: 378; 496–498, 1995.

Le Bihan D, Turner R, Zeffiro TA, Cuenod CA, Jezzard P, Bonnerot V: Activation of human primary visual cortex during visual recall: A magnetic resonance imaging study. Proceedings of the National Academy of Science, USA: 90; 11802–11805, 1993.

Le Bihan D, Turner R, Zeffiro TA, Cuenod CA, Jezzard P, Bonnerot V: Activation of human primary visual cortex during visual recall: a magnetic resonance imaging study. Proceedings of the National Academy of Sciences of the United States of America, in press.

Levine DN, Warach J, Farah MJ: Two visual systems in mental imagery: dissociation of 'What' and 'Where' in imagery disorders due to bilateral posterior cerebral lesions. Neurology: 35; 1010–1018, 1985.

Maunsell JHR, Newsome WT: Visual processing in monkey extrastriate cortex. Annual Review or Neuroscience: 10; 363–401, 1987.

Mellet E, Tzourio N, Crivello F, Joliot M, Denis M, Mazoyer B: Functional anatomy of spatial mental imagery generated from verbal instruction. Journal of Neuroscience: 16; 6504–6512, 1996.

Mellet E, Tzourio N, Denis M, Mazoyer B: A positron emission tomography study of visual, and mental spatial exploration. Journal of Cognitive Neurosciences: 7; 433–445, 1995.

Paivio A: Imagery and Verbal Processes. New York: Holt, Rinehart, and Winston, 1971.

Pylyshyn ZW: What the mind's eye tells the mind's brain: a critique of mental imagery. Psychological Bulletin: 80; 1–24, 1973.

Pylyshyn ZW: The imagery debate: analogue media versus tacit knowledge. Psychological Review: 88; 16–45, 1981.

Riddoch MJ: Loss of visual imagery: a generation deficit. Cognitive Neuropsychology: 7; 249–273, 1990.

Roland PE, Eriksson L, Stone-Elander A, Widen L: Does mental activity change the oxidative metabolism of the brain? Journal of Neuroscience: 7; 2373–2389, 1987.

Roland PE, Friberg L: Localization of cortical areas activated by thinking. Journal of Neurophysiology: 53; 1219–1243, 1985.

Roland PE, Gulyas B: Visual imagery and visual representation. Trends in Neurosciences: 17; 281–286, 1994.

Servos P, Goodale MA, Humphrey GK: The drawing of objects by a visual form agnosic: Contribution of surface properties and memorial representations. Neuropsychologia: 31; 151–159, 1995.

Shepard RN: The mental image. American Psychologist: 33; 125–137, 1978.

Stangalino C, Semenza C, Mondini S: Generating visual mental images: deficit after brain damage. Neuropsychologia: 33; 1473–1483, 1995.

Uhl F, Goldenberg G, Lang W, Lindinger G, Steiner M, Deecke L: Cerebral correlates of imagining colours, faces and a map — II. Negative cortical DC potentials. Neuropsychologia: 28; 81–93, 1990.

Ungerleider LG, Mishkin M: Two cortical visual systems. In Ingle DJ, Goodale MA, Mansfield RJW (Eds), Analysis of Visual Behavior. Cambridge, MA: MIT Press, 1982.

Subject Index *

* Underlined page numbers indicate in-depth treatment.